Electricity & Buildings

Electricity & Buildings

Edited by G. J. Hughes

Peter Peregrinus Ltd
On behalf of the Institution of Electrical Engineers

Published by: Peter Peregrinus Ltd., London, UK.

Reprinted 1986

British Library Cataloguing in Publication Data

Hughes, G.J.
Electricity and buildings.
1. Electric wiring, Interior
I. Title
621.319'24 TK 3271

ISBN 0-86341-015-4

Printed in England by Short Run Press Ltd., Exeter

Contents

Foreword

Buildings can utilise energy in different forms according to the economy and convenience of particular applications, but electricity is indispensable. Electricity can be applied directly to improve the internal environment, to provide motive power and communications and also to control the use of other forms of energy so that the overall management of a building can be conducted more efficiently. Wisely applied in the course of the integrated design, particularly at the conceptual stage, electricity offers the means by which the very best use can be made of all the energy inputs to a building, whether these are purchased, obtained from natural sources, as a by-product or even as waste heat.

Efficient use of energy in this way benefits the building owner, the occupier and the community at large. I welcome the publication of 'Electricity and Buildings' and commend it to all those who are concerned with the use of electricity in new buildings and old.

M. N. John, B.Sc., F.Eng., F.I.E.E.
President 1983–1984
Institution of Electrical Engineers

Introduction

'Electricity and Buildings' is intended as a comprehensive guide to the utilisation of electricity in buildings, setting out the ways in which electricity may be usefully employed, and the provisions which must be made if it is to be used most effectively and safely.

It is expected that amongst those who will find this book to be helpful will be architects, building designers, developers, installation and maintenance engineers, and quantity surveyors, as well as students of building design and technology. Electrical engineers will also find much of interest. Further, the many references should provide the route to enable particular aspects to be studied and pursued in greater detail, when necessary.

Topics in 'Electricity and Buildings' are covered under three broad headings. Parts One and Two deal with electricity itself and how it reaches the consumer. In Parts Three and Four, installation and environmental aspects are dealt with in detail, whilst in Part Five the use of electricity is discussed in relation to the particular needs of eighteen different classes of buildings, from factories to prisons. Some overlap of subject matter will be met, but this is no more than is necessary to cover all aspects of a situation, and often serves to emphasise important points. On occasion the reader is taken outside the building, as in external lighting, and in food production, whilst appropriate emphasis is placed on electronics, as in the chapters on control, communications and security. The woman's point of view is represented, particularly in the use of electricity in the home, and reference is made to the special needs of the disabled. Finally, in the belief that "Electricity and Buildings" will have a readership beyond the United Kingdom, consideration is given to the precautions necessary to meet conditions in hot countries.

The 45 authors who have contributed to "Electricity and Buildings" represent Government Departments, Industry, Consulting Engineers, Contractors, Education, the Electricity Supply Industry, and other bodies; all are expert in their respective fields, and the Institution and myself are grateful for their contributions. The varying styles of authorship add variety to the book. We are also indebted to our sister Institution, the Chartered Institution of Building Services, for generous provision of tables and other references; several chapter authors are members of both bodies. The Electricity Council, too, has been of great assistance in allowing use of material from 'Electrics' and other publications.

Finally, as Editor, I acknowledge the guidance and help given by colleagues in the Power Division of the Institution, particularly A. S. Kennedy, J. C. Lane, T. E. Marshall, J. R. Platts and J. Savage.

G. J. HUGHES B.Sc.(Econ), C.Eng., F.I.E.E.
Editor

Part 1
Principles of electricity

Chapter 1.1

Principles of electricity

John Platts B.Sc.(Eng)., C.Eng., F.I.Mech.E., F.I.E.E., F.C.I.B.S.,
Energy Sales Manager, The Electricity Council

1.1.1 Simple circuits

1.1.1.1 Introduction

The flow of electricity through a wire can be likened to the flow of water through a pipe. A simple analogy with water is shown in Fig. 1.1.1. Water is pumped into tank 1 through pipe x and passes down through the discharge pipe back into tank 2, into pipe y and through the pump flow round the system again. Water will not flow up pipe x until there is a difference in pressure between the end of the pipe connected to the pump and the end which is connected to the top of tank 1. This

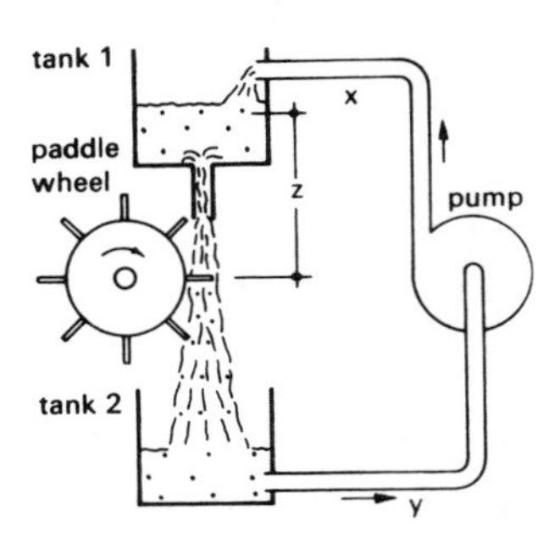

Fig. 1.1.1. *The analogy of electricity with water*

difference in pressure only exists when the pump is operating. The water in the system is being drawn from tank 2 at low pressure and forced through pipe x at high pressure into tank 1. It will be seen that the greater the pressure supplied by the pump, the quicker the rate of flow into tank 1. The pipework offers a frictional resistance to the flow of water and, in addition, the pump must produce sufficient pressure to overcome this. The larger the bore of the pipes, the smaller the resistance offered. The electrical measure which corresponds to the pressure of water is called the potential difference or voltage. The rate of flow of water measured at any point in the system corresponds to the electric current or amperage. The flow of water through the system is harnessed for work and depends on the head of water, z; the rate of travel of the paddle wheel, or the rate of working, is proportional to the head of water multiplied by the rate of flow.

In electrical terms power is equal to the product of the voltage and amperage. Power is the working rate, which may be the rate of emission of heat, light, or mechanical energy. The unit of power is the watt and is the rate of working when a current of one ampere flows at a potential difference of one volt. Energy is the result of power exerted over a period of time (i.e. work done) and is expressed in joules. (1 joule = 1 watt second).

1.1.1.2 Electrical units

The pipework in the system offers resistance to the flow of water, and, similarly, an electric wire or conductor offers a resistance to the flow of electricity. A resistance of one ohm (the unit of electrical resistance) will allow a current of one ampere to pass when a potential difference of one volt is applied. The following equations can be formulated.

$$\text{W (watts)} = \text{V (volts) multiplied by A (amperes)} \tag{1.1.1}$$

$$\text{V} = \text{A multiplied by R (ohms)} \tag{1.1.2}$$

From these equations, others can be derived, e.g.

$$\text{W} = \text{A}^2 \text{ multiplied by R} \tag{1.1.3}$$

The relationship between voltage, current and resistance (Ohm's Law) is extremely important. It can be expressed as

$$A = \frac{V}{R} \tag{1.1.4}$$

Using international symbols, Ohm's Law is expressed as

$$I = \frac{E}{R} \tag{1.1.5}$$

In practical terms, 1000 watts are 1 kilowatt (kW) and 1000 kilowatts are 1 megawatt (MW). Also, 1000 watt hours are 1 kilowatt hour (kWh).

1.1.1.3 Electrical circuit

A simple electrical circuit is shown in Fig. 1.1.2. As with the water system in Fig. 1.1.1, a difference in pressure must be provided before current will flow. This difference in electrical pressure is provided by the generator which supplies the electromotive force (emf). The unit of electromotive force (corresponding to potential difference) is the volt. Included in the circuit are a rheostat (a variable resistance), a voltmeter, a switch and an ammeter. It can be seen by reference to the diagram that, as the pointer is moved along the rheostat more resistance is included in the circuit. The switch in the electrical circuit is analogous to the valve in the water circuit. When the switch is closed to provide a continuous path, the current will flow in the direction of the arrows. The voltmeter measures the potential difference or voltage in the circuit and the ammeter measures the current. The larger the cross-sectional area of the wires in the electrical circuit, the smaller the resistance offered to the flow of electricity. The total resistance in this simple circuit is the sum of the internal resistance of the generator, the maximum value of the rheostat when the total resistance is included in circuit, and the resistance of the ammeter and of the conducting wires.

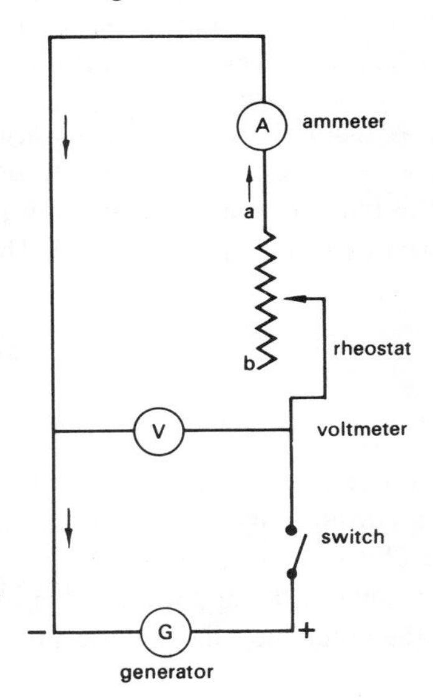

Fig. 1.1.2. *A simple electrical circuit*

1.1.1.4 Electrical conductors

The wires or conductors of an electrical circuit must be capable of withstanding sufficient pressure or voltage to perform the required task, which may be supplying power to a motor, or to a lighting or heating system. The effect of voltage reduction at lamps and heating appliances is readily apparent and the design of an installation must allow for the effects of voltage drop. The IEE Wiring Regulations (Ref. 1) state that every conductor in a circuit shall be capable of carrying the maximum current which can flow in it under normal conditions of service, and the conductors shall be so selected that the drop in voltage from the consumer's terminals to any point in an installation shall not exceed 2.5%. Thus, if the supply is taken at 240 V, the voltage drop at any point in an installation must not be more than six volts. The resistance of any conductor is dependent upon the material. One of the best conductors of electricity is silver but obviously, for economic reasons, this material cannot be employed for common use, although electrical contacts are frequently silver-plated to improve conductivity. The best practical conductors are copper and aluminium, and these are most commonly used in cable manufacture. The resistance of a conductor is directly proportional to its length and inversely proportional to its cross-sectional area. Temperature also affects the resistance of a conductor. Practically all metals, and certainly those used for electrical purposes, increase in resistance with an increase in temperature.

All these factors are taken into account in the tables of current ratings included in the IEE Regulations. These tables include, for various types of cables and methods of installation, the size of the conductor, indicated by cross-sectional area, the current rating and volt drop per ampere per metre. In addition, correction factors are applied for different ambient temperatures, particularly important in many industrial applications, and also for cables laid in groups and in enclosed trenches. For example the ambient temperature correction for non-armoured single-core p.v.c. insulated copper cables with or without sheath is 1.06 at 25°C and 0.79 at 45°C, indicating that the temperature at which cables are required to carry current is an extremely important consideration.

1.1.2 Alternating current

1.1.2.1 Single phase a.c.

In describing a simple circuit and the various units, it has been assumed that direct current (d.c.) is used, ie a current which flows in one direction only. Alternating current (a.c.) is represented by a sine wave in Fig. 1.1.3. The wave above and below the zero line is described as one cycle, and the number of these cycles occurring in one second is known as the frequency of the alternating voltage of the supply.

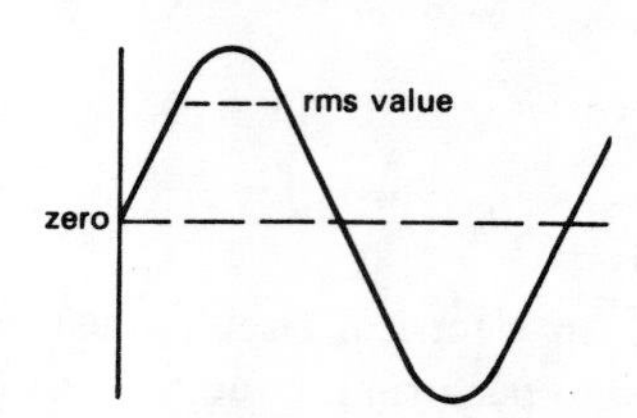

Fig. 1.1.3. *Wave form of one cycle of an a.c. supply*

The standard frequency in Great Britain is 50 cycles per second ie 50 Hertz (Hz); in North America the standard is 60 Hz. Below the frequency of 50 Hz, a noticeable flicker of lights can be detected, particularly with incandescent lamps. Clearly, the voltage and amperage of an alternating supply vary continuously, and by convention the nominal voltage and amperage of a supply of this kind is that of a direct current which will give the same heating effect. This equivalent value of direct current is used to represent the alternating value of direct current. Simply, this means that an alternating current flowing through a resistance in a circuit produces a heating effect which changes at any given point throughout the cycle, but the total of heat produced has a definite value and can be measured.

1.1.2.2 Three phase a.c.

Electricity is generated and distributed in Great Britain and other countries as a three phase supply. This means that there are three separate single phase supplies, as shown in Fig. 1.1.3, out of step with each other by an equal amount, normally 120°, produced by an alternating current generator (alternator) with three sets of symmetrically arranged field windings. A supply of this kind is shown in Fig. 1.1.4, which is distributed locally through a transformer. It is possible to take three pairs of conductors from the transformer, thus providing three separate single

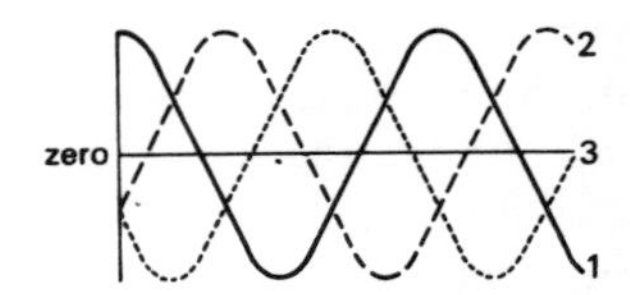

Fig. 1.1.4. *Wave form of three phase a.c. supply*

phase supplies, but it is more economical to arrange the windings as indicated in Fig. 1.1.5, and use three live (or 'line') conductors and one common return conductor (or 'neutral'); the alternating voltage between each of the line conductors and the neutral is 240 in Great Britain. Loads may be connected between any of the line conductors and neutral and if the loads are equal there will be no current at all flowing in the neutral, the three return currents having cancelled each other out. This is known as balancing the load across the phases. Even if the three loads

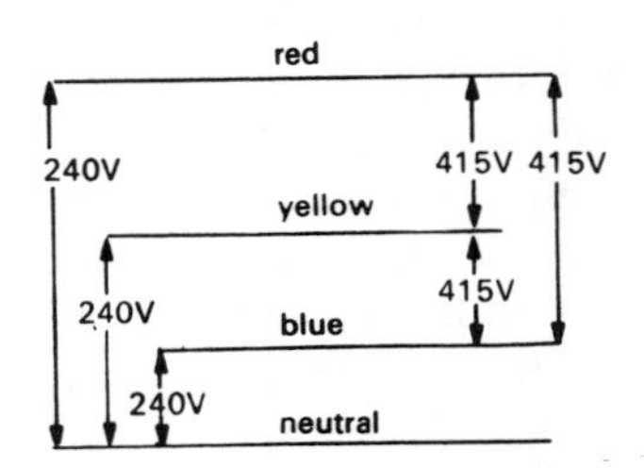

Fig. 1.1.5. *Voltages between conductors of a three phase supply*

are not identical, the current in the neutral conductor can never exceed the greatest current in any one of the line conductors. It is desirable that the current in the neutral conductor should be kept to a minimum and the objective should always be to have loads as nearly as possible equal, connected to each phase. The voltage between any line conductor and neutral ('phase voltage'), is 240, and between any two line conductors ('line voltage'), $\sqrt{3}$ (i.e. 1·73) times the phase voltage, in this case 415 V. When a three-phase supply is brought into a building, single-phase services such as lighting, heating and single-phase motors are connected between one line conductor and neutral, and three-phase appliances such as motors are connected across the three line conductors. In most cases three-phase motors do not require a neutral connection.

1.1.3 Effects of electricity

1.1.3.1 Heating

The heating effect of an electric current is determined by the resistance of the conductor through which it flows. In an electric cable, the resistance is low, to minimise the loss of power, but in an electrical appliance in which the heating effect of electricity is used, the resistance of the heating element is high and the wire will be coiled, so concentrating the heat. Electric heating and cooking appliances make use of this, as do incandescent lamps in which light is produced by a filament glowing at white heat.

1.1.3.2 Electromagnetic

Other wide areas of use for electricity depend on electromagnetism. A stationary charge will produce only an electric field in surrounding space, but if the charge is moving i.e. there is a movement of electrons through a conductor, a magnetic field is also produced around the conductor. If this electric current is steady and in one direction, the magnetic field is stationary. But with an alternating current or a fluctuating direct current the magnetic field is continuously changing its value and direction. This change in magnetic field can produce an electric field, and the mutual interaction of electric and magnetic fields produces an electromagnetic field. In a generator mechanical energy is used to rotate an electromagnet (the rotor) inside coils of wire held in a stationary frame (the stator). As the rotor revolves, pulses of electric current are generated in the coils of the stator. An electric motor uses the same kind of equipment to convert electrical into mechanical energy. By applying a current to a motor's windings, two magnetic fields are produced, one in association with the stator, and the other with the rotor; the interaction between the two fields causes the rotor to rotate. Electric motors are complex arrangements of coils and their specialist designs determine the kind of magnetic fields established and shaped by the respective conductors.

1.1.3.3 Electrochemical

A third effect of electricity is electrochemical, in which the passage of an electric current can be used to bring about a chemical change. This property of electricity is used in d.c. batteries, which by relying on the difference in voltage between two dissimilar substances, can store limited amounts of electricity, and for electroplating, in which one metal may be given a coating of another.

1.1.3.4 Electronic

Electronics is a further aspect of electricity which is rapidly expanding in application to building services. The subject is too vast to permit other than passing reference and is based upon modern atomic theory. Basically electrons are particles of the atoms of solids and gases which possess an electrical charge, which under predetermined physical conditions are released. Thereby, potential energy is transferred from one atom to another atom in a continuous stream. The phenomenon occurs by ionisation in gas discharge tubes used for fluorescent lighting. Indeed, the conduction of electricity in solid metals, approached from a microscopic stance, is an electronic process.

Any building services process involving elements of measurement, control communication or data processing is now a likely candidate for microelectronics design. Microelectronic devices are electronic components (including semiconductors) made to very small dimensions.

A semiconductor is a material in which the electrical conductivity lies between that of conductors and insulators. It also has a crystal structure whose atomic bonds allow the conduction of current by either positive or negative electrons when addition is made of the appropriate dopant, i.e. an impurity introduced to achieve the desired characteristics.

A microprocessor is an integrated miniscule circuit design which provides through semiconductors similar functions to those contained in the central processing unit of a computer. It interprets and executes instructions and usually incorporates arithmetic capabilities.

1.1.4 Earthing

The objective of earthing is to ensure that dangerous potential differences cannot exist, either between different metal parts, or between metals and earth. As the earth can be considered to have zero potential, and people are usually in direct contact with it, any person is at risk who touches a metal part that has become charged with electricity. Thus all metalwork, other than that which carries current, is connected together and connected to earth. Earthing secures the system by limiting the difference in potential between the live conductors and earth to values that their insulation will stand.

The earth circuit must provide a return path for earth fault currents without the hazards of electric shock, fire or explosion. Earthing of distribution systems and the bonding of metal enclosures are the most important means of overcoming the dangers due to faults to earth. Most consumers are supplied by an Electricity Authority distribution system employing a neutral conductor, connected to earth usually at more than one point. The consumer's earthing system is then connected to an earthing terminal or to his own earth electrode. Although a consumer is responsible for the earthing of his own installation the Electricity Authority may be able to provide assistance in obtaining a satisfactory system. Otherwise, one or more residual current operated devices should be installed as required by the IEE Regulations. (Section 3.1.6)

1.1.5 References

1.1.5.1 References in text

(1) Regulations for Electrical Installations. ('IEE Wiring Regulations'). 15th Edition 1981. (Institution of Electrical Engineers.)

1.1.5.2 Bibliography

JENKINS, B. D. 'Commentary on the 15th Edition of the IEE Wiring Regulations'. (Peter Peregrinus Limited).

NEIDLE, M. 'Electrical Installations and Regulations'. (MacMillan)

REEVES, E. A. (Editor) Newnes Electrical Pocket Book. (Butterworth)

SEIP, G. G. Electrical Installations Handbook. (2 vols) (Heyden) (English translation of German handbook)

WHITFIELD, J. F. 'A Guide to the 15th Edition of the IEE Wiring Regulations' (Peter Peregrinus)

WHITFIELD, J. F. 'Electrical Craft Principles'. (Peter Peregrinus) (Student Textbook)

Part 2
Electricity supplies

Trawsfynydd Magnox Nuclear Power Station *(CEGB)*

Chapter 2.1

Public electricity supply

John Platts B.Sc.(Eng)., C.Eng., F.I.Mech.E., F.I.E.E., F.C.I.B.S., Energy Sales Manager, The Electricity Council

2.1.1 Electricity supply organisation: UK

The industry responsible for the supply of electricity in Great Britain was nationalised by the Electricity Act of 1947, although there had previously been a large measure of public ownership and central control. It is now the largest interconnected system under unified control in the Western World.

Changes to the structure of the industry were made by the Electricity Act of 1957 and there are now fourteen statutory bodies for England and Wales, the Electricity Council, the Central Electricity Generating Board (CEGB) and twelve Area Electricity Boards. The Electricity Council, as the central body for the industry, is responsible for the shaping of general policy. Its functions are to advise the Secretary of State for Energy and to promote and assist the maintenance and development of an efficient, co-ordinated and economical system of electricity supply. The Council also has specific functions, particularly in matters of finance, research and industrial relations. The Central Electricity Generating Board owns, maintains and operates the power stations and main transmission lines. It is responsible for the bulk supply of electricity to the Area Boards and also bears responsibility for the provision of new generating and transmission equipment. Each of the Area Boards operates its own distribution network and maintains supplies to the final consumer.

Electricity generation, transmission and distribution in Scotland is the responsibility of the North of Scotland Hydro-Electric Board and the South of Scotland Electricity Board. In Northern Ireland the Northern Ireland Electricity Service is an autonomous body responsible for generation, transmission and distribution of electricity throughout the province.

Until 1 June 1983 only a publicly owned Electricity Board could supply electricity as a main business, but the Energy Act 1983 removed the statutory restrictions on the private generation of electricity. Providing the terms and conditions are reasonable, an Electricity Board must satisfy the request of a private generator or supplier for a supply of electricity either for his own use or that of his customer, must purchase electricity generated by the private generator and allow the private generator to use the Electricity Board's transmission and distribution system.

2.1.2 Electricity supply organisation: overseas

2.1.2.1 Australia

In Australia the organisation for electricity supply is such that each State or Territory has a statutory undertaking with the overall responsibility for electricity supply. New South Wales, Victoria, Tasmania, Queensland, Western Australia and the Northern Territory have Commissions, South Australia has the Electricity Trust, and the Capital Territory has the Electricity Authority. The Government has developed the Snowy Mountains Hydro-Electric Scheme, which sells electricity to NSW, Victoria and the federal capital. Most of these undertakings generate and distribute electricity, but some distribution is also provided by District, County and City Councils, except for Queensland which has a Generating Board, and Electricity Boards for distribution.

Water power contributes about one-fifth of the national electricity requirements, gas-turbine and internal combustion engine driven generating sets together provide about 2%, and the remainder comes from indigenous hard coal and brown coal. The only imported fuel is heavy oil, used mainly for boiler lighting-up purposes.

There are about 120 undertakings which distribute electricity. The Commissions are usually the inspection and approvals body for wiring and appliances, and also the licensing authority for electrical contractors and electricians. Most consumers are supplied at 240/415 V, except in Western Australia where the standard is 250/440 V; all systems are 50 Hz.

2.1.2.2 USA

Electricity supply in the USA is predominantly provided by private investor-owned companies. These 200 companies provide 78% of the national generating capacity. In the public sector some 80 Federal projects, including the Tennessee Valley Authority and the Bonneville Power Administration, provide 10% of capacity, about 500 municipal utilities and projects provide another 10%, and the remainder is owned by many hundreds of co-operatives.

2.1.2.3 Republic of Ireland

Electricity Supply in the Republic of Ireland is provided by the Electricity Supply Board, a statutory body which was set up by the Government in 1927. It generates, transmits and distributes electricity to the entire area of the Republic. The Board operates 10 hydro-electric stations; 11 peat fired stations; 6 oil fired stations and 2 which use natural gas, which is brought ashore from about 30 miles off the south coast of Ireland. In addition, there is a pumped-storage station in the mountains of Co. Wicklow and a small station in Co. Leitrim which uses local deposits of coal.

2.1.2.4 Other countries

Variations on these types of organisation apply to the Electricity Authorities in other countries of the world. It is necessary specifically to check the available supply voltage and the applicable frequency (i.e. 50 Hz or 60 Hz) at the earliest design stage of building electrical services. Assumptions should not be made regarding consistency between States in the USA, Provinces of Canada, countries in the Middle East or any Continental neighbouring countries. In this respect British Electricity International (BEI) is a reliable reference source. BEI is the overseas consultancy company of the British Electricity Supply Industry. (Ref. 1)

2.1.3 Fuel for generating plant

Conventional generating plant utilises steam at pressure to drive a turbine rotor, which in turn drives the actual generating equipment. The heat source used to produce the steam can be either a boiler fired by coal, fuel oil or natural gas, or a nuclear reactor.

2.1.3.1 Coal

Coal has been the traditional primary fuel of the generating industry in the UK and in recent years has accounted for more than 80% of the electricity generated by CEGB power stations. The large amount of relatively new coal-fired equipment, will result in the CEGB continuing to rely heavily on coal for many years to come, up to a level of about 80 million tonnes per annum. (Fig. 2.1.1).

2.1.3.2 Oil

At present oil accounts for about 4% of the electricity generated in CEGB power stations, but the use of oil depends on availability and price. Six large oil fired power stations have been commissioned, one of which can burn either coal or oil.

2.1.3.3 Nuclear power

Britain pioneered the production of electricity from nuclear power. The CEGB has twelve nuclear power stations in operation and one under construction. The South of Scotland Electricity Board has two in operation and another under construction. All the nuclear power stations now in use are equipped with gas-cooled graphite-moderated reactors; nine use natural uranium fuel canned in magnesium alloy, the Magnox stations; five use uranium dioxide fuel in stainless steel cans enriched to about 2·3% U235 content and are known as advanced gas-cooled reactor (AGR) stations. (Fig. 2.1.2). The stations under construction are

Fig. 2.1.1. *500 MW turbo-alternators* (CEGB)

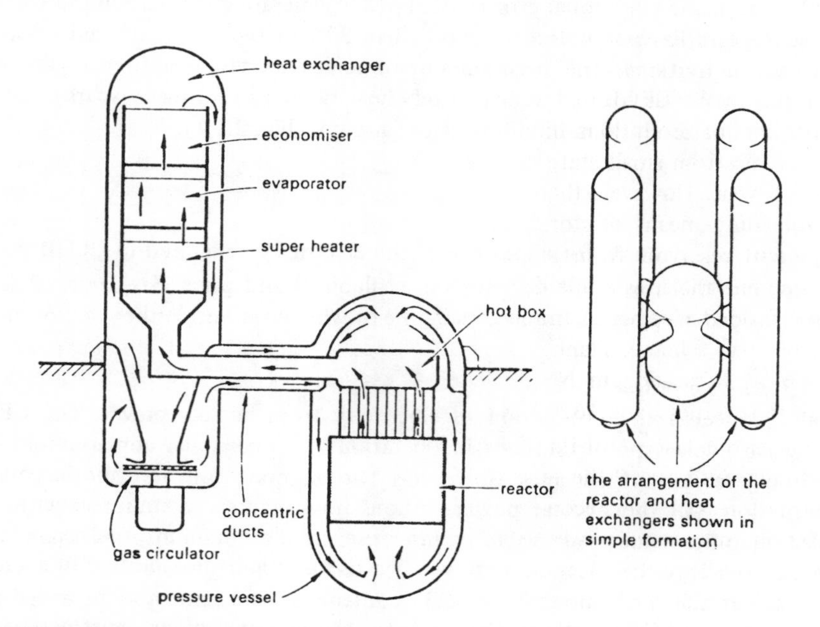

Fig. 2.1.2. *Basic principles of AGR reactor*

also AGRs, and are planned to be followed by a pressurised water reactor to be built at Sizewell in Suffolk, subject to receipt of all necessary consents following a Public Enquiry. The moderator used in the Magnox, AGR and PWR reactors slows down the speed of neutrons because slow neutrons are most effective for producing fission in U235. Another element, the artificially produced Pu239, bred in U238 at these stations, is readily fissioned by fast neutrons that have not been slowed down by a moderator. Fast neutron reactors using Pu239 (as well as uranium) can produce more fissile material than they consume and are called fast breeder reactors (FBR). The FBR might be able to double the amount of plutonium in an original fuel stock in 25 years given present reactor and fuel reprocessing plant development, and its maximum development, assuming the repeated re-cycling of the fuel, could lead eventually to an electrical energy equivalent to 1·5 million tonnes of coal-fired generation being obtained from one tonne of natural uranium.

2.1.3.4 Natural gas

The first gas-fired power stations in Britain were the 366 MW Hams Hall C power station in Warwickshire, converted from coal-firing to dual operation on coal or natural gas in 1971, and the 1240 MW West Thurrock power station in Essex, similarly converted in 1972. By 1980/81 the use of gas at these stations tailed off as it was no longer attractive on grounds of price and availability. The 1320 MW Peterhead station of the North of Scotland Hydro-Electric Board can burn natural gas liquids from the North Sea.

2.1.3.5 Renewable Energy Sources

Conventional hydro-electric plant in Britain in 1984 amounted to 1293 MW, of which 1052 MW was located in the North of Scotland. There is little prospect of any further major stations in Britain although some additional generation might be economic from small stations, generating the equivalent of 0·25 million tonnes of coal a year. However, there is scope for pumped storage hydro schemes that offer the only means of storing electricity on a large scale. Water is pumped into a high-level reservoir from a low one during off-peak periods, or when cheaply generated electricity is available. Then, at peak periods, the stored water is allowed to flow from the upper to the lower reservoir, generating electricity like a normal hydro-electric scheme. Planned capacity will reach 2560 MW from four stations, 360 MW at Ffestiniog in North Wales, 400 MW at Cruachan, Argyll, 300 MW at Foyers in Inverness, and 1620 MW at Dinorwig in North Wales.

As a further aspect of its strategy the Electricity Supply Industry in Britain is maintaining interest in the renewable energy sources, and will be exploiting them when it is feasible and economic to do so. The prospects encompass electricity generation from wave power, tidal power, geothermal hot rocks, wind power and direct solar energy. Of these sources, wind power appears to be most immediately promising in the UK climatic conditions. Experimental installations have been sited in Wales and Scotland, and when proven commercial designs become available the CEGB intends to seek consent to build a large wind-powered generator, and this could be a prelude to a possible array of similar machines.

2.1.4 System control

The Electricity Supply Regulations (1937) state that consumers must be supplied at a frequency of between 49·5 and 50·5 Hz. Operationally, the CEGB aims to work between 49·9 and 50·1 and is usually outside those limits for only a few hours a year and always well within the statutory limits. The Area Electricity Boards also have a statutory duty to maintain the voltage to the user at plus or minus six per cent of the figure they have declared for this purpose.

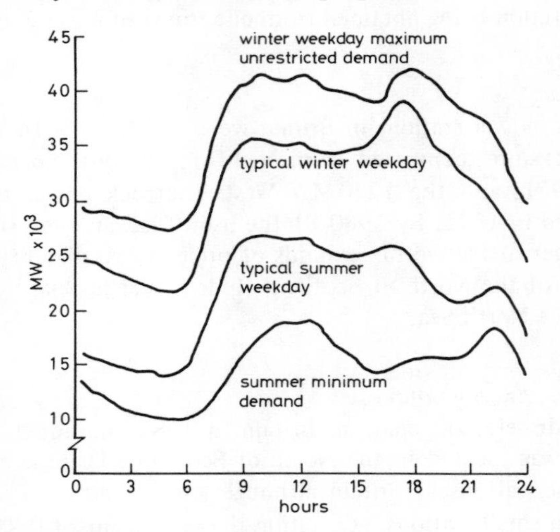

Fig. 2.1.3. *Typical daily load curves*

Obviously, the level of generation must be balanced at all times with the national demand in order to maintain this declared frequency of supply. It is therefore necessary to have a control organisation, one of whose functions is to direct the level of output from the power stations to meet the varying demand. This is known as system control and has a two tier structure. In England and Wales, the National Control Centre co-ordinates generation in the various areas by directing economic transfers of power from one to another. There are seven area control centres responsible for the switching and safety precautions of the grid network. The task that is set for the system control organisation is to meet the instantaneous power demand at the lowest production cost commensurate with security of supply throughout the network, at the same time maintaining the frequency and voltage at the declared standards. The problems of control within the CEGB are so complex that the use of computers is essential for the solution of daily operating problems. Fig. 2.1.3 illustrates the demand made on the CEGB on certain summer and winter days.

2.1.5 Electricity supply economics

Power stations generate electricity most economically when they operate for twenty-four hours a day but, because the demand for electricity is never constant, changes in the rate of consumption have to be balanced by starting up or closing down some of the generators. The bulk-supply tariff sets out the prices charged by the CEGB to the Electricity Boards for the energy generated and supplied to them for distribution. The tariff has been devised to recover the costs of generation and bulk transmission, taking into account the cost of fuel, and to reflect as closely as possible in the prices the actual cost of changes in the quantity of electricity supplied to each segment of demand. A variable tariff results because the capital and running costs may differ according to the level of demand at any given time. This is because plant is operated in cost 'merit' order: the newer stations, including all the nuclear ones with the lowest costs, meet the base load and the older stations, which are more expensive to operate, are brought into use as demand increases. To provide an incentive for customers to use electricity outside the normal peak hours, the Area Electricity Boards offer cheaper off-peak tariffs, thereby cutting their costs and partially 'smoothing' the load.

2.1.6 Transmission

Having produced electricity in generating stations, it is necessary to distribute it to each individual user at the time and place required. This can be done by having many small power stations located near to the load, or alternatively, by major power stations with a transmission system to connect them to the main distribution points. The larger stations are more economical both from the point of view of capital and running costs, and the interconnecting transmission system means that each generating station can rely on the others during maintenance or in the event of breakdown, the amount of spare plant needed being thus kept to a minimum.

Electricity is produced in the stator windings of the generators at up to 23·5 kV and is fed through terminals to one side of the generator transformer, which steps up the voltage usually to 132 kV, 275 kV or 400 kV. Generators are normally switched at the transmission voltage because of the cost and difficulty of switching heavy currents at the lower voltages. The generators feed to a main conductor, the 'omnibus bar', with main and reserve circuit arrangements to give necessary security and flexibility in operation. Bus-bar selector switches, which also function as isolating switches, allow each generator circuit to be connected to either the main or reserve bus-bar. On load bus-bar changeover by isolation is a normal provision with open-type switchgear. Bus-bar sectioning is normally necessary to limit the amount of generation at hazard from a bus-bar fault. Isolator switches and earthing switches are arranged so that any part of the equipment may be disconnected and earthed in order to allow safe access for inspection and maintenance. A similar protection arrangement covers the supply from the bus-bars to the grid.

The original grid in Great Britain was established in the 1930s, and was designed to work at 132 kV. It was strengthened by the 275 kV system which began operating in 1953 and which allows the transmission system to be run on a fully national basis. In 1960, the CEGB decided to adopt 400 kV for major new lines in order to increase the carrying capacity and to reduce to a minimum the number of new lines needed: one 400 kV line has three times the power-carrying capacity of one 275 kV line and eighteen times the capacity of a 132 kV line. In 1969 the 132 kV system was transferred to the Area Boards for primary distribution. The 400 kV system should be capable of meeting system loads of 175 GW, four times the present level, without the need for an even high voltage network. A 2000 MW d.c. cross-Channel link with France will enable some pooling of spare capacity and facilities between the two countries, particularly as peak demand occurs at different times of day and at different seasons of the year in each country; it will be completed by 1986. The CEGB possesses 7682 route kilometres of overhead and underground transmission lines and 207 substations. (Fig. 2.1.4).

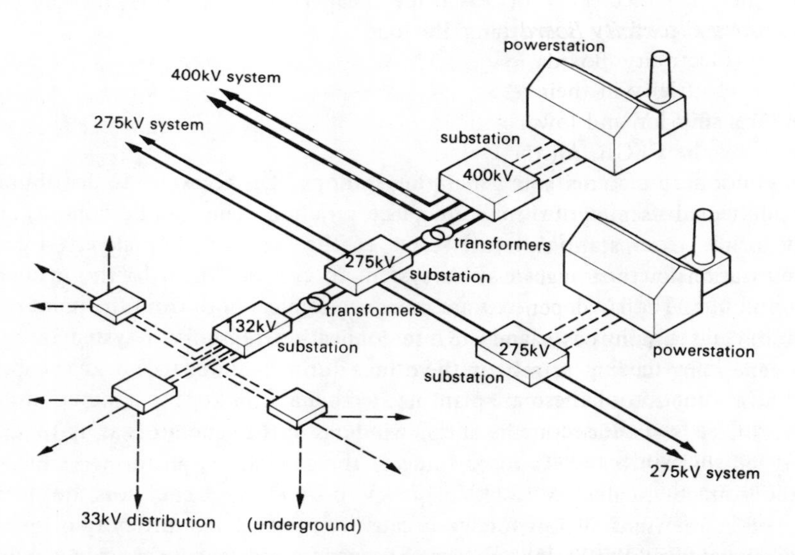

Fig. 2.1.4. *Typical transmission system from 400 kV to 33 kV showing power lines transformers and substations*

2.1.7 Distribution

2.1.7.1 Powers and functions of Area Electricity Boards

In England and Wales the twelve Area Electricity Boards and CEGB have powers and functions laid down by statute. The primary duty of the Area Boards is to take electricity from the CEGB, and to plan and carry out an efficient and economical distribution of supplies to all classes of consumer. After consultation with the CEGB, Area Boards may acquire bulk supplies from another board or from any other body or, after consultation with the CEGB, and the Electricity Council, and with the approval of the Department of Energy, they may generate electricity. By agreement a Board may supply consumers in an adjoining area. Also, an Electricity Board has powers to sell, hire, repair and install appliances and equipment of all types, and to carry out other activities, such as electrical contracting, maintenance and repair work.

In addition to their generation and transmission responsibilities, the South of Scotland Electricity Board, the North of Scotland Hydro-Electric Board and the Northern Ireland Electricity Service possess similar distribution and other powers as those of the Area Boards in England and Wales.

The addresses of local offices of the Electricity Boards can be found by referring to the Yellow Pages section of the telephone directory, to the Electricity Supply Handbook published annually by the Electrical Times (ref. 2) or by communicating with the Head Office of the Board concerned.

2.1.7.2 Area Electricity Board supplies

The Area Electricity Boards in England and Wales are responsible for the distribution of electricity in their respective territories. They obtain their supplies from the 400 kV, 275 kV and lower voltage lines that make up the transmission network operated by the CEGB. All the electricity required by an Electricity Board for use by its consumers is taken and metered at points of supply which may be located either at the substations of the transmission system or at the generating stations or, for historical reasons, at substations on the 132 kV system. The Area Boards distribute electricity through four principal networks operating at 132 kV, 33 kV, 11 kV and 415 V/240 V depending upon the load to be supplied.

Primary distribution is carried out at 132 kV, frequently using double-circuit steel-tower lines feeding primary substations, which in turn feed supplies out at 33 kV. The function of these primary networks is to supply larger industrial installations and to feed the secondary distribution networks in urban areas. Secondary distribution networks radiate from the primary substations in the form of either underground cables in urban areas or as overhead lines on wooden poles in rural areas. These networks carry the power from the heavier primary system in to the areas where consumption takes place. Consumers are usually connected to the lower voltage networks which are fed from the distribution substations. Medium and low voltage networks operate at 415 V/240 V three phase or 240 V single phase and may be either overhead or undergound.

Where consumers use electricity in large quantities, they may be supplied direct from the high voltage networks and transform on their own premises to meet particular requirements. Heavy industries are sometimes supplied direct from the primary distribution network; light industries and large commercial premises are frequently supplied from the secondary distribution system or from the 415 V/240 V system. (Figs. 2.1.5, 2.1.6).

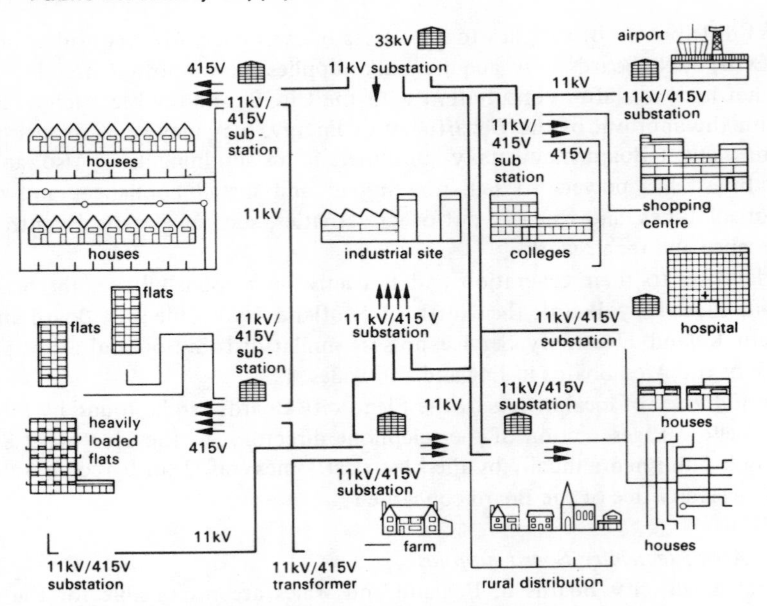

Fig. 2.1.5. *Distribution from grid supply points to consumers*

Fig. 2.1.6. *33 kV/11 kV substation* *(Electricity Council)*

2.1.7.3 Provision of electricity supply
Under reasonable circumstances, the Electricity Boards are obliged to provide a supply of electricity to anybody who applies, who is prepared to allocate space in his building for the Board's equipment, contribute towards the costs incurred, and whose electrical installation (i.e. the wiring and control equipment) is of a satisfactory standard. Charges to the consumer for the provision and connection of a supply vary from Board to Board but are usually related to the expected consumption.

Application for a supply should be made at the earliest possible opportunity. For new premises, the Board will want to know the nature of the development, the approximate installed load and the date on which the supply is required. Where a supply is also required for construction purposes, an overall saving can usually be achieved by the installation of part of the permanent supply for use during the construction period.

2.1.8 Tariffs

2.1.8.1 General
The Electricity Boards sell electricity to consumers according to a range of tariffs, consumption of electricity being measured in units (kilowatt hours) (kW h). Costs of supplying electricity vary over the day and year, depending on variations in demand, and the demand and location of individual consumers.

Tariffs are structured to recover total expenditure and to reflect as far as practicable the costs of supply. Each Electricity Board fixes its own tariffs, after consulting the Area Consultative Council and the Electricity Council; standard tariffs are published for the main classes of consumer i.e. industrial, commercial, farm and domestic.

Generally tariffs may be based either on the metering of kWh alone, or, for larger supplies on the separate measurement of demand (kW) and energy (kWh). Most tariffs are available with the separate registration of day and night kWh as an option. In this variant considerably lower kWh rates apply at night although the day rate is often slightly higher than the single rate version, and the additional metering costs are recovered through the tariff's fixed charge.

2.1.8.2 Types of tariff
The main types of tariff offered by Electricity Boards are:–

(a) *Flat rate tariff*
A tariff comprising a single kW h hour rate for small supplies given for a specified purpose (e.g. access lighting, power, catering).

(b) *Two-part tariff*
A tariff in which there is a single kW h rate (or two time of day rates) and a standing charge payable monthly or quarterly. The standing charge may be related to

installed load, maximum power required, size of premises, or fixed for all consumers on the tariff.

(c) *Block tariff*
A tariff in which the charge is based on a series of reducing kWh rates applying to successive kWh blocks of a given size, supplied during a specified period. The size of the blocks may be varied according to installed load, maximum demand or size of premises. However, when applied to smaller supplies the usual practice is to employ blocks of a fixed size for all consumers.

(d) *Maximum demand tariff* (See sec. 2.1.9)
This type of tariff is designed for consumers with higher levels of demand (usually above 40 kVA) and involves the separate measurement of energy and maximum demand. The demand may be recorded in kVA or kW, in which case there will be a separate charge for reactive power. The demand charge may be based on the consumer's annual demand, but the more usual practice is to link this charge to the monthly demand with winter demands charged at a higher rate than those in the summer. Where the maximum demand is established at night, terms may be available where the excess over the daytime demand is charged at a lower rate; kWh rates are linked to the replacement cost of the supply industry's fuel, and adjusted monthly. The cost of assets local to the supply may be recovered through a service capacity charge.

Whilst the type of load does not usually dictate which tariff is most appropriate, Boards may offer tariffs for specific uses with non-standard load characteristics (e.g. public lighting). Restricted hour (or off-peak) tariffs have now mainly been superseded by the day/night variant of the standard tariff, and are generally no longer available to new consumers.

2.1.8.3 Industrial and commercial tariffs
New high voltage supplies must be the subject of special negotiation as regards the supply voltage, estimated demand, general supply and metering arrangements. Consumers are normally required to provide their own transformers and the Board's staff should be consulted on the design and planning of the substation access, layout and equipment specification. The tariff depends on the circumstances; the appropriate published high-voltage tariff usually applies unless there are special conditions such as facilities for standing-by to private generation, a pattern of demand with higher demands at night time, or where special load control arrangements are possible.

For smaller supplies in the range 100 kW to 500 kW, and which are normally given at low voltage, consumers may be required to provide facilities for network transformers which will be owned by the Board. Here also early consultation with the Board is necessary to agree the substation location and access, general supply arrangements and the choice of tariff.

Where the supply is required for a commercial development involving a number of consumers, discussions on the supply arrangements should also encompass the layout of internal wiring to cater for any separate metering that may be required. For premises where the accommodation may be let in a number of ways as the result of changing requirements (such as in offices), the wiring arrangement adopted should be sufficiently flexible to enable separate metering of each tenant's supply.

If the consumer is making use of a cheap night rate for storage water or space heating, the Board may be able to make available a timed controlling facility operated from the meter's time switch. For heating loads of less than 20 kVA this can be achieved by direct switching of circuits taken back to the meter position. For larger loads operation would be by energising a separate controller.

2.1.8.4 Domestic tariffs

Individual dwellings will normally be supplied under the standard domestic tariff, comprising a fixed quarterly charge and a single kWh rate, or the 'Economy 7' variant which has separate day and night kWh rates. The Economy 7 tariff is usually applicable to those consumers with storage water or space heating but may also be economic where appliances can be operated during the seven low priced night hours. The Board's time switch also provides a facility for switching storage loads at the appropriate times, but this requires the wiring to be taken back to the meter for these circuits.

In domestic premises Boards will provide meter boxes for locating the supply termination and meter, and these should be sited to allow ease of access. For blocks of flats, the question of tariffs, substation accommodation and the provision of individual meters, rising mains, lateral connections and separate landlord supplies should be discussed as early as possible with the Board.

2.1.8.5 Agricultural tariffs

The choice of tariff for a farm or horticultural supply will depend upon the size and nature of the electrical load. For very large establishments, where extensive use is made of electricity, a maximum demand tariff would be appropriate, but for smaller loads a block-tariff comprising a quarterly fixed charge, an initial block of higher priced kWh and a follow on kWh rate would apply. In some Boards special tariffs are available for loads which operate only during summer months, such as grain dryers. Boards can advise if significant night use for operations such as heating or irrigation would make the variant of the tariff with a separate night rate appropriate.

2.1.9 Power factor

2.1.9.1 Introduction

The power factor is the percentage of current in an alternating current circuit which can be used as energy for the intended need. For example, a power factor of 0·7 indicates that 70% of the current supplied is usefully employed. The power factor is the ratio of useful power in watts to the apparent power taken by the load, and is usually below unity because the current and voltage are not in phase. The current can be divided into two components, the active component which is in phase with the voltage and does the useful work, and the reactive component which is out of phase with the voltage and does no work. The sum of the two components is known as apparent power and is measured in kilovolt amperes, kVA.

$$\text{power factor} = \frac{\text{useful power (kW)}}{\text{apparent power (kVA)}}$$

$$\text{reactive factor} = \frac{\text{reactive power (kVAr)}}{\text{apparent power (kVA)}}$$

An inductive circuit, such as is produced by a solenoid or motor, induces electromagnetic force which opposes the applied voltage and causes the current wave to lag the voltage wave. If the current lags by 90°, the useful power is exactly offset by the reactive power with the result that there is no true power. Magnetic energy is stored up in the load during one half-cycle and returned to the circuit in the other half-cycle. Where a capacitive circuit is employed, the current leads the voltage since the capacitor stores energy as the current rises and discharges it as the current falls. Where the current leads the voltage by, for instance, 30°, the

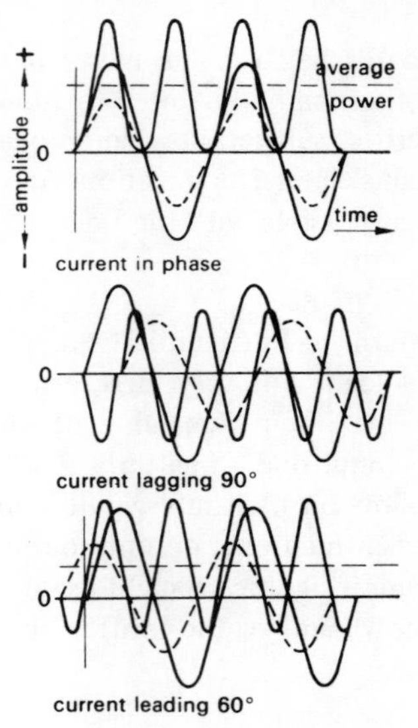

Fig. 2.1.7. *Wave diagrams*

reactive power is small and the true net power is substantial. Since most a.c. equipment is inductive, it is usual for the current to lag the voltage and so the whole of the current available is not used. A pure resistance load such as used for electric heating will cause no displacement between current and voltage waves, and such loads operate at unity power factor. (Figs. 2.1.7, 2.1.8).

Motors, transformers, chokes for fluorescent lights and welding plant all have an inherently low power factor because they operate on electro-magnetic principles. When this type of equipment is in operation, the reactive current uses some of the capacity of the distribution network although it is doing no work. Consequently, in order to obtain the required power an excess of current is taken and the network is used less efficiently than it could be, and at peak times may become overloaded.

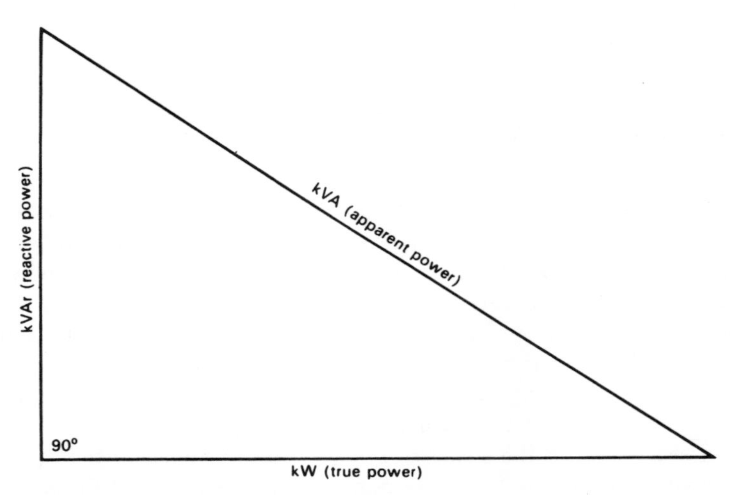

Fig. 2.1.8. *Relationship between kW, kVA and kVAr*

2.1.9.2 Power factor measurement

The most convenient and easiest method of measuring power factor at any point in a circuit or installation is by means of a power factor indicator. Where an instrument of this type is not available, accurate calculation for three phase systems can be made by taking watt, volt and ampere measurements and using these values in the following equation:

$$\text{power factor} = \frac{\text{kilowatts} \times 1000}{1.73 \times \text{volts} \times \text{amperes}}$$

2.1.9.3 Power factor improvement

The power factor at which consumers take their electricity is outside the control of the Electricity Board. It is governed entirely by the electrical plant and equipment which is installed and operated within the consumer's building. Electricity Boards discourage the use of equipment and installations with a low power factor since it absorbs part of the capacity of the generating plant and the distribution network but has no useful effect. Consequently, power factor improvement warrants consideration from an economic viewpoint to achieve a reduction in Electricity Board charges resulting from lower costs of supply.

Table 2.1.1 *Relationship between useful and reactive currents (415 v 3 phase supply*

Power Factor	Power Delivered (kW)	Useful Current (A)	Reactive Current (A)	Total Current (A)
1·0	10	13·9	0	13·9
0·9	10	13·9	6·7	15·4
0·8	10	13·9	10·4	17·4
0·7	10	13·9	14·2	19·9
0·6	10	13·9	18·5	23·2
0·5	10	13·9	24·1	27·8

The benefits of good power factor are indicated in Table 2.1.1 which shows the total current and its useful and reactive components when supplying 10 kW at different power factors. It can be seen that to deliver power at a power factor of 0·5, the mains have to carry a current which is twice as great as if the power factor were unity. This means that copper sections of the generating machines, of the main and subsidiary feeders, the transformers, and, in fact, of the whole complex system extending from the power stations to the load terminals are determined by the current to be carried. Furthermore, the energy lost in the form of heat in every item of the electrical system is proportional to the square of the current passing; so that the lower the power factor the greater is the energy lost in all this apparatus.

When power factor is low, equipment can be installed to correct it to the level recommended by the Electricity Board. Even where the cost of energy supply is not reduced, power factor correction equipment may confer other advantages. For example, where equipment and cables are operating at maximum rating, power factor correction may reduce the loading to safe limits and avoid overheating. By reducing the current, losses in the system are cut down. Better voltage regulation is usually obtained by the reduction in loading. The savings to be made in cabling costs can be illustrated by the fact that double the amount of copper is required to transmit 200 kW at 0·6 power factor on 415 V, than for the same load at 0·9 power factor.

The reactive current illustrated in the table occupies copper sections which could be utilised to pass profitable, useful current. This applies not only to the electricity supply authority's mains, but also to the building distribution mains. Low power factor means unprofitable use of capital for supplier and user alike.

The power factor of motor-driven equipment can be kept as high as possible by closely matching the horsepower of the motor to the load. The more accurately this is done, the higher the power factor for the type of motor employed. It is possible however, that even at this maximum value the power factor will not reach the required figure. In this case satisfactory results can only be obtained by the installation of power factor improvement equipment.

2.1.9.4 Equipment for improvement of power factor
The equipment available for improvement of the power factor can be divided into two main groups, namely capacitors and synchronous motors. Each system has particular applications.

(a) *Power capacitors*
The use of capacitors for improvement of the power factor is reliable, economical and practical for a wide variety of commercial and industrial applications. Capacitors for low voltage are designed for connecting either to individual items of equipment or to distribution centres: alternatively, banks of capacitors may be connected to main bus-bars. High-voltage capacitors available for individual correction of large motors offer many advantages and the rating of a capacitor used for the purpose should provide as high a power factor as possible without exceeding 85% of the no-load magnetising kVA of the machine. Leading power factor should not be obtained under any circumstances.

The advantages of capacitors are as follows:

(i) They require little or no maintenance
(ii) No special structural work or foundations are required for installation
(iii) Capacitors are flexible and additional units can be installed as a project or system is extended
(iv) Correction equipment can invariably be installed adjacent to the machine concerned.

(b) *Synchronous motors*
Large synchronous motors are used on systems with long transmission lines for power factor correction, and hence voltage regulation. In industrial practice, the synchronous motor has been largely superseded by the capacitor, the cost of which, in relation to rotating plant, is very low.

2.1.9.5 Savings from improved power factor
A significant requirement by a consumer for reactive power will result in an Electricity Board incurring additional costs in the provision of distribution equipment to accommodate the reactive power flows and as a result of the increased electrical losses on the system. These costs are passed on to the consumer through the demand charges in the maximum demand tariff. Where demand is metered in kVA a falling power factor will automatically increase the recorded kVA and thus the demand change for the same flow of energy. Boards which base their demand charges on kW include in the tariff a clause which surcharges the demand charge if the power factor falls below a datum level, usually 0·9.

Lightly loaded motors, such as air conditioning fans and compressors, will often have a substantial need for reactive power but correction capacitors may be installed either locally to the equipment or at the point of supply to ensure that the reactive power taken from the Electricity Board's system is kept to a minimum. Boards will advise on the specification of the equipment but for loads which are not running continuously, capacitors should be automatic in their operation. The installation of power factor correction equipment will produce a saving to the consumer through the reduction of his demand charges. An investment in this type of equipment will usually produce a payback in less than three years and sometimes in under 18 months.

2.1.10 References

2.1.10.1 References in text

(1) British Electricity International, Thames House North, Millbank, London, SW1P 4QF
(2) The Electricity Supply Handbook, published annually by IPC Electrical Electronic Press Ltd, Quadrant House, The Quadrant, Sutton, Surrey, SM2 5AS.

2.1.10.2 Legislation (See also Appendix 6.1)

Electric Lighting Act, 1882
Electric Lighting Act, 1888
Electric Lighting (Clauses) Act 1899
Electricity (Factories Act) Special Regulations 1908
Electric Lighting Act 1909
Electricity (Supply) Act 1919
Electricity (Supply) Act 1926
Electricity Supply Regulations 1937
Electricity (Factories Act) Special Regulations 1944
Electricity Act 1947
Electricity Reorganisation (Scotland) Act 1954
Electricity Act 1957
Electricity (Scotland) Act 1979
Energy Act 1983

2.1.10.3 Bibliography

CHARD, F de la C: 'Electricity Supply, Transmission and Distribution.' (Longman)
Electricity Council (eds): 'Power System Protection.' (Peter Peregrinus Limited)
Electricity Council Intelligence Section. 'Electricity Supply in the United Kingdom: a Chronology.' (Reference Paper RP3)
Electricity Council Intelligence Section: 'Electricity Supply in the United Kingdom: Organisation and Development.' (Reference Paper RP1)
HANNAH, L: 'Electricity before Nationalisation: a study of the development of the Electricity Supply Industry in Britain to 1948.' (MacMillan)
HANNAH, L: 'Engineers Managers and Politicians: the First Fifteen Years of Nationalised Electricity Supply in Britain.' (MacMillan)

2350 kVA packaged power plant *(Dale Electric)*

Chapter 2.2

Alternative electricity supplies

J.P. Milne B.Sc.(Eng)., C.Eng., F.I.E.E., F.C.I.B.S.,
Partner, Kennedy and Donkin Associates

2.2.1 Classes of supplies

2.2.1.1 Introduction

The standards and quality of the public supply in Great Britain are contained in the Electricity Supply Regulations 1937, which set down the permitted variations in voltage and frequency of the supply. (Section 2.1.4) The Regulations also state that the supply shall be continuous except when emergencies arise, or (provided notice is given) when operations are carried out. These standards adequately control the quality of the public supply, but consumers may elect to provide their own electricity supply or provide a back-up or standby supply. (Refs. 1, 2)

There is often a statutory requirement for a standby supply to be provided, usually with particular reference to the safety of personnel. Relevant Acts and Regulations are given in Para. 2.2.4.2.

Although these Acts indicate the legal requirements for the provision of standby supplies, they do not provide advice on the scope of supply required, using terms like 'adequate' and 'sufficient', and thus leaving the consumer to look elsewhere for advice on the degree and quality of supply needed.

An important source of guidance in one particular area occurs in the January 1983 Amendments to the IEE Wiring Regulations, which make specific provision for electricity supplies for safety services. Also, the Energy Act 1983 sets out the arrangements under which privately generated electricity may be supplied to the public network.

2.2.1.2 Total on-site energy generation

If consideration is being given to the total on-site generation of energy at any particular location, usually it will only be economic where one or more of the following conditions apply:

(a) where the required energy is a significant portion of the manufactured product cost, say ten per cent or more.
(b) where there will be access to low-cost or waste fuel.
(c) where power generation can be associated with the production of heat needed in the manufacturing process, thus effectively raising the efficiency of power production above the normal levels attainable. This can take several forms. Steam can be produced in a boiler to power a turbine and also be used in the manufacturing process; a gas turbine can be used to produce electricity, and its hot exhaust gases fed to a waste heat boiler which produces steam for the manufacturing process; a diesel engine/alternator unit can be used to produce electricity, and the waste heat from the engine's water jacket can be used in the manufacturing process, or perhaps to heat the factory.

For total on-site generation of energy, the quality of the generating plant itself may well have to be better than would otherwise be required for standby duties, to ensure that it will run for long periods without discontinuity after making due allowance for maintenance and overhaul. For example, in the case of diesel plant, slower speed machines should be used, but these are more expensive.

Additional plant must be installed to allow for machines to be taken out of service for maintenance and repair. Extra staff may need to be employed to cover the full 24 hour generation period. Also, the running cost of the plant will be of major importance, a point not significant when considering standby duty only.

2.2.1.3 The need for standby supplies

Loss of electric power in the home is inconvenient. In the shop it means loss of sales, in the office a reduction in efficiency, in the workshop or farm a loss of production. But its loss can be more disastrous. Computer records can be lost, essential communications can be disrupted, and in hospitals human lives can be at risk. In the developed world the reliability of the public electricity supply has reached a very high standard, but interruptions do take place on occasions and this must also be taken into account when deciding on the need for a standby supply.

The prospective purchaser of standby plant must therefore determine whether the expenditure is justifiable. Is it simply for convenience, or is it absolutely necessary? Also is the standby supply required for a short time only, or must it be maintained for several hours? Must the supply be available instantaneously or can there be a break in supply after the mains fail? The answers will determine whether the cost of installing a standby supply is justified, and if so, the scope and type of supply that should be provided.

2.2.1.4 Peak lopping

An additional aspect of a separate source of power generation in industrial or commercial applications is peak lopping. This involves the use of private generating plant at times of high load, to reduce the demand on the public electricity system. Where the plant is installed solely for peak lopping its capital and running costs have to be set against the savings in cost to the consumer of importing the peak power. Where the plant already exists for standby purposes, there will usually be a marginal increase in capital expenditure, but of a relatively small amount.

2.2.2 Provision of standby supplies

2.2.2.1 Duplicate mains supply

A consumer may require a duplicate supply for added security and the Electricity Authority may agree to install an extra mains supply cable. This cable will operate in parallel with the original supply but from a different point in the supply network and will thus provide a back-up in the event of failure of the original supply. It should be noted, however, that should there be a widespread failure in the electricity supply itself, then the value of the standby supply could be negated. Where the supply is required for a particularly sensitive consumer, like a hospital, the public supply authorities can usually be relied upon to do their best to provide the alternative supplies from different sources if at all possible, but this is nevertheless unlikely to be as completely reliable as an independent power source provided this is properly installed, maintained and supervised.

2.2.2.2 Standby generating plant

Money spent on standby generating plant can be described as a non-productive expenditure of capital. It is therefore in the consumer's interest to keep the capital expenditure to a minimum and also to minimise the amount of fuel that needs to be stored. It is therefore usual to install high speed sets, using premium fuel, and care should be taken to provide only the capacity needed to cater for the emergency loads.

The most commonly used prime mover for standby sets is the diesel engine, but petrol and gas-driven engines and gas turbines are also to be found. Today it is more usual for them to drive alternating current (a.c.) generators (alternators). Direct current (d.c.) generators can be provided where d.c. is the required standby supply, but d.c. systems cannot operate in parallel with the public supply.

Alternative starting techniques are possible:

(a) Automatically, following the failure of the mains supply, with the generator being run up to speed and switched in immediately.
(b) Automatically, when power is actually required after mains failure. The standby system is initiated when the mains supply fails but only comes into operation when required.
(c) Manually, from a push button on a control panel adjacent to the generator.
(d) Manually, from a remote push button.
(e) For small sets, by using a starting handle.

Diesel sets require about 30 seconds, gas turbine sets about 45 seconds to run up to speed and take load. Quicker starting times are possible by adding such refinements as pre-heating, continuous lubricating oil priming and other devices, all of which add considerably to the cost of the installation, and therefore the question must always be asked if these refinements are justifiable in cost/benefit terms.

2.2.2.3 Battery supplies

A battery's ability to provide its output instantaneously makes it a very satisfactory source of standby power. Even in installations using generators, batteries usually provide the starting power, and are often used to provide power to the essential loads for the initial period, while the generator is running up to speed.

Batteries supply direct current only, but in many installations this is not a disadvantage since the standby supply is for emergency lighting only. Where an alternating current supply is needed the battery can be used in conjunction with static inverter equipment or to drive a d.c. motor/a.c. generator unit.

2.2.2.4 Emergency lighting

The most common use of any standby supply is for the provision of some form of emergency lighting, which may be required to meet two needs:

(a) Escape Lighting: Lighting provided to ensure that means of escape can be safely used.
(b) Standby Lighting: Lighting provided to enable essential activities to continue following failure of the main lighting supply.

There are two commonly used systems of emergency lighting:

(a) Maintained: A system in which the emergency lighting is kept in use at all times.
(b) Non-Maintained: A system in which the emergency lighting lamps are alight only when the normal lighting fails.

Both systems are used extensively. The maintained system is an essential feature in certain public buildings and is usually preferred for standby lighting although it is also used for escape lighting. Standards of emergency lighting have proved hard to define. (Ref. 3) In Britain BS 5266 and the CIBS Guide for Interior Lighting provide useful guidance and the Industry Committee for Emergency Lighting have produced ICEL 1001. This Industry Standard for the Construction and Performance of Battery Operated Emergency Lighting Equipment gives specific guidance on the design of the luminaires. ICEL 1003 provides a Guide for Emergency Lighting Applications. (Ref. 4).

In the past most emergency lighting systems were supplied from a central battery and charger unit, but more recently the self-contained emergency lighting luminaire has become readily available for both maintained and non-maintained systems. Each unit comprises a lamp, battery, charger and control equipment. Usually a neon or light emitting diode (LED) indicator is incorporated to provide a visual indication that the battery is under charge. In general, any installation comprising fewer than twenty lamps is likely to be most cost effectively met using self-contained luminaires, but the dividing line is not hard and fast.

2.2.2.5 Uninterruptible power supplies

For applications where no interruption of supply can be tolerated even for a fraction of a second, an uninterruptible power supply (UPS) is needed. Several methods of providing this are available. Formerly it almost always entailed the use of rotating plant. In one method, an alternator and a large flywheel were coupled to an a.c. motor, and through an electromagnetic clutch to a diesel engine. Under normal circumstances, the a.c. motor would drive the alternator which supplied power to the essential loads. When the mains supply failed, the clutch engaged, the diesel engine was started, and as the engine ran up to full power, the alternator continued to supply power, its energy being supplied from the flywheel.

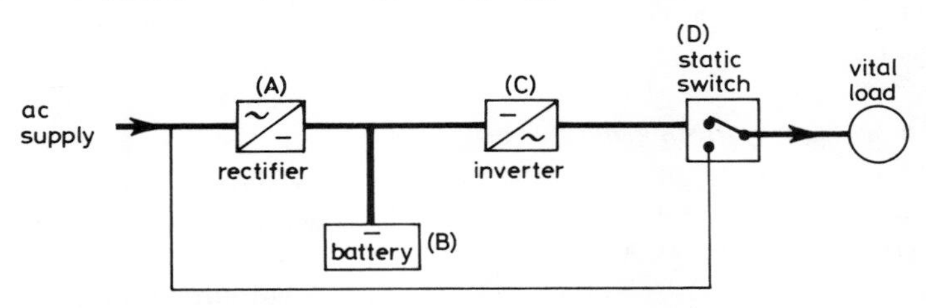

Fig. 2.2.1. *Circuit for uninterruptible supply*

An alternative method is to use static equipment and in the past decade this has been developed rapidly so that it can now be used to supply loads of several hundred kilowatts. Many systems are available but they broadly follow the same concept of an a.c. supply backed up by a d.c. supply and the use of a static change-over switch. One arrangement is shown in Fig. 2.2.1. Under normal circumstances the a.c. supplies the charger rectifier unit (A) which supplies the inverter (C) with d.c. and maintains the battery (B) in a fully charged condition. The a.c. output from the inverter, suitably smoothed to a sinusoidal a.c. waveform, is fed to the essential load via a static electronic switch (D). If the a.c. mains should fail, supply to the inverter, and hence to the essential load, is maintained from the battery. If any part of the rectifier/battery/inverter circuit should fail, the electronic switch (D) will bring in the a.c. mains supply as a further back-up.

Usually the battery will be rated to provide the back-up supply for a period of up to an hour. If it is considered likely that a mains failure will last for longer than this, the a.c. mains can be backed up by a diesel alternator set which may well be used to provide standby lighting and small power in addition to the vital loads which will continue to be supplied via the rectifier/inverter unit.

2.2.3 Equipment for the provision of alternative supplies

2.2.3.1 Alternators

Most alternators used for private generation today are of the brushless, self-regulating type and designs are available to meet almost any specific requirement.

The standard machine is usually of the screen protected, drip-proof type and is mounted on a common base plate with the prime mover, to which it is flexibly coupled. For sizes up to 400 or 500 kVA, the control panel including the voltage regulator and the output circuit-breaker, can be mounted on the machine. For larger machines, separate floor-mounted panels are used.

An analysis of the expected load must be carried out to determine the size of alternator required. As well as meeting the steady state peak running load of the system for which supply is provided, the alternator must be capable of handling motor starting currents, which can be six or eight times greater than the full load running current of the motor. It is therefore advisable when placing an order, to give the manufacturer full details of all loads, particularly motor sizes and starting characteristics.

2.2.3.2 Diesel engine driven generator sets

Today the vast majority of generators are diesel-engine driven. Sets are available with capacities from less than 10 kVA upwards, with the most common sizes ranging between 100 and 1000 kVA. The usual speed of operation for diesel sets in standby situations is 1500 rev/min for 50 Hz units (1800 rev/min for 60 Hz systems). These speeds provide a reasonable balance in terms of reliability, performance, size, weight and cost.

Starting is usually effected from a battery, although compressed air is also used, particularly for large units. Starting batteries, with lead-acid high performance cells are the most suitable, although nickel-cadmium batteries are also satisfactory, but expensive. About 80% of all failures of machines to start are associated with the batteries and their chargers, and it is imperative that these are checked at least once a week to ensure that they are in a healthy condition.

For smaller sets, air-cooled diesel engines are sometimes used, but most sets are water cooled. The hot water from the engine jacket is then cooled either by a radiator or heat exchanger. Wherever possible it is preferable on grounds of cost and convenience to mount the radiator on the engine block as shown in Fig. 2.2.2.

Although the exhaust system will be provided by the manufacturer of the set, particular care should be taken in its installation. A flexible connection should be installed at the machine end, to prevent vibration being transmitted to the structure and to allow for expansion of the exhaust system when hot. The silencer should be located as near the engine as practicable, since the high temperature of this location prevents a build-up of carbon in the silencer. Horizontal silencers should be mounted at a slight angle so that any condensation will flow to the low end where a drain hole is fitted. A common exhaust system for multiple installations is not acceptable, since exhaust gases from operating engines tend to flow to the units which are shut down causing condensation to form in the exhaust manifolds of these machines.

2.2.3.3 Gas engine generator sets

The gas engine is a spark-ignition engine operating on natural gas. Invariably sets based on the gas engine are supplied to organisations already using large quantities of gas and are not found in general industrial and commercial use. In carrying out any design studies the tariff under which gas is sold for electricity generation should be ascertained, since this could be a decisive factor in the choice of machines.

Fig. 2.2.2. *315 kVA diesel engine generating set* *(Dale Electric)*

2.2.3.4 Petrol engine generator sets

Generators are also available powered by petrol engines, but these are usually the small models, and are perhaps most commonly found for outputs of less than 10 kVA.

2.2.3.5 Gas turbine generator sets

A development in recent years has been the increasing use of gas turbine generating sets for alternative and standby supplies. Units are now available from about 500 kVA upwards.

At ratings below about 4000 kVA the gas turbine is more costly than the equivalent diesel driven set and its fuel consumption is much higher. However, the gas turbine has the advantage of being more compact and lighter in weight. Also, although basically very noisy, it is easier to apply acoustic treatment since gas turbines do not suffer from low frequency vibrations like diesel engines. Hence it is possible to consider installing gas turbine plant on the roofs of buildings, which has the incidental advantage of reducing the noise problem and eliminating the cost of installing an exhaust flue through the building.

2.2.3.6 Batteries

Two basic types of battery are in use for standby supplies, the lead-acid battery and the nickel-cadmium battery.

Two main versions of the lead-acid battery cell are used, the Planté cell with pure lead positive plates, and the flat plate cell utilising alloy positive plates. The latter are less expensive and more compact but have a life expectancy of about 10 or 12 years compared with 25 years for the Planté cells.

The nickel-cadmium battery is of very robust construction and is capable of withstanding considerable electrical and mechanical abuse. It has a very long life, retains its charge for long periods and is tolerant of extremes of temperature. However it is expensive when compared with the lead-acid battery and its use is therefore usually reserved for special applications.

The capacity which can be taken from a battery varies with the discharge rate and is also affected by temperature. It is measured in ampere hours and is usually quoted at the 10 hour discharge rate.

Most batteries used for standby supplies today are equipped with constant voltage chargers. The principle of these is that after a discharge of the battery its voltage will be depressed and this enables a relatively large current to flow from the charger to recharge the battery. As the battery becomes more fully charged its voltage will rise until it reaches the constant voltage level where the current output from the charger will drop until it will be just sufficient to balance the battery's internal losses. The main advantage of this system is that the battery controls the amount of charge it receives and is therefore automatically maintained in a fully-charged condition without human intervention, and without the use of any elaborate control circuitry. (Fig. 2.2.3)

2.2.3.7 Solar panels

Two forms of solar panel are available:

(a) Where a photovoltaic cell produces electricity directly.
(b) Where the solar energy is converted into heat.

The photovoltaic cell now offers a practical solution to the problems of supplying power to remote-located communications or signalling equipment, and the same technique is used for satellite applications. The panels are relatively expensive at present, but indications are that the cost of manufacturing them is likely to drop during the next decade.

The more commonly found solar panels are those where the collector comprises an absorber plate in close contact with tubes through which the medium to be heated, usually water, flows. It is usual to insulate the back and the sides of the collector panel to minimise heat losses and to have a glass cover on the front, facing the sun.

Active solar heating is possible in the UK, but studies already done have thrown some doubt on its economic viability except for certain specialist applications, such as the heating of swimming pools, and any scheme put forward needs to be looked

Fig. 2.2.3. *Automatic battery charging system* *(Chloride)*

at critically to ensure that it is cost effective and that the equipment is itself reliable and long-lasting. Improvements in the design of solar collectors, and increasing real prices of fuel could improve the situation and make solar heating economically viable in the UK in the future.

A major drawback of solar energy is that it is generally most abundant when it is least required and there is considerable difficulty in storing the energy collected for later use. Hence its obvious attraction for heating swimming pools, and similarly it can be applied to domestic water heating, although in the UK it is necessary to supplement the solar heating by a conventional system, even during the summer months when sunlight is at its most abundant.

In climates enjoying much longer periods of sunlight, for example in the Middle East, the economic use of solar heating panels is more assured, and in addition to water heating, there would appear to be possibilities for the heat to be used to power absorption type chillers in the provision of air conditioning. A photograph of a typical roof-top water-heating installation in the Middle East is shown in Fig. 2.2.4.

Fig. 2.2.4. *Roof top solar panels*

2.2.3.8 Location of standby equipment

Diesel engines and other large plant should be located in a well ventilated room with adequate space between machines to allow for easy repair and maintenance. Diesel generating sets are normally supplied with the engine and alternator on a common base plate but massive concrete foundations are neither necessary nor recommended. As a rule the machines should be supported on anti-vibration mountings to reduce the transfer of vibration through the structure of the building. Anti-vibration mountings should be considered essential when the machines are in an occupied building. Even so, noise emission can be high, although a greater level of noise may be tolerated for short term generation than would be accepted for continuous operation.

Small batteries, usually supplied in a cabinet with their associated charger, can be located in almost any room that is reasonably well ventilated. Large batteries are supplied on open wooden stands and are often housed in a room specially reserved for the purpose. When possible a water supply and a low level sink should be provided where large batteries are housed.

2.2.3.9 Maintenance of standby equipment

Plant provided for standby purposes, whether powered by rotating plant or batteries, is very reliable and requires little attention to keep it in good condition. However, maintenance must not be neglected and satisfactory performance is best guaranteed by regular, routine maintenance.

In rotating plant this calls for:

– a check on general cleanliness
– a check on fuel tank level
– a check on lubricating oil level
– a check on radiator/cooling water jacket level
– a check on starting battery condition

For battery equipment this calls for:

– a check on general cleanliness, particularly cell tops and terminals
– a check on electrolyte level (and occasionally on specific gravity)
– a check on battery voltage (and occasionally on the voltage of each cell)
– a check on charger output

In all cases the maintenance data should be logged, and the plant should be operated on test at regular intervals, say once a month.

2.2.4 References

2.2.4.1 References in text

(1) Electricity Council Engineering Recommendation G 26. 'The Installation and Operational Aspects of Private Generating Plant'
(2) Electricity Council Engineering Recommendation G 47. 'Notes of Guidance for the Parallel Operation of Private Generators with Electricity Boards' Low Voltage Networks'
(3) DAVID, JONATHAN. 'Emergency Lighting' (Building Services. September 1981.) (The Journal of the CIBS)
(4) Industry Committe for Emergency Lighting (ICEL) 207 Balham High Road, London, SW17 7BQ

2.2.4.2 Legislation (see also Appendix 6.1)

Explosives Act 1875
Electricity (Factories Act) Special Regulations 1908 & 1944

Cinematograph Act 1952
Mines and Quarries Act 1954
Factories Act 1961
Offices Shops and Railway Premises Act 1963
Health and Safety at Work Etc Act 1974
Electrical Equipment (Safety) Regulations 1975
Energy Act 1983

2.2.4.3 British Standards (see also Appendix 6.2)

BS 440 Stationary Batteries (Lead-Acid Planté cells)
BS 5266 Emergency Lighting
BS 5514 Performance of Internal Combustion Engines.
BSCP 1007 Maintained Lighting for Cinemas.

2.2.4.4 Bibliography

CIBS (formerly IES) Code for Interior Lighting.
Diesel Engines for the World – Yearbook and Buyers' Guide (Whitehall Press, Maidstone)
Electric Power Plant International, (ERA Technology Limited Cleeve Road, Leatherhead.)
HOWELL, DEREK. 'Your Solar Energy home (including Wind and Methane Applications.)' (Pergamon Press)
LAZER, IRWIN. 'Electrical Systems Analysis & Design for Industrial Plants', (McGraw-Hill Publishing Co.)
SMITH, G. 'Storage Batteries', (Pitman)
WOZNIAK, S.J. 'Solar Heating Systems for the UK. Design, Installation and Economic Aspects'. (HMSO)

Part 3
Electrical installation technology

IEE Wiring Regulations

Chapter 3.1

Electrical installation practice

Philip J. Champ, C.Eng., F.I.E.E., F.B.I.M.
East Midlands Electricity Board

3.1.1 General

3.1.1.1 Introduction

The design and execution of a satisfactory electrical installation is a complex process requiring the application of knowledge and skills no less demanding than those involved in any other aspect of the building process. Each electrical installation, whether in domestic, industrial or commercial premises, requires to be conceived and executed with due regard to the requirements of the building and its users. Thus although an electrical installation usually comprises mass-produced components, their co-ordination into an effective whole results in an unique assembly suited to the particular purposes of a given premises. This chapter will outline the significant features of electrical installation practice and will indicate in broad terms the design and practical decisions which will be required in the more frequently met situations.

An electrical installation, whether for a small flat or a large factory must meet certain basic criteria. It must convey electrical energy in an efficient manner from the point of origin (usually the load terminals of the Electricity Authority's meters, but occasionally the terminals of a privately owned generator) to the locations within the premises where it is to be employed. It should also provide for foreseeable changes in the location or nature of use which will occur during the life of the property. These functions must be performed safely, without risk of injury to the occupants of the premises or people who may have to maintain the installation, without risk of fire or other damage to the structure and without damage to the installation itself.

3.1.1.2 IEE Wiring Regulations

The principal guide to good electrical installation practice in the United Kingdom is the 15th Edition of the Institution of Electrical Engineers Regulations published in

1981, together with later amendments. The Society of Telegraph Engineers and Electricians published the first wiring regulations under the title 'Rules and Regulations for the Prevention of Fire Risks arising from Electric Lighting' in 1882, a little over one year after the first public electricity supplies were inaugurated in England. These Regulations have been continuously reviewed and updated to reflect the evolution in knowledge and application of electrical technology.

The 15th Edition of the Regulations owes much to international work on installation standards in two bodies, the International Electrotechnical Commission (IEC) and the European Committee for Electrotechnical Standardisation (CENELEC) and represents a major step towards adoption of internationally agreed rules for electrical installations.

In the United Kingdom the IEE Regulations enjoy a wide measure of regard and respect. However, they do not, in themselves, have the force of law. The Scottish Building Regulations embrace the IEE Regulations, and other United Kingdom legislative measures (Factories Acts, Electricity Supply Regulations, etc) make reference to the Regulations in such a way as to either accord them a 'deemed to satisfy' status or to render it difficult to meet the mandatory requirements without at least complying with the IEE Regulations.

In Great Britain, an Electricity Board's responsibility in respect of electrical installations is limited to the requirements of the Electricity Supply Regulations 1937. These provide that a Board may refuse a supply to an installation 'unless they are reasonably satisfied that the connection, if made, would not cause leakage from the consumer's installation exceeding one ten-thousandth part of the maximum current to be supplied to the said installation'.

A further, more discretionary and little used, clause states that the Board is not compelled to commence (or continue) a supply unless they are reasonably satisfied that the consumer's installation meets certain basic safety requirements. The Electricity Supply Regulations do however provide that compliance with the IEE Regulations is deemed to satisfy the requirements of the Electricity Supply Regulations. Thus while compliance with the IEE Regulations will, in general, ensure the connection of an electricity supply, the provision of a supply is no guarantee that anything more than the most basic safety requirements have been met. Many consumers mistakenly believe that connection of an installation by an Electricity Board is their assurance of its safety.

The responsibility for the acquisition and maintenance of a safe, adequate electrical installation lies with the owner or occupier of the property who should, as a minimum, seek to ensure that any new installation complies with the IEE Wiring Regulations.

Where factories and other premises governed by the Electricity (Factories Act) Special Regulations 1908 and 1944 are concerned these Regulations take precedence; during the construction period the effect of these Regulations is that the electrical contractor has the responsibility for the operation of the installation until the time of the formal handover. Overall, however, the IEE Wiring Regulations constitute a valuable guide to safe construction and installation.

Certain premises e.g. hospitals, cinemas, garages and special process plants, have additional special requirements which are in general more onerous than the IEE Wiring Regulations.

3.1.1.3 Consulting engineers

The prospective building owner or developer is – as with all aspects of the building process – confronted with the need to translate his generalised requirements into a practical reality. When the developer employs his own electrical staff they will normally initiate the design work even if at a later stage the work is executed by an external contractor. In most situations however, such capability does not exist in-house and a Consulting Engineer will be brought in to undertake the design and supervision of the contract to completion. He will explore with the client and the other members of the building team the electrical needs of the project and translate these into practical designs. Consulting Engineers are permitted no financial involvement with prospective contractors and are bound to act in the best interests of their client throughout the project. Advice on the location and selection of Consulting Engineers can be obtained from the Association of Consulting Engineers, Alliance House, 12, Caxton Street, London. SW1H 0QL.

3.1.1.4 Electrical contractors

For smaller projects, it is often the practice for the client, or his architect, to deal directly with the prospective electrical contractors. In this situation it is vital that the client produces a detailed brief or specification of his requirements, so that a common basis exists for the comparison of tenders. Any vagueness or omission will lead to costly additions, variations, and delays at a later stage, and to prospective contractors making assumptions which are not necessarily in keeping with the client's requirements.

The specification or design brief together with drawings of the proposed building will be sent to a number of electrical contractors to price. The number of contractors invited to tender should be as small as possible and there is rarely good reason for more than three of four tenders being invited. The practice of allowing large numbers of contractors to tender is to be deprecated as it inevitably leads to considerable amounts of wasted effort by the unsuccessful contractors which in turn must be reflected in higher tender prices generally. The selection of prospective contractors is a difficult and yet vitally important process. Electrical contracting organisations vary from small, one or two man firms to large international organisations. Local knowledge, reputations and the prospective contractor's past record of undertaking similar projects will assist selection. In the UK, the Electrical Contractors Association and the Electrical Contractors Association of Scotland, offer a 'guarantee of work' scheme to cover installations carried out by their members.

The National Inspection Council for Electrical Installation Contracting (NICEIC) publishes a Roll of Approved Contractors. The Council, through a team of regional inspecting engineers ensures that Approved Contractors have the plant, skill and experience to undertake installations in conformity with the IEE Wiring Regulations.

Each contractor is visited regularly and a random sample of his work inspected; repeated failure to adhere to the appropriate standards will result in deletion of the offending Contractor from the Roll.

Most reputable contractors value their membership of the Roll and many public authorities and specifying organisations use only NICEIC approved contractors. In this way they not only safeguard their own interests but also help to raise standards in the contracting industry by encouraging membership of the NICEIC. Copies of the NICEIC Roll can usually be found in Public Libraries, Electricity Board shops, or can be obtained from NICEIC 237 Kennington Lane, London SE11 5QJ.

The Electricity Boards operate their own competitive electrical contracting units throughout the country and are members of the NICEIC.

3.1.1.5 Certification

As in the field of switch gear (section 3.2.4) ASTA – the Association of Short Circuit Testing Authorities – is the oficially recognised UK certification authority for electrical installation equipment such as plugs, sockets, light switches, consumer units, miniature circuit breakers and residual current devices (r.c.d.). Manufacturers can be licensed to use the ASTA Diamond Mark which demonstrates compliance with a specified British Standard and involves both factory and market surveillance. ASTA publishes a list of approved products and licence holders.

BSI also operates certification schemes in certain industrial and commercial areas (see appendix 6.2) whilst BEAB certifies domestic appliances for safety (see section 5.2.2.7) and BASEC acts similarly in the field of cables. (section 3.3.7)

3.1.2 Structural considerations

3.1.2.1 Benefits of early consultation

The electrical installations in many existing buildings bear witness to the regrettably frequent practice of regarding such installations as a minor ancillary which need only be considered after the design of the buildings has been finalised. This practice has probably occurred because of a general lack of appreciation on the part of architects, designers and building users of the benefits of planning the incorporation of electrical services at the earliest design stage. Not only will early consideration of the electrical requirements minimise problems of space, congestion, and the need for costly amendments to design, it can offer positive benefits to architect or designer. The electrical specialist will be able to suggest installation techniques which will minimise inconvenience to other trades, speed the installation process and lead to an integrated finished project in which the electrical installation is as unobtrusive as possible.

3.1.2.2 Accommodation for incoming supply

The first aspect to be considered is the provision for the connection to the source of supply – usually the Electricity Authority's mains. In domestic premises the use of outdoor meter boxes offers many advantages both to the builder and to the final occupier. An outdoor meter box is usually a fibre-glass or plastic box set into the outer leaf of an outside wall with provision for housing the incoming service cable, meters and any necessary timeswitches. In the UK, Electricity Boards will often supply such boxes free of charge but alternative purpose-made boxes will also be considered and early negotiation is advantageous. The installation of an outside meter box not only facilitates meter reading when the house is unoccupied but also allows the installation of service cables to be undertaken at an earlier stage in the construction process. The consumer's main switch, or consumer unit, will normally be situated inside the premises within 2–3 metres of the meter box.

A block of flats can be regarded in many respects like a row of houses except that where houses can be serviced from the road, services to each flat must be run within the building. Provision for these cables within the building structure will be necessary and this must take the form of ducts and pipes formed in the structure to allow cables to be taken from a central position to the supply point of each flat. Since the design of blocks of flats varies so widely, again it is essential that discussions are held with the Electricity Authority regarding the methods of and provision for services and meters in such buildings.

Installations in commercial and industrial buildings are invariably more extensive. Where the expected total load of a building exceeds about 300–500 kW the Electricity Authority will usually require a substation on the premises and detailed discussions will be necessary regarding location, size and structural requirements. It should, however, be noted that even where a substation is being provided on the premises, separate provision will be necessary for a switchroom.

The switchroom should as far as practicable be sited near to the centre of the electrical load, thus minimising the need for long circuits of large cable. The switchroom needs to be large enough to permit the installation of all the required switchgear on one uninterupted wall with at least 25% additional wall space for future modifications and extensions. In addition, ample space needs to be provided for cables to be taken from the switchboard in all directions and for operation and maintenance of the switchgear. Too often switchboards are sited in cupboards or storerooms which are inadequately sized, forcing the site operatives and future maintenance personnel to work in cramped and dangerous locations, and creating hazards when faults occur. The requirements of the Factories Acts in regard to the costruction, siting and security of substations must also be taken into account.

3.1.2.3 Cable routes

The routes to be followed by each main cable or group of cables from the switchroom need to be identified and checked to see that there are no obstacles along that route caused by other services, structural supports, etc; where possible, ducts should be provided solely for the purpose of electrical services. It will be necessary to provide access for cables to pass through walls, floors and ceilings and such provision needs to be planned at an early stage. Not only is it infuriating and costly to have to drill holes through recently erected structures, but in extreme cases the integrity of the structure can be put at risk. Thus the planning of major cableways and the provision of floor channels, rising ducts and lateral cable channels makes for a superior finished job at lower overall cost.

In larger buildings distribution boards will be established at strategic sub-centres throughout the building thus avoiding the need for numerous long circuit cables. For example, in a multi-storey office block a switchroom would normally be sited on the ground floor and would feed one or more distribution boards on each floor via a rising service duct situated within the central core.

3.1.2.4 Trunking and conduit

The distribution of circuits from distribution boards to individual points of use will usually be via trunking or conduits. Where a building is being provided with false ceilings these can usually be readily accommodated in the ceiling void but care will need to be taken if, as often happens, the ceiling void also contains hot water pipes or other heating plant.

Large areas of open plan office or display space are increasingly popular but present the problem of providing electrical services to the furniture and equipment to be used in them. A floor and/or skirting trunking system is usually the most effective answer, but again requires consideration and incorporation at the structural design stage. Skirting trunking, although often used, permits socket outlets and telephone connections to be provided only at the walls; this results in the use of dangerous and unsightly lengths of flex to connect apparatus. Floor trunking can be laid in lengths across a floor at say, two metre intervals and connection boxes can be provided at any required frequency. Such connection boxes will be constructed so as to be flush with the floor finish so that unused boxes present no hazard to pedestrian traffic.

The selection of types of floor trunking will depend upon the type of floor finish to be employed, the range of facilities required (power, telephones, visual display units, alarm circuits, etc.,) and budget considerations. A minimum of 15 mm concrete cover is required above a floor duct.

For lighting circuits and power circuits where the degree of flexibility required is not significant, conduits can be incorporated into floor slabs. This is done by laying conduits into the structure just before the slab is poured and should invariably serve outlets in the area beneath in order to avoid forming U-bends in which condensation will form. Since such conduits are rarely more than 25 mm diameter an alternative approach is to lay conduits in the floor screed, passing down through pre-formed holes in the slab to serve outlets on the ceiling beneath.

3.1.2.5 False ceilings

False ceilings can present opportunities or problems to the electrical installation installer. Some ceiling systems comprise lightweight metal supporting skeletons suspended on wire from the underside of the roof slab. Such systems are often not adequate to bear the additional weight of luminaires, giving rise to the need for additional supports. Further, the vertical alignment of luminaires against such ceilings can often be unsatisfactory. The better solution lies in the use of luminaires recessed into the false ceiling and using a common adequate mechanical support. The ceiling tiles are then selected or cut to form a close fit with the luminaires, giving an integrated and satisfactory overall finish. Close liaison between electrical and ceiling installers is essential in order to ensure that such composite installations are satisfactory.

3.1.2.6 Fixings and supports

A considerable amount of time, effort and expense in electrical installation work is devoted to making fixings for cables, conduits and equipment. Wherever possible, therefore, fixings should be provided along cable routes by the incorporation of timber pieces in cast slabs, steel hangers, brackets or other fixing points. In factory and workshop environments where finished appearance is less critical, conduits and trunking are usually fixed to the surface of the structure. It should be noted however, that conduit and trunking need to be supported at regular intervals to avoid risk of mechanical stress. Appendix 11 of the IEE Regulations gives the maximum support spacing for both conduit and trunking.

An interesting and economical recent innovation which not only overcomes the need for fixings but also provides an unobtrusive installation is the introduction of trunking systems which use the lower limb of structural roof members as part of the trunking, adding a purpose made lid to enclose cables.

In industrial situations, particularly where other piped services are present, it is important that electrical conduits are clearly distinguishable from other pipes and services in order to minimise the risk of confusion and consequent hazard. BS 1710 lays down the agreed colour coding for each factory service and in accordance with this Standard, electrical conduits should be coloured orange.

3.1.2.7 Electrical connections between buildings

Industrial sites often comprise two or more detached buildings, giving rise to the need for electrical interconnection between buildings. There are two principal ways in which this can be achieved – overhead or underground. When cables are taken overhead it is necessary to avoid the risk of mechanical damage from external sources, e.g. traffic passing beneath and also to provide adequate support to prevent the weight of the cable causing mechanical stresses. This support is usually achieved by using cable with an integral catenary wire or by placing normal p.v.c. insulated and sheathed cable in a continuous length of heavy duty conduit. In both cases careful consideration needs to be given to the type of traffic likely to pass beneath and even where no traffic is expected a ground clearance of at least 3·5 m is required.

Where buildings are separated by considerable distance or where traffic is likely, overhead systems are unsuitable and cables should be laid underground. While it is permissible to bury cables directly in the ground provided the depth is adequate and they are marked by cable covers or tapes, it is preferable to install such cables in buried conduits or pipes. A number of pipes of 75 mm or 100 mm diameter should be laid in a trench usually not less than 0.5 metres deep. To avoid the need for subsequent re-excavation in the event of a fault or an increase in load it is good practice to lay at least one or two more pipes than are immediately required. Such pipes should terminate in slow bends or covered pits just inside each building so that cables can be drawn in at a later stage without damage.

3.1.3 Principles of electrical installation design

3.1.3.1 Assessment of general characteristics

Past experience has indicated that inadequate consideration is often given to the circumstances and requirements of an installation before detailed design and installation work commences. Part 3 of the IEE Regulations therefore calls attention to the need for a careful, in-depth, consideration of the circumstances of the proposed installation. This assessment will involve the installation designer in consultation with the Electricity Authority, the architect, the building user and equipment suppliers.

3.1.3.2 Diversity and maximum demand

The maximum electrical demand of the proposed installation has to be estimated with care. Too low a figure will result in overloading of the cables and switchgear and the operation of fuses or other protective devices. The adoption of too high a figure without paying due regard to diversity will cause unnecessary expense in the employment of oversized cable and switchgear. It follows therefore, that the designer needs an intimate knowledge not only of each item of equipment to be used but also the manner and frequency of its use in order to estimate the simultaneous maximum demand of the installation. He must also make an informed estimate of likely future changes in the nature and pattern of usage if costly alterations and extensions to the installation are to be avoided at a later date.

Table 4B of the IEE Regulations gives a general guide to the determination of the likely maximum demand to be expected from an installation. The current demanded from each circuit is assessed by applying the percentages shown in the table to the current demand or the rated full load current of the equipment. However, it must be stressed that these figures are a general guide only. The more extensive and complex the installation is, the more important it is that the assessment of demand is carried out by a competent engineer fully acquainted with the equipment and the way it is to be used.

3.1.3.3 Supply characteristics

Armed with an assessment of the expected demand, the designer can then seek information from the Electricity Authority regarding the proposed supply arrangements. Demands of up to 100 A (25 kW) will usually be supplied from a single phase two-wire 240 V service, larger requirements will be met by a three-phase

240/415 V four-wire supply and the proposed load will need to be divided and balanced across the three phases. Where the proposed load exceeds around 300–500 kW the provision of high voltage (6.6 kV or 11 kV) supplies will be considered and one or more transformers will be necessary to reduce the voltage to the normal working level.

At the same time the designer will need to ascertain from the Electricity Authority the availability and type of external earthing arrangement to be used for the supply including, and in the case of supplies yet to be installed, an estimation of the maximum impedance of the earth fault loop external to the installation, and of the prospective short circuit current. Further development of this important subject follows in Sections 3.1.5.7 and 3.1.10.2.

3.1.3.4 External influences

Consideration must be given to the external influences under which the installation will operate. The IEE Regulations make reference in Appendix 6 to the present international classification of external influences but note that work on the application of these classifications is insufficiently advanced to be adopted as a basis for Regulations at this time.

Nevertheless the designer must give thought to the circumstances in which his installation will be required to operate. These will include ambient temperatures, the presence of water or corrosive substances, the likelihood of damage due to vibration, mechanical impact, or even insects and small rodents. He must also consider the type of users on the premises who may be children or handicapped people and their requirements in terms of action or evacuation in emergency conditions and in terms of special facilities. (Low level sockets and chest-high switches may be inaccessible to wheel-chair bound people).

3.1.3.5 General arrangement of the installation

The installation designer may now consider the general arrangement of the proposed installation. This will include consideration of the number and location of distribution boards and the individual circuits required. Each installation must be divided into a number of distinct circuits in order that each circuit and its associated control and protective devices may be related to the use of the circuit. The decisions regarding the sub-division of the installation into circuits will inevitably involve an element of judgment and experience but Regulation 314-1 requires that such sub-division be made so as to avoid danger and minimise inconvenience in the event of a fault, as well as facilitating the safe operation, inspection, testing and maintenance of the installation. (Fig. 3.1.1)

The design process will normally start at the point of use of equipment, progressively building back via circuit distribution boards to the point of supply.

The lighting installation will be planned, often in consultation with specialist designers or equipment suppliers, to provide the requisite levels of illumination. Compliance with Regulation 314-1 and commonsense precautions dictate that the lighting in a dwelling or in any work area should be divided across two or more circuits so that in the event of a fault the whole area is not plunged into darkness. This precaution is particularly important where hot or moving plant is involved or where exit routes, or stairways have to be negotiated. One of the preferred ways of meeting this requirement is to arrange for alternate rows of lighting to be fed from separate circuits and protective devices so that in the event of a fault an adequate overall illumination is maintained to enable safe evacuation to be effected. The designer of a lighting installation can choose from a variety of control facilities ranging from simple manual local switches to automatic time or photo-electric controls designed to optimise energy utilisation. The selection of the appropriate control techniques should be a matter of guided discussion with the building user.

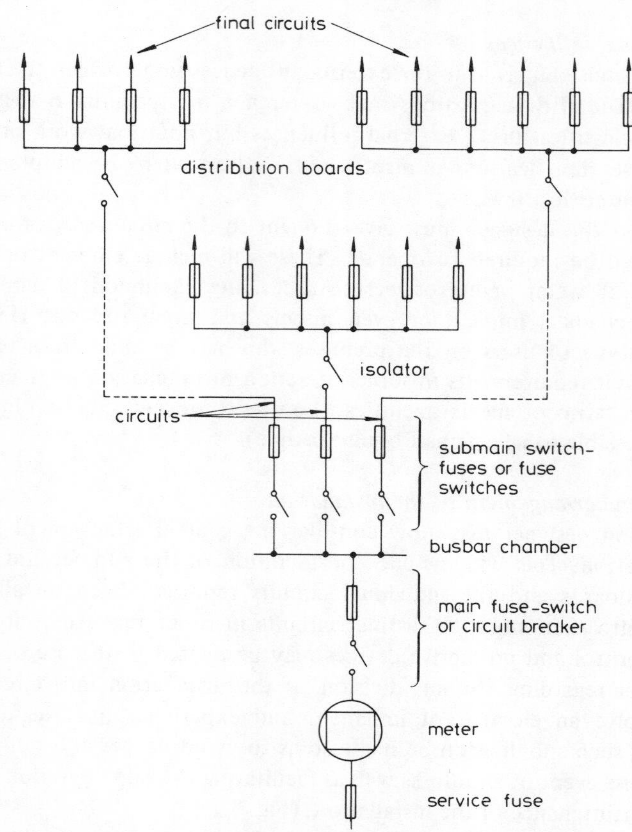

Fig. 3.1.1. *Arrangement of main and final circuits in a large installation.*

The prospective maximum load of each piece of electrical equipment must be identified and a circuit installed to suit the purpose. Every circuit must be provided with means of isolation and switching in both normal and emergency conditions.

While this requirement is readily appreciated and met in respect of a simple piece of equipment, it is more onerous where large machines employing several separate motors and operating components are concerned. Switching arrangements must include the facility to switch off the whole of the equipment under full load conditions, instantaneously.

Circuits feeding individual items of plant will be connected to distribution boards and protected by devices to prevent the persistence of overload or short circuit conditions, and the relevant protective devices must be labelled to indicate the circuit and apparatus protected.

3.1.3.6 Socket outlets

The concept of the socket outlet is one which provides for flexibility. It recognises the needs of the user to connect different appliances at different times and places, and to reposition them more or less frequently at will. The principles suggest a large number of circuits each terminating in a socket outlet, each capable of supplying the largest available appliance, and each separately wired back to the source. But because the outlets will be close together, it is unlikely that more than a small proportion will be utilised to their maximum capacity at any one time. By applying this principle of diversity sensibly, a single 30 A protective device may protect 20 or more 13 A socket outlets. However, the individual outlets need to be provided with a greater degree of protection than is afforded by the 30 A amp protective device alone. The standard British socket outlet is covered by BS 1363, and the plug therefore incorporates provision for a fuse with a maximum rating of 13 A.

The 30 A protective device protects the circuit cables and the sockets connected to it. The fuse in the plug protects the appliance and is related to the current rating of the flex connecting it to the plug. 13 A fuses should be fitted to the plug of a high load appliance while a small appliance or a lamp should be connected via a 3 A fuse.

The development of the BS 1363 plug and socket system and the associated concept of the ring circuit have made possible the provision of large numbers of socket outlets at lower cost than would otherwise be possible. (Fig. 3.1.2) The requirements for a ring circuit using BS 1363 socket outlets are set out in Appendix 5 of the IEE Regulations and include the following:

(a) The floor area served by any one domestic ring circuit must not exceed 100 m^2. In non-domestic premises the expected demand may indicate that a smaller area be served by each ring.

(b) Kitchens and similar high load areas should be provided with separate circuits.

(c) Non-fused spurs, not exceeding the number of sockets in the ring, may be connected to the ring.

(d) Permanently connected equipment must be fed from an appropriate fused spur unit. Fixed space heaters, water heaters and immersion heaters must not be connected to the ring circuit, but should be supplied from their own separate circuits.

The use of BS 1363 socket outlets does not however inevitably require the provision of a ring circuit. A single radial circuit may serve an unlimited number of sockets provided the floor area served is limited to 50 m² if the circuit protection is 30 A, or 20 m² if the circuit protection is only 20 A. (Fig. 3.1.3).

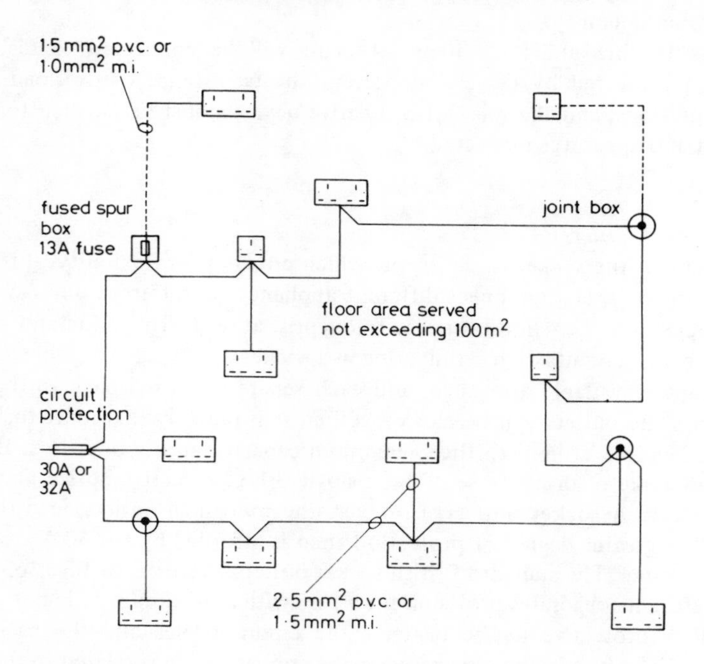

Fig. 3.1.2. ***Ring circuit for socket outlets to BS 1363***

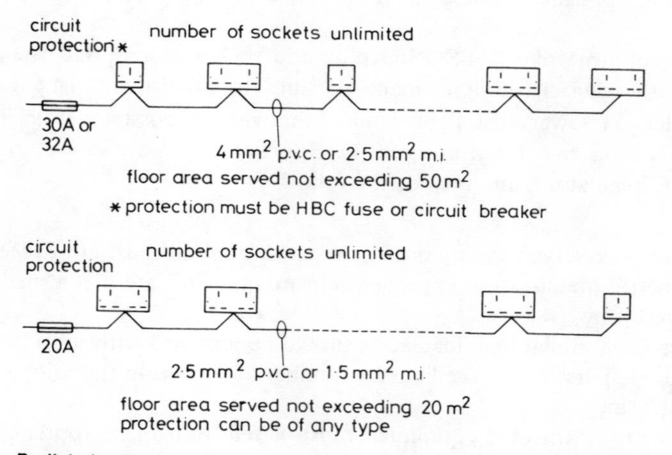

Fig. 3.1.3. ***Radial circuits***

3.1.3.7 'Clean' supplies

Certain communications and data processing equipment is sensitive to variations in the uniformity of the 240 V 50 Hz supply and in particular to distortions caused by other pieces of electronic equipment, or frequently switched loads. While they will take every reasonably practicable measure, the Electricity Authority cannot always ensure that the supply they provide is free of such distortions, which can in many cases arise within the premises concerned.

For this reason, it is sometimes necessary to arrange for the provision of so-called 'clean' supplies to certain equipment. This provision may range from the installation of a dedicated circuit directly from the consumer's main switchboard to the equipment concerned, to the installation of specialist equipment capable of removing any distortions, if circumstances demand it. Where sensitive equipment of this kind is to form part of the installation early consultation between manufacturers, the user, and the Electricity Authority, are essential.

3.1.4 Control of electrical installations (See also chapters 3.2 and 3.5)

3.1.4.1 Functions of control devices

The various control devices – switches isolators, links, etc, – which may be incorporated in an installation have four functions to perform:

(a) Functional switching; i.e. switching apparatus on and off or regulating its speed.
(b) Isolation; i.e. cutting off a piece of equipment or the whole or part of an installation from every source of electricity in order that work may be done on it in safety.
(c) Switching for mechanical maintenance, which relates to the electrical disconnection of equipment in order that non-electrical maintenance can be undertaken by electrically unskilled people, e.g. lamp changing, cleaning.
(d) Emergency switching, which implies the facility rapidly to cut off the supply to remove an electrical or mechanical hazard.

As we shall see, these four functions do not necessarily have to be performed by four separate devices; one device may perform more than one function. However, it is unlikely in practice that any one device will perform all four functions.

It is axiomatic that any device designed to control an installation in the interests of safety must itself be safe. In general this means that such devices must conform to the relevant British Standards and must be safely and properly installed in a position where their use will not create a hazard and where their function will not be impeded by other activities in the premises.

3.1.4.2 Functional switching

A functional switch may be a simple on-off plate switch on a bedroom wall or a complex assembly of speed and time control devices or other controls. The use of semi-conductor devices such as thyristors and triacs is increasing in industry, commerce and even in the home. While such devices can be used for functional control, they are not at this stage considered adequate as isolators and must therefore be augmented by a means of isolation. Any functional switch must be capable of performing its task and in the case of fluorescent lighting this can, for example, mean using a switch with a rating of twice the normal steady current of the circuit in order to allow for the high currents which flow in such circuits momentarily when they are switched on.

3.1.4.3 Isolation

Isolators must break all the phase conductors of the supply but the neutral conductor need not be broken except in the case of

(a) The main switch of a single phase installation.
(b) Heating appliances with exposed elements.
(c) Auto-transformers feeding discharge lamps.

Isolators are intended to be off-load devices, their purpose being to ensure that operators are not put at risk by the inadvertent closure of a switch. The isolating distances between contacts when in the open position is prescribed in BS 5419 and it is essential that, if the contacts are not visible, there is a reliable clear indication of the isolated position of the isolator such that there can be no confusion about its state.

Depending upon the type of device used and the circumstances it may be necessary to provide an isolator with a means of padlocking in the OFF position, or a removable handle so that personnel working on the isolated installation have total assurance against inadvertent energising of the circuit. While separate isolators are used for certain functions, particularly in industry, the functions of an isolator are more often incorporated into a switch or switch fuse unit. One simple means of combining the function of isolation with other functions is to use a plug and socket, while another is the removal of fuse carriers or links in a switch or distribution board, providing of course that this can be done in safety.

The number and disposition of isolators, or means of isolation combined with other functions, is a matter of judgment bearing in mind the need to provide means of isolation for work to be done while minimising inconvenience. Every installation must have a means of isolation at its origin, i.e. the point of entry of the supply and this may be adequate for a domestic installation. However, an industrial installation would invariably have means of isolating circuits or groups of circuits separately.

3.1.4.4 Switching for mechanical maintenance

Often, the means of isolation and/or functional switching off is also used to allow mechanical maintenance to be carried out. However, such devices must then be capable of breaking the full load of the circuit, and should preferably do so directly rather than through an indirect control circuit. They must also be selected having regard to the fact that mechanical maintenance may be undertaken by electrically unskilled people, and must therefore be effective without affording access to live parts. In other respects a switch intended to facilitate mechanical maintenance must fulfil the requirements of an isolator in that it must clearly indicate the OFF position and be designed or sited in such a way as to prevent unintentional re-closure.

3.1.4.5 Emergency switching

Emergency switching devices are similar again, except that plugs and sockets are not regarded as adequate emergency switching facilities and the handles or buttons of emergency switches should be coloured red.

Where the occurrence of an emergency necessitates the disconnection from one of several locations, emergency STOP buttons will usually be installed so as to be readily accessible to the operators of, say, a large piece of machinery. Such STOP buttons would disconnect circuit breakers or contactors situated remotely. It is vital in such circuits that the emergency switching circuits are fail-safe, that is they switch off the machine if the emergency switching circuit is defective.

The design and layout of any installation should be such that all controls, particularly those designed to be operated in emergency, can be readily located, identified and associated with the relevant apparatus or circuit, and not concealed so that their location or purpose appears a mystery. In considering his layout therefore, the designer must have regard to the users of the premises and the extent of their knowledge and capability. Switches mounted at high level – above 2 metres from the floor – or in locked or obstructed cupboards, garages and the like can hardly be said to be 'readily accessible'.

3.1.4.6 Application of controls in domestic installations

The practical effect and application of the requirements for control of an installation can be appreciated more readily by considering typical installations.

The domestic installation will have an isolator as close to the meter as possible, and this isolator will also fulfil the functions of a switch for mechanical maintenance and emergency purposes. It must therefore, be accessible to the householder. Isolation of individual circuits will also be available in most cases by the removal of fuses or the operation of circuit breakers.

The lighting circuit will of course incorporate a number of functional switches which will also fulfil the role of maintenance and emergency switches. Where such switches are mounted within a luminaire, for example, a mirror light, the connections and structure of the luminaire must be such that normal maintenance, including lamp changing, can be carried out without exposing live parts.

In the use of BS 1363 (13 A) sockets and plugs, the combination may be used as an isolator, but does not fulfil the role of an emergency switch. Whenever emergency switching facilities are needed, the socket outlet must incorporate a double pole switch, and that switch must clearly indicate whether it is 'on' or 'off'. It is often considered that switched socket outlets are safer and more convenient for the user, than the plain socket, but for complete assurance that an appliance is isolated, the plug must be withdrawn from the socket.

Fixed appliances such as immersion heaters, and storage heaters, should be supplied by their own separate circuits and should each have a switch adjacent to them fulfilling the roles of isolator, functional and emergency switch.

IEE Regulation 476-20 deals specifically with domestic cookers and requires there to be a switch within 2 metres of the appliance. The two components, hob and oven, of a split level cooker may be controlled by one switch provided each is within 2 metres of the switch. If the hob and oven units are more distant that this or are, for example, on opposite walls of the room two switches will be required. One of the regrettably too common emergencies which occur in kitchens is the overheated chip pan. In such circumstances the cooker switch which is often found immediately above the cooker would be useless. It is thus desirable that the switch be positioned to one side of the cooker and never above it.

3.1.4.7 Application of controls in non-domestic installations

In an industrial situation the installation must similarly incorporate an initial isolator which may even be a high vcltage switch when supply is provided at 6.6 kV or 11 kV. However, if the supply is provided at high voltage a switch will also be required on the low voltage side of the transformer. The initial fuse-switch or circuit breaker will be connected to a bus-bar of sufficient size and capacity to enable each of the outgoing circuits to be connected to it via its own switch. A busbar chamber is a convenient and safe means of connecting a large number of outgoing circuits to a single incoming circuit and it is common to find several such chambers of varying size used within an installation to provide the means of 'branching' one high capacity circuit into a number of smaller ones. Individual circuit switches will be connected to a busbar chamber and the outgoing circuit may terminate at a single piece of apparatus, a distribution board or another busbar chamber. In each case a further switch will be placed at the remote end.

Individual circuits may incorporate some or all of the following control devices:

(a) Circuit-breakers are switches with integral protective capabilities which enable them to break circuits automatically under specified fault conditions.
(b) Contactors are switches operated electromechanically by control currents from detectors or other apparatus situated remotely. Large numbers of contactors will often be found associated with process machinery, controlled either automatically or manually from remote locations.
(c) Switch fuses are factory produced assemblies in which, for convenience, a switch and one or more fuses for circuit protection purposes are enclosed within a single chamber usually constructed of steel. The design is such that access to the fuses and other live parts can only be obtained with the switch in the OFF position.
(d) Switches vary in size, shape and capability from miniature lamp switches for the control of individual luminaires to large 1600–2000 A switches for the control of whole installations. Switches for domestic applications are usually of plastic con-

struction except where high durability or improved appearance is required. Switches for industrial use are usually of steel construction, with cast iron being employed for flameproof and other similar applications.
(e) Photo-electric switches are increasingly being used to control both indoor and outdoor lighting. They are sensitive to the level of light falling upon them and can be used to ensure that lighting is operative during hours of darkness.
(f) Solid state controls are now widely used to monitor and control electrically a wide range of processes. They can be used to vary the speed of motors, stop or start machines or vary the intensity of heating or cooling in response to detected events. The art and application of solid state and programmable controls is developing rapidly. However, in accordance with Regulation 537-4 semi-conductor devices controlling circuits or appliances must be supplemented by a directly operating conventional isolator.

3.1.5 Protection of an electrical installation

3.1.5.1 Purposes of protective measures

The provision of protective devices in an electrical installation is fundamental to the whole concept of the safe use of electricity in buildings. The electrical installation as a whole, and each of its constituent parts, must be protected against overload or short circuit, and the people in the vicinity must be protected against the risk of shock, fire or other risks arising from either their own misuse of the installation or from fault. A number of the other measures previously described have the same fundamental objectives, the protection of the installation and its users from the effects of unplanned occurrences. However, the installation and maintenance of adequate and appropriate protective measures is a vital constituent of the safe deployment of electrical energy.

3.1.5.2 Insulation

Insulation is an important aspect of protection against contact with an electrical conductor, and the IEE Regulations identify two classes of insulated equipment:

(a) Class I equipment, in which protection against electric shock does not rely on basic insulation only, but which includes means for the connection of exposed conductive parts to a protective conductor of the fixed wiring of the installation.
(b) Class II equipment, in which protection against electric shock does not rely on basic insulation only, but in which additional safety precautions such as supplementary insulation are provided, there being no provision for the connection of exposed metalwork of the equipment to a protective conductor, and no reliance upon precautions to be taken in the fixed wiring of the installation.

BS 2754 gives information on the classification of equipment with regard to the means provided for protection against electric shock.

3.1.5.3 Protection against shock

The human body's movements are controlled by the nervous system. Minute electrical signals travel between the central nervous system and the muscles, stimulating operation of the muscles. Thus, if the body becomes part of a more powerful external circuit and current flows through it, the body's normal electrical operations are disrupted. Such shock currents cause unnatural operation of the muscles which the body's own electrical signals are unable to overcome and the result can be that the patient is unable to release the conductor which is causing the shock. In simple terms therefore the body becomes a conductor and part of a circuit through which current is flowing. It is however, important to recognise that the current which flows through the body is a function not only of the body's inherent resistance but also of the surface resistance of the skin of the hands and feet. This leads to the consideration of exceptional precautions where people with wet skin or the presence of wet surfaces are involved.

Two types of contact will result in a person receiving a shock:

(a) Direct contact with live parts, for example, a phase conductor in a piece of apparatus.
(b) Indirect contact, resulting from contact with the metal structure of a piece of equipment which has become live as a result of a fault. This might happen for example if an internal fault caused the metal case of an electric cooker to become and remain live.

In installations operating at normal mains voltages the primary method of protection against direct contact is by insulation. That is, all live parts are enclosed in some insulating material e.g. plastic, or rubber, which prevents contact with those parts unless the insulation is destroyed. Such insulating materials must of course be suitable for the circumstances in which they will be used, and the stresses to which they will be subjected.

Other methods of protection include the provision of barriers or enclosures which can only be opened by the use of tools, or when the supply is disconnected. Protection may also be provided by the provision of fixed obstacles such as a guard rail around an open switchboard, or by placing the live parts out of reach, as with an overhead line.

3.1.5.4 Protection against indirect contact

There are five methods of protection against contact with metalwork which has become unintentionally live recognised in the IEE Regulations. These are:–

(a) earthed equipotential bonding coupled with automatic disconnection of supply
(b) The use of Class II equipment and equivalent insulation
(c) The provision of a non-conducting location
(d) The use of earth-free equipotential bonding
(e) electrical separation

The use of methods (c) and (d) is limited to special situations under the effective supervision of trained personnel. Electrical separation is little used but does find an application in the domestic electric shaver supply unit which incorporates an isolating transformer.

The use of Class II insulation and equipment (other than for individual appliances) is similarly limited because it relies upon effective supervision to ensure that no metallic equipment or extraneous earthed metalwork ever enters the area of the installation.

The protective measure which is therefore almost universally used in the United Kingdom is method (a) – earthed equipotential bonding and automatic disconnection of supply.

3.1.5.5 Protection by equipotential bonding and automatic disconnection

This method relies upon all exposed metalwork being electrically connected together and to an effective earth connection. Not only must all metalwork associated with the electrical installation – conduits, metal switches, and the metalwork of appliances – be so connected, but extraneous metalwork such as gas and water pipes, radiators, structural steelwork and so on must similarly be connected to earth. In this way the likelihood of a voltage appearing between two adjacent exposed metal parts is removed.

The second element of this method of protection is the provision of a means of automatic disconnection of the supply in the event of a fault which causes exposed metalwork to become live.

The IEE Regulations recognise that the risk of an injurious shock is greater when the equipment concerned is portable and likely to be hand-held (e.g. an electric drill) than when the equipment is fixed. It is therefore specified that disconnection must be effected within 0·4 second for circuits which include socket outlets but within 5·0 seconds for circuits connected to fixed equipment. The achievement of these disconnection times is a function of the protective device (fuse or circuit breaker), the circuit to the fault, and the provision of adequate equipotential bonding. These aspects will therefore be considered further in the next section.

3.1.5.6 Residual current protection

The IEE Regulations recognise the particular problems created when electrical equipment (lawnmowers, drills, lights) are used outside the building. In these circumstances the availability of an adequate earth return path is a matter of chance.

The Regulations therefore require that any socket outlet intended to be used to supply equipment used outside the building shall have the additional protection of a residual current device (r.c.d.) having a rated residual operating current of not more than 30 milliamperes (mA). An r.c.d. is a form of circuit breaker which continuously compares the current in the phase and neutral conductors of a circuit. These currents in a healthy circuit will be equal. In a circuit which develops a fault some of the current flows to earth and the currents in the phase and neutral conductors will no longer be in balance. The r.c.d. detects this imbalance and if it exceeds a predetermined level, say 30 mA, disconnects the circuit (Figs. 3.1.10 and 3.1.11).

Having regard to the wide variety of unforeseeable factors which will be operative at the time a fault occurs an increasing number of installation designers consider that r.c.d. should be incorporated into most installations.

Such devices are available to control a single circuit or a whole installation. However, if consideration is being given to the use of a single r.c.d. to control the whole of an installation it should be remembered that its operation will disconnect all the circuits connected to it, including lighting circuits. The consequences of plunging a dwelling or other premises into darkness can, at times, be as serious as the consequnces of the fault the device was seeking to guard against. Fortunately assemblies are now available which enable an installation to be subdivided and protected by one or more r.c.d. in order to overcome this difficulty. (Fig. 3.1.4)

Fig. 3.1.4 *Split-load consumer unit* *(Crabtree Electrical Industries)*

3.1.5.7 Protection against excess current

Excess currents will occur in a circuit for two reasons. Overload, in which currents of up to a few times the rated current flow occur when the circuit is sound, but the load exceeds design expectations due to machine overload, departure from the assumed diversity, or the addition of some new unforeseen load. Short circuits on the other hand can result in current flows of many thousands of amperes and occur under fault conditions.

The object of any form of protection against excess current is to disconnect the affected circuit or apparatus before temperature rise in the cable conductors, or at the site of the short circuit, causes permanent damage to the installation or its surroundings. The devices used for overload and short circuit protection fall into three main categories:

(a) Semi-enclosed (rewireable) fuses designed to BS 3036
(b) High Breaking Capacity (h.b.c.) fuses to BS 88 or BS 1361
(c) Miniature or Moulded Case circuit breakers (Fig. 3.1.5).

Fig. 3.1.5. *Interior of miniature circuit breaker* *(MEM)*

Fuses operate because the wire in them has a low melting point and will vapourise before the excess current has time to cause damage. They are not instantaneous in operation, their speed depending upon the current flowing in them, and their design. Semi-enclosed fuses consist of a length of copper wire contained in a purpose made carrier usually within an insulating, heat resistant, tube so that the metal dispersed when the fuse operates does not cause damage.

High Breaking Capacity fuses utilise more sophisticated configurations of wire within an insulated body such that the performance characteristics of the fuse are both superior to and more predictable than the semi-enclosed fuse.

Circuit breakers use a combination of thermal (bi-metallic) and magnetic effects to separate a pair of contacts when the current exceeds a pre-determined level. Circuit breakers are increasingly used because their characteristics can offer a closer degree of protection than fuses and because they can be reset after the overcurrent has ceased. There is therefore no need for 'spare' fuses and no risk of oversized fuses or fuse wire being substituted.

Since the primary objective of all protective devices is to prevent damage, due to overheating, to the conductors, it follows that the protective devices must be related to the lowest rated cable in the circuit they are protecting.

Semi-enclosed (rewireable) fuses have been extensively used in the United Kingdom for many years, particularly in domestic and other smaller installations. This leaning towards the semi-enclosed fuse arises because of their relatively low initial cost, and the ease with which the fusible element can be replaced. Where h.b.c. fuses have been used in domestic situations it has been known for the fuse link to be 'repaired' by bridging the fuse with tin-foil; to prevent this, spare fuses must be readily available. Miniature circuit breakers have hitherto been relatively more expensive than semi-enclosed fuses and have been resisted by cost-conscious developers having no concern for future maintenance.

IEE Regulation 433-2 highlights a disadvantage of semi-enclosed (rewireable) fuses. These rupture at current flows so far above their nominal rating that it is necessary to use a factor of 0.725 applied to the rating of the conductor to arrive at the correct fuse rating. Put another way, a circuit required to carry a certain load will, all other things being equal, often require a larger cable if it is to be protected by a semi-enclosed fuse.

Reference was made in Section 3.1.3.3 to the need for the installation designer to identify the prospective short circuit current at the supply terminals. The prospective short circuit current is the value of current which would flow in the event of a short circuit fault occurring at that point and can in certain circumstances reach several thousand amperes. It is essential, therefore, for the designer to ascertain, either by consulting the Electricity Authority or by conducting his own investigations, the magnitude of such prospective currents. He must then ensure that any switchgear, fuses or circuit breakers he proposes to use are capable of withstanding the stresses which would arise in the event of a short circuit.

There are a limited number of occasions when it is permissible to omit overcurrent protective devices. These are when the consequences of the operation of the protection would be dangerous, as for example where the circuit supplies an electromagnetic crane or hoist or the field coil of a d.c. motor. In such cases disconnection of the supply would create a hazard and therefore reliable overload detection and alarm systems should be used to call attention to the faulty circuit and the cables provided with a high degree of mechanical protection to minimise the risk of short circuits.

3.1.5.8 Protection against thermal effects

The protective measures required under this heading are concerned with avoiding the effects of heat created either intentionally or under fault conditions by the installation. The precautions are generally readily appreciable if the risks are known. Thus for example electrical appliances which get hot must not be allowed to come close to material which might create a fire hazard. Transformers and other large items of plant containing flammable oil or other liquids must be surrounded by pits or channels to prevent burning spilt liquid spreading fire to the rest of the building.

In general however, precautions against heat effects are a matter of appreciating the likely incidence of heat and taking sensible precautions to avoid its consequences. Perhaps the simplest illustration of this principle is the domestic decorative lampshade which usually has adequate ventilation for a 60 W lamp. If a larger lamp is fitted overheating occurs and the lampshade will char or ignite with potentially disastrous consequences.

3.1.6 Earthing

3.1.6.1 The purpose of earthing

Earthing is perhaps one of the aspects of an electrical installation least understood by the layman. It can appear to be an unnecessary expense and an inconvenient nuisance without which the installation appears to work perfectly well. This erroneous impression arises from an understandably limited awareness of the role and purpose of earthing. The purpose of earthing is to connect all metalwork,

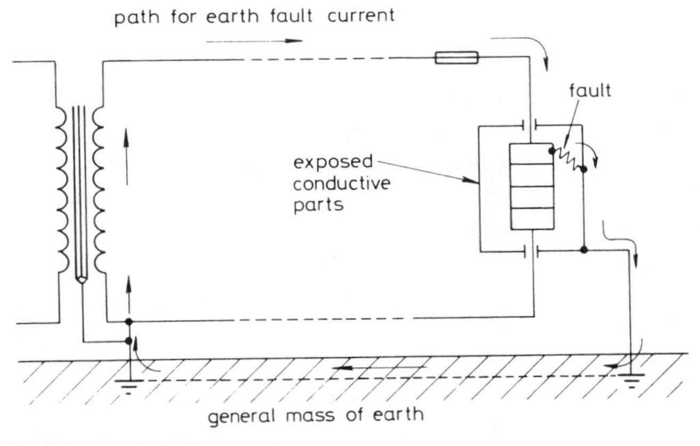

Fig. 3.1.6. *Path for earth fault current*

other than that intended to carry current, to the earth. In this way, dangerous potential differences cannot exist either between adjacent metallic objects, or between metal parts and earth. In the event of fault conditions arising, the fault current will normally flow via the earth conductors to the earth, from where it returns to the supply transformer as shown in Fig. 3.1.6.

At each supply transformer owned by the Electricity Authority, and at privately owned transformers and generators, the neutral point of the secondary (low voltage) winding is connected to earth. This is usually done by burying one or more copper electrodes deep into the earth until a satisfactorily low resistance connection is achieved. This connection provides the prospective return path for any currents which may, under fault conditions, flow from the supply system to earth. Without an effective connection to earth at the transformer no path would exist for a leakage current and hazardous conditions could then persist at the scene of a fault on a piece of apparatus.

3.1.6.2 Earthing systems

There are several methods or systems of employing earthing and these have been classified in the IEE Regulations by a three or four letter designation.

(a) The first letter indicates the supply system earthing arrangements. T: one or more points of the supply are directly connected to earth. I: the supply is either not earthed or is earthed through a current limiting impedance.
(b) The second letter indicates the installation earthing arrangements: T: all exposed conductive metalwork is connected directly to earth. N: all exposed conductive metalwork is connected directly to the earthed supply conductor.
(c) The third and fourth letters indicate the earthed supply conductor arrangement. S: separate neutral and earth conductors. C: neutral and earth combined in a single conductor.

Although in theory many permutations of arrangements are possible only three are of practical concern to the general user. (Fig. 3.1.7).

(a) TT system. This is the system which generally applies when no earth terminal is available from the supply authority and will be found in many older properties and some isolated premises fed by overhead lines. The earth and the neutral conductors are kept separate within the installation and the consumer's earth terminal is connected to an earth electrode buried in the ground outside the premises. Since such earth connections are difficult to obtain – involving sometimes the driving of multiple earth rods – and are unreliable in service because of changing ground moisture conditions, this system is rarely used now; it requires residual current devices for protection.
(b) TN–S system. This is the system which was extensively used until the late 1960's, making use of the fact that in the UK, Electricity Boards employed underground cables with metallic (usually lead) sheaths. The metallic sheath formed a continuous path from the consumer's earth terminal to which it was connected back to the earthed point of the transformer. Thus, any fortuitous earth currents occurring in the consumer's installation followed a continuous metallic path back to the supply transformer and the effectiveness of that path was independent of soil conditions.
(c) TN–C–S system. This system is becoming the universal earthing arrangement

for new and many existing supplies in the UK. The consumer's installation consists of separate phase, neutral and earth conductors in the normal way. The supply to the premises is provided by a system known as Protective Multiple Earthing (PME) which will be considered in more detail in section 3.1.6.3.

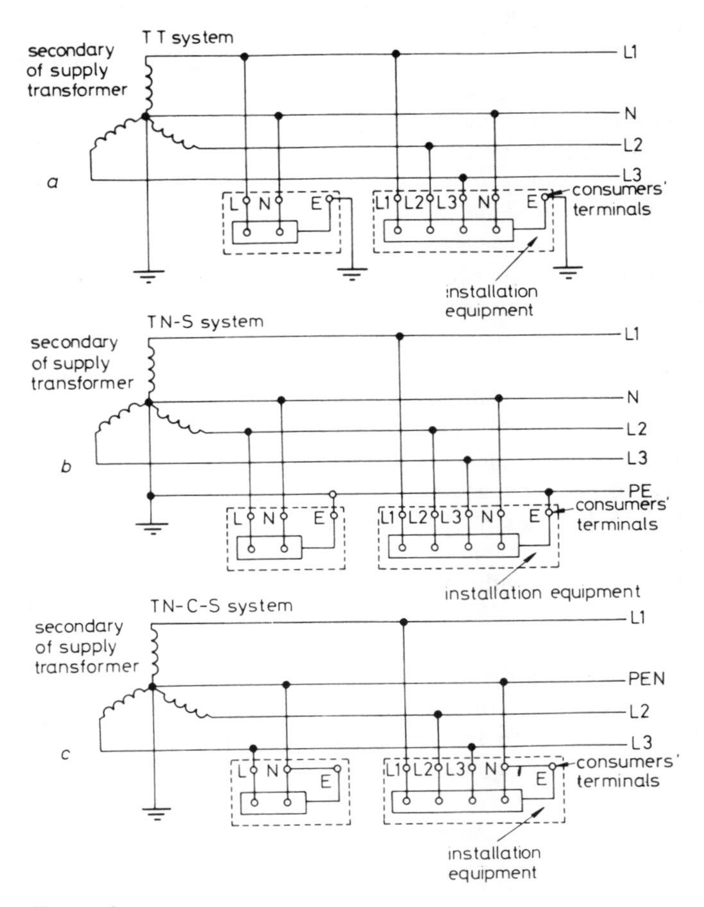

Fig. 3.1.7. *Types of earthing system*

The other, little used, earthing arrangements are:–

(d) TN–C systems. These systems involve the use of a combined neutral and earth not only for the supply but for the installation also. In Great Britain, such installations require the specific prior approval of the Secretary of State for Energy or the Secretary of State for Scotland and are subject to stringent requirements as to the types and sizes of cables which may be used. Such systems are very unusual and require careful consideration by qualified engineers before being initiated.

(e) IT–systems. Such a system would involve the deliberate introduction of an impedance into the earth circuit at the supply transformer which would limit the operation of protective devices (fuses and circuit breakers). Such systems may not be directly connected to Electricity Board networks in Great Britain.

3.1.6.3 Protective Multiple Earthing

Since the neutral point of the supply transformer is connected to the general mass of earth at the substation, the neutral conductor is at earth potential at that point and will remain at approximately earth potential throughout its length. The Protective Multiple Earthing (PME) approval granted by the Secretary of State to the Electricity Board requires that single earthing points be reinforced by multiple earthing of the neutral along the length of the outgoing cable. The neutral conductor then becomes an earth conductor at the same time and, subject to certain conditions, the Electricity Board will offer the consumer an earthing terminal connected to this combined neutral – and – earth conductor.

These conditions, imposed by the Statutory Approval, require the Board to take the necessary steps to ensure that their network is adequately earthed at several points and that it will remain so earthed. They also require that any installation connected to a PME earth terminal meets with certain standards. These include the provision of adequate bonding between the earthing terminal and all other metallic services (e.g. gas and water) and exposed metalwork in the premises. Compliance with Regulation 413–2 of the IEE Regulations will normally ensure compliance with the requirements for the provision of a PME terminal, but it is also advisable to check with the Electricity Board in case of any special requirements.

The purpose of the bonding required in PME installations often appears to cause misunderstanding and is therefore worthy of comment. It is sometimes thought that the object of bonding the earthing terminal to gas and water pipes and other metalwork is to use these services as auxiliary earth electrodes. This is not so. The objective is to ensure that all metalwork within the premises is and remains at substantially the same potential. For this reason connections to gas and water sevices are to be made as close as practicable to the point of entry of those services but on the consumer's side of any meter or stop-tap. Such meters and stop-taps often incorporate non-metallic insulating parts which would negate the effect of the bonding if connection were made on the external side of them. (Fig. 3.1.8).

It is the policy of the Electricity Boards in Great Britain to seek to offer an earthing terminal which will usually be a PME terminal to all new consumers, and to certain existing consumers as soon as practicable. Early consultation with the Board regarding the availability of an earthing terminal and any special conditions which may be attached to its use, is essential.

3.1.6.4 Protective conductors

Once an earth has been established within a premises, whether from a PME system or one of the alternatives, the consumer's main earth terminal is connected to it by an earthing conductor. Since the whole of the safety system of the installation relies upon this connection great care must be taken to guard against its inadvertent damage or disconnection. A label bearing the words 'Safety electrical connection – do not remove' in clear and permanent lettering not less than 4·75 mm high must be fixed to the conductor which must be of a certain minimum size – usually not less than 16 mm^2 – and must be protected against damage or corrosion.

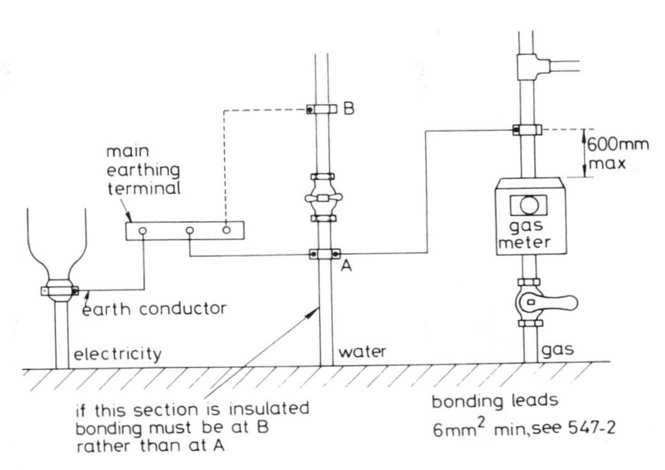

Fig. 3.1.8. *Main bonding conductors*

An earthing bar or set of terminals must be provided for the connection of each of the protective conductors which will be required in the installation. This will usually be located within or adjacent to the main switchgear. Every circuit in the premises must then be provided with an adequately sized circuit protective conductor (c.p.c.) in order to provide a path for any fault current which may occur at the point of use. The c.p.c. (Fig. 3.1.9) may consist of one or more of the following:

(a) a separate conductor forming part of the same cable as the live conductors (the familiar 'twin and earth' cable).
(b) separate independent conductors insulated with distinctive green-and-yellow insulation.
(c) the metallic enclosure of switchboards or other apparatus, providing the continuity is good, and the cross-sectional area is adequate for the purpose.
(d) the metal sheath and/or armour of a cable, providing again that the cross-sectional area is adequate.
(e) metal trunking or conduit systems used to enclose cables, provided that the cross-sectional area is adequate and that all joints in them are either screwed or of a mechanical type which ensures electrical continuity.

Where conduit, trunking or cable sheaths are used to provide the c.p.c to a socket outlet there must be a separate protective conductor – usually a green-and-yellow insulated cable – connecting the earthing terminal of the metal forming the c.p.c.

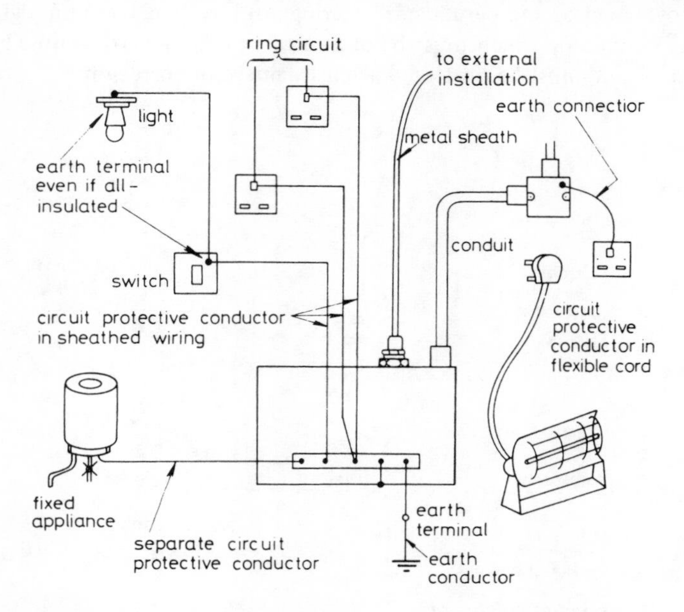

Fig. 3.1.9. *Types of circuit protective conductor*

to the earthing terminal of the socket outlet. This ensures that the earth terminal of the socket will remain effectively earthed even if the fixing screws holding the socket to the box fail or are removed.

Flexible conduits cannot be relied upon to provide earth continuity and a separate c.p.c. must be provided between the fixed ends of each piece of such conduit. This conductor should preferably be inside the conduit in order to afford it mechanical protection.

The objective of the protective and bonding conductors refered to above is to ensure that no dangerous potential can exist between earthed installation metalwork and other metalwork on the premises. However, since connection of the bonding conductors is made at the point of entry of the gas and water services reliance is being placed upon the electrical continuity of the joints in the pipework to continue this assurance throughout the building. In situations where the consequences of a fault could be particularly serious, supplementary bonding conductors may be necessary. Such situations include kitchens, bathrooms and other similar locations where water and large areas of extraneous metalwork (sinks, baths, etc.) are present. In these circumstances supplementary bonding conductors of not less than $4{\cdot}0\ \text{mm}^2$ should be provided between the various items of metalwork and the nearest available protective conductor. In this way even if continuity of the water pipe system is lost – for example by the insertion of a plastic fitting – the exposed metal bath, sink etc., cannot assume a dangerous potential relative to earth and cause a person touching it to receive a shock.

3.1.6.5 Residual current devices

The provision of earthing does not in itself provide protection against shock, or fire hazards. Earthing by the use of earth electrodes, c.p.c. or supplementary bonding conductors seeks to ensure that a continuous low resistance path exists between the site of a fault and the supply transformer such that a current will flow which will be of sufficient magnitude to operate the protective devices in the circuit while at the same time seeking to keep the voltage difference between any two pieces of exposed metalwork to acceptably low levels. However, there are circumstances when the current flowing as a result of an earth fault or inadvertent contact with live parts is insufficient to operate the protective device. The current required to operate a 5 A minature circuit breaker in a reasonable time can be up to 10 A and excessive impedance in any part of the fault loop can be such as to prevent this level being reached.

Circumstances which can contribute to this situation can include:

(a) The contact between the phase conductor and the surrounding metalwork at the site of the fault is less than perfect due to arcing, paint finishes, etc.,
(b) The user is away from earthed metal but in contact with the ground which may have a variable level of resistance.
(c) There is no earth terminal available and dependence is thus being placed upon an earth electrode buried in the ground which has dried out.

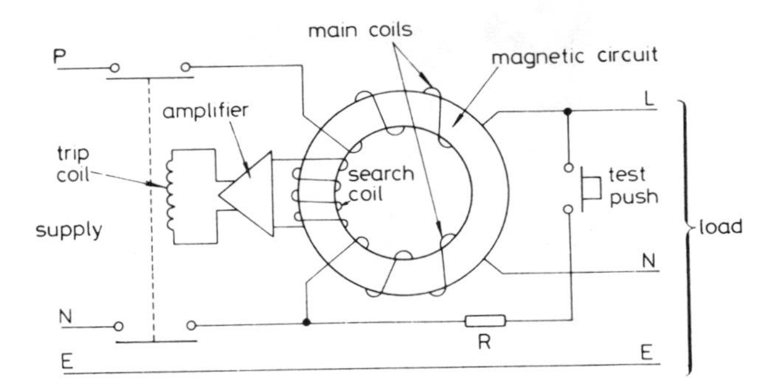

Fig. 3.1.10. *Diagram of residual current circuit breaker*

In all cases of difficulty the use is recommended of a residual current circuit breaker (current operated earth leakage circuit breaker) which compares the current flowing in the phase and neutral conductors and disconnects the circuit in the event of an imbalance indicating that current is flowing to earth. (Figs. 3.1.10 and 3.1.11).

The IEE Wiring Regulations recognise the growth of electrical equipment designed for use outside the building (electric drills, lawnmowers, etc,) and the fact that in such circumstances the efficiency of the earth connection is unpredictable. They therefore require sockets supplying such equipment to be protected by a 30 mA residual current circuit breaker. Similarly where reliance is being placed on a buried earth electrode rather than an Electricity Board earth terminal a residual current device is highly desirable, and in certain circumstances may be required.

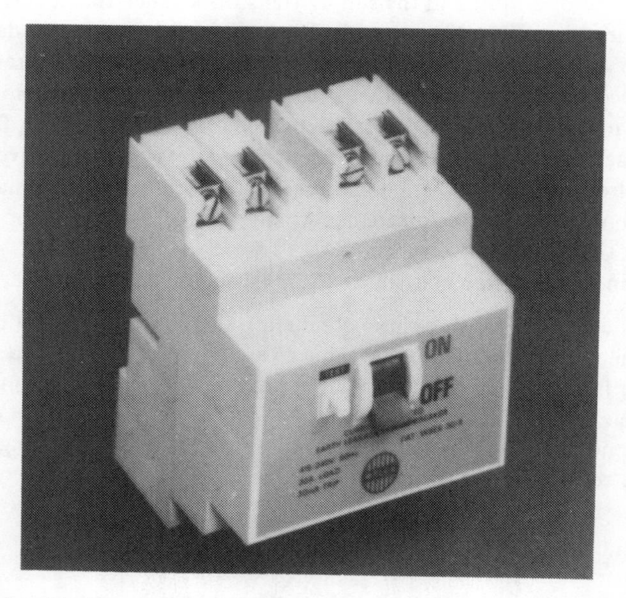

Fig. 3.1.11. *A residual current circuit breaker* *(George H. Scholes plc)*

Residual current devices cannot be used in TNC systems, but as has been noted above, such systems are rare in Great Britain. Conversely, where the electrical system is a TT system (i.e. there is no earthed return conductor to the source of supply), an r.c.d. is obligatory for compliance with the IEE Regulations.

3.1.6.6 Earthing of communications equipment

The special requirements of earthing of communications equipment, involving the concept of 'noisy' and 'silent' earths, are described in section 4.13.6.4.

3.1.7 Cable systems

3.1.7.1 Cable selection

This section is concerned with the selection and utilisation of cable systems for the wiring of buildings rather than with the design and construction of the cables themselves and the provisions necessary for their installation, which will be dealt with in chapter 3.3.

While other relevant factors need to be taken into account, probably the most significant factor in cable selection and installation is temperature. Most materials used to insulate and sheath cables are liable to failure in the presence of excessive temperatures, and all wire used in cable making has a resistance which, when current is passed through it, gives rise to heat. Cable selection therefore is primarily related to the size of cable which will carry the required current without the temperature of the surrounding insulation rising above a tolerable level. The current carrying capability of a cable is thus a function of:

(a) the material of the conductors
(b) the type of insulation material
(c) the temperature of its environment
(d) the prospective heating effect of other adjacent cables

PVC insulated cables to BS 6004 for example are suitable only as long as the conductor temperature does not exceed 70°C, whereas mineral insulated cables fitted with high temperature terminations can be operated up to 135°C (provided of course that damage or injury will not result).

If the environment in which the cable is to be installed is subject to extremes of temperature, or to fire or other abnormal hazards, consideration should be given to the selection of cables with appropriate insulation and sheathing materials.

3.1.7.2 Current rating of cables

Clearly it is not normally practicable for the design engineer to determine directly the likely operating temperature of a range of cables. He relies therefore on tabulated current carrying capacities such as those in Appendix 9 of the IEE Regulations which are based upon data provided by ERA Technology Ltd and the Electric Cable Makers Confederation, and which will ensure that excessive temperatures are not reached. It should however be pointed out that the tabulated current ratings are based upon a given set of conditions:

(a) an ambient temperature of 30°C
(b) no other cable is adjacent to the cable under consideration.
(c) the cable is installed in a way which corresponds to the rating table being used.
(d) there is no surrounding thermal insulation.

Should any of these conditions be varied then the cable rating has to be adjusted by reference to a correction factor. It is therefore, dangerous for the unwary to buy or sell so called '30 ampere cable' as a cable carrying 30 A in one set of conditions may be suitable for carrying only 10 A or 15 A in others.

Tabulated cable ratings are based upon 30°C as this is the temperature most commonly experienced in normal occupied premises, but even in such buildings higher temperatures can occur in the vicinity of heating equipment or other sources of heat, which the designer must identify and allow for by the application of a correction factor. Similarly a cable which is bunched with others will receive heat from adjacent cables and will be less able to dissipate heat. If the spacing of cables is greater than twice their diameter this grouping effect can be ignored but at closer spacings a further correction factor is needed.

The increased awareness of energy costs generally has led to a much wider use of building insulation products, roof insulation, cavity wall and underfloor insulants, which, if they enclose a cable, limit its ability to cool. If he is to avoid the application of yet another significant correction factor the installation designer must seek cable routes which avoid contact with thermal insulation materials.

3.1.7.3 Voltage drop in cables

The same tables in Appendix 9 of the IEE Regulations also set out voltage drop values. In order that the voltage at the point of use remains at an adequate level the Regulations stipulate that the maximum voltage drop in any circuit from the point of supply to the point of use must not exceed 2.5% of the nominal voltage, i.e. 6 V in a 240 V supply. This, coupled with the maximum permissible variation in the mains supply voltage (6%), can result in a voltage at the point of use as low as 220 V, a fact which needs to be borne in mind when voltage sensitive equipment is to be used.

Voltage drop occurs because all cables have some inherent resistance and the flow of current through them results in some reduction in the voltage. Thus the longer the circuit length the greater the voltage drop. Situations will often occur in large buildings where cables of greater size than appears justified for current carrying requirements are made necessary by the requirement to keep the voltage drop within the aggregate 2.5% limit.

3.1.7.4 Mechanical stresses

Since one of the objectives of good installation design is to ensure the safe durable working of the installation through its life, it follows that cables must not be subjected to mechanical stresses or the risk of mechanical damage. Cables must therefore be provided with mechanical support throughout their length. The spacing of supports is related to the type of cable. For example, small twin and earth p.v.c. cables need to be supported every 250 mm along accessible horizontal runs, and every 400 mm on vertical runs. (Appendix 11 of the IEE Regulations).

Where it is necessary for cables to pass through floor joists there is an obvious risk of subsequent damage from nails, screws and the like. Protection against this risk may be afforded either by ensuring that the cable passes through at least 50 mm from the top of the joist or is provided with protection by enclosure in steel conduit or some similar equivalent protection. If such drilling or cutting of joists is to be undertaken, consultation with the appropriate structural specialist is highly desirable in order that the strength of the structure is not inadvertently impaired.

In industrial and many commercial situations, conduit and trunking systems are chosen to afford mechanical protection to the cables, coupled with a neat and accessible installation. Obviously any conduits or trunking must be supported to prevent mechanical stresses damaging them and again the parameters for spacing such supports are given in Appendix 11 of the IEE Regulations.

The Regulations have also set out a tabular method of determining the size of conduit or trunking required for any selection of cables. It is essential that conduits and trunking are not overcrowded, otherwise cables will be damaged during the drawing-in process.

In larger buildings certain walls and floors are designed to act as fire barriers and this function will be defeated if a cable duct or trunking passes through that barrier and is capable of transmitting fire. A fire barrier, usually comprising a glass fibre mat or similar, must therefore be installed after the cabling has been completed. Similarly the ability of a vertical cable duct in a multi-storey building to act as a chimney is often overlooked. Heat barriers should be installed at each floor to prevent the accumulation of heat at the top of the duct.

3.1.7.5 Cable identification

The overall colouring, where it is desirable to distinguish electrical conduits, trunking etc., from other services, is orange, and the same colour is often used to identify switchgear and distribution boards. However, the requirements for testing, repairs and alterations to be carried out on an installation make it essential that the functions of the various cables within an installation are readily identifiable, and for fixed wiring the colour identification scheme set out in Table 52A of the IEE Regulations should be used. Colour identification of fixed wiring need however only be applied at the ends of cable lengths, by coloured tapes or sleeves.

The colour combination green-and-yellow is reserved exclusively for protective (earth) conductors in order that they are readily distinguishable from live conductors. Under no circumstances should this colour combination be used for any other purpose.

Flexible cables and cords must be identified by colour throughout their length, in accordance with the following:

Phase – Brown
Neutral – Blue
Protective
(earth) – Green-and-Yellow

3.1.7.6 Segregation of circuits

In industrial and commercial buildings it is usual to find circuits other than normal mains power and lighting circuits following the same general route, particularly where service ducts or channels have been formed within the building to accommodate such services. These other services may include radio, telephone, burglar alarm systems, emergency lighting and fire alarm circuits. Strict precautions are necessary to ensure that a fault on a mains (low voltage) circuit does not adversely affect these other circuits which may be vitally necessary in an emergency.

Circuits can conveniently be classified into three groups.

(a) Category 1 – Mains-fed circuits other than fire alarms and emergency lighting
(b) Category 2 – Communications circuits including burglar alarm, telephone and similar systems.
(c) Category 3 – Fire alarm and emergency lighting circuits.

The main risks which it is desirable to guard against are overheating caused by one category of circuit rendering the other circuits inoperative, or breakdown of insulation causing mains voltage to be applied to the other circuits. This can be avoided by segregation of circuits into separate enclosures and/or by enhanced insulation of the vulnerable circuits by one of the following methods:

(a) Trunking with built-in separate compartments which – for fire alarm circuits at least – must be fire resisting. While trunking with separate compartments is readily available however, the provision of fire-resistant compartments is difficult and costly.
(b) Totally separate conduits or trunking can of course be used and this is often a perferred alternative where the length of the common route is relatively short.
(c) Category 1 and 2 cables can be placed in the same conduit or trunking provided the Category 2 circuits are wired in cable insulated to the same level as the mains fed circuits. This is an economical option where short bell or alarm circuits are involved.

Fire alarm circuits can also be installed in the same enclosures provided they are wired in mineral insulated cable. Alternatively, fire alarm and emergency lighting circuits can be wired in physically separate enclosures.

Communications circuits, although electrically regarded as Category 2 circuits, should nevertheless be physically segregated from mains fed circuits in order to minimise the risk of disturbance to the signals thereon.
(d) Multi-compartment trunking for wall, skirting and floor mounting is available commercially to facilitate multi-service installations but care must be taken to maintain the appropriate segregation fully where junctions or outlets occur in such trunking. It is not unusual to find that the effectiveness of such screening has been totally destroyed by compartment barriers being cutaway in order to take one circuit across to reach an outlet point.

3.1.7.7 Economics of cable systems

The selection of a cable system for internal wiring purposes will involve consideration of p.v.c. sheathed cables, m.i.m.s. cables, p.v.c. cables in conduit or trunking of various kinds, and armoured multicore cables. While it would generally be true to say that on a unit length basis p.v.c. insulated and sheathed cable will usually be the cheapest cable system, it does not follow that this makes it the preferred system for any given installation. As has been indicated above, there are many applications (particularly in industry and commerce) for which p.v.c. sheathed cable is inappropriate because of the need for mechanical protection, because of environmental conditions or for some other reason.

The decision as to the most appropriate system for a given application involves consideration of all the circumstances of the installation. The prospective life of the installation, the need to provide for future alterations, the degree of mechanical protection required, the number of circuits following a given route and many other considerations will each tend to influence the choice of system. Further consideration of various systems and their suitability for particular applications follows in later parts of this chapter.

3.1.8 Reduced voltage insulations

3.1.8.1 Types of reduced voltage installations

The vast majority of electrical installations operate at normal mains voltage, (in the UK, 240/415 V). However, there are certain situations where the use of lower voltages is necessary or desirable either in order to afford added safety or because of the nature of the equipment they supply. Such installations might include communication circuits alarms, and control circuits, and certain emergency lighting installations, as well as supplies in construction sites, laboratories and other similar high-risk situations.

Extra low voltage is defined as not exceeding 50 V a.c. (120 V d.c.) between conductors or between any conductor and earth. Because such installations are likely to co-exist in the same premises as mains voltage installations precautions are necessary not only to ensure that the reduced voltage systems do not cause harm, but also to ensure that they do not inadvertently become energised at mains voltage.

A number of types of reduced voltage system are recognised in the IEE Regulations, including:

(a) Safety extra-low voltage (SELV)
(b) Functional extra-low voltage (FELV)
(c) Reduced voltage

3.1.8.2 Safety extra-low voltage

Safety extra-low voltage (SELV) systems are not so low a voltage that they can be regarded as touchable. On the other hand, it is generally considered that shock, at 50 V a.c. (120 V d.c.) is less likely to be serious, hence the attraction of this system for high risk locations. To be regarded as a SELV system an installation must derive its supply from a safety isolating transformer, a suitable generator or a battery, and none of the conductors of the SELV system must be connected to earth or to protective conductors of the normal mains voltage installation. This is to avoid any risk that a fault on the higher voltage system could energise the SELV system. For the same reason the wiring of SELV systems must either by physically separate from the mains voltage wiring at all times, or the wiring must be insulated to the same standards as the mains voltage wiring. (Fig. 3.1.12).

For obvious reasons any plugs and sockets used on extra-low voltage equipment must be physically different from normal low-voltage plugs and sockets so that no interchange of equipment can possibly occur.

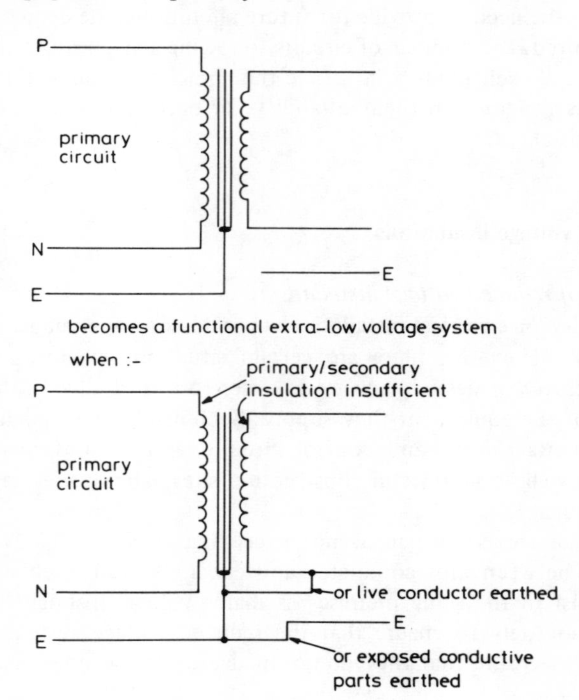

Fig. 3.1.12. *SELV and FELV systems*

3.1.8.3 Functional extra low voltage

Functional extra-low voltage (FELV) systems are similar to SELV systems except that either there may be an earthed protective conductor present and/or the insulation between the extra-low voltage source and the primary circuit is insufficient. These installations are used to meet certain specific functional requirements such as control circuitry and while safer than mains voltage systems do not offer the same degree of safety as SELV systems. They must therefore always be insulated to a level capable of withstanding 500 V for one minute, which usually means the use of mains voltage cables.

3.1.8.4 Reduced voltage systems

The most common form of reduced voltage system is the 110 volt centre-tap earthed system recommended for building and construction sites, which will be described in Section 3.1.13.2. Such systems must be supplied from isolating transformers or similar safety sources, the neutral point of which must be earthed, there must be protective devices (fuses or circuit breakers) in each phase conductor and a unique, non-interchangeable, type of plug and socket must be used. In a three-phase system, the neutral point of the transformer must be earthed, and in a single phase system the midpoint of the transformer secondary winding must be earthed.

3.1.9 Industrial installations (See also chapter 5.1)

3.1.9.1 Primary distribution

Distribution of electricity within the factory will start from a main switchboard containing a main fuse-switch or circuit breaker, a busbar chamber and a number of circuit switch-fuses, which will in turn feed small switchboards or distribution boards close to the locations of the electrical load.

The circuit wiring of factories can take several forms. The selection of the most appropriate technique in any situation depends upon an economic evaluation of the available alternatives.

Major circuits such as those between switchboards or supplying major single items of plant will often utilise four-core composite cables in which the four live cores are laid together, insulated and then protected with an overall sheath of p.v.c., lead, aluminium and/or steel wire. Such cables are semi-rigid and usually need no additional mechanical protection except where there is an obvious risk of physical damage. They can be fixed to wall or roof structures with special cleats or hung on specially formed hooks. Alternatively, where a number of such cables run along the same route, it is convenient to install a cable tray – a continuous shelf of open-mesh metal – onto which the cables are laid and clipped.

3.1.9.2 Trunking and conduit

Rectangular steel trunking to BS 4678 is normally used where a number of smaller circuits follow the same route. Trunking is available in a range of sizes from 50 × 37·5 mm up to 150 × 150 mm and guidance on the number and size of cables each will contain is given in Appendix 12 of the IEE Regulations. The capacity of trunking is such that the space factor – the proportion of the internal space occupied by cables – must not exceed 45% in order that cables can be drawn in without damage to each other. As steel trunking provides the cables with mechanical protection, the cheaper p.v.c. insulated non-sheathed cables can be used for the circuit wiring provided that at no point is the cable left without the mechanical protection of either trunking or conduit.

It should be recalled that all cables have a heating effect and that cables in trunking will tend to be less able to cool than those in free air. The relevant cable rating for the type of installation must therefore be employed and where appropriate a de-rating (grouping) factor (Table 9B of the IEE Regulations) must be applied to allow for the mutual heating effect. For similar reasons additional cables must not be placed in existing trunking without an evaluation of the effect on all the circuits in that trunking.

Individual circuits and small groups of circuits are normally installed in conduit of either steel or plastic. While plastic conduits are convenient and easy to handle and form on site, steel conduit, providing it is of adequate cross sectional area, can act as a protective (earth) conductor. As with trunking, conduits must not be over filled, so that cables are not damaged during the drawing-in process; a series of factors relating cables to conduit sizes is given in Appendix 12 of the IEE Regulations.

In factories where machines are liable to be re-located at intervals, or, where a large number of small machines are to be used, overhead busbar trunking offers a convenient, flexible and cost effective answer. Busbar trunking consists of continuous lengths of steel trunking in which copper busbars are mounted on insulated supports. Protective devices related to the capacity of the busbars are provided at the origin of the trunking circuits. Fused take-off units are then connected to the busbars above each machine and short lengths of conduit taken to the isolator on or adjacent to the machine. The rating of the take-off unit – which is, in effect, a large plug – is related to the requirements of the individual machine and take off units can be added at 1 m intervals as required up to the total capacity of the busbar system.

The busbar trunking system is usually more costly initially than wiring individual circuits from strategically placed distribution boards, but it has the merit of enabling machine layouts to be determined at a late stage and altered quickly and cheaply as production requirements alter. For this reason the system is often used in assembly line situations where work stations may be re-located or altered frequently to suit product changes.

3.1.9.3 Special enclosures for adverse conditions

Attention has already been drawn to the importance of the installation designer being aware of and responding to factors external to the installation itself which may affect either the design or the safe operation of the installation. Such external factors can require the introduction of special features or equipment.

The presence of water, for example, can require the adoption of mineral insulated metal sheathed (m.i.m.s.) or special rubber insulated cables, and any electrical equipment present must be suitably constructed. Because the degree of exposure can range from an occasional occurrence of dripping water, through the possibility of sea-water waves or exposure to hose-jets to total submersion, it is not practicable to generalise about the nature of a protective enclosure. However, BS 5490 establishes a system of classifying enclosures according to the degree of protection they afford. Reference to this system of classification enables a designer to match his circumstances to the degree of protection required and thus to specify the class of protected enclosure or equipment. Thus, an enclosure specified as having a classification IPX3 offers protection against water falling as a spray at an angle of up to

60° from the vertical, whereas an enclosure classified as IPX6 is protected against heavy seas and powerful jets of water.

Manufacturers of specially enclosed switchgear and apparatus normally indicate the relevant classification in their literature but in cases of doubt reference should be made to the manufacturer to verify that the selected equipment is appropriate to a particular location.

The same system of classification extends also to the degrees of protection provided against solid objects. In certain situations dust, wire probes or fingers must be excluded. An enclosure having a classification IP6X is dustproof, whereas a product with a classification IP5X is protected against excessive dust entry but is not totally impervious to such ingress.

Where protection against both solid (dust) and liquid (water) entry is required, the two classifications can be combined and, for example, an enclosure classified as IP44 is protected against the penetration of solid objects greater than 1·0 mm diameter and against splashing water.

In industry and commerce today use is made of a wide range of substances which, in gaseous vapour, mist or dust form, are highly flammable and while it is always preferable to avoid exposing any electrical installation to such substances, in many cases the presence of electrical equipment in potentially explosive atmospheres is unavoidable. Appropriate precautions must therefore be taken to protect such equipment and thus minimise the risk of ignition. Precautionary measures extend to both the apparatus and the system of wiring supplying it. Before decisions regarding the selection of a wiring system or appropriate apparatus are made, it is essential that the installation designer is fully familiar with the nature of the flammable materials likely to be present. While the risks associated with petrol vapour are fairly well recognised, the potential risks arising from less frequently found chemicals may involve close consultation with the client and the manufacturers of the product.

In order to assist the selection of apparatus appropriate to a given circumstance, a system of approval and marking of apparatus has been established. The British Approvals Service for Electrical Equipment in Flammable Atmospheres (BASEEFA) is the UK Certifying Authority for such equipment and they operate a system of equipment testing and certification which enables the installation designer to select with confidence apparatus appropriate to his requirements. An outline of this scheme of classification and marking is contained in BS 5345 Part 1, while subsequent parts of this standard deal with the installation and maintenance requirements appropriate to one or more of the different degrees of protection available. Other relevant British Standards are BS 1259, BS 4533, BS 4683, BS 5000 and BS 5501.

3.1.10 Domestic installations (See also chapter 5.2)

3.1.10.1 Scope of the installation

Until fairly recently the majority of domestic supplies in the United Kingdom were provided on a simple domestic tariff with a single scale of charge, with the option of a separate meter supplying separate circuits on an off-peak tariff for storage heaters and storage water heaters. This approach has been superseded by the 'Economy 7' and other similar time-of-day tariffs which allow the consumer to use any apparatus during the specified night hours at a substantially lower unit price. This fundamental change in approach opens up new possibilities for the installation designer to provide the consumer with a flexible and economical means of using electricity for all purposes.

It is one of the long standing anomalies of British housing design that the electrical services which can offer the occupier such a wide range of facilities represent little more than 1%–2% of the selling price of a house. The perceived value of a home can be greatly enhanced by the provision of an adequate electrical installation at little extra cost.

3.1.10.2 Service terminations

Domestic installations in the United Kingdom are normally supplied by a 240 V single phase service cable from the Electricity Board's distribution mains. In new premises arrangements are usually made for the Board's meter to be located in an outside meter cupboard so that meter reading can be effected even when the house is unoccupied. Also housed in the same cupboard will be the service termination cut-out incorporating a 60 A or more usually, a 100 A BS 1361 h.b.c. fuse. These items of equipment will be sealed by the Board and only their staff are permitted to alter or connect to them.

Meter tails, usually single core p.v.c. insulated and sheathed, will connect the meter to the service cut-out and the consumer's main switch, which must be located outside the meter cupboard. As the majority of services are of 100 A capacity the usual size for meter tails is 25 mm^2. It is, however, the installation designer's responsibility to satisfy himself that the prospective maximum demand of the installation is within the 25 kW service capacity allowed for by the Board, and to liaise with them should he consider this provision inadequate.

For new supplies the Board will normally provide an earth terminal which may be either a PME connection or a direct connection to a cable sheath. The installation designer will need to know not only what type of earth connection (if any) he will be offered but also the impedence of the earth loop up to the service connection in order to design his installation.

It is unlikely that the Board will be able, in practice, to give a precise figure for the earth loop impedance; rather they are likely to indicate a range or a maximum figure, which for PME terminals is likely to be 0·35 ohms and for cable sheath connected terminals 0·8 ohms.

In addition to his meter tails the installer will need to provide a main earthing conductor of 16 mm^2 cable to connect the consumer's main earth bar to the earthing terminal provided by the Board, and main equipotential bonding conductors, usually 10 mm^2, between the bar and the other metallic services in the dwelling (e.g. water, gas and central heating pipes).

Consideration should also be given at the earliest stage to the prospective short circuit current at the origin of the installation. This is, in practical terms, the current which would flow if a short circuit occurred in the consumer's main switch. The level and duration of this current is dependent upon the Board's network and fuse characteristics and therefore again, close liaison is necessary. The designer needs to satisfy himself that the main switch or consumer unit he propose to use will withstand the worst short circuit condition that could be imposed upon it and must therefore relate the data provided by the Board with the manufacturer's data.

In countries other than the United Kingdom, circumstances will vary, and early contact should be made with the Electricity Authority to ascertain local requirements.

3.1.10.3 Consumer units

For many years, the most popular configuration of the consumer's main switch and circuit protective devices has been the 'consumer unit' containing a main switch of 60 A to 100 A rating and 4 to 8 semi-closed (rewireable) fuses. Many millions of these devices have been used with little reported ill-effect. However, many engineers and householders will attest to the events which follow the blowing of a semi-enclosed fuse; hairpins, nails and oversized pieces of wire have been found to have been used to overcome the pressing problem of the unavailable fuse wire. Further, it is now recognised that the degree of protection offered to both the user and his installation by such fuses is limited by the inherent slowness and inaccuracy of the semi-enclosed fuse element.

Reference has already been made to the need for residual current protection of sockets supplying equipment out of doors. The householder will be still better protected from shock and the risk of fire if this same degree of protection is applied to the whole installation. Favourable consideration should therefore be given to the selection of a consumer unit combining residual current protection of the socket outlet circuits with miniature circuit breaker (m.c.b.) protection of each individual circuit.

3.1.10.4 Circuits for domestic installations

In selecting his consumer unit the designer should consider:

(a) The adequacy of the main switch for the maximum demand of the installation
(b) The number of circuits required to be connected to it and their respective loadings.
(c) the benefits to his installation and to the ultimate user of miniature circuit breakers rather than fuses.
(d) the added safety provided by one or more residual current devices.
(e) the desirability of providing at least one spare way for future needs.

The main switch should normally be of 100 A rating unless the designer is aware of circumstances which clearly justify a different size.

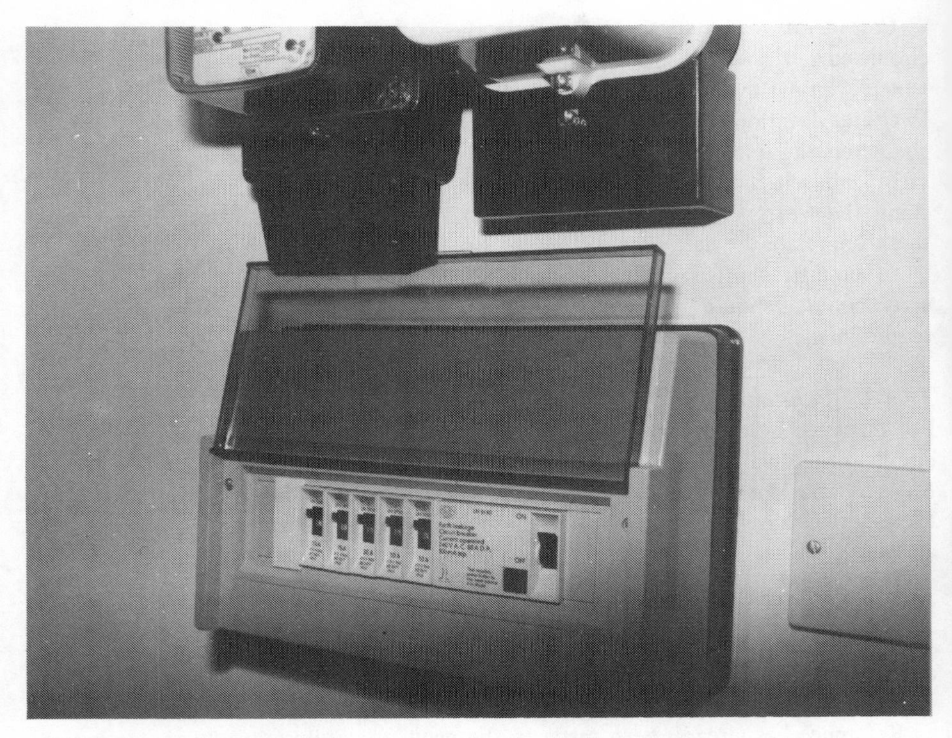

Fig. 3.1.13. *Domestic consumer unit with m.c.b. circuit protection* *(MK Electric)*

The decision regarding the number of circuits is to some extent subjective but the following represents a typical selection: (Fig. 3.1.14)

(a) lighting circuit, ground floor
(b) lighting circuit, first floor (although the total prospective load could be contained by one 5 A circuit, the consequences of a circuit failure plunging the whole dwelling into darkness should persuade the designer to use two circuits).
(c) immersion heater(s) (which must be on separate circuits, not connected to a ring main).
(d) kitchen/laundry area socket outlets
(e) socket outlets – ground floor
(f) socket outlets – first floor
(g) cooker circuit(s)
(h) electric shower unit

3.1.10.5 Domestic kitchen installations

The electrical load of domestic laundry appliances can alone reach 5–6 kW, and other kitchen appliances can lift this demand to 10–12 kW, excluding cooking appliances. For this reason the IEE Regulations urge designers to consider the provision of a separate circuit for the kitchen area.

Each working surface should be provided with at least one and preferably two dual socket outlets with special consideration being given to the likely location of electric kettles, food mixers, microwave ovens and the like. In addition, outlets should be provided under work-tops for washing machines, refrigerators, tumble dryers, waste disposal units and in a convenient accessible location for floor cleaning appliances.

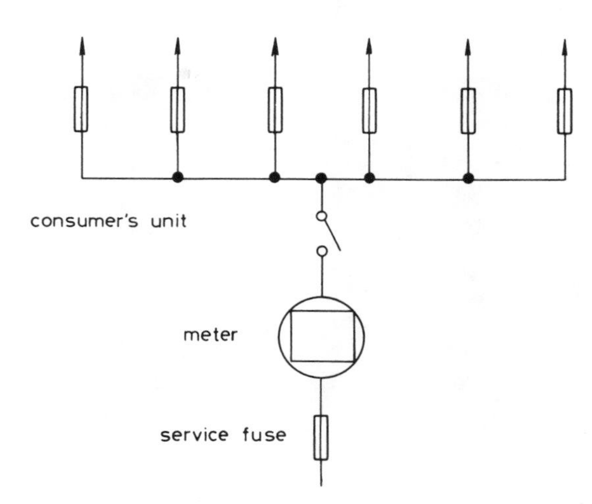

Fig. 3.1.14. *Typical arrangements for feeding final circuits in a domestic situation*

Domestic cookers can have a theoretical maximum load of 10–20 kW. However, the flexibility of their use in domestic situations allows the designer to apply a degree of diversity in accordance with table 4A of the IEE Regulations, resulting in the provision of a 30 A or 45 A circuit.

The cooker control unit must be located within 2 metres of the cooker and should be at the side and not above the cooker. This will allow ready isolation of the cooker should this be necessary. If the cooker is of the split-level type, either both parts of the cooker (hob and oven units) must be within 2 metres of the cooker control or two separate controls must be installed.

3.1.10.6 Domestic socket outlet circuits

Ring final circuits using socket outlets complying with BS 1363 have been used extensively in the United Kingdom for over 30 years. The principle of the ring circuit recognises that the total load in a given area is not likely to exceed 30 A, but that the location of small loads within that total is likely to be variable. (Fig. 3.1.2).

A domestic ring circuit may serve any number of socket outlets within a floor

Fig. 3.1.15. *Domestic switches and 13 A plug and switched socket outlets (Ashley Accessories)*

area of 100 m^2. However, consideration of the probable growth of electricity usage in future years makes the use of two or three ring circuits (ground floor, first floor and kitchen) highly desirable. The maximum load which may be supplied by a 13 A socket is 3 kW, at 240 V, and appliances of larger capacity will require different arrangements.

Table 3.1.1 compares the number of socket outlets recommended by official bodies in the new housing sphere, and the desirable minimum indicated by a reasonable consideration of the growth in ownership of appliances over the next few years.

Not only must the number and distribution of socket outlets provide for the appliances the householder may own, it must also provide for the fact that the positioning of furniture and the utilisation of appliances varies from family to family with time. Flexible cords between sockets and appliances must always be as short as possible and never longer than 1·5–2 metres, from which it follows that a dual socket should be available within 1·5 metres of every point in a room at which a future occupier may wish to utilise an appliance or portable luminaire. Only the provision of outlets to, at least, the level in Column 3 of Table 3.1.1 approaches this standard.

It is not necessary for every socket outlet to be connected into a ring circuit.

Table 3.1.1. *Recommended minimum provision of socket outlets in domestic premises*

Area of the Home	Recommendation of 1961 Parker Morris Report (Note 1) Desirable Provision	National House Building Council (1974)	Author's Recommendation (Note 2)
Working kitchen	4	4	8–10
Dining Room area	2	2	4–5
Living rooms	5	3	8–10
First Bedroom	3	2	4–5
Each other double bedroom	2	2	4
Each single bedroom	2	2	3
Hall or landing	1	2	2–3
Store/Garage	1	1	2–3
Typical 3 Bed House	20	18	35–43

NOTES

1. The Parker Morris Report "Homes for Today and Tomorrow", published in 1961, recommended at least 15 sockets and preferably 20, but suggested that a dual socket fulfilled the requirements for 2 outlets.
2. This Recommendation is based upon consideration of Regulation 553–9 "Provision shall be made so that every portable appliance and portable luminaire can be fed from an adjacent and conveniently accessible socket outlet" and on the reasonably foreseeable future needs of families occupying new homes of 100–110 m². The majority of such socket outlets should be dual outlets and such dual outlets may be regarded as two outlets for this purpose provided that their location has regard to the likely disposition of furniture and appliances.
3. Permanently connected equipment must be fed from an appropriate fused spur unit. Fixed space heaters, water heaters and immersion heaters must not be connected to the ring circuit but should be supplied from their own separate circuits.

Non-fused spurs may be taken from the ring to feed single or dual sockets provided the number of such spurs does not exceed the number of socket outlets and items of stationary equipment connected directly into the ring. Small fixed appliances such as extractor fans, waste disposal units and central heating pumps, should not be connected via socket outlets but should be connected to the circuit by a fused spur connection unit which, like the 13 A BS 1363 plug, houses a 3 A or 13 A fuse.

3.1.10.7 Special precautions in bathrooms

Socket outlets are not permitted in bathrooms nor within 2·5 metres of a shower cubicle or bath in a bedroom. This is because the consequences of a shock when the person is wet, has bare feet or is in contact with earthed metal are far more likely to prove fatal than if the same shock were sustained elsewhere. For the same reason, lampholders within 2·5 metres of a bath must be shrouded or totally enclosed and no fixed wall switches or heaters may be installed within reach of a person using a bath or shower. Pull cord switches are permissible and are indeed the preferred way of meeting the switching requirements of a bathroom.

Provision can and should be made for an electric shaver in a bathroom. A special shaver socket to BS 3052 must be used. Such sockets, which may be either self-contained or incorporated into a mirror light, have a built-in isolating transformer which limits the current which can flow in the event of a fault and isolates the socket from earth so that any shock is unlikely to be sustained.

A separate circuit is always required for an electric shower unit and isolation is most conveniently provided by means of a double-pole pull switch. If a wall mounted switch is used it must be placed out of reach of persons in contact with the bath, which usually means outside the bathroom.

3.1.10.8 Special regulations for outdoor installations

It should be recognised that portable tools and other equipment for use outdoors are growing in popularity and at least one socket outlet should be provided in a convenient position for the connection of such equipment. This socket, at least, must be provided with the protection of a residual current device (earth leakage circuit breaker) with a tripping current not exceeding 30 mA and must be labelled 'FOR EQUIPMENT OUTDOORS'.

A higher degree of overall safety can however, be provided by selecting a consumer unit in which certain outgoing circuits (those supplying socket outlets) are controlled by a 30 mA r.c.d and the remaining circuits are controlled by a higher level (100 mA–300 mA) r.c.d.

3.1.10.9 Cable installation in domestic premises

The routing of all cables within a dwelling needs consideration during the planning stages. The bunching or adjacent running of cables should be avoided where two or more circuits run along the same route. Cable routes should be chosen to avoid locations where thermal insulation will be installed later. Failure to observe these precautions may result in cables becoming overheated and deteriorating. Where cables have to pass through timber joists holes should be drilled at the mid-point of the joist and not less than 50 mm from the top face in order to minimise the risk of damage by nails or screws later. It is not normally considered necessary to provide additional sheathing over cables which are to be concealed in plastered internal walls. However, where cables are to be concealed by plaster they should run vertically between the ceiling and the outlet they serve so that their presence can be ascertained and they can be avoided when picture hooks and other fixings are being installed.

Modern rapid-construction techniques and the increased interest in the refurbishing of older dwellings call for a more radical and yet flexible approach to the wiring of houses. Commercially available systems now make use of hollow plastic skirting trunking and door frames as the housing for cables, and the decorative appearance of these mouldings mean that wiring or re-wiring can be undertaken with the minimum of building work. These systems have the added advantage that they lend themselves to the addition of further socket outlets without the need for major structural work at their point of attachement. Since the objective is to connect metalwork within the building, these connections must be made on the user's side of any meter or insulating insert.

The areas of special risk where supplementary bonding is required are primarily bathrooms and kitchens but may also include laundry rooms and boiler rooms. In these locations supplementary bonding in the form of green-and-yellow conductors not less than 2·5 mm² should be connected between the extraneous metalwork (sinks, baths, hot and cold water pipes, etc.) and the nearest convenient protective conductor, usually the protective (earth) conductor at a circuit outlet. (Fig. 3.1.16)

There is an increasing use being made of non-conductive joints, fittings and sealing compounds in water installations and where these occur special precautions need to be taken to ensure that isolated metallic structures are bonded separately.

3.1.10.10 Bonding and earthing

In order to minimise the risk of dangerous potential difference ocurring between adjacent exposed metalwork, it is necessary to bond together the main metallic services (gas, water, central heating pipes, etc.) at a point as close as practicable to their point of entry to the premises and provide supplementary bonding at locations of special risk. Protective (bonding) conductors must be connected from the main earth bar to the gas, water and other metallic services using reliable mechanical clamps. These conductors should be at least 6 mm², coloured green/yellow and be labelled "Safety electrical connection – do not remove".

3.1.11 Commercial installations

3.1.11.1 Supply and distribution considerations

In this section consideration is given to some of the special features and requirements of the installations in retail store, office and leisure premises and other non-domestic medium sized installations.

While single phase 100 A services are adequate for the smaller shop or office unit, premises with a prospective maximum demand in excess of about 25 kW will be provided with a three phase 240/415 V supply; outdoor meter cupboards are not usually used.

The service cable will be terminated in a cut-out located in agreement with the Electricity Authority. This should preferably be in a separate room away from stored materials, work areas etc., with adequate wall space for the meters, and the consumer's switchgear, together with access space for maintenance and alterations later. The switchboard will consist of a main fuse-switch or circuit breaker adequate in capacity for the installation, a busbar chamber and a number of circuit switch-

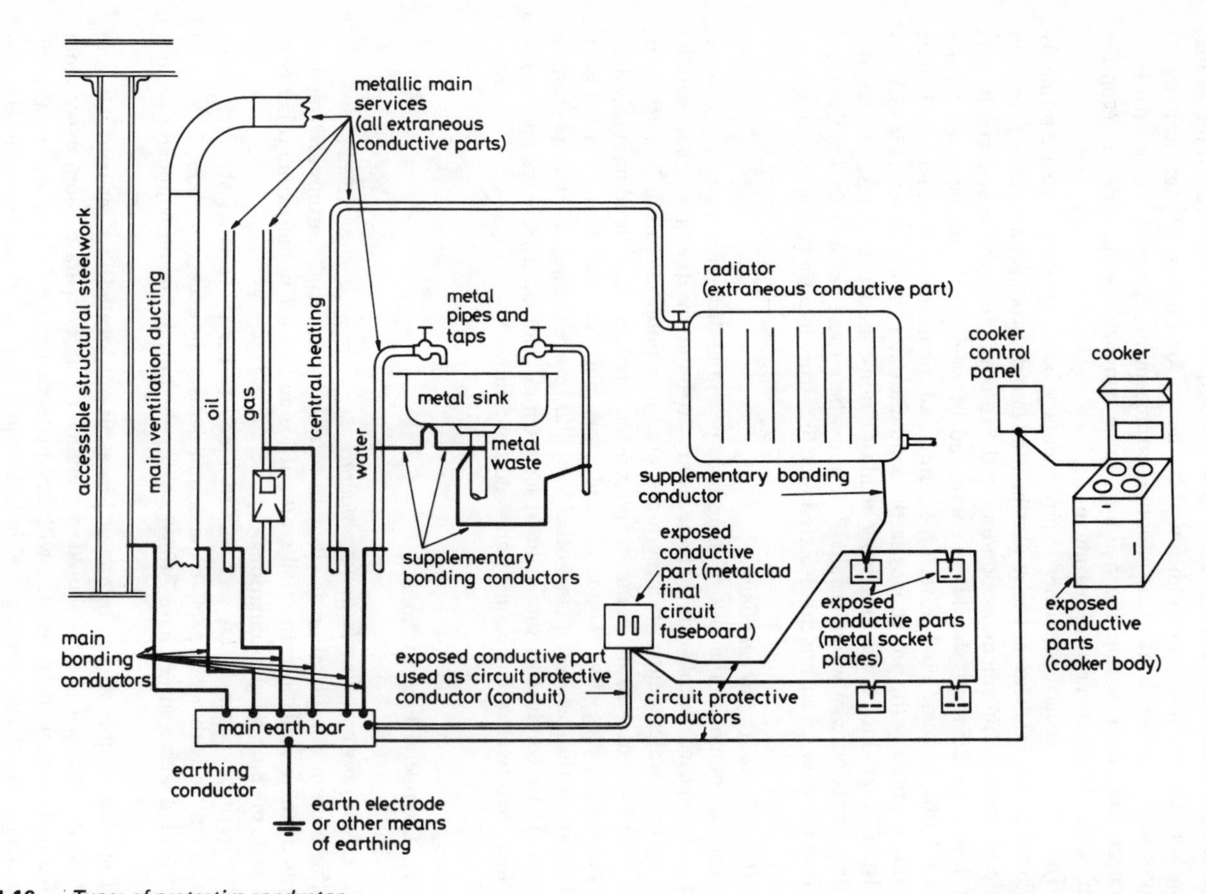

Fig. 3.1.16. *Types of protective conductor*

fuses or circuit breakers which will in turn supply distribution boards. It is usually more economic to locate distribution boards as near as possible to the centres of the electrical load. Thus a building on three floors would have a distribution board on each floor fed by sub-main cables from the main switchboard.

Unless three-phase motors or other three-phase equipment are to be installed, the three phases of the supply should be segregated within the building. The lighting and all power circuits in any one area should be connected to the same phase so that the risk of 415 V appearing between two adjacent outlets or pieces of equipment is minimised. Where, for good practical reasons, this separation cannot be achieved warning notices are required wherever two items of equipment connected to different phases are simultaneously accessible.

3.1.11.2 Circuits for power-using equipment (See also section 4.13.6.1)
The growth in the use of telecommunications equipment, office machinery and data transmission equipment means that almost every desk and work station may need access to such facilities. The trend away from small offices towards large flexible open-plan areas which can be replanned to suit changing needs makes the provision of such facilities somewhat more difficult. However, the recognition of these requirements at the design stage opens the way to the installation of a network of floor trunking which, if laid in a 2 metre matrix, provides the flexibility the user will require in the future without the risks which follow the use of long trailing flexes. Floor and skirting trunking systems are available with two or three compartments so that circuits supplying socket outlets, telephones and data processing equipment can be carried along the same route. (Para. 3.1.7.6(d)). A wide variety of floor trunking systems are available which are adjustable to match the finished floor level and carpet or other floor finishes can be applied to them to render them unobtrusive.

General purpose power circuits in commercial premises will usually be wired on the ring circuit principle, an unlimited number of outlets within a 100 m^2 area being connected to a 30 A fuse or circuit breaker. However, this wide licence to connect sockets to a single ring should be exercised with care. The installation designer must be satisfied that the prospective demand on that circuit will not exceed the 30 A rating of the circuit protection, and table 4B of the IEE Regulations gives guidance on how this demand should be assessed.

3.1.12 Agricultural installations (See also chapter 5.18)

3.1.12.1 Special precautions on farms
Electrical installations on farms are potentially more hazardous than most other situations for three main reasons. There is a high probability of moisture in and around farm buildings, the nature of farming activities tends to be less disciplined and confined than factory situations, and livestock are more susceptible to shock than human beings. Nevertheless electricity has become as indispensable in farming

as in any other activity, in the pursuit of higher productivity. Special precautions are therefore essential to meet and overcome these risks, and the IEE Regulations incorporate special provision to meet these circumstances.

It is desirable, but rarely possible, to keep electrical installations well away from livestock. Certainly as far as possible the electrical conduits and fittings should be installed well above the height which livestock can reach. It should also be recognised that livestock areas are often washed down with hosepipes and any electrical apparatus in such areas should be of a type which will withstand such treatment.

Consideration should be given to the desirability of using a voltage lower than 240 V, whilst electrical equipment in livestock areas should if possible be of durable insulated construction. At the same time the risks of physical damage to the installation by livestock, rodents or farm machinery should be recognised.

3.1.12.2 Bonding and earthing

Supplies to farm buildings should be protected by residual current devices (earth leakage circuit breakers). All metallic services – water, compressed air, oil, etc., – must be effectively bonded together and to the earth terminal. In addition all exposed metalwork of the buildings should be bonded to the earth terminal. This precaution, which is designed to remove any risk of the steel-work of the building becoming and remaining live under fault conditions, can be a major undertaking. Where effective metal-to-metal contact exists between building components this will provide some of the bonding but it may be necessary to supplement this with additional cable connections. Often the electrical continuity of metallic structural sections can only be ascertained by testing after the structure is complete.

The desirability of keeping earth fault currents away from livestock makes the use of plastic conduit preferable to steel and at the same time removes the problems of corrosion. Galvanised steel conduits may be used in some situations where mechanical protection is needed, but enamelled conduit is liable to corrode too quickly to be worth considering.

Many farm buildings should for all practical purposes be regarded as outdoor installations. Switches and sockets which have unavoidably to be located in such areas should be of a weatherproof variety and either of plastic or galvanised steel construction. However, controls and switches should as far as possible be located away from such areas, and luminaires should be of a moisture-proof type.

3.1.13 Special installations

3.1.13.1 Temporary installations

Temporary installations, because of the nature of the environments in which they occur, are often the source of greater risk than are permanent installations. There are therefore, no grounds for exempting such installations from any of the considerations which apply to installations generally.

The word 'temporary' is not a synonym for 'less safe'. In particular, careful consideration must be given to the circumstances in which the installation will be required to operate, the extent to which it will be accessible to untrained people and its expected life. In general however, a temporary installation will require all the features of switchgear, control and protective devices, and mechanical protection required by any other installation. The IEE Regulations recognise only one respect in which a temporary installation may differ from a permanent one. Cables forming a temporary installation need not comply with the requirements of the Regulations in respect of the spacing of supports, clips etc., providing supports are installed such that there is no appreciable mechanical stress on any cable termination.

3.1.13.2 Construction site installations (See also chapter 3.7)
Electricity is usually required on construction sites from the earliest stage for site accommodation, tools and equipment, and for site lighting, and early and close liaison with the Electricity Authority can often ensure the provision of a supply for construction purposes before the building is ready to receive its permanent supply cable. Generators are sometimes used to provide short term power to remote sites but they are only adopted where economic and practical considerations preclude the use of a mains supply.

Because of the particular problems associated with construction sites, the IEE Regulations devote special attention to them. A most important feature of construction site installations is the fact that a reduced voltage 110 V (55 V to earth) single phase system must be used for site lighting and all portable tools and equipment with a loading of up to 1.8 kW. Where there are special dangers, for example in the construction of boilers, even lower voltages are recommended. Normal mains voltages may be used for the electrical installation in site offices, stores and fixed plant.

The distribution system on the site will require to be efficiently earthed and desirably connected via one or more earth leakage circuit breakers (residual current devices). Because of the constant risk of mechanical damage to cables, the absence of close control over circuit lengths and the nature of any fault current only such devices provide a reliable degree of protection against shock. Minature or moulded-case circuit breakers should be used to control and protect individual circuits as fuses are liable to abuse by site operatives, who may be inclined repair a fuse with any piece of wire which comes to hand.

For the majority of medium to small sites the site electrical facilities are best controlled and distributed from a purpose-built distribution unit complying with BS 4363. Such units are transportable from site to site and provide facilities for the connection of the supply, and socket outlets for the connection of 110 V single phase tools, together with sensitive earth leakage protection. It is strongly recommended that such purpose made units are employed wherever electricity is used on construction sites.

The electrical installation on a construction site must be inspected no less frequently than once every three months. However, it is preferable that a weekly, monthly and quarterly routine be established under which pre-determined checks will be undertaken. This might involve, for example, a visual inspection of the installation every Monday morning looking for evidence of abuse, damage, or malpractice, and insulation resistance tests and tests of the residual current devices. A more extensive examination should be undertaken monthly and every 3 months the full Inspection prescribed in the IEE Regulations should be undertaken and an Inspection Certificate carefully completed and retained. Such a certificate can be a valuable safeguard for a site operator in the event of incidents occurring later affecting the safety of the site.

Underground cables in and around construction sites are a constant source of concern and hazard. Cables should only be buried on a working site if it is absolutely necessary. In that event they should be buried at least 500 mm deep and clearly marked with distinctive markers and tapes to avoid the risk of damage. The alternative of erecting cables overhead has its own hazards: minimum height recommendations must be met (Table 11B of the IEE Regulations) and conspicuous warning signs provided.

Unforeseen risks arise frequently from the presence of Electricity Authority cables on or adjacent to a site. Not only can damage to such cables prove dangerous and inconvenient to the neighbourhood, it can also prove costly as the responsible party will be required to bear the costs of repairs. Before work starts on any site, therefore, the exact location of electricity cables and other services should be ascertained and then marked on site. Should excavation in the vicinity of such cables be necessary it should be undertaken by hand and the Electricity Authority advised so that, if necessary, the cable can be supported or moved. It cannot be overstressed that the indiscriminate excavation on unknown land and roadways can be both dangerous and costly.

Guidance on electrical installation practice on construction sites is contained in BS CP 1017.

3.1.13.3 Petrol station installations (See also chapter 5.13)

The licensing conditions covering the storage and sale of petrol include exacting requirements for the installation of electric wiring in and around such locations. These requirements are set out in a Home Office Model Code of Practice (now administered by the HSE) but may be augmented by local licensing authority regulations. Enforcement of these requirements is by annual inspection and licensing without which the operation of the premises must cease.

Petrol station wiring falls into three types in three parts of the installation. The distinction which is made recognises that petroleum vapour is heavy and tends to accumulate at low levels. The area in and around petrol pumps is therefore divided into designated areas based upon the degree of explosion hazard which is present. A "Zone 1" area is one in which the hazards of explosion are normally present, and these include the interior of pump enclosures up to 230 mm from floor level and the area within 1·5 metres of the vent pipes. Any wiring within this area must be carried out in armoured or mineral insulated cable or enclosed in heavy duty conduit. In any event any terminations and fittings must be certified flameproof.

"Zone 2" areas are those areas in which dangerous atmospheric conditions might be expected in the event of an emergency and are generally regarded as extending 4·25 m laterally from the petrol pumps up to a height of 1·25 m. In this area too, mineral insulated or conduit enclosed wiring is required but flameproof fittings are not normally regarded as necessary.

Outside the designated areas the normal considerations for an industrial outdoor installation apply, and this influences the layout of petrol stations. If the sales/cash kiosks and other buildings can be placed outside the hazardous areas – i.e. more than 4·25 m from the nearest pump or storage tank – considerable expense and difficulty in the design of the installation can be avoided.

Lighting fittings on the canopies above petrol pumps or illuminating other parts of the forecourt do not need to be of special design but do need to be of weatherproof construction to withstand the normal exposure to the elements.

At a conspicuous position on the outside of the building there must be a master – or fire – switch which, in emergency situations, will isolate the supply to all pumps and pump lighting. This switch must be clearly identified by a sign "PETROLEUM SPIRIT PUMPS: SWITCH OFF HERE". This master switch – which must be painted red – will normally be a simple isolator connected so as to operate a contactor or group of contactors which will isolate supplies to all the pumps and associated lighting in the forecourt area.

The increasing popularity of self-service operation of petrol stations, even if only at low traffic periods, gives rise to certain additional requirements. The attendant must have ready access to an isolator to enable him to disconnect supply to any pump and its associated lighting in the event of emergency. He must also have a loudspeaker system to enable him to advise or warn customers, without leaving the control desk.

3.1.14 Caravan installations

3.1.14.1 The need for additional precautions

There are two aspects of caravan installations to be considered, the caravan site and the caravan itself, and in this context consideration will be given only to caravans intended for human occupation. The IEE Regulations make several references to caravans and caravan sites, whilst the Department of the Environment have issued Model Standards as guidance for Local Authorities. Caravans used as mobile workshops may be subject to additional requirements under the Electricity (Factories Act) Special Regulations 1908 and 1944.

There is sometimes a misconception that caravan sites, because of their short life nature, are in some way exempt from or in less need of certain electrical precautions. The converse is in fact the case, the possible mobility of caravans, the extent of metal used in their construction, and their exposure to the weather, call for special additional precautions. It must be clearly stated that such additional precautions are supplemental to, and not in substitution for, the requirements for comparable fixed premises. For example, the requirements for the installation of socket outlets in a caravan are the same as those for a fixed dwelling. Indeed it should be remembered that some larger caravans are in effect fixed dwellings, with the additional risks referred to above.

3.1.14.2 Caravan site distribution

Permanently established caravan sites frequently provide access to an electricity supply. The problems here are that electricity is being distributed around a wet plot of land, caravans may be moved on and off the site, and the site will be used by adults and children unfamiliar with it.

Good earthing – the effective connection of protective conductors and extraneous metalwork to the general mass of earth, and thereby either directly or indirectly to the earthed point of the supply transformer–is absolutely vital throughout the site.

In planning the distribution network of a caravan site the objective will be to provide a socket outlet as close as practicable to the intended location of each caravan and in any case not more than 20 m from each caravan intake. It is most desirable not to have flexible connections between caravans and supply sockets crossing paths and walkways and a favoured layout is to establish groups of four caravan socket outlets at the mid point of a square of four plots where pedestrian traffic is at a minimum.

The load to be assumed for each caravan will depend upon whether they are for summer only occupation or will be used in cold weather too, and what facilities are provided by other fuels (e.g. bottled gas). It should be noted that hair-care appliances with loadings of up to 1·2 kW are now popular, as are portable television sets and, in English summers, portable space heaters and even electric blankets.

While overhead distribution is generally cheaper to install, underground distribution is preferable, on both safety and aesthetic grounds, as well as being more reliable and less prone to interference by children.

If the supply to the site is provided from a TN–S system (with a continuous, separate protective conductor to the point of supply) the earth connection from this system can and should be used to earth the protective conductors for the site supply. However, because of the vulnerability of overhead lines on a site, the protective conductor to each socket outlet must be duplicated. That is, there must be two separate protective conductors connected to each socket so that in the event of accidental breakage or failure of one, protection is maintained. Where underground cable is used there is no need to duplicate the protective conductor.

New supplies, and most existing supplies, will form part of a TN–C–S system (I.e., in Great Britain, a PME earth terminal is provided by the Electricity Board). In this case the cable used for site distribution must be armoured concentric cable or another similar type and close consultation with the Board at the design stage is essential as additional earth electrodes may be required on the site.

The connection from the site supply to each caravan should be via a splash proof socket outlet complying with BS 4343 with a rating of 16 A unless the expected load from any of the caravans exceeds about 3·5 kW. Each socket outlet, either separately or in groups of not more than six, must be protected by a residual current device (r.c.d.) with an operating current of not more that 30 mA. If, as suggested earlier, caravan supply sockets are provided in groups of four, one such residual current device can control the group, and if no protective conductor has been distributed around the site, each device will require the provision of earth electrodes. (Fig. 3.1.17).

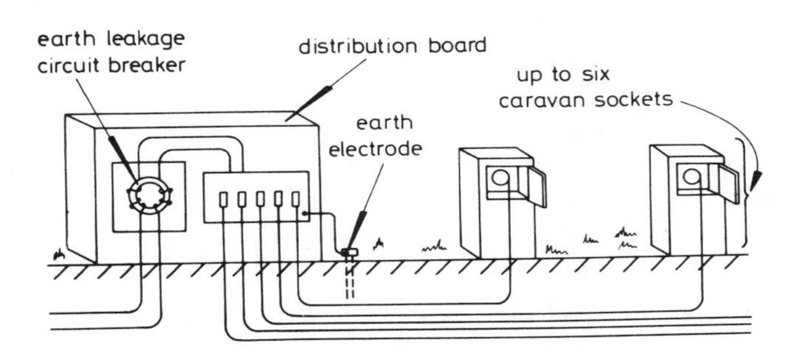

Fig. 3.1.17. ***Residual current e.l.c.b. protecting caravan site sockets***

Residual current devices are sensitive instruments with electro-mechanical parts which will not be called upon to operate until a fault occurs. It is therefore essential that either a fully weatherproof device is chosen, or the device is so housed that it is not exposed to damp, rain etc., even when the sockets are in use. Cases have been found where r.c.d. when called upon to operate under fault conditions have been corroded or infested with flora or fauna.

It is desirable to have, at each supply socket outlet, or issued to each caravan user on arrival (or preferably both) a clearly worded notice regarding the use of the electricity supply on similar lines to the notice which should be posted inside caravans (IEE Regulation 514–6). The connection between the socket and the caravan forms part of the caravan installation. However, where this flexible cable will have to cross paths, or accessible land, the provision of protective tiles or plate should be considered.

3.1.14.3 Caravan installations

The electrical installation within the caravan will be similar to other domestic installations. The point of supply will however be an inlet coupler to BS 4343 which must have provision for protection against rain etc., when not in use. Adjacent to the inlet coupler, on the outside of the caravan, there should be an indelible notice indicating the voltage of the installation within it. This is particularly important with the growing number of caravans which are taken abroad.

There must be, immediately inside the caravan, an isolator and either fuses or circuit breakers for the protection of each circuit. Each circuit will incorporate protective (earth) conductors and it is usual to use domestic BS 1363 13 A socket outlets to facilitate the transfer of appliances between home and caravan.

Luminaires of the pendant type should not normally be used in caravans because they are prone to damage during travelling and because of restricted head room. Some form of enclosed ceiling or wall mounted luminaire is preferable and these should be installed with careful regard to the fabric and structure of the caravan.

The wiring of caravans will normally be carried out in twin and earth p.v.c. insulated and sheathed cables concealed either in the structure or by plastic sheathing. Such cables must be supported at least every 250 mm on horizontal runs or every 400 mm on vertical runs. However, the presence of thermal insulation and structural members between the inner and outer leaves of the caravan often provides adequate support. The presence of thermal insulation does however mean that a correction (de-rating) factor should be applied to the cables. (Section 3.1.7.2)

It is essential that all metal parts of the caravan, which will include the chassis, and other structural parts as well as sinks, taps, gas pipes, and the like, are bonded together and to the protective conductor with a cable not less than 4 mm^2 in cross section. This cable must be securely fixed with clips or clamps to all the extraneous metalwork and labelled "Safety electrical connection – do not remove" at each point of connection.

Finally, for touring (mobile) caravans there must be a permanently fixed notice, inside the caravan, adjacent to the main switch giving clear instructions as to the procedure to be adopted on arriving at and leaving the site. (IEE Regulation 514–6).

3.1.15 Lightning protection

The protection of buildings and their installations against lightning is an inexact science because the behaviour of lightning is unpredictable and subject to all manner of external variables. What is known is that lightning discharges can take the form of electric currents of up to 200 000 A and that a series of discharges may last for up to a second, causing grave thermal, mechanical and electrical consequences.

Overhead lines, particularly in exposed locations, are equipped with a variety of arc gap and surge divertor devices designed to facilitate the safe discharge of any lightning strike to earth before it causes damage to terminations, plant, or other equipment. Owners of private overhead lines which may be prone to lightning strikes would be well advised to consult the local Electricity Authority engineers whose knowledge of the locality and its risks will prove invaluable.

Since, in general, lightning from a storm cloud will discharge to the nearest prominent feature of the landscape, it follows that high or isolated structures such as tall chimneys and church steeples are most likely to need protection from such effects. The principle of lightning protection of such structures is the provision of one or more metallic air terminations above the highest point of the structure, and connected directly to earth via copper or aluminium down conductors connected to rods driven into the ground. It is essential that metallic conduits, cables and other structures forming part of an electrical installation do not come into fortuitous contact nor run in close proximity to any part of the lightning protection installation.

Authoritative guidance on the assessment of the need for, and the principles and practice of the installation of, lightning protection is contained in BS CP 326, to which reference should be made whenever this topic is under consideration.

3.1.16 Static electricity

Static electricity occurs frequently in industrial and domestic situations and, for certain special applications, e.g. paint spraying, can be deliberately generated. Unintentional and undesirable static electricity can be a source of shock, fire and accident and while having no direct relationship with the electrical installation, is often mistaken for 'leakage' from adjacent wiring.

Static electricity can occur in situations remote from electrical supplies. In simplified terms, it is most likely to occur when two dissimilar insulating materials are separated, creating a potential between them. The effect is enhanced, for reasons not yet fully understood, if the contact between the two materials involves rubbing. One of the more common manifestations of static electricity occurs therefore when a person's dry shoes rub along a synthetic fibre floor covering, giving rise to a static charge on the wearer. Only when the person concerned comes into contact with earthed metal, e.g. a handrail, does he become aware of the electrostatic charge which is at that instant dissipated. In industry, static electricity can be created in any process involving the transmission of powder or suspended particles passing along insulated pipes or channels.

The hazards of static electricity, whether to human beings or in industrial processes, occur in the discharge of the stored energy. This can, in certain circumstances, give rise to sparks which in turn can create fire or explosion hazards.

The basic approach to the prevention of hazards from unwanted static electricity is to connect all conductors together and to earth by electrical paths which will allow the relaxation of stored charges. This can in extreme cases be an elaborate and necessarily costly process, but one which will avoid the even more costly consequences of resulting incidents.

One of the more frequently encountered and disturbing manifestations of static electricity is that which occurs in offices and similar carpeted areas. The combination of synthetic carpets, man-made footwear and dry atmospheric conditions contribute to the creation of static electrical charges on people moving around the area. The individual only becomes aware of the charge, however, if he comes into contact with some earthed metal before static electricity has been dissipated. The effect can in extreme cases, be a visible spark and a sensation of momentary shock.

Erroneously, these symptoms are sometimes attributed to the electrical installation, leading to unnecessary and misdirected alarm.

The precautions against this problem include the use of floor coverings treated to increase their conductivity or containing a proportion of natural fibres which have the same effect. The wearing of leather soled footwear also reduces the likelihood of a static charge persisting, as does an increase in the humidity of the air in the area, where this is practicable.

Where special circumstances make the avoidance of static electric shocks particularly important, reference should be made to BS 5958 for general advice and to BS 2050 and BS 5451 for specifications for conducting flooring materials and footwear respectively.

3.1.17 Identification, inspection and testing

3.1.17.1 Labelling and drawings

One of the most frequent and regrettable omissions from any electrical installation is the adequate labelling of the various components and the provision of "as-installed" drawings and diagrams. Even installations which have been well designed and competently installed are found afterwards to be lacking in this respect despite the fact that specifiers see the need for them and the IEE Regulations require at least a minimum provision. The omission becomes apparent and often costly when repairs, alterations and periodic inspections are required and the building occupier then finds himself obliged to bear the cost of an extensive survey to ascertain and record what should have been recorded when the installation was being carried out.

The following identification work should be undertaken before an installation is regarded as completed.

(a) A durable label reading 'Safety electrical connection – do not remove' should be fixed at the point of connection of every earthing conductor and every bonding conductor to either earthing terminals or the extraneous metalwork.
(b) In most circumstances where a voltage exceeding 250 V may exist between live parts or adjacent pieces of equipment, a warning label should be fixed indicating the maximum voltage present. (IEE Regulation 514–4).
(c) A notice at or near the main distribution board or main switch reading 'IMPORTANT. This installation should be periodically inspected and tested and a report on its condition obtained, as prescribed in the Regulations for Electrical Installations issued by the Institution of Electrical Engineers'.

The same label should show the date of the last inspection and the recommended date of the next inspection. (Section 3.1.17.3).

(d) Labels should be fixed on each piece of switchgear, each fuse board and each piece of control equipment indicating the apparatus it controls. It is permissible to omit these labels where the function of a switch or control is obvious, but the more extensive the installation the more important do such labels become.

(e) Labels should be fixed in or adjacent to distribution boards indicating the circuits or equipment each protective fuse or circuit breaker controls, so that isolation and repair can be quickly and reliably effected. This requirement extends even to domestic consumer units where each fuse should be suitably labelled to indicate clearly its purpose.
(f) Drawings or tables should be available showing what each circuit serves, the size and type of cable in each circuit and the type of fuse or circuit breaker intended to protect it.
(g) If the installation is extensive and not readily visible, physical "as-fitted" drawings are required, showing the location of cables, trunking, conduits and equipment in relation to the structure. Invariably these are not the same as the plans drawn up at the design stage as some re-routing or amendment will have been made during the construction process. Equally inevitably if these drawings are not prepared during the installation process it will be time consuming and sometimes impossible to draft them after cables etc., have been concealed behind structures or finishes.

Neglect of these important aspects of identification and recording occurs because their absence does not immediately impede use of the installation and occupation of the premises is usually the priority concern of all parties as completion approaches. The result can often be embarrassingly costly when inspection, testing and alterations are required later.

3.1.17.2 Initial inspection and testing

On completion every new installation or addition to an existing installation should be subjected to visual and electrical inspection and testing. The owner of the premises should be provided with a Certificate of Completion and an Inspection Certificate in the form set out in the Regulations.

It is customary for the client or his representative to witness at least some of the inspection process if only to satisfy himself as far as possible that the finished installation complies with his requirements and his specification. The visual inspection, in addition to confirming that the installation conforms with the specification, must include verification that no damage or interference has occurred during the building of finishing process. Regrettably it is far from uncommon in large installations to find that cables, conduits and switchgear have been damaged or even removed between their installation and the final handover. It should also include confirmation that the various items of equipment comply with and have been installed and connected in accordance with the relevant standards, specifications and regulations. The presence of the various labels and notices referred to earlier should be verified at the same time.

Once the visual inspection has been made, electrical tests must be carried out. These tests include:–

(a) A test to verify the electrical continuity of each ring circuit including tests of the neutral and protective conductor continuity.

(b) Earth loop impedance tests to ascertain that the path taken by fault currents is sufficiently low to ensure the rapid operation of the protective devices.
(c) Measurement of the insulation resistance to confirm that the insulation between each live conductor and each other live conductor and earth is such that no leakage or damage due to overheating will occur.
(d) Verification of polarity, confirming that switches are in the phase conductors and that socket outlets etc., are correctly connected.
(e) Other tests to verify that the installation is safe and that the components of it are correctly installed. These include special tests to confirm the effectiveness of residual current devices.

The full sequence of tests must be carried out on every installation and only then can the prescribed Inspection Certificate be completed. Such certificates can of course only be of value when signed by or on behalf of a competent person who should be either

(a) a professionally qualified Electrical Engineer
(b) a member of the Electrical Contractors Association or the ECA of Scotland
(c) an approved contractor on the Roll of the National Inspection Council for Electrical Installation Contracting (NICEIC)

3.1.17.3 Periodic re-inspection

The need for period re-inspection and reporting on existing installations is regrettably little recognised. Every installation is liable to accidental damage, overloading and changes of use. Further, during the life of an installation alterations, repairs and additions are often made by untrained people, both in the home and in work situations. Well-intentioned DIY repairs can frequently create unseen hazards ranging from oversized fusewire to the exposure of live conductors. In addition the execution of other work in the vicinity of an electrical installation can introduce hazards which were not present when the wiring was carried out. Examples might include the addition of thermal insulation around cables, the removal of walls, the introduction of sources of heat.

The advent of 'Health and Safety at Work' legislation has alerted employers to the need to take steps to ensure that their electrical installations to not constitute a hazard to their work people or to visitors. The periodic inspection of the installation and the careful retention of the resulting Certificate goes a long way towards providing the necessary assurance. In certain activities, particularly those subject to petroleum and entertainment licensing, regular inspection is a mandatory condition for the renewal of the licence.

The following are the recommended maximum intervals between inspections:

(a) temporary installations on construction site – 3 months
(b) caravan site installations – 1–3 years
(c) agricultural installations – 3 years
(d) all other installations – 5 years

It should be stressed that these periods are the maximum intervals between inspections recommended in the IEE Regulations. They would not necessarily be regarded as sufficiently frequent by authorities responsible for safety legislation enforcement.

The selection of the appropriate period will normally be made by consultation beween the user, the contractor, and the appropriate authorities. Many employers feel that where an installation is not under the day-to-day supervision of an electrical engineer e.g. most installations in shops, offices and smaller factories, an annual inspection is one way to head-off problems before they become serious; on large construction sites weekly electrical inspections are quite common. Even where constant supervision of an installation is apparently present, periodic inspection is still required, in much the same way as a financial audit of the Company's monetary affairs is conducted annually.

Re-inspections of domestic installations rarely take place except, occasionally, if premises change ownership or the wiring is manifestly suspect. This neglect of the most elementary precaution – a competent inspection – is all the more regrettable in view of the proliferation of amateur alterations and additions to domestic wiring. It is to be hoped that those concerned in financing and insuring domestic premises in particular will encourage the practice of having regular inspections undertaken at not more than 5 yearly intervals.

3.1.18 References

3.1.18.1 Legislation (See also Appendix 6.1)
Electricity (Factories Act) Special Regulations 1908 and 1944
Electricity Supply Regulations 1937
Factories Act 1961
Health and Safety at Work, etc, Act 1974
Model Code of Principles and Licensing Conditions (HSE)
Model Standards for Caravan Sites, Department of the Environment
Scottish Building Regulations 1971

3.1.18.2 British Standards (See also Appendix 6.2)
BS 1363 refers to 13 A domestic plugs and sockets, and BS 4343 to industrial types; BS 3052 covers shaver units. Fuses are covered by BS 88, BS 1361, BS 1362 and BS 3036. BS 4768 relates to cable trunking, BS 4363 to distribution units, BS 5419 to air-break switchgear, BS 5490 to protection provided by enclosures and BS 2754 to the construction of electrical equipment. BS 1710 covers pipeline identification.
Anti-static precautions are referred to in BS 2050, BS 5451 and BS 5958.
Amongst codes of practice, BS 5345 covers the use of electrical equipment in explosive atmospheres, BS CP 1017 is the code of practice for electricity distribution on building sites and BS CP 326 for lightning protection.

3.1.18.3 Bibliography

Regulations for Electrical Installations (15th Edition and subsequent amendments) (Institution of Electrical Engineers)

JENKINS, B.D. 'Commentary in the 15th Edition of the IEE Wiring Regulations' (Peter Peregrinus Limited)

WHITFIELD, J.F. 'A Guide to the 15th Edition of the IEE Wiring Regulations' (Peter Peregrinus Limited)

'A Handbook on the 15th Edition of the IEE Regulations in Electrical Installations' (The Electrical Contractors' Association)

PORGER, F, 'The Design of Electrical Services for Buildings'. (Spon)

Mc GUINNESS, WILLIAM, J and STEIN, BENJAMIN 'Mechanical and Electrical Equipment for Buildings'. (John Wiley & Sons Inc)

BENYON, E.R. and CUMMINS, T.J. 'Electrical Installation Work'. (Vols 1, 2, 3). (Hutchins)

Caravan Sites and Control of Development Act 1960: Model Standards. (Department of the Environment) (HMSO)

Chapter 3.2

Switchgear and transformers

A.S. Kennedy, B.Sc., C.Eng., F.I.E.E.
Director of Works (RAF)
Property Services Agency

3.2.1 Switchgear

3.2.1.1 General

Switchgear is a generic term for switching devices which are used in connection with the generation, transmission, distribution and conversion of electricity. This chapter deals with the forms of switchgear most commonly found in buildings, but it excludes consideration of items such as light switches and socket outlets. The purpose of switchgear is either to control, or control and protect, the apparatus which is supplied. It controls by providing means whereby the making or breaking of load current can be effected. It protects by affording the disconnection of a circuit under overload conditions and fault conditions. Switchgear is categorised into that used for voltages above 1000 V a.c. (high voltage) and that for voltages up to and including 1000 V a.c. (low voltage).

Switchgear comes in different forms, the main classes being disconnectors, switches and circuit breakers. There are important differences between the functions of each class. Disconnectors, whilst designed to carry full load current, are not intended to either make or break a circuit under load conditions. They are devices solely used to isolate equipment which has already been removed from a source of supply. Switches on the other hand are designed to not only carry the full load current, but also to be able to make and break a circuit under load conditions. Furthermore they usually have the capacity to make a circuit under fault conditions but they are not designed to break a circuit under fault conditions. This is often referred to as fault make load break. Circuit breakers go that stage further and are able to break a circuit under fault conditions.

These considerations lead to a number of design parameters which are used in the choice of switchgear. These include the rated voltage, the rated frequency, the rated normal current, the short time withstand current and the rated short circuit breaking current. Most of these terms are self-explanatory, but the last two need special mention.

The short time withstand current is that current which the equipment can carry in the closed position during a specified short time under prescribed conditions of use and behaviour. Typical short times often quoted by manufacturers are 1 second or 3 second, eg an LV air circuit breaker may have a short time rating of 50 kA for 1 second, or 43·3 kA for 3 seconds. The short circuit breaking current is the maximum value of the current that the device shall be able to break, eg the air circuit breaker mentioned above is stated by the manufacturer to have a breaking capacity of 50 kA. The designer must therefore work out the prospective fault levels in his system, together with their likely duration, so that appropriately rated equipment can be selected.

3.2.1.2 HV switchgear

The most commonly used components of HV switchgear are circuit breakers, oil switches and fused switches. Circuit breakers come in different forms and are classified according to the medium in which the arc resulting from the separation of electrical contacts during a breaking operation is extinguished. Thus oil circuit breakers (OCB) use oil as the extinguishing medium, and air circuit breakers (ACB) use air. A more recent development, and one finding general favour, is the use of a vacuum as the interrupting medium, giving rise to the term 'vacuum circuit breakers'. Another recent arrival on the market are breakers incorporating the use of the gas sulphur-hexafluoride (SF_6) as an extinguishing medium, but to date there is not a lot of operational experience with them at 11 kV and below. Vacuum circuit breakers have advantages over oil circuit breakers in terms of constant interrupting times regardless of current flow, minimal maintenance costs and minimum fire risk. They are however more expensive. Circuit breakers by their nature can be fitted with protective devices which when operated will initiate circuit interruption by opening the breakers. Such protective devices include fuses and relays with time delay arrangements such that both short circuits and overcurrents can be dealt with as appropriate. Some manufacturers are now offering vacuum breakers and SF_6 breakers which can be retro-fitted in oil circuit breaker equipment.

Oil switches are considerably cheaper than oil circuit breakers, but are not fitted with protective devices and therefore cannot be used in circuits where time graded discrimination between one part of the circuit and another is required. The fused oil switch which is fitted with high voltage fuses offsets this disability to some extent and is often used to protect the high voltage side of transformers.

Standard rated voltages for equipment likely to be encountered in buildings are 3·6, 7·2 and 12 kV. Typical normal rated currents are 400, 500, 630, 800, 1250, 1600 and 2000 A, and similarly typical rated short circuit breaking currents are 8, 12·5, 16, 20, 25, 40 and 50 kA. A very common rating is 12 kV, 630 A with a rated short circuit breaking current of 25 kA for 3 seconds.

In the event of system faults large currents can flow which unless interrupted can cause extensive damage to the electrical installation. For this reason HV switchgear usually incorporates protective devices which serve to interrupt fault currents before they reach dangerous levels. For buildings, the devices most commonly seen comprise inverse definite minimum time (IDMT) relays, overcurrent trips with time limit fuses, and HV high rupturing (or high breaking) capacity (HRC) fuses.

IDMT relays, usually fed from current transformers, (CT), can sense overcurrent and earth faults and in doing so will actuate the tripping circuit within the switchgear, thereby opening the breaker. The relays are designed with an inverse minimum time characteristic which means that the greater the fault current the quicker the response. The relays can also be set for a given minimum time of operation and this feature is used for discrimination purposes.

Overcurrent trip coils are a cheaper form of protection. They are usually fed from CT and employ the attracted armature principle to initiate the circuit breaker trip circuit. Sometimes they are wired in parallel with time limit fuses so that the fuse must melt before the coil sees sufficient current to actuate the tripping mechanism, and this feature imparts a minimum time characteristic to the device.

HRC fuses are mostly used for the protection of transformers up to around 1000 kVA. They are located within fused oil switches and incorporate striker pin devices to ensure that if one phase is blown then all three phases are isolated.

3.2.1.3 LV switchgear

The main components of LV switchgear are circuit breakers, control gear, fusegear and distribution boards. These components are usually combined with a busbar system to form LV switchboards from which the lighting, small power and motor circuits are distributed to the various parts of the building. It is becoming common practice for switchboards to be assembled and tested at the manufacturer's works and then delivered to site as composite units. These are known as Factory Built Assemblies (FBA). A further variation of this theme is the package substation, which comprises a transformer as well as the LV switchboard, the whole being packaged as a complete unit. Typical current ratings for both FBA and package substations run from 800 A to 3500 A at 433 V rating.

LV circuit breakers are generally of the air break type and oil circuit breakers are becoming increasingly rare. Typical ratings for air circuit breakers range from 1000 A to 4000 A, with breaking capacities of up to 50 kA. The 50 kA breaking capacity will meet the requirement of most LV applications. Moulded case circuit breakers (MCCB) range from 30 A to 4000 A but have much lower breaking capacities.

Fusegear is a term used to describe switches incorporating fuses, and these are commonly used to control and protect outgoing circuits.

Control gear is a similarly general term used to describe motor starters which may be direct on line (DOL), auto-transformer, star delta or liquid resistance type depending on the kW rating and particular application. Direct on line devices contain fuses for short circuit protection, an air break switch for local isolation, and protective relays for over current and earth leakage protection. They also have push buttons energising contactors for start and stop opertions. These devices can be selected to supply motors from a few watts to several kilowatts.

Distribution boards are used to feed final circuits and incorporate either fuses or miniature circuit breakers for protection of the circuit. Miniature circuit breakers are usually backed up by fuses.

3.2.2 Transformers

3.2.2.1 General

A transformer is a static device used to convert the voltage of an alternating current supply from one value to another. As an example, power might be generated within the power station at 22 kV, but transformed to 132 kV for power transmission lines – or again power may be taken from an 11 kV distribution system and fed to industrial premises at 415 V

3.2.2.2 Principle of operation

The power transformer works on the principle of electro-magnetic induction. In its conceptual form it comprises two windings wrapped round an iron core. The winding which is connected to the supply side is called the primary winding, whilst the other, connected to the output or load side, is called the secondary winding. An alternating voltage applied to the primary winding circulates an alternating current which produces an alternating magnetic flux through the iron core (Fig. 3.2.1). This flux cuts the secondary winding and in doing so induces an

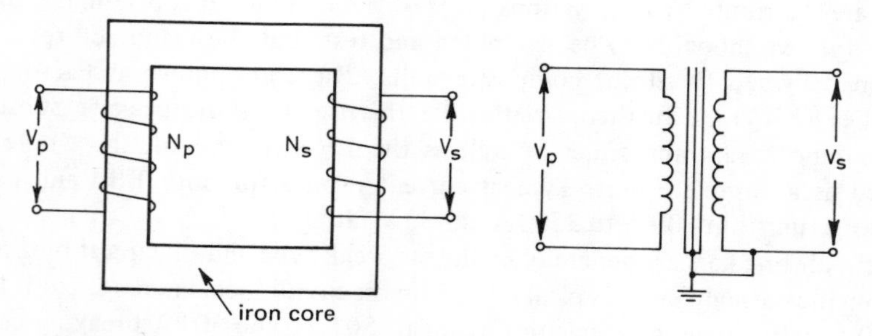

Fig. 3.2.1. *Conceptual arrangement of transformer*

electro-magnetic force (EMF) in each turn of this winding. Since the same alternating flux passes through both windings the volts induced per turn in each winding must be the same, leading to the approximate relationship:

$$\frac{V_p}{N_p} = \frac{V_s}{N_s} \quad \text{or} \quad V_s = \frac{N_s}{N_p} V_p \tag{3.2.1}$$

where V_p and V_s are the primary and secondary voltages, and N_p and N_s are the number of turns on the primary and secondary coils.

3.2.2.3 Winding arrangements

Transformers can be wound in either single phase or three phase configurations, but three-phase transformers are generally used for supplies within larger buildings. These transformers have the three separate phase windings interconnected in star, delta and interstar arrangements. The most commonly encountered arrangement is for step down transformers (eg 11 kV/433 V) to have the primary 11 kV side connected in delta (often denoted by Δ or *D*), and the secondary 433 V side connected in star (often denoted by Y). (Fig. 3.2.2). In the figure, '*R*' '*B*' '*Y*' (primary) and *r*, *b*, *y* (secondary) denote red, blue, and yellow, the conventional colours of cables in a three-phase system.

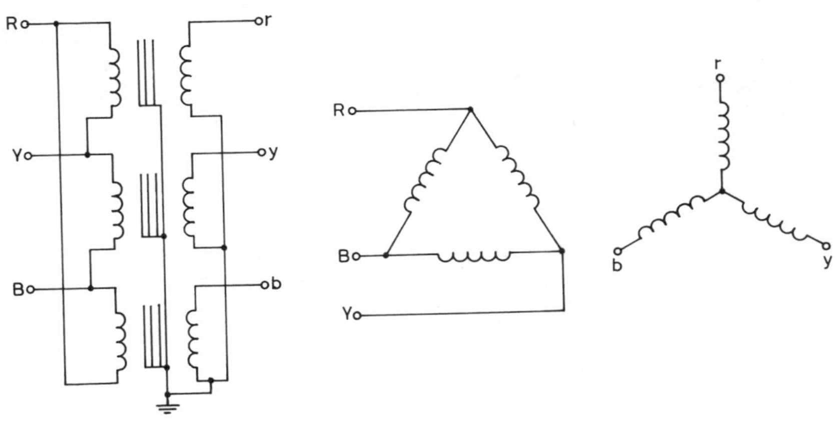

Fig. 3.2.2. *Conceptual arrangement of delta-star connected three phase transformer*

Another winding arrangement is that associated with an auto-transformer. In this device the input voltage is applied to the primary winding and the output voltage derived from the same winding (Fig. 3.2.3). Auto-transformers are not used for electrical distribution purposes but are commonly in use in motor starter and discharge lamp circuits.

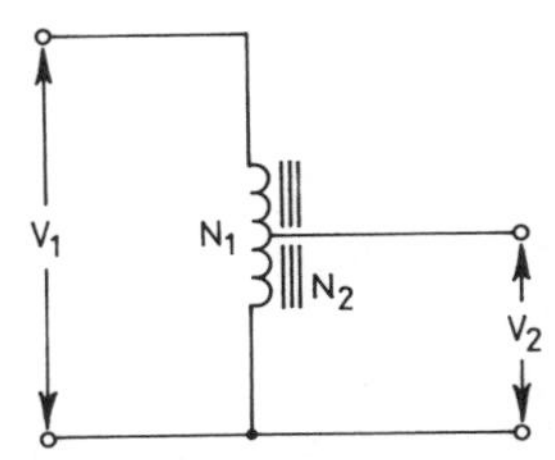

Fig. 3.2.3. *Conceptual arrangement for step-down auto-transformer*

3.2.2.4 Tap changing

Under load conditions the secondary voltage may become less than the statutory limit. As may be deduced from the foregoing equation, one solution is to vary the number of turns on either the primary or secondary windings. This process is called tap changing and most transformers for use in buildings are fitted with a tap changing switch on the HV winding so that the number of turns can be varied. These switches when incorporated in distribution transformers are always off-load devices so that the transformer must be isolated before the tap changing operation is undertaken. It is good practice to padlock these switches to prevent unauthorised operation.

3.2.2.5 Transformer ratings

Typical standard power ratings for transformers used within buildings are 315, 500, 800, 1000, 1250, 1600 and 2000 kVA. It is normal practice to quote the rated voltage of a winding or the open circuit or off load value. Thus an 11 kV/433 V transformer would be used with a three-phase system working at 415 V.

The line currents flowing in the primary or secondary sides can be determined from the formula:

$$I_L = \frac{\text{kVA}}{\sqrt{3}\,V_L} \qquad (3.2.2)$$

where I_L is the line current and V_L is the line voltage in kV. e.g. in a 1000 kVA 11 kV/433 V transformer wound in delta/star the line currents are:

HV side line volts 11 kV

$$\therefore \quad I_L = \frac{1000}{\sqrt{3} \times 11} = 52\text{ A}$$

LV side line volts 433 V (0.433 kV)

$$\therefore \quad I_L = \frac{1000}{\sqrt{3} \times 0.433} = 1333\text{ A}$$

3.2.2.6 Transformer losses and efficiency

The transformer is inherently an efficient device and except at very low loads the efficiency will usually be between 96% and 98·5%. The losses in a transformer comprise:

(a) iron losses;
(b) copper losses.

Iron losses are due to the hysteresis loss from magnetising effects and eddy currents in the iron core. The iron losses are usually determined by a standard test called the no load (or open circuit) test on the transformer, carried out at the manufacturer's works. These losses are constant and independent of load current.

Copper losses are due to the resistance of the primary and secondary windings and are proportional to the square of the current being taken. They are therefore dependent on the load. The copper losses of a transformer are derived from a standard test known as the short circuit test.

Transformer efficiency is given by the expression:

$$\text{efficiency} = \frac{\text{output power}}{\text{input power}} = \frac{\text{input power} - \text{losses}}{\text{input power}}$$

$$= 1 - \frac{(\text{copper losses} + \text{iron losses})}{\text{input power}} \qquad (3.2.3)$$

and it can be shown that transformer efficiency is a maximum when the constant iron losses are equal to the variable copper losses and typically may be around 98·5%.

3.2.2.7 Percentage impedance voltage

A further important characteristic of a transformer is the impedance voltage. This is formally defined as the voltage which when applied to the terminals on one winding will cause full load current to flow in that winding when the other winding is short circuited. This voltage when expressed as a percentage of the normal winding voltage is called the percentage impedance voltage, thus

$$V_z\% = \frac{V_A}{V_N} \times 100 \qquad (3.2.4)$$

where V_z is the percentage impedance voltage, V_A is the voltage applied to the winding, and V_N is the nominal voltage of the winding.

As an example, if the secondary winding of a 11 kV/433 V transformer is short circuited and the voltage necessary for full load current to flow through the primary winding is 529 V, then the percentage impedance voltage V_z is given by:

$$\%V_z = \frac{529}{11000} \times 100 = 4{\cdot}8\% \qquad (3.2.5)$$

This percentage impedance voltage is of great significance during fault conditions as the fault current available is given by the expression:

$$\text{Fault current} = \frac{100}{V_z\%} \times \text{ full load current (flc)}$$

Thus in the transformer given above

$$\text{Fault current} = \frac{100}{4{\cdot}8} \times \text{flc} = 20{\cdot}8 \times \text{flc}$$

Typically the percentage impedance voltage will range from 4·5 to 6·0%.

3.2.2.8 Types of transformers

Transformers are usually classified by the nature of the winding insulant and five types of transformer are found in general use, namely oil immersed, askarel immersed, dry type, dry type resin cast and silicone fluid filled.

The oil immersed transformer is probably the most widely used and has its winding and core immersed in mineral oil. The windings are generally covered with Class A insulation (enamel or paper) which has an extremely long life if the temperature is kept within British Standard limits (hot spot temperature of 98°C). Experience has shown it to be very reliable in service. A problem is however the fire risk associated with the insulating oil and special precautions may often have to be taken for fire protection and oil spillage containment within buildings. These transformers are very suitable for outdoor use.

The askarel transformers were developed to obviate the fire risk. Askarels are fire resistant synthetic fluids. A major disadvantage is however that serious pollution can be caused by spillage or incorrect disposal and the product is dangerous to animals and humans. Some local authorities and government departments no longer permit their use.

Silicone fluid is becoming increasingly popular as a power transformer coolant. It is an extremely stable liquid, does not pollute, and is harmless to humans and animals. It has very low flammability and when burning forms a crust of silica which produces a self-extinguishing effect. It is now being used for re-filling askarel transformers and since it is not a fire risk can be used in buildings without the need for fire protection equipment. Other fluids with similar characteristics are now becoming available.

Dry type transformers have exposed windings and core and are normally enclosed. The insulation standard is usually rated as Class C which permits a higher temperature rise than the Class A insulation used with oil immersed transformers. These transformers are not suitable for use in external locations, or where conditions are humid or particularly dusty. They are often used in package substations. They have a reputation for being noisy in operation and should not be located adjacent to noise sensitive areas.

Resin cast dry type transformers have their windings encapsulated in a resin material. They are a good choice for locations where a fire risk is unacceptable and where conditions could be damp or humid. They need a smaller amount of space than dry type or fluid filled transformers, but on the other hand are more expensive. These transformers can be easily arranged for forced cooling by fans and this permits an increase in rating. Both the dry type and cast resin type trans-

Table 3.2.1

Capacity	Transformer type	No load loss W	Full load loss W	% Impedance V	Noise dbA	Cost
1000 kVA	Oil filled	1770	11 800	4.75%	55	least costly
	Silicone filled	1770	11 800	4.75%	55	
	Dry type	2400	11 000	5.0%	59	
	Cast resin	3000	8 500	4.75%	57	most costly

formers are contained within cabinet type enclosures. These enclosures are often interlocked with switchgear so that transformer enclosures cannot be entered unless the circuit is disconnected.

Table 3.2.1 shows typical data for each kind of transformer, the example chosen being a 1000 kVA 11 kV/433 V transformer.

As a general rule the fluid filled transformers will have similar losses and the cast resin transformers will have the lowest copper losses. The resin cast transformer losses at full load will be superior to those of fluid filled and Class C transformers.

3.2.3 Siting and building considerations

A typical HV switchgear/transformer and LV switchgear complex is illustrated in Figs. 3.2.4 and 3.2.5 in both schematic form and general arrangement. A number of points should be noted:

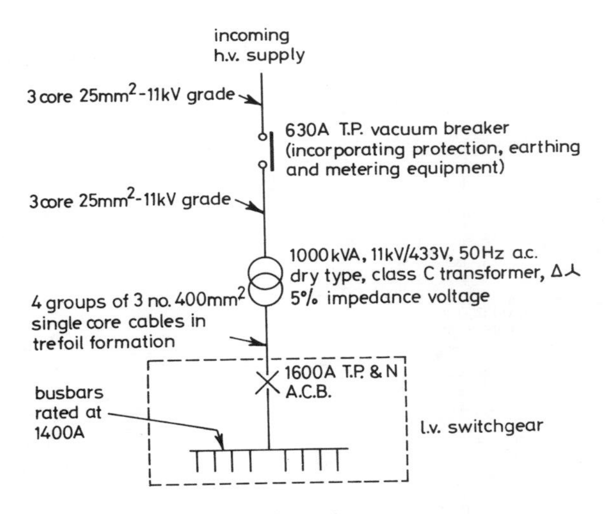

Fig. 3.2.4. *Typical HV/LV distribution schematic*

(a) Good access must be available to switchgear and transformer rooms to allow replacement, and the main access doors should not be less than 1800 mm wide and 2700 mm high. Some relaxation on door height is permissible for transformers of 500 kVA and less.

(b) Fluid filled transformers contain significant quantities of oil (e.g. a 500 kVA transformer would contain approximately 700 litres of oil), and containment arrangements in the form of a bund should be provided. It is good practice to locate fluid filled transformers in the basement or at ground floor.

(c) The losses of a transformer generate a considerable quantitiy of heat, e.g. a 1000 kVA fluid filled transformer on full load generates over 13 kW and adequate means of ventilation must be provided. In some locations insufficient natural ventilation will be available and forced ventilation will be necessary.

(d) Sufficient space must be left for movement around the gear (usually not less than 700 mm. Sufficient headroom should be allowed and 1000 mm from the top of the transformer to the ceiling or any projecting obstruction is recommended. Withdrawal space for circuit breakers and associated equipment must also be remembered.
(e) Cable ducts in floor slabs should not be less than 600 mm wide and 750 mm deep in order to allow access and proper cable bending radii.
(f) Provision should be made for any ductwork, tripping and closing batteries, general lighting, emergency lighting and socket outlets for maintenance.
(g) Where it is proposed to use oil filled transformers indoors, then a check should be made with the Fire Officer to determine the need for fixed CO_2 fire fighting equipment.

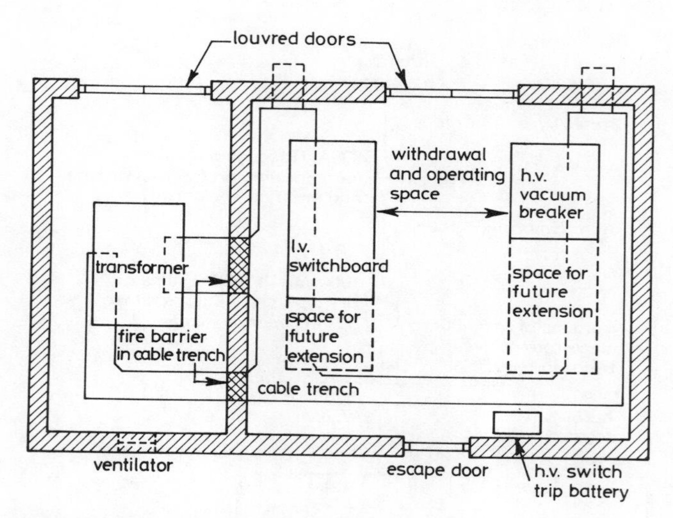

Fig. 3.2.5. *Typical substation layout (not to scale)*

3.2.4 Certification

The Association of Short Circuit Testing Authorities (ASTA) is the officially recognised body in the UK for the certification of electrical transmission and distribution equipment e.g. power transformers, high and low voltage circuit breakers and motor control gear. ASTA issues Certificates for such products based on type testing to British Standards, IEC Standards and the recognised Standards of other countries. In the absence of a Standard ASTA will prepare and publish its own rules for type testing.

3.2.5 References

3.2.5.1 British Standards (See also Appendix 6.2)
BS 171 relates to power transformers, BS 88 covers cartridge fuses up to 1000 V a.c. and BS 4752 and BS 5419 include specifications for switchgear up to 1000 V a.c. Switchgear above 1000 V a.c. is covered by BS 5227 and BS 5311.

3.2.5.2 Bibliography

The J & P Switchgear Book. (Butterworth)
The J & P Transformer Book. (Butterworth)

Cables suspended in service tunnel *(GTE Unistruct)*

Chapter 3.3

Cables

John Lane, C.Eng., M.I.E.E., F.C.I.B.S.
Electrical Engineering Consultant

3.3.1 Introduction

3.3.1.1 General

Cables are the means by which electrical energy is distributed from its source to its point of use. This chapter is concerned with the selection, design and construction of cables installed in buildings but not the distribution supply cables normally provided by an Electricity Supply Authority. The design of cable systems forming part of an installation is contained in section 3.1.7.

Reference to IEE Regulations in this chapter is to the Fifteenth Edition 1981 of the IEE Wiring Regulations and where applicable the terms used are taken from Part 2 (Definitions) of those Regulations. The importance of cables within an installation is emphasised by the devotion of the whole of Chapter 52 of the IEE Regulations to this subject and by their significance elsewhere in the Regulations, particularly Part 4.

No reference is made in this chapter to systems operating at over 11 kV, which is considered to be the upper limit of voltage available in an installation in a building. As described elsewhere systems using voltages above low voltage require special operating management and separate switchrooms. Whenever voltages in excess of low voltage are to be provided, building designers are advised to ensure that any special requirements for the routing and termination of the associated HV cabling are determined in association with the supply authority and/or the system designer.

Cables also form an essential part of communications, security and control systems. Cables for these systems must be chosen to avoid interference from other sevices particularly a.c. distribution systems, and must be suitable for their particular application. It is good practice to keep mains voltage systems segregated from each other (e.g. 11 kV separate from 415 V) but also to segregate other systems from each other and from mains voltage cable runs. Section 525 of the IEE Regulations gives important guidance on this subject, particularly on the segregation of fire alarm circuits and emergency lighting circuits from other circuits. These requirements are particularly relevant when using common enclosures (e.g. a trunking system) for several systems and can be expensive to provide.

A number of British Standards relate to electric cables. (Section 3.3.8.1). Fig. 3.3.1 illustrates a typical cable made to BS 6346.

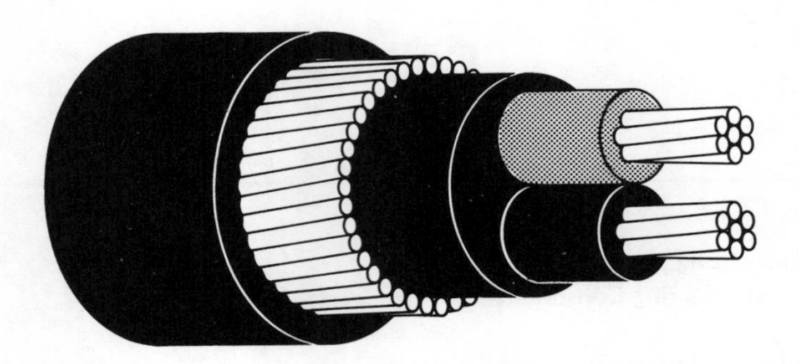

Fig. 3.3.1. *Twin core p.v.c. insulated, p.v.c. bedded, steel wire armoured, p.v.c. sheathed cable to BS 6346* (Pirelli General Ltd)

3.3.1.2 Types of cable

Varying operating conditions both electrical and environmental create the need for the multitude of types of cable which are available for incorporation in building electrical services. Guidance on the selection of types of cables is given in chapter 52 and Appendix 10 of the IEE Regulations. (Table 10A is reproduced as table 3.3.1)

The current carrying capacity of a cable must be sufficient to cater for the maximum sustained current which will normally flow through it. The insulation must be adequate to deal with the voltages of the system and must not be damaged by the heat caused by current flow, high ambient temperatures or heat transfer from hot objects (e.g. luminaires); volt drop and short circuit stresses must be catered for and provision made for an adequate protective conductor if this is to be incorporated in the cable.

Certain types of cable are precluded from use in specified circumstances. Because of the current which would be induced in the armour, Regulation 521–8 forbids the use of single core cables having steel armouring on a.c. systems.

Environmental conditions may require cables capable of operation in the presence of water or moisture, or subjected to fire risk, or in extremes of temperature (e.g. on a refrigeration plant or in a boiler house), in contact with corrosive or polluting substances, subject to mechanical stress and vibration both during installation and ultimate use, or liable to damage by fauna, including vermin, and to damage from solar radiation. If the environment is such that the cable is subjected to such hazards, cables should be selected with appropriate insulation and sheathing materials.

Table 3.3.1 *Application of cables for fixed wiring*

Type of cable	Uses	Additional precautions (if any)
P.V.C.- or rubber-insulated non-sheathed	In conduits, cable ducting or trunking, but not in such conduits etc. buried underground	
Light circular p.v.c.-insulated and sheathed	(i) General indoor use other than embedding	Additional protection where exposed to severe mechanical stresses
	(ii) Underground in conduit or pipes	
Flat p.v.c.-insulated and sheathed	(i) General indoor use	Additional protection where exposed to severe mechanical stresses
	(ii) On exterior surface walls, boundary walls and the like	
	(iii) Overhead wiring between buildings	
	(iv) Underground in conduits or pipes	
Split-concentric p.v.c.-insulated	General	
Consac	General	
Mineral-insulated	General	With overall p.v.c. covering where exposed to the weather or risk of corrosion, or where installed underground, or in concrete ducts
P.V.C.-insulated and armoured	General	With overall p.v.c. covering where exposed to the weather or risk of corrosion, or where installed underground, or in concrete ducts
Paper-insulated lead-sheathed	General	(i) With armouring where exposed to severe mechanical stresses or where installed underground
		(ii) With serving where installed in concrete ducts

1 The use of cable covers (preferably conforming to BS 2484) or equivalent mechanical protection is desirable for all underground cables which might otherwise subsequently be disturbed.
2 Cables having p.v.c. insulation or sheath would preferably not be used where the ambient temperature is consistently below 0°C. Where they are to be installed during a period of low temperature, precautions should be taken to avoid risk of mechanical damage during handling.

In building services the usual types of cables used are

(a) Non-armoured p.v.c. insulated only, installed in conduits and trunking systems (except where conduits are buried underground)
(b) Non-armoured p.v.c. insulated and sheathed for general indoor use, particularly in domestic and commercial applications and for use in conduits buried underground
(c) Armoured p.v.c. insulated cables for mains and sub-mains applications and for control cabling.
(d) Mineral insulated metal sheathed (m.i.m.s) cables are often used in place of p.v.c. cables in conduits or trunking, particularly in areas of extreme temperature.
(e) Heat, oil and flame retardant (h.o.f.r) cables are intended for use in severe conditions; examples of these are c.s.p. (chlorosulphinated polyethylene) and p.c.p. (polychloroprene) sheathed cables.
(f) Communications cables of small cross-sectional area, with plastic insulation and sheathing, and sometimes with metallic screening, generally co-axial or multi-core. Such cables are sometimes known as 'soft' wiring, in contrast to 'hard' wiring, i.e. relatively stiff lighting and power cables.

It should be noted that the use of split concentric copper conductor, p.v.c. insulated cable, and Consac cable ('concentric solid aluminium conductor') in which the concentric outer forms the neutral conductor, referred to in Regulation 521–1, are not suitable for use on systems other than TN–C (Section 3.1.6.2), which requires special authority, which is unlikely to be given for normal building projects. (Appendix 3 of the IEE Regulations).

3.3.2 Physical laws

Conductors in cables are low value resistors and they therefore behave in accordance with the following physical laws.

(a) Resistance (ohms) is proportional to length.
(b) Resistance is inversely proportional to area.
(c) Resistance depends on the specific resistance of the material. This has a different value for each material

e.g.	Copper	0.017 ohms at 20°C
	Aluminium	0.0283 ohms at 20°C

(d) Volt drop caused by the passage of a current I amps through a conductor having resistance R, equals $(I \times R)$ volts.
(e) The passage of a current (I) through a resistance produces heat. The heat produced is proportional to I^2 and results in a conductor operating at a temperature above ambient.
(f) A temperature rise within a metal resistance directly increases its resistance. The ratio of the increase of resistance per °C rise of the temperature is known as the Temperature Coefficient of Resistance and for copper is 0.004264. If therefore

the resistance of a conductor at 20°C ambient is 1.0 ohms, its resistance at 70°C will be $1 + (50 \times 0.004264) = 1.2132$ ohms.

To take countenance of the above statements, allowing for conductor length and electrical load being pre-determined by other factors, the choice of a particular material for, and for the cross-sectional area of, a conductor must be dictated by:

(a) The current to be carried.
(b) The need to avoid an excessive voltage drop.
(c) The restriction, under Regulation No. 522–8 of the IEE Regulations, of the volt drop in a consumer's installation between the origin and any point in the installation, to $2\frac{1}{2}\%$ of the normal voltage at full load current (viz. 6 V maximum on a 240 V supply).
(d) The normal operating temperature of the conductor – which in turn will dictate the type of insulation to be used.

3.3.3 Construction of cables

3.3.3.1 Components

The components of electric cables used in buildings are:

(a) *Conductors*
A conductor or several conductors which provide electrical paths. They are fabricated from metals having low resistivity. A conductor may be formed from solid material (e.g. small copper wiring cables, some aluminium conductors and mineral insulated cables) or be made up from a number of strands of smaller wire. Conductors are made in a number of standard metric cross sectional areas. Detailed information is available in BS 6360: 1981.

(b) *Insulation*
The insulation surrounds each conductor to prevent direct contact between individual conductors or conductors and earth. The type of insulation will depend on the voltage of the system, the operating temperature of the conductors and the mechanical and environmental conditions affecting the cable during both installation and operation. Typical insulation ranges from p.v.c. compounds and synthetic rubbers to oil impregnated paper tapes.

A conductor and its immediate insulation is colloquially known as a core. A cable may comprise a single core with or without further mechanical protection or a number of cores laid up together and held in position by a sheath or tape binding.

Cable cores are identified in accordance with various British Standards and conventions which are referred to in Section 524 of the IEE Regulations.

Colours of the cores of non flexible cables are detailed in Table 52 A of the IEE Regulations. The most important are red for the phase conductor of a single phase a.c. circuit, black for the neutral conductor and green-and-yellow for the protective conductor.

Wiring cables intended for installation in a conduit, trunking or similar enclosure are usually single core, insulated only, and are unsuitable for installation in other circumstances. Other types of cable are provided with further external protection.

(c) *External protection*
External protection applied over the various cores of the cable (one core or more) is intended to provide protection against mechanical damage and hostile environmental attacks. It is also intended in the case of power cables, particularly HV cables, to provide resistance to the considerable mechanical forces which may occur under short circuit fault conditions. In the case of conductors insulated with oil impregnated tapes the external sheath is usually extruded lead or lead alloy, designed to form a moisture excluding protection for the hydroscopic insulation. For other cables the external protection may comprise metallic or plastic sheaths, or a combination of these, with a layer of metallic armour being provided where extra mechanical protection has to be incorporated; a circuit protective conductor can be conveniently provided by this armouring (Para. 3.3.4.2.)

3.3.3.2 Choice of conductor material

In recent years aluminium had become a major alternative to copper as a conductor material because of its attractive price. However, as indicated in section 3.3.2, aluminium has a higher specific resistance than copper and is therefore, size for size, not such a good conductor as copper. For the same load capacity it is necessary to provide a larger aluminium conductor than copper and as an arbitrary guide aluminium cables have approximately 70% of the conductivity of a similar sized copper cable.

Whereas aluminium has become established as the principal conductor material in cables used for distribution systems, motorway lighting and similar applications, it has not supplanted copper in building service applications.

This is not only because of the superior electrical properties of copper but because copper conductors are available over the complete range of sizes required for both wiring and mains usage. There is a long established compatability between switchgear and copper cables, which are more easily jointed and less susceptible to corrosion and oxidisation, than aluminium. It is also possible because of the smaller overall diameter of copper cables compared to aluminium cables of the same load capability, to claim that they are more easily handled, particularly when bending radii are considered, as the minimum acceptable values for these are functions of diameter. Regulation 521–1 requires that conductors of 10 mm² cross-sectional area or less shall be of copper, or copperclad aluminium.

3.3.4 Cable systems

3.3.4.1 General

Table 10A of the IEE Regulations (Fig. 3.3.1) gives guidance on the type of cables suitable for particular installations. Having considered these environmental conditions, the building construction and its utilisation, the cable system chosen has also to be compatible with the supply system. Guidance on this is given in Part 3 of the IEE Regulations. The type of cable system chosen must also be compatible with the requirements of Regulation 312–3 (Type of Earthing Arrangement) (including Appendix 3) and the system must incorporate protective conductors to satisfy the requirements of Parts 4 and 5 of the Regulations.

3.3.4.2 Protective conductors

'Protective Conductor' is the generic name given to the means of bonding together exposed conductive parts, extraneous conductive parts, the main earthing terminal, earth electrodes and the earth point of the source of supply.

Section 413 of the IEE Regulations deals with methods to prevent danger arising from indirect contact (i.e. contact with exposed conductive parts made live by a fault). In buildings the practical solution is to use regulation 413–1 (i) (earthed equipotential bonding and automatic disconnection of supply) rather than the alternative methods. This solution entails providing protective devices for automatic disconnection which operate within defined time limits. (Regulation 413–4). To ensure that these time limits are met, a low resistance path to earth allowing the fault current to flow and operate the protective device is required. This low resistance path is provided by the protective conductor. Regulation 413–5 gives details of the maximum earth fault impedances allowable for various types of circuit and protective device.

The protective conductors must be considered as part of the cable system. They may be conductors external to and separate from the cables or they may form part of the cable – either as separate core or utilising the mechanical protection – metal sheath and/or armouring provided in the cable construction.

In cable applications where the wiring system is housed in a metallic conduit or trunking system the metallic housing may be adequate to provide the protective conductor. In the case of a wiring system housed in plastic conduit or trunking a separate protective conductor system will have to be provided.

The topic of Earthing Arrangements and Protective Conductors is dealt with in Chapter 54 of the IEE Regulations and rules for the sizing of protective conductors are contained therein. Cable manufacturers can supply cables with armouring to meet the requirements of Table 54F but in certain sizes this is a non-standard requirement which needs to be specified when ordering.

In the case of wiring systems using p.v.c. sheathed cable with incorporated earth wire complying with BS 6004 Table 5 (usually domestic buildings), Appendix 8 of the IEE Regulations should be referred to (particularly Tables 8A–D.)

3.3.4.3 Cable sizes

The standard circuit arrangements outlined in Appendix 5 of the Regulations give information which affects cable sizing for domestic type arrangements.

When assessing the cables to be utilised in an HV system, having considered the voltage and current constraints, the determining factor of the size and type of cable to be used may be its short-circuit capacity (Regulation 313–1 item 3). In the case of a low voltage system the parameter which normally determines the size of cable to be used is the volt drop, which has to be restricted to $2\frac{1}{2}\%$ at full load current between the origin of the system and any point on the system. (Regulation 522–8).

The current carrying capacity of HV cables can be obtained from the manufacturers or from the several ERA reports on cable ratings. LV cable system ratings are dealt with in Appendix 9 of the IEE Regulations.

The current carrying capacities given in the various tables are designed to avoid deleterious temperatures being attained in the conductors, sufficient to damage the insulation. Care must be taken to ensure that the correct method of installation is selected (Table 9A), that the correction factors for grouping cables (Table 9B) are taken into account and, if relevant, that the derating factor applicable to cable protected by rewireable fuses is implemented. It is possible to avoid the penalty of the grouping factor by ensuring that adjacent cables are spaced from one another by a distance equal to twice the diameter of the larger cable.

3.3.4.4 Exceptional temperature constraints

Exceptional environmental reliability or operating temperature restraints may require consideration of cables having characteristics to meet these. Where low temperatures (below 0°C) are encountered, for example in refrigerated areas, the use of general purpose p.v.c. insulation or sheathing must be avoided.

Mineral insulated metal sheathed (m.i.m.s.) cable is an example of a cable suitable for operating in hot conditions. The conductors are insulated with compressed magnesia oxide and sheathed overall with a metal tube. These cables are available in various combinations of core material and metal sheath (copper, aluminium, stainless steel). They may also be obtained with external sheathings of various materials to provide further protection against corrosion and weather conditions. These cables are designed for long life, do not support combustion and are not subject to derating if protected by semi-enclosed fuses to BS 3036. Each cable termination needs to be provided with a non-hydroscopic seal and arrangements such as a gland or 'earth tail' for the continuation of the protective conductor. The maximum operating temperature of an m.i.m.s. cable depends on the type of cable seal chosen (see note to Table 9JA).

The performance requirements for cables required to maintain circuit integrity under fire conditions are set out in BS 6387: 1983.

3.3.4.5 Protection against overcurrent

It is essential to ensure that cables do not become overheated due to their having to carry overcurrent. Chapter 43 of the IEE Regulations deals with the devices which are used to ensure automatic disconnection of the supply in the event of overloads or short circuits causing overcurrent. These devices are either fuses or circuit breakers and they are designed to operate before the current flowing exceeds 1.45 times the lowest of the current-carrying capacities of any of the conductors of the circuit. Overload protection must be provided wherever cable current capacities are reduced and the characteristics of the short-circuit protection provided must be co-ordinated with the overload protection to ensure that this cannot be damaged by excessive energy let through by the short-circuit protective device. Overcurrent automatic disconnection devices are also used to provide circuit protection in the cause of earth faults.

The detailed choice of overcurrent protective devices and their relationship is dealt with in Chapter 3.1.

3.3.5 Installation of cables

3.3.5.1 Building design constraints

The long term management of an electrical installation ideally calls for the provision of ducts, risers and access for the mains cable systems and distribution equipment to be isolated from other services. Cables need support throughout their length, whether run horizontally or vertically. These provisions are described in Appendix II of the IEE Regulations and it is advisable that consideration is given both to the room available for the installation of cables and also to the method of their fixing to the structure so that the cost of these fixings may be minimised. (Figs. 3.3.2, 3.3.3).

Mechanical restraints of short-circuit forces also have to be provided by the fixing system; this is particularly important on bends. The use of standard 'built in' fixings can effect overall economies of installation cost. Straight runs of cable are preferable to runs which have to be diverted to avoid other services or building obstructions, but to accomplish this needs liaison with other services at the planning stage. Lift shafts must not be used as routes for any cables except those directly associated with the lift system.

3.3.5.2 Cables and fire hazards

Some of the p.v.c. and bitumen materials used in the insulation and sheathing of cables pose a threefold threat when cables are involved in fires.

(a) Flame propagation
(b) Corrosive aftermath
(c) Dense smoke

The flame propagation qualities depend on the weight of the combustible material and a 'bundle' of cables is more likely to spread flame than a single cable. Reduced Propagation (RP) cables are available and their use is advisable in multi-core vertical runs. Normal grades of p.v.c. when burned produce about 30% by weight of hydrochloric acid gas. Grades of p.v.c. producing lower volumes of this corrosive agent detract from the RP characteristics, but it is possible to produce p.v.c. insulated or sheathed cables having limited flame propagation and corrosive potential. Dense

Fig. 3.3.2. *Cabling to factory distribution boards*

black smoke is produced whenever p.v.c. of any grade is burned and this feature may influence the choice of cable to be used.

3.3.5.3 Fire barriers

Regulations 523–6 and 528–1 give guidance as to the provisions to be made. It is recommended that these provisions be incorporated in the original design rather than as an afterthought. Fig. 3.3.4 illustrates one type of barrier suitable for cables laid in ducts or trunking.

Fig. 3.3.3. *Cable tray installation in a steel works* *(Swifts of Scarborough)*

3.3.5.4 Bending radii

The insulation of cables can be damaged if they are installed with very sharp bends. In Table 52C of the IEE Regulations guidance is given to the minimum internal radii of bends for various types of cable. It must be emphasised that these are minimum requirements and the design of ducts and cable ways in a building should avoid the necessity for sharp bends. Conformity with Table 52C would ensure that the p.v.c. armoured cables, which are a popular choice for sub-main cabling, are installed with a minimum internal bending radius of either 6 or 8 times their overall diameter. For example a p.v.c. armoured cable having shaped conductors with an overall diameter of 50 mm would need a minimum internal bending radius of 400 mm.

It is a common fault in the termination of an underground duct system for cables to be provided with a 90° elbow for the transition between the horizontal and vertical run. It is desirable that such duct runs should terminate in the horizontal plane in an adequately sized pit or alternatively that any bend should afford at least the minimum radii referred to in Table 52C and preferably offer a 50% improvement on these minima.

In designing cable access pits consideration must be given to the method of cable installation and adequate room provided to allow the cable to be drawn in and out of the ducts emanating from the pits without damage to the cables.

Special attention must be given to the requirements of the Electricity Authority for the provision of access for their cables.

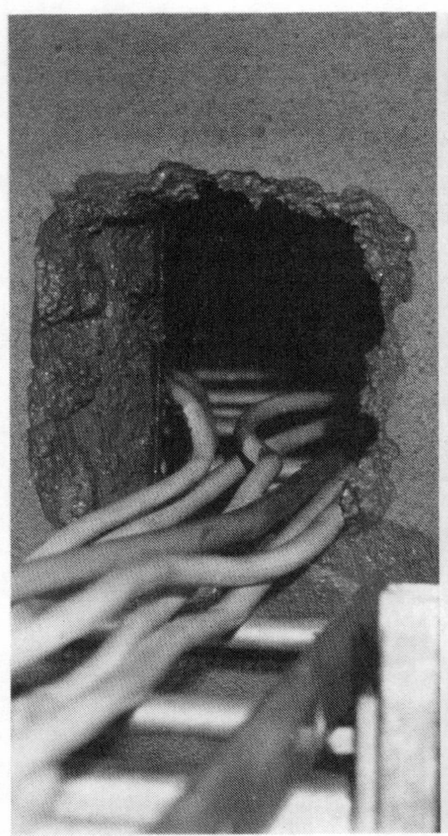

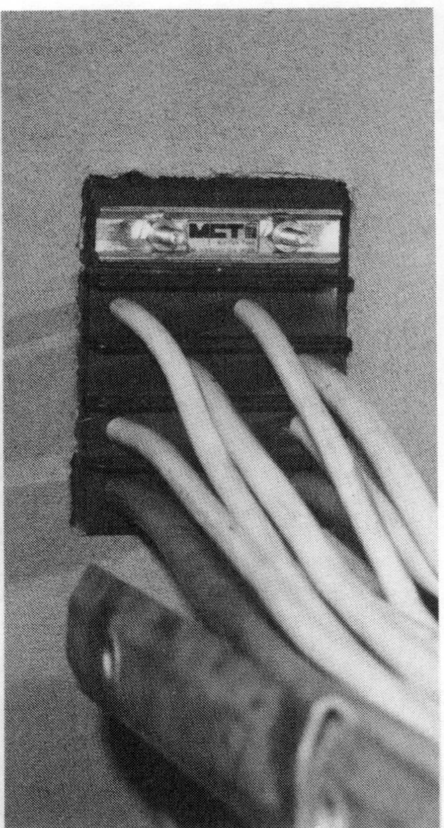

Fig. 3.3.4. *Fire Barrier (Hawke Cable Glands)*

3.3.5.5 Joints and terminations

Cables are joined by means of joints, which must be as sound, electrically and mechanically, as the cable itself. Joints may be soldered or brazed, provided it is possible to apply heat at the site, or a compression technique may be employed, using ferrules or lugs compressed by a special tool, preferably of the same manufacture as the accessory, and incorporating a mechanical interlock to ensure that the correct pressure has been exerted on to the ferrule or socket. However, screwed mechanical clamps are now widely used to through joint and terminate cables. Joints in continuous runs of cable should be avoided wherever possible, but where these joints are unavoidable they should be enclosed in non-flammable boxes and identified.

Cables terminate at switchgear or other equipment, at which terminals are provided. It is important to provide proper means of termination, which comprise a gland, electrical insulation and cable sockets to connect the cores to the equipment. The purpose of the gland is to provide:

(a) A non-hygroscopic seal for cables having paper or mineral insulation.
(b) Continuity of the protective conductor system if this is in the sheath of the cable
(c) Mechanical rigidity to the cable
(d) A seal to the equipment being entered

Cable glands can be obtained in materials and designs to suit any environment or size and variety of cable. (Fig. 3.3.5).

Fig. 3.3.5. *Cable gland for m.i.c.s. cable* *(BICC)*

It is also important to ensure that adequate room is available outside the equipment to assemble the gland over the cable, and that inside the equipment there is proper provision for the cable cores and their terminating sockets. Cable sockets, compressed on to cable cores, must be correctly chosen and used with the correct compression tool, preferably of the same manufacture as the cable sockets.

3.3.5.6 Underground cables

Connections between buildings can often be best made by underground cables laid in trenches or pulled into duct systems. Regulations 523–23, –24 and –25 specify the acceptable types of cable for this type of installation. Cables buried direct in the ground must be armoured or have a metal sheath or both. Underground cables should be marked with cable covers complying with BS 2484, or plastic marker tape. Cables should be buried at a sufficient depth to avoid their being damaged by any disturbance of the ground reasonably likely to occur during the normal life of the premises.

3.3.5.7 Overhead cables

It is unusual in modern practice to use overhead cable systems as part of the consumer's installation although their use by Electricity Authorities is widespread on their distribution networks.

Where it is expedient to use overhead cables as part of an installation in a building project Regulation 521–1 allows for the standard types of cable to be provided with catenary wire if they are to be used for aerial suspension. Regulation 523–26 and its notes give further guidance for short connections. The use of cables envisaged in Regulation 521–4, the provisions of the Overhead Line Regulations and of

IEE Regulation 412–9 require bare or lightly insulated cables to be out of reach of any source of mechanical damage and of persons or livestock.

3.3.6 Future developments

Two development which will effect cables in the future are the introduction of Fibre Optic cable systems and new insulants for mains voltage cable systems. Development of fibre optic systems will dramatically reduce the number of cables required for control and communications systems which will in turn reduce the physical room required for such systems. The cables are also not subject to electrical pick-up and can be run adjacent to mains cables.

The introduction of new insulants such as XLPE (Cross linked Polyethylene) and EPR (Ethylene Propylene) will enable mains cables to have improved short-circuit characteristics and higher conductor operating temperatures compared to the traditional cables of the same current ratings; these cables may ultimately replace the traditional types of cable for heavy current distribution in buildings.

3.3.7 Certification of cables

A number of British Standards relate to cables, and are listed in section 3.3.8.2 and Appendix 6.2. The UK certifying body for electric cables is the British Approvals Service for Electric Cables (BASEC). The BASEC mark is applied to cables within the scope of the scheme which have satisfied the appropriate British Standard, and the BASEC HAR mark in the case of cables also meeting harmonised international standards. These marks, and the symbol denoting the scheme, are illustrated in Fig. 3.3.6.

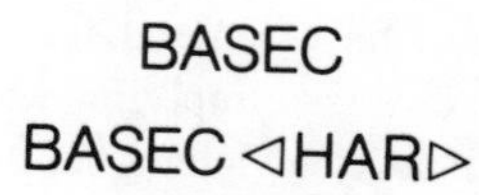

Fig. 3.3.6. *BASEC Marks*

3.3.8 References

3.3.8.1 British Standards (See Appendix 6.1.2)
British Standards relating to cable specifications include the following: BS 2136,

BS 6004, BS 6007, BS 6207, BS 6231, BS 6346, BS 6360, BS 6387, BS 6480, BS 6899 and BS 6977. Joints, glands and terminations are referred to in BS 4579, BS 6081 and BS 6121, whilst BS 2484 refers to cable covers.

3.3.8.2 Bibliography

Regulations for Electrical Installations (15th Edition and subsequent amendments) (Institution of Electrical Engineers)

JENKINS, B. D. 'Commentary on the 15th Edition of the IEE Wiring Regulations'. (Peter Peregrinus Limited)

WHITFIELD, J. F. 'A Guide to the 15th Edition of the IEE Wiring Regulations'. (Peter Peregrinus Limited)

Memorandum on the Electricity (Factories Act) Special Regulations 1908–1944. SHW 928 (HMSO)

LARMAN, W. E. 'The Importance of Cable Glands' (CMP Limited, Newcastle-upon-Tyne)

McALLISTER, D. 'Electric Cable Handbook'. (Granada) 'Current Rating Standards for Distribution Cables'. (ERA Technology Limited).

Overhead Line Regulations (HMSO)

Chapter 3.4

Motors and generators

Professor Arthur J. Ellison, D.Sc.(Eng.), C.Eng., F.I.Mech.E., F.I.E.E., Sen.Mem.I.E.E.E.

Head of Electrical and Electronic Engineering Department, The City University.

3.4.1 Introduction

Motors and generators, though sometimes superficially different e.g. in their protective features, are actually internally, and so far as the operating principles are concerned, identical. If the torque applied to the shaft of a rotating machine is changed in sign (i.e. driving becoming braking) then the flow of energy through the machine will be reversed, electrical energy output then becoming electrical energy input.

There have been rapid developments in practices using rotating electrical machines in recent years and these will continue. The causes have been the introduction of solid state power conditioning equipment (altering voltage and frequency at will) and microprocessors, and of dramatic improvements in the design of certain types of electric machine, making some traditional types obsolescent. There is also a growing emphasis on environmental factors, especially quietness, and on energy conservation. Emphasis continues on safety. It is becoming appreciated that the whole-life cost of installing and running a drive system (a machine with its associated equipment) is often of greater importance than is first cost.

The subject of electric machines and their use is therefore in a state of rapid change. The reader who wishes to specify appropriate electric machine installations for a modern building is therefore unable to base his recommendations on even quite recent practices without very careful consideration as, though working well, they may be in fact obsolescent. The possession of up-to-date manufacturers' data is today vital and recommendations from manufacturers who build both the machine and the power electronics are especially relevant.

Another factor of great importance in regard to the specification of appropriate equipment is the need to appreciate the growing shortage and increasing cost of skilled manpower. The highest practicable reliability is therefore to be emphasised with, in addition, consideration of the availability of equipment which indicates where a fault has occurred. The increasingly ubiquitous microprocessor and its proper application and use must therefore be appreciated.

These introductory remarks will indicate why this Chapter has its characteristic features. It is necessary to provide brief information on machine types in a more or less traditional way but, above all, it is essential to indicate the rapidly changing aspects of the subject and the need to assess continuously the current state of the art. There is much more to the enlightened selection of electric motors (and generators) and their associated control and protection equipment than can be found in textbooks on machines, even of quite recent date.

3.4.2 Electricity supply

3.4.2.1 Type of supply

The supply of electrical energy available in every modern building is of alternating current. If the total load is small the supply will be a single phase, having a line wire and a neutral wire (between which the loads are connected), and also an earth wire, now known as a circuit protective conductor (for safety reasons). (These features are those of most domestic supplies.) Motors must therefore be of the single-phase types, and necessarily small. A direct current supply or a 3-phase alternating current supply can be produced by appropriate power electronic equipment, if necessary, but a limit of size is set by the power requirements.

Large buildings will have a power supply of 3-phase alternating current and the power supplied can be as high as necessary. Small motors can still be connected between one of the three lines and the neutral, as for a single-phase supply, but larger motors (say greater than about 1 kW rating) will be supplied with 3-phase power, all three lines being connected to the machines. Single-phase loads are distributed between each of the three lines and neutral and the distribution is often by floors, loads on adjacent floors being connected to different lines to give an approximate balance of power on the three phases.

Very large buildings will receive a 3-phase power supply at high voltage and one or more transformers will reduce this to the low voltage required for distribution throughout the building. Large motors can thus be fed directly at the higher voltage and the choice of voltage is usually based on cost as there is a most economical voltage for a given size of motor (the size varying slightly with the manufacturer).

3.4.2.2 Standby supplies

Standby power supply equipments are usually integrated diesel-engine driven synchronous generator sets, though gas turbines are sometimes used as the prime movers. The supply features are the same as those of the normal supply because the loads are of course identical. Means of automatic starting and change-over of connections are normally available as part of such standby plant. Standby supplies for emergency lighting have to supply only a very small power and batteries are usually used.

3.4.3 Choice of motor and ancillary gear

The factors governing the type and size of motor used, with its associated equipment – and the whole must be considered together – are predominantly as follows:

(a) *Performance required*
Normal (or equivalent) full load power, starting torque, maximum torque, speed and any variation needed or permissible, starting current permissible, duty cycle (all machines do not run continuously on full load, nor at constant speed).

A machine may be designed for say a 1-hour rating and cost less than if it were made suitable for a continuous full-load duty. Details of the duty cycle if the load varies are important in so far as the equivalent full-load rating is concerned and on which the size and cost of the machine will be based.

(b) *Ambient conditions*
Temperature, cooling air supply (clean or polluted), vibration present (if any), noise level permissible.

(c) *Whole life cost*
That is, first costs plus estimated working life running costs, allowing for energy supply, servicing, amortization. Some of these are difficult to estimate in the presence of unknown future inflation, but should be attempted.
(d) *Degree of reliability*
The degree of reliability necessary and probable cost of breakdowns.

Alternative ways of doing the job must also be considered (e.g. fluids may be circulated by a motor-driven pump and rate of flow controlled by a valve, or the valve may be left fully open and the speed of the motor varied with a consequential saving in energy). The saving over the whole life of the equipment may more than cover the present cost of the extra equipment for speed variation.

3.4.4 Types and characteristics of motors

3.4.4.1 Introduction
There are two general types of motor – suitable for connection to a.c. or to d.c. supplies. Some small motors are 'universal' and may be connected to both a.c. and d.c. supplies (of appropriate voltages). There are a number of sub-types of these general types, some being still in use while others are obsolescent or obsolete (primarily due to developments in solid state power conditioning equipment). New types are under development.

3.4.4.2 Induction motors (Figs 3.4.1, 3.4.2)
By far the most widely used type of motor, for reasons of cheapness, robustness and reliability, is the induction motor, the common version being the cage type. For certain purposes wound rotor ('slip ring') machines are used. The cage type

induction motor operates from an a.c. supply and has a single-phase or 3-phase winding on the stationary member (the 'stator'). It is the cheapest and most robust of rotating electric machines as the rotating member (the 'rotor') consists only of a laminated steel cylinder (carried on the shaft) having uninsulated copper or aluminium bars inserted through slots at its periphery, all being joined together at the ends by rings to form the 'cage'. In small examples the complete cage is of die-cast aluminium. Slip ring motors have a rotor carrying instead of a cage a 3-phase insulated winding, the ends being connected to 'slip rings', with carbon 'brushes' so that additional resistance may be externally inserted into the rotor circuits for alterations of the performance. These latter machines are not made in very small sizes as are the cage types. The performance of cage type machines can be altered by special design of the cage.

Fig. 3.4.1. *30 kW 3-phase Induction Motor* *(Brook Crompton Parkinson)*

An induction motor runs at almost constant speed, decided by the number of pairs of poles for which it is wound and the supply frequency. The light-running speed will be almost one pole-pair per cycle of the supply i.e. for 2 poles, 50 rev/s (3000 rev/min), called 'synchronous speed'. When load is applied 'slip' occurs and the speed drops by a few per cent (say by 2% for large motors and 5% for small). Full-load speeds available are therefore in the region of 2850, 1440, 960, 720, 570 . . . rev/min. The cost of a motor of given power becomes progressively greater the lower the speed. Lower speeds than those listed are probably best obtained by a higher-speed motor built integrally with a speed-reduction gear box. Above a certain torque (the maximum or 'breakdown' torque) an induction motor will slow down and stop, this torque (available for a short time only or over-heating would occur) being normally about 150% of the full-load value. Cage-type induction motors can carry stator windings suitable for more than one speed. Switching the supply from one winding to another (which may be the same conductors reconnected or an entirely different winding in the same slots) will then change the synchronous speed and other characteristics.

3.4.4.3 DC motors

DC machines are much more expensive than induction machines as the rotating member (the 'armature') has a commutator and brushes. The stationary member, the 'field system', has electromagnets carrying d.c. windings or permanent magnets. The commutator and brushes both wear and must receive regular maintenance.

DC motors are designed (for convenience of standardization) for the speeds suitable for induction motors but also for any practicable speed required. While induction motors are usually available 'off the shelf' a d.c. motor would, especially if of a non-standard speed, have to be designed and made specially. Its expensive construction (especially of the commutator, to the segments of which the armature (rotor) winding coil ends have to be individually connected) plus the extra cost of often being 'special' rather than 'stock' mean that other types of machine plus additional equipment may in total be cheaper, while producing an equivalent performance. An induction motor plus solid state power electronic control equipment to produce a variable frequency may be more appropriate if the use of a d.c. machine is being considered because the speed must be varied, and would probably be more reliable. Similarly, reluctance and permanent magnet machines of the newer types becoming available, fed from a similar power electronic supply, should be investigated.

3.4.4.4 Reluctance motors (and permanent magnet motors)

Important developments have taken place in reluctance motors and with appropriate power electronic equipment they may well replace more traditional machines in some applications as regards cost, performance and reliability. Some reluctance machines may have an improved performance by having in-built permanent magnets.

The reluctance motor is therefore likely to come into prominence soon and is built in two types, the rotating field type and the switched type. The rotor is a robust laminated steel member of simple salient form (having projections around a cylinder) carrying no windings. The stator carries (normally) a 3-phase winding in the rotating field version. In the switched version, the windings of polar projections are fed with pulses of current from an appropriately controlled electronic power source. Such a controlled drive is applicable to controlled-speed or controlled-position applications and has certain advantages over conventional machines by way of high performance, low cost, simplicity and reliability.

3.4.4.5 Synchronous motors

The other important type of a.c. machine is the synchronous machine: it is more expensive and less common than the induction machine but has particular and distinct properties. It is the type almost invariably used (as an a.c. generator) in power stations of all kinds and sizes, including for standby and emergency purposes.

The principal feature of this motor is that its shaft speed is precisely constant for all load torques within its normal rating, this speed being decided (as is the synchronous speed of an induction motor) by the number of pairs of poles for which the stator and rotor are wound. Synchronous motors are made in smaller sizes where a constant speed independent of the proportion of normal load is required. In the smaller (and increasingly larger) sizes permanent magnet 'secondary' members (usually the rotor, the 'primary' member carrying a 3-phase winding) are becoming commoner. At a certain overload torque the synchronous motor will lose synchronism and stall. ('Synchronism' refers to the pattern of rotating magnetic poles on the secondary member running at the same speed as the set of corresponding poles produced by the 3-phase primary winding, which condition is essential for normal functioning.)

A synchronous motor has the useful property of running at a power factor which may be chosen, and depends on the value of the field current in the secondary member. It can thus (at extra cost) improve the power factor of the total load on the system and, with an appropriate tariff, reduce the energy costs.

3.4.4.6 Linear motors (Fig. 3.4.3)

Linear motors are, in the commonest form, built like cage-type induction motors, but having the stator opened out flat. The 'rotor' rather than being of the cage type is often a long sheet of aluminium with or without a steel backing, and can be used (rather inefficiently) with a steel sheet only. Held stationary against a lift door or a roller shutter door, for example, they can cheaply simply and effectively, move the door one way or the other without contact (and without gears or chains). They are built in 3-phase or single-phase versions.

3.4.5 Starting and control of motors

Unless they are small, motors cannot usually be started by connecting them directly to the supply by a simple switch or circuit-breaker as there may be restrictions on the maximum current permissible. A reduced voltage is therefore often applied for starting and then increased to normal for running.

Induction motors larger than about 3 kW full-load rating are often started in the star (wye) connection (so reducing the current to one-third of what it otherwise would be) and then changed (manually or automatically) to the normal delta connection for running. When the speed is controlled by power conditioning equipment, interlocks are often arranged so that starting is possible only at a low-speed setting.

DC machines always have a starter which inserts resistance into the armature circuit for starting and removes it in steps during the run-up in speed. Such machines may have their speed raised by lowering the current flowing in the field windings; the speed may be lowered by reducing the voltage applied to the armature winding, by inserting series resistance or otherwise.

Synchronous machines usually require rather more elaborate controls, beyond the scope of this Chapter.

All machines normally have means for automatic disconnection from the supply in cases of excessive overload and for restarting in the normal way after an interruption.

3.4.6 Environmental features

3.4.6.1 Enclosures

Although most motors function in 'normal' indoor conditions it is frequently appropriate for various reasons to mount motors in exposed places or in other environments hazardous to the motor. Appropriate enclosures are available for most environmental conditions and are as follows. All normal motors require ventilation (so that internally produced heat can be removed) or they have to be oversize and therefore expensive.

Fig. 3.4.2. *Induction Motor driving ventilation fan* *(GEC Small Motors Ltd)*

(a) Screen protected: live and moving parts are protected from accidental contact without obstructing the ventilation. Used in clean dry locations and not in corrosive or flammable atmospheres.

(b) Drip proof: as screen protected but ventilation openings protected to exclude water or dirt falling vertically. Not suitable for 'hosing down.'

(c) Totally enclosed: the enclosed air has no direct connection with the ambient atmosphere – but not air tight.

Cooled by internal circulating fan with radiation/convection from external cooling fins or by an external fan blowing air across the cooling fins. Used where clean cooling air not available or in the presence, for example, of water, steam, wood shavings, cement dust or dirt.

(d) Pipe or duct ventilated: not now widely used. In corrosive or otherwise objectionable atmospheres clean cooling air is brought from a more distant point.

(e) Weatherproof: motor may be mounted without further protection from the weather specified.

(f) Flameproof: used where the motor may contain flammable or explosive gases or dusts. The motor enclosure should withstand any explosion occurring within it and prevent the spread of explosion or flame to the surrounding atmosphere. Can be described as flameproof only if certified by competent authority. (BS 5000: Part 17: 1981).

(g) Closed air-circuit water-cooled: larger machines may be cooled by arranging for the circulating air to pass through water/air heat exchangers.

3.4.6.2 Noise: acoustic

With the growing emphasis on the quality of the environment machines must not be allowed to produce excessive noise. 'Standard' machines are limited to sound levels tabulated in the relevant British (or other) Standard. Several other sound levels are specified. Where special quietness is an important requirement permissible sound levels must be specified. A noisy machine cannot normally be quietened by a sound attenuating enclosure as the ventilation necessary for cooling may be obstructed.

If a motor is driving equipment which is much noisier than itself there is no point in concern over the motor noise. Noisy equipment can be installed in special rooms or enclosures but must be resiliently mounted to prevent appreciable noise and vibration being transmitted through the building via the mounting. Plant rooms attenuate noise transmitted to the building, dependent on the mass of the material in the walls, floor and ceiling. If equipment is noisy, lining the plant room with light acoustic tiling will not lower the sound level elsewhere appreciably.

Motors supplied from power conditioning equipment will almost certainly be noisier than those connected directly to the supply mains. Allowance must be made for this and the manufacturer's advice sought in important cases of doubt.

3.4.6.3 Noise: electrical

Motors having rubbing electrical contacts, especially commutators, where sparking is likely to occur emit objectionable interference, both along the mains and radiated. Such machines must be 'suppressed' by the use of capacitors and inductors and by careful earthing of frames. (Such electrical interference can also be produced by power conditioning equipment.)

3.4.6.4 High ambient temperature

Motors required to perform in ambient temperatures greater than 40°C, i.e. in which the cooling air is at an abnormally high temperature, can be supplied with suitable insulation. It is usually best to specify the ambient temperature and permit the motor manufacturer to offer suitable machines rather than to specify the class of insulation.

Fig. 3.4.3. *Linear Motor operating cold room door* *(Linear Motors Ltd)*

3.4.6.5 Condensation

Where machines are shut down at night in relatively high humidity and there is a large temperature drop, condensation of water will take place on the windings, possibly leading to breakdowns. Such machines should be fitted with heaters to prevent such a drop in winding temperature. Machine manufacturers should be consulted.

3.4.7 References

3.4.7.1 British Standards (See also Appendix 6.2)

BS 2048 Dimensions of fractional horse-power motors
BS 4999 General requirements for rotating electrical machines
BS 5000 Part 3 Generators to be driven by reciprocating internal combustion engines
Part 10 General purpose induction motors
Part 11 Small-power electric motors and generators
Part 15 Machines with type of protection 'e' (increased safety)
Part 16 Motors with type of protection 'N'
Part 17 Machines for flameproof enclosure
Part 40 Motors for driving power station auxiliaries
Part 99 Machines for miscellaneous applications
BS CP 1011 Maintenance of electric motor control gear
BS CP 1013 Earthing
BS CP 1015 Electrical equipment of industrial machines

3.4.7.2 Bibliography

Regulations for Electrical Installations (Institution of Electrical Engineers)

Chapter 3.5

Automatic control systems

D.M. Lush, B.Sc.(Eng.), C.Eng., M.I.E.E., M.C.I.B.S.
Technical Director, Ove Arup Partnership

3.5.1 Introduction

3.5.1.1 Applications (See also section 3.1.4)
Automatic control systems are accepted as common-place in modern buildings, so much so that their importance is often not fully recognised. Their correct selection and application is crucial to the overall satisfactory operation of all building services systems and an acceptable internal environment. The multiplicity of services in buildings often accounts for up to 50% of the total cost of the building and can cover the electrical distribution system, heating, ventilating and air conditioning (HVAC), lighting, plumbing and public health system, communications, fire defence, security and vertical transportation. There may also be some services such as mechanical handling or conveyor systems which can be treated as building services or process cum production systems, depending on their application.

Each of the systems listed requires some form of control, which may range from manually operated devices, through stand alone automatic control systems, to fully automated computer based building automation systems. Each of the systems may be the most suitable for a particular set of circumstances but only the latter two are examined here in detail. The term "automatic control systems" is often shortened to "control systems" or "controls" and the terms are frequently used synonymously without confusion. Until quite recently these terms were applied to the thermostatic controls for the HVAC systems but generically they cover all the elements which permit the building and its services to meet a specified level of performance. This chapter is confined to the use of controls for building services and does not cover process and industrial applications, although the principles are the same in all cases.

3.5.1.2 Interfaces

The complexity and variety of services in modern buildings is such that interface and boundary conditions between the services are numerous and interactive, e.g. the operation of a fire alarm in an air conditioned building may require fans and dampers to operate in an emergency mode, while at the same time normal lift control will be over-ridden and the lifts returned to the main entrance level. Thus the controls may be considered as the mortar which binds together individual services into a comprehensive and cohesive entity. For this reason, as well as many others, the control systems for building services should be considered as an overall package from the inception stage of design, rather than a set of discrete packages to be added after the individual services systems are designed.

3.5.1.3 Classification of functions

Automatic controls should be selected on the following basis:

(a) To control the internal environment within the limits of its designed and specified performance.
(b) To allow the automatic functioning of equipment and services to preselected levels and patterns of operation.
(c) To act as safety devices to prevent or give warning of undesirable conditions in the plant or environment.
(d) To provide maximum economy in fuel and energy consumption.
(e) To save labour.

3.5.1.4 Types of control system

(a) *General*

Control systems may be electric/electronic, pneumatic, hydraulic, self acting, or hybrid, i.e. a combination of systems. There is also the possibility that emerging systems such as fibre optics will in future become standard for the control of particular elements of building services. In this chapter emphasis will be placed on the application of electric/electronic systems (shortened subsequently to electric systems) but some very brief details of the other common systems are given below:

(b) *Pneumatic systems*

Pneumatic controls for building services are normally used for HVAC systems and can provide a range of facilities comparable to those of the electric system, with the exception of building automation centres. The choice between the two is normally based on cost differential rather than differing performance. All pneumatic systems are hybrid because they are always associated with some electric components necessary for the overall operation of the controlled plant. The system uses compressed air and pipework distribution for the transmission of signals and the operation of actuators on control valves, dampers and associated electrical devices. A compressor installation providing clean dry air is an essential element of such systems. Due to the compressibility of air, signals may take a considerable time for transmission.

(c) *Hydraulic systems*
Hydraulic systems are not commonly used in building services systems, hydraulically operated lifts being the most common exception. Again the system is hybrid, having an associated electrical element which may constitute a major part of the system. As distinct from pneumatic systems the signal transmission is made via a fluid in pipework which is then pumped or forced into actuating mechanisms operating control valves, etc. The most common fluids are water or oil which may be considered incompressible so that signal transmission may be faster than that in pneumatic systems. Such systems will be found most frequently in industrial applications.

(d) *Self acting systems*
Self acting systems cover such items as thermostatic radiator valves and direct acting devices for calorifier controls, etc. The former items are widely used for individual space control.

3.5.2 Economics and energy conservation

3.5.2.1 Cost evaluation
These two topics are relevant to all elements of the building construction and services content, but in no context are they more important than the field of control systems. Some simple guidelines illustrate these points. In terms of economic factors the cost evaluation of proposed systems should not be based wholly on first cost, which may be very misleading. It should cover:

(a) Cost of control equipment including data centres, valves, sensors, controllers, motor control centres, loose starters (i.e. starters mounted outside motor control centres) etc.
(b) Overall installation cost of all the equipment and the electrical inter-wiring (for pneumatic systems, inter-connecting pipework and compressor costs also need to be included).
(c) Cost of supervising the installation.
(d) Cost of suitable software for any data centres or building automation systems.
(e) Cost of testing and commissioning and the associated instrumentation and specialised labour.
(f) Costs of spares to be held on site.
(g) Operating costs of the control systems over the life of the building.
(h) Servicing and maintenance costs over the life of the system, which is normally different to the life of the building.
(j) Cost benefit of available spares and servicing over the full life span of the system.
(k) Cost benefit from reduced energy consumption provided by the different control systems under consideration.

3.5.2.2 Areas for design consideration

The relationship between energy consumption and control systems is generally acknowledged but not always pursued in the design of the building services and their associated controls. Particular control applications will be described later for a range of services systems but at a very basic level it can be stated that a space temperature in a heated building which is controlled, or uncontrolled, at 1°C above a design temperature of 19°C, adds between 5% and 10% to the energy costs. This alone, in times of expensive and ever increasing fuel costs, should make the selection and design of suitable plant and control systems a mandatory requirement. Without going into detail the following points identify the major areas to be considered:

(a) Plant operating periods: these need to be minimised by careful selection of plant size, zoned distribution and suitably controlled switching.
(b) Matching plant output to load: plant selection has to permit efficient operation of boilers or chillers under part load conditions, which exist far more frequently than the design load situation. Control systems for suitable sequential operation of such plant items under varying load conditions are essential, if this match is to be maintained.
(c) Temperature control: the effects of inadequate space temperature control have already been mentioned. Ensure that the systems are designed and the distribution is such that each space may be individually controlled. Consider air conditioned buildings, where the control temperature may be raised for the summer, or cooling, sequence. Controlling the space temperature at, say, 19°C in winter is required for comfort but if this is still maintained in summer when 23°C is acceptable there is a 4°C cooling penalty, which is directly reflected in energy consumption.
(d) Elimination of simultaneous heating and cooling: paradoxically this is not a statement applied only to air conditioned buildings. In any heated building where windows are opened because of overheating, this situation exists. Properly selected controls can eliminate this problem. In air conditioned buildings some systems, notably non-changeover induction unit systems, suffer from the problem. When fossil fuels were considered to be abundant and energy was regarded as cheap, this was accepted, but in the present situation a more careful system and controls selection will virtually eliminate the problem.
(e) Efficiency of energy usage: the choice of fuel(s) for a building, to obtain the most efficient energy usage for particular applications, is beyond the scope of this chapter. However, after the selection is made it is the control system which will largely determine whether the conversion efficiency can be achieved and maintained.
(f) Monitoring and optimisation of control systems: individual plant control systems are designed and selected on the basis of being able to maintain the required performance criteria. The use of building automation systems (BAS) (section 3.5.13) is an acknowledged method of monitoring and optimising the use of particular plants and their controls. The BAS may vary from a time switch to a computer based centralised system and each has its own range of suitable applications. Both, however, are relevant to energy conservation and will be considered later.

3.5.3 Electrical installation

There are very few problems of principle related to the wiring and installation of control systems but there are a number concerning details. In general, control wiring may be run with other electrical distribution wiring so long as cable insulation standards and identification accord with the requirements of the 15th Edition of the IEE Wiring Regulations. Exceptions to this are:

(a) Control wiring associated with the fire alarm system, which is specifically covered in the Regulations and may also have to comply with local by-laws and insurance company requirements.
(b) Security system wiring which may need to be segregated for insurance purposes or purely security reasons. In the absence of such requirements this wiring may be treated as control wiring.

Power requirements are normally so low on control systems that the stipulated current carrying capacities of cables quoted in the Regulations are not normally significant. The main consideration is the possibility of unacceptable volt drop on very long wiring runs where the control system voltage is below 50 V. Different suppliers use a variety of voltages, both a.c. and d.c., below this figure and this point should always be queried for any proposed system.

A different but related consideration is that of screening. Most modern control systems have been designed to eliminate, as far as possible, the need for screened cable. There are no hard and fast rules but in some circumstances screening will be advisable when the control cabling is run together with heavy power distribution cables, particularly where frequent load switching occurs. In other cases screening will be advisable for sensor wiring, either generally or for runs over a given length, irrespective of whether such wiring is being run independently or with other cabling. Voltage spikes, etc. can damage microprocessors and erase software but their source is not always identified nor understood. If in doubt, ask. It can be expensive to remedy an unstable system once it has been installed.

Another matter which is of a practical nature with financial connotations concerns the actual number of inter-connecting cables. Systems from different suppliers, or different systems from the same supplier, may have the same number of basic components to perform identical tasks but the inter-connecting wiring can vary markedly. What is known as two wire control, i.e. a pair looped from item to item with spurs as required, is quite common, but in many cases three wires are required to sensors, and up to six normal connections to motorised valves. Very occasionally, compensated cable may also be required for resistive sensor elements. From a technical point of view it is imperative that the wiring diagrams are correct in this respect and the financial consequences of mistakes may be painful.

When low voltage controls are being considered ensure that suitable transformers are included as part of the control system. Many such systems are complete in themselves except that they still require a voltage supply of less than 50 V a.c., which is not normal in most buildings. Control systems also mix 240 V a.c. line voltage with other elements running below 50 V.

The fusing and protection of control system circuits does cause occasional difficulties. Because of the low current in these circuits the smallest standard fuses tend to be too large and it is common to run very large numbers of control circuits from the same control panel mounted fuse. Apart from the question of the Regulatory sizing of such fuses a very practical problem can ensue. The fuse may be blown by a fault in a single controller but every other control circuit will also be disabled. It is therefore necessary to limit the number of control circuits on a single fuse and to group such circuits so that they are all associated with a given plant. This will then restrict the inconvenience caused by a single fault to only one already disabled plant system. Wherever possible all control circuits should be fed from the same phase.

Connections to all actuators should always be made in a flexible form of termination to avoid any potential problems due to vibration of plant etc. and to facilitate servicing and maintenance.

3.5.4 Equipment components and modes of control

To control plants or systems having different characteristics and to meet varying control requirements, a controller may be made to operate a final control element (FCE). Various modes of control may be used to achieve this, with a wide variety of components. Before describing the application of control systems to particular plants a brief summary of these elements is provided below:

3.5.4.1 Components

Equipment components in a control system are simply described, although in practice each item may be extremely complex. In essence the components are sensors, controllers and final control elements which may be independent or combined items. Each control loop is some combination of these elements connected together in order to achieve the control of some specified parameter, e.g. temperature.

(a) *Sensor*

This is a detecting element sited in the variable being controlled, which registers the actual conditions of the controlled variable and transmits a signal either directly, or via a controller, to the FCE. The sensor may detect temperature, flow, pressure, humidity, products of combustion, open doors, etc. by means of a bimetal element or thermally sensitive resistance, orifice plates, Bourdon tubes, nylon filaments, ionisation chambers, and microswitches, respectively. The signal may be transmitted directly either electrically or pneumatically, or via a transducer which converts the signal from one form to another e.g. a pressure drop across an orifice plate may be converted into an electrical or pneumatic signal for transmission purposes. The term 'controlled variable' refers to the actual condition being sensed, e.g. space temperature, chiller outlet temperature.

There is also a range of specialist sensors such as photo-electric devices, which may include the necessary controller, or which may work via an independent unit. These devices are used for the control of lighting (switching or dimming), lifts, sunblinds, etc.

(b) *Controller*
This accepts the signal from the sensor, compares it with the desired value (set point) setting at the controller, to determine the error, and provides a corrective signal to the FCE. Modern electric, or more correctly in this instance, electronic controllers may still basically be considered as Wheatstone bridges where there is only one correct balance point for the variable resistance leg, which is represented by the signal from the sensor. The modes in which the controller may operate are described later. The controllers are powered by any voltage between 20 V a.c. and 240 V a.c. (pneumatic equivalents exist for the various types available). The action of comparing sensor signals with desired value settings is, in the majority of cases, a continuous operation and so is the corrective action.

(c) *Final control elements (FCE)*
These are most frequently motorised valves or dampers. They respond to the signals from the controller and vary the quantities or temperatures of the water and/or air to the plant serving the controlled variable in which the sensor is situated. Motors used for these applications are normally part of comprehensive ranges of equipment produced by specialist controls manufacturers. There are line voltage or extra low voltage versions for particular applications most commonly of the reversible type and frequently with internal switches to limit their travel. They normally drive the valves and dampers via internal gear boxes and purpose made linkages and can also be used to drive step controllers, etc. Equally the FCE may be a luminaire which is switched on or off, or dimmed, according to the dictates of a sensor/controller or, alternatively, a fire alarm bell actuated by a smoke detector.

3.5.4.2 Modes of control
Modes of control may be split principally into two, on/off and modulating. The former is a discontinuous control action which provides only two plant outputs 'maximum' and 'nil'. For temperature control a room thermostat acts as both the sensor and controller and the FCE could be a two position motorised valve, a fan, or electric heater, etc. In these cases there is a finite and discernible temperature gap between the thermostat going from 'on' to 'off' and vice versa and this is commonly known as the differential of the thermostat. Various means are employed to minimise this differential in practice, e.g. a minute internal heater which operates in the 'on' position causing the thermostat to anticipate the output from the FCE and thus turn off earlier than would otherwise be the case.

(a) *On/off*
Where the detecting sensor is sited so that the heater is both controlled and continuously monitored by the sensor the operation is said to be closed loop control.

On/off control is normally suitable for systems with a high degree of thermal inertia such as domestic hot water storage calorifiers, individual radiators and recirculating fan heaters. It is not suitable for non-storage calorifiers and heater and cooler batteries on fresh air plants.

In a fire or security system the sensors would be set to detect a fire condition or break-in, respectively, and operate in an on/off mode. However, each would initiate some particular FCE providing an audible or visual warning, which would not be reset or monitored by the initiating sensor, and these cases are said to be open loop control.

(b) *Modulating*

The modulating control mode is associated mainly with HVAC system controls, to a lesser extent with lighting and possibly to some public health applications. There are several identifiable forms of modulating control which may be categorised as proportional, floating, integral or derivative, either independently or in combination. The various modes are described in more detail elsewhere (Ref. 1). In the modulating modes the FCE is theoretically capable of being held at any position between, and including, the two extremes. In this way the input of air or water which causes changes to the controlled variable may be very finely controlled to give the desired result. Modulating systems are suitable for use on systems with little thermal inertia, such as non-storage calorifiers and fresh air heater and cooler batteries.

(c) *Proportional control*

The use of simple proportional controllers has a particular effect known as offset which needs to be identified and explained, particularly as this mode of control is often selected as the most basic modulating controller. Fig. 3.5.1 illustrates the operation of such a controller where the controlled variable is temperature. Under proportional control the actuator on the FCE will move in a correcting manner proportional to the deviation of the controlled variable from the desired value or set point. In effect this means that valve will have one position where there is no error signal, i.e. the controlled variable corresponds to the set point. By convention this is assumed to be the mid-position between open and closed (in practice this would frequently not be so). The valve can then only vary its position as the controlled variable deviates from the set point and the amount of movement is literally governed by the deviation. The permitted deviation from the fully open to the fully closed position is known as the proportional band. It can be seen from the diagrams that for a given load, corresponding to a particular valve position, the controlled temperature is determined by the width of the proportional band. Thus for any constant load other than that at the 50% position there will always be a sustained deviation from the set point. This is the offset.

At first sight the solution to offset appears simple – reduce the proportional band to zero. This has several effects in that any minute change in temperature from the set point immediately causes the actuator to move from one extreme to the other so that the output from the controlled device varies very rapidly between 0% and 100%, just like an on/off controller. The occupants in the controlled space will feel discomfort as the temperature attempts to swing violently due to this extreme change in output, and the control system will be unstable, because the sensor will almost immediately reverse the action of the controller. The proportional band must therefore be widened to a point where instability cannot occur under any load conditions and it may then be found that the offset is unacceptable to the occupants.

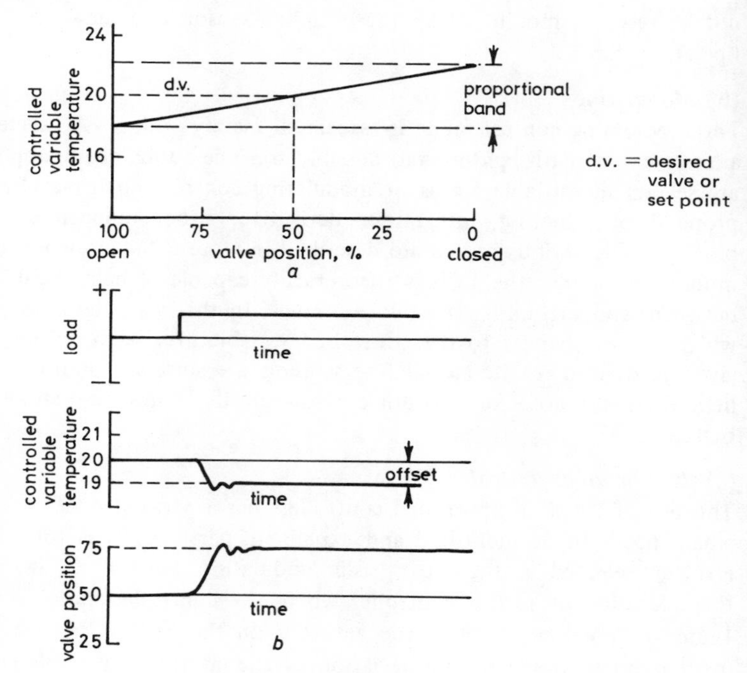

Fig. 3.5.1. *Proportional control operation demonstrated by space temperature control of a heater battery valve* (CIBS)

Offset can sometimes be used to advantage. The form of operation is such that a proportional controller set to control a heater battery to maintain a space temperature of 20°C, with a proportional band of 2°C, will be controlling at 19°C in cold weather and at 21°C in warm weather. If 19°C is acceptable to the occupants less energy will be used to maintain this condition than a constant 20°C. This principle can be employed on air conditioning systems using a set point of 21°C with a proportional band of 4°C which would give 19°C as the lowest temperature in winter and 23°C in mid-summer on the cooling cycle. Thus the use of these controllers can contribute to energy conservation as described in section 3.5.2.

The actual proportional band which gives stable operation is a function of several parameters including the various time lags which occur in the system operation. These time lags have different causes and will not be analysed in detail. Their effect is such that when a sensor detects a change in the controlled variable and signals back via the controller to the FCE, there will be a finite time before the change at the FCE is detected by the sensor. The complexity of the plant, the distance of the plant from the controlled variable and the velocity of transfer of output changes all have an effect on the optimum setting.

(d) *Non-proportional control*
Where offset is unacceptable, or close limits are specified for the controlled variable, it is increasingly common to use the other modulating modes of control or their combinations. The rapid adoption of micro-electronic technology now makes the use of more sophisticated controllers a realistic proposition at little or no extra cost whereas only a few years ago there was a very wide cost differential between proportional and other modulating controllers which eliminate offset. System configuration and time lags can also affect the operation and selection of the other types of controller.

3.5.5 Design and specification of control systems

3.5.5.1 The brief

It has already been stated that control systems should be considered from the inception of any building design rather than as add on features to a completed design. This requires the application of a co-ordinated and integrated design approach which considers the interaction between the various services. The largest element of controls is still that related to the HVAC system and, where applicable, the building automation system. The controls brief is part of the overall client requirements. It needs to be far more specific than in the past about the following parameters:

(a) Usage patterns.
(b) Hours of occupation for parts or all of the building.
(c) Acceptable comfort criteria with specified limits.
(d) Possible zoning.
(e) Flexibility for future modifications.
(f) Single or multiple tenancies.
(g) Energy metering.
(h) The quality of staff who will be maintaining and servicing the building and its mechanical and electrical systems after completion or refurbishment.

While these factors will affect the overall system design and possibly the building fabric, they are crucial to the effective and efficient operation of the control system.

3.5.5.2 Specifications

The brief has to be developed into a fully detailed and specified control system which should include the performance criteria for every control loop (section 3.5.4.1), a comprehensive description of the complete functional sequences of the controls in relation to the plant operation, detailed plant schematics which show all the controls and instrumentation and testing and commissioning details. Ideally the specification should include the associated control and motor starter panels, the interconnecting wiring and installation, testing, commissioning and spares, all as one single contract or sub-contract. The complexity of modern systems and the number of interfaces makes this composite approach a much easier system for the designers to supervise during the construction process. Where applicable, building automation, fire and security systems should be included in the same package and, at the very least, the boundaries and interconnections to each of these systems should be clearly defined with precise details as to who is responsible for any particular interconnection, coordination and commissioning.

3.5.5.3 Access

One particular aspect of design which affects control systems more than most services is access. The most comprehensive, correct and complete controls specification will ultimately be wasted if the plantrooms, ceilings and items of equipment are not selected and laid out in a manner which permits readily available access to control items. In this context one would also include access to the instrumentation and equipment required for testing and balancing the overall plant prior to the commissioning and testing of the controls.

3.5.6 Environmental control systems

3.5.6.1 Temperature

Temperature control is the most common feature of HVAC systems. This may generally be broken down into space or plant temperature control. Internal or space temperature should be controlled at the level required for comfort and energy economy, as dictated by the design specification. It has already been stated that 1°C overheating can increase energy consumption by as much as 10% and uncontrolled installations can increase fuel consumption by 30% or more. It is therefore important to ensure that each space may be individually controlled to the requisite level, over the minimum period possible. The degree of accuracy required may affect the selection of the system and the capital cost. There are relatively few occasions when commonly available commercial control systems will be incapable of achieving the desired accuracy.

It is now commonly accepted that modern air conditioned systems are provided with individual space control but in non-domestic heated buildings this still has to be fully recognised and in domestic premises this approach is, regrettably, uncommon. Capital cost is the reason most frequently given for the omission of such controls but a life cycle costing analysis would often show these additional controls as being cost effective.

While individual space control appears to offer the ideal system in non-domestic heated premises there are situations where the capital investment may not be cost effective, or the capital is simply not available, or refurbishment to this level is not practicable. The use of a single compensator system has been, for many decades, the mainstay of energy conserving and temperature control systems in heated buildings.

Where electricity is being used throughout a building for convective, fan assisted convective, or radiant heating it is unlikely that it would be installed without individual space temperature control in the first instance. If such a system were installed without these controls, a specialised energy regulator could be used to control the input to the individual heaters in unison on a timed pulse system, the pulse length depending on the external temperature and wind conditions. This type of system is now uncommon and unlikely to be proposed.

Where hot water heating is used via radiator or convector systems, compensators are still the most consistently used primary space temperature control. Fig. 3.5.2 shows such a system in schematic form. The external temperature detector (T1) on the North face of the building, to avoid solar effects, adjusts the set point of the mixed flow detector (T2), via controller C 1, in accordance with the typical flow characteristic shown in the Figure. Detector T2 then modulates the three port mixing valve (V1) to a position where water at boiler outlet temperature mixed with water returned from the load in correct proportions achieves the necessary temperature. The flow characteristic may be adjusted at C 1 for upper and lower limits and slope. Windage effects may also be impressed on the system to alter the characteristic.

One compensator used for a total building cannot provide the correct water temperature for all the different aspects of the building, solar gains, internal gains and variations in infiltration. The most frequent outcome of these elements is overheating in many areas of the building because the compensator has been adjusted to satisfy the coldest areas. To overcome this, compensator systems, each with its own pump, are often recommended for each aspect of the building with the external detectors mounted on the aspect face and subject to solar effects. Often these compensators are specified with external detectors calibrated for solar effects and with solar adjustments at C 1. It is difficult to set these compensators correctly for solar gains, whether the external element is specially calibrated or not. The other problems mentioned above still exist, plus the additional factor of shade patterns which often negate solar compensation.

The best intermediate solution is probably a single compensator and some zoning controls, i.e. motorised valves serving particular aspects, or floors of particular aspects, controlled from a room thermostat(s). This arrangement limits the upper level of temperature in the space(s) being controlled, but representative positioning of the themostat(s) may be difficult. The optimum solution is probably a single compensator system and thermostatic radiator valves (TRV) as shown in Fig. 3.5.2. The compensator ensures that the water temperature will not permit excessive space temperatures by simply turning up the TRV setting, while at the same time mains losses are minimised (circulating water in large mains, in spring and autumn, at 82°C rather than, say, 40°C is expensive in energy terms). At the

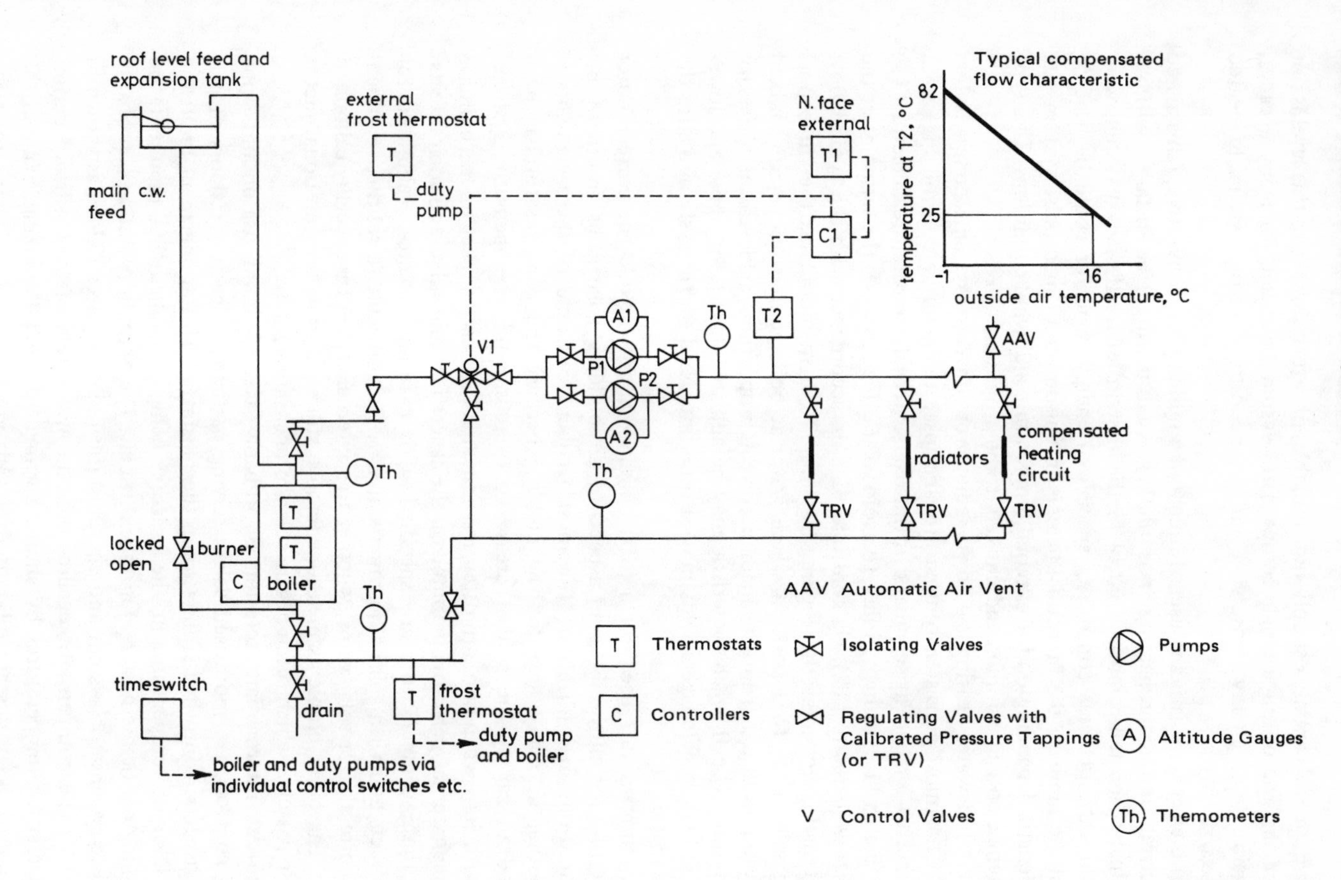

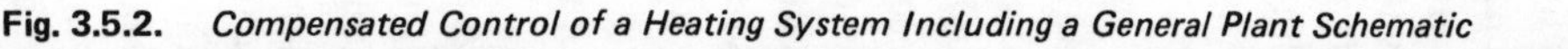
Fig. 3.5.2. *Compensated Control of a Heating System Including a General Plant Schematic*

same time the TRV's control individual spaces at an equable temperature by varying the heat output with variations in extraneous gains and losses.

3.5.6.2 Humidity

While humidity is an important factor in environmental comfort conditions a fairly wide range of relative humidity is normally acceptable. Because this range is approximately 40% to 70% at the space temperatures adopted for buildings, the UK climate is generally such as to naturally satisfy these requirements in non-air conditioned buildings. Humidity control is therefore confined to air conditioned buildings and special or processing areas within other buildings where the humidity control is critical for the process. Some details of this are provided in section 3.5.9.2.

In buildings which are only heated, humidities below 40% occur rarely and only during sustained periods of cold weather. This is generally acceptable but, when the relative humidity drops below 35%, nose and throat irritation can occur and static electricity may become a problem. If these points are considered harmful in any identifiable occupation situation, very simple pan humidifiers may be used where water is evaporated into the air under the control of a space mounted humidistat which switches an immersion heater in the humidifier. Excessively high humidity is normally encountered only in hot weather and the best solution is to encourage additional ventilation, by opening windows.

3.5.6.3 Time

Plant or plant items are normally started or stopped by means of an automatic timing device. In its simplest form the device is the long established time switch which consists essentially of a clock mechanism, operated either electrically or by a spring, which actuates a switch to make or break an electrical circuit. The method of drive can be a self-starting synchronous motor, clockwork with an electric wind, or synchronous motor with spring storage to drive the mechanism if the electricity supply fails. The switching sequence usually operates on either a daily or weekly cycle, and the following programmes are commonly encountered: twenty-four hour cycle with one or two switching operations per day; twenty-four hour main dial with auxiliary seven-day dial to provide alternative daily operations; or seven-day cycle with provision for individual daily cycles.

The contacts of time controls are normally rated up to 20 A and 30 A but, for a very heavy electrical load, the contacts of the clock control can be used to operate a contactor of adequate current-carrying capacity. More sophisticated time switches are available for complex functions, e.g. process timers which are used for interlocking and timing functions. Such timers exist as standard items but some are purpose made.

While the majority of time switches control plant via relays, it must be remembered that where the time switches are carrying direct power loads their ratings are for single phase resistive heating loads.

At the domestic level there is a large and constantly changing range of programmers which are basically time switches with multiple choice timing sequences serving more than one switched control circuit. The latest versions of these programmers are based on microprocessor technology and digital visual displays. In all cases it must be ensured that the ultimate user has sufficient knowledge and manual dexterity to fully utilise the selected programmer.

In commercial and industrial situations a common variation of the conventional time switch is the optimum start controller (which may also provide optimum stop in some instances). In essence these are microprocessor based time switches with variable switch-on times, computated by associated software which compares internal and external temperatures against a time base.

The effect of these devices is to ensure that environmental plant is switched on at the latest possible time in order to achieve the desired internal conditions at the time of occupation and not before. This is illustrated in Fig. 3.5.3 which demonstrates the energy saving against conventional time switching for a heating system. Modern versions of optimisers are simple to set up and in many cases have self-adaptive software. Thus the optimiser will use the previous day's predictions and performance to make the final adjustments to the necessary heating characteristic for the next day. In some cases, the optimisers will achieve their maximum performance after several days iteration, even without any real attempt to set the correct initial settings.

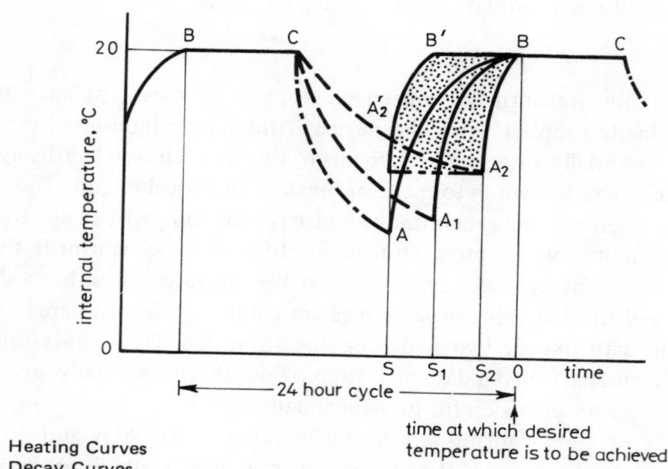

——— Heating Curves
– – – – Decay Curves
A_2-B Heat-up curve when the optimiser is used on a mild day
A'_2-B′ Heat-up curve when a time switch is used on a mild day
A'_2-B′-B-A_2-A'_2 Represents energy saving on a mild day by the use of an optimiser
B Normal time for which desired temperature is required
B-C Period for which desired temperature is to be maintained
C-A Temperature decay on coldest day
C-A_1 Temperature decay on an intermediate day
C-A_2 Temperature decay on a mild day
S Conventional time switch on point for all days
S-O Optimiser range of switch on points according to day and internal temperature

Fig. 3.5.3. *Optimum start control of heating plant* (JIEE) Jan 81

Optimiser costs are still far in excess of those which are acceptable in the domestic sector. There is, however, a vast potential market in this sector which, with its simpler and more consistent requirements, may lead to domestic versions. The functions of optimum start controllers are also available from building automation systems which are described in Section 3.5.13.

3.5.7 Control of heating and cooling sources

3.5.7.1 General

In HVAC terms these comprise fossil fuel fired boilers, electrode boilers, various forms of direct electric heating, chilled water machines (chillers) and direct expansion refrigeration units. The control of the conventional boilers, chillers and their associated heat rejection systems will be treated first, followed by the wholly electrical heating devices and systems.

3.5.7.2 Boilers and chillers

The control of these sources resolves itself into individual control and multiple control. The former is normally very simple and the latter frequently complex.

(a) *Individual control*
The vast majority of both boilers and chillers are supplied with their own packaged control systems. Where only one source unit is required at any time, i.e. there is only one unit or one plus another with total standby capacity, the use of the packaged control is better than any other solution.

(b) *Multiple control*
With multiple boiler or chiller combinations the first choice to be made is whether

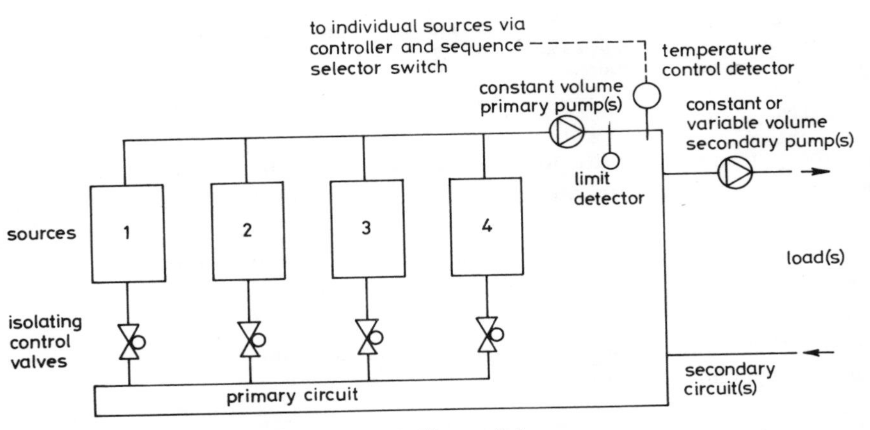

Fig. 3.5.4. *Schematic of sources controlled in parallel*

Parameters for Control:
1. Three sources to operate
2. Constant volume flow through sources
3. Modulating output from sources control from the flow
4. Manual or automatic selection of standby source
5. Constant or variable volume flow in secondary circuit

to connect them hydraulically for parallel or series operation and control (see Figs. 3.5.4 and 3.5.5). Sequential control is normally employed with a selected lead unit followed by others in a nominated order. The operation of the normal standby unit(s) may be carried out either manually when a failure is signalled or automatically through the control system – when an alarm should also be indicated.

The following considerations affect the control system:
In the parallel mode:

(i) The amount of over-temperature (boilers) and sub-cooling (chillers) which can be tolerated during sequence operation over the total load span.
(ii) The choice of primary plus secondary pumps or primary only, in conjunction with the valving off, or not, of inoperational units.
(iii) The permitted variation in flow through the units.
(iv) Flow balance between individual units.
(v) The maximum number of units which can reasonably be controlled in sequence.

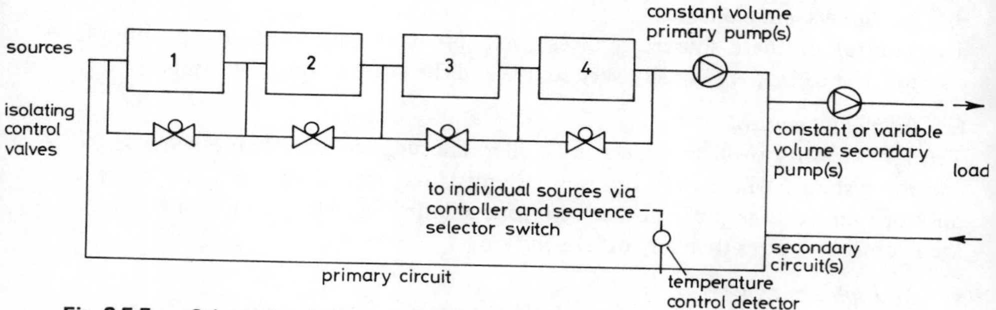

Fig. 3.5.5. *Schematic of sources controlled in series*

Parameters for Control:
1. Three sources to operate
2. Constant volume flow through sources
3. Modulating output from sources
4. Control from the return
5. Manual or automatic selection of standby source
6. Constant or variable volume flow in secondary circuit

In the series mode:

(i) The problems of over temperature and sub-cooling do not occur, but what is the minimum temperature rise (boilers) or fall (chillers) acceptable across each unit?
(ii) The choice of primary plus secondary pumping, or primary only.
(iii) Does the selected sequence of operation for the sources affect their output capability?
(iv) Is the operation of a series system of such an advantage as to outweigh the additional pumping costs for units in series?

For both series and parallel operation:

(i) The choice between modulating or stepped mode of temperature control.
(ii) The choice of temperature control from flow or return circuits.
(iii) Is there a suitable sequence control system available for the proposed arrangement?

(iv) What is the effect of superimposing an overall control system over that of the individual units?
(v) Are the unit sizes selected so that operation at low partial loads creates no more problems than operating at maximum load? On multiple unit installations one unit normally operates at minimum load far more frequently than the overall system operates at maximum load.
(vi) Do the limit devices have the span to cope with the unit operation over the full range of loads?

(c) *General controls*
Some control features should be considered for all sources whether used individually or in multiple systems:
(i) Manual override of the time switch.
(ii) The necessity to keep all isolating valves continuously open on the leading unit, except for actual maintenance periods.
(iii) Proving that the isolating valves are open before the sources are permitted to operate.
(iv) Ensuring that a failed source is locked out.
(v) Inclusion of all external interlocks into source starting circuits, e.g. proof of water flow.
(vi) The possible requirements for limitations on low return water temperature to boilers, or low flow temperatures from chillers.
(vii) On solid fuel boilers, kindling controls during normal off periods, with limit alarm and heat dissipation facilities if the water temperature rises too high under these conditions.

In all cases of individual control it is essential to check:

(i) That the source unit package controls are supplied already mounted on the unit and that all the interconnecting control wiring/piping is also part of the package.
(ii) The type of electrical equipment supplied as part of the package. Does it include isolators, fuses and starters? Are there multiple drives, for which additional external equipment and power supplies are required?
(iii) That remote starting features are provided, i.e. time switch or hand switch.
(iv) That external interlocking connections to the control package are possible, e.g. flow switch or pump starter auxiliary contacts.
(v) That control package and power wiring diagrams are available at tender stage.
(vi) Whether run-on timers are required to keep the primary circulating pumps running for a period after the sources are shut down. This prevents residual heat (or coolth) tripping out the limit devices.

Figures 3.5.4. and 3.5.5 are typical examples of the boiler and chiller configurations described above. Each of the schemes carries with it advantages and disadvantages. There are some aspects of all multiple source systems, in respect of hydraulics, excessive pump head, and energy management, which affect the choice of control system. One particularly important element of boiler controls which applies to both multiple and individual systems is examined below:

(d) *Boiler return temperatures*
Under system design conditions the return water temperature in a boiler system is a primary design parameter and should always be high enough to prevent corrosion of the boiler by condensation in the flue. There are however, flow conditions and systems, e.g. compensated circuits, which on part load provide much lower return temperatures, below the acid dewpoint of the flue, causing corrosive conditions. The same situation occurs during the warm up period of boilers after a plant shut-down. Special arrangements can be made to maintain the return water temperature or minimise the warm up period, and the same control arrangement can usually be used for both purposes.

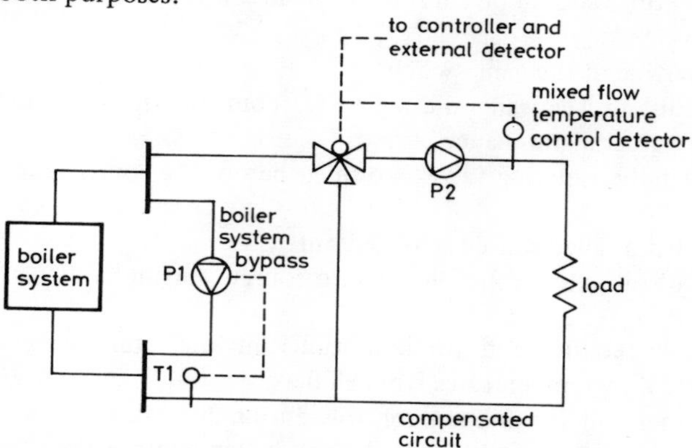

Fig. 3.5.6. *Basic schematic of boiler return water temperature control*
Note. Isolating or regulating valves not shown

A common system is shown in Fig. 3.5.6. A thermostat (T1) in the return from the load circuit controls a pump in the bypass to the boiler system. The setting of T1 is the lowest permissible return temperature and at any condition below this the pump (P1) in the bypass is started, but only during periods when the boiler system is operating. Thus P1 runs while at the same time the compensator circuit pump (P2) is also circulating water from the boiler. During start up this allows the boiler return temperature to rise very rapidly, due to P1, while the compensator circuit is also slowly warming up. This method prevents cold slugs of water being returned to the boiler during the start-up period. Thermostat T1 should not be positioned in the return from the bypass pump as this would cause rapid switching of P1 and the return from the bypass pump as this would cause rapid switching of P1 and would not be monitoring the main circuit. During normal operating periods this system also protects the boiler when the compensator flow temperature is reduced, causing a lowering of the mains return temperature.

3.5.7.3 Cooling towers
Towers are used to reject the heat extracted from a building, by chillers, to atmosphere. A general schematic for cooling tower control is shown in Fig. 3.5.7 which is also annotated with design notes for good practice. There are basically two types of cooling tower:

(a) An open circuit tower, where condenser water is discharged directly over the cooling tower pack, collected in a low level pond, then pumped back to the condenser.
(b) A closed circuit tower where condenser water is circulated through a heat exchanger within the tower and a separate, local, water supply is pumped up from a low level pond and discharged over the secondary side of the heat exchanger.

In both cases the air is induced or forced over the pack in contra-flow to the secondary water. Towers may be controlled in three ways:

(a) Air side, by fan and/or damper control;
(b) Water side, normally using bypass control;
(c) A combination of (a) and (b).

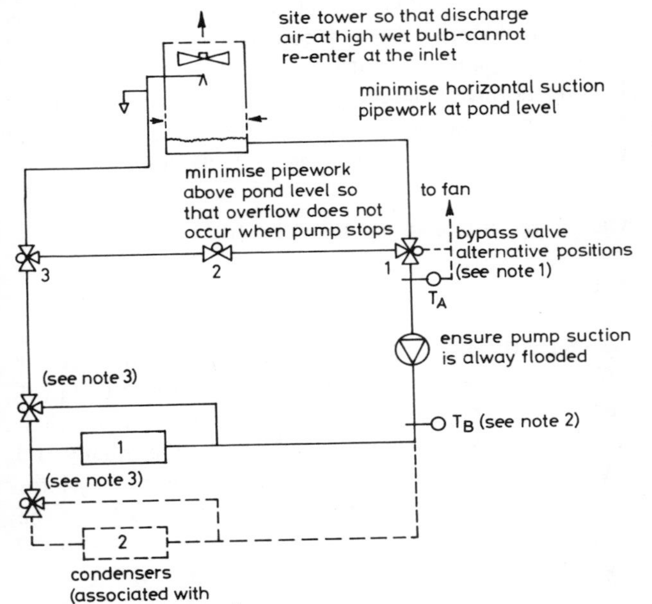
site tower so that discharge
air–at high wet bulb–cannot
re-enter at the inlet
minimise horizontal suction
pipework at pond level
minimise pipework
above pond level so
that overflow does not
occur when pump stops
to fan
bypass valve
alternative positions
(see note 1)
3
2
1
T_A
ensure pump suction
is alway flooded
(see note 3)
T_B (see note 2)
1
(see note 3)
2
condensers
(associated with
chiller evaporators)
Notes
1. Three possible valve positions are shown. Position 1 is very common but may cause cavitation. Position 2 avoids cavitation but needs a diverting type value. Position 3 utilises a two part valve and is common on large projects
2. T_A and T_B are alternative positions depending on length of vertical pipework and plant operation.
3. When multiple chillers are served by one tower water is automatically bypassed for non-operating chillers
4. Isolating or regulating valves not shown

Fig. 3.5.7. *Schematic of cooling tower temperature control*

The three options listed above apply equally to open or closed circuit towers, although the actual methods of achieving control may differ. The controlled variable can be flow or return water temperature or refrigerant head pressure. Heat reclaim requirements on modern sophisticated systems may necessitate complex variants of these arrangements.

3.5.7.4 Air cooled condensers

Air cooled condensers are an alternative means of heat rejection for cooling towers which are generally associated with smaller refrigeration plants. Physical size has normally dictated current practice of limiting single air cooled condenser systems to about 300 kW refrigeration effect, but 1000 kW units are now available. For the refrigeration system to function properly the condensing pressure and temperature must be maintained within certain limits. Abnormally high condensing temperatures cause reduction in capacity, extra power consumption and overloading of the compressor motor with the possibility of permanent damage to the compressor and motor. Safety limit controls normally protect against such conditions. Air cooled condensers are normally controlled by modulating the internal refrigerant flow to maintain the condensing pressure, or air flow control externally to achieve the same result.

3.5.7.5 Protection for chiller and tower systems

Chillers normally require flow switches or differential pressure switches to prove cooling water flow before starting the chiller. Protection against frost damage must always be considered. Exposed closed circuit pipework may be trace heated or filled with a water/ethylene glycol mixture, but open circuit systems and tower ponds will always require heating, normally electric. An economical form of control is an immersion thermostat in the pond, set at 2°C to control the heaters, operating only if a fresh air thermostat set at 0°C indicates that freezing is likely to occur.

3.5.8 Control of electric heating (see also chapters 4.8 and 4.10)

3.5.8.1 Electric space heating

(a) *Storage radiators*

Storage radiators, consisting of heavily insulated high mass storage media, require control at three stages, tariff control, charging or input control and output control, but many do not provide the latter. Tariff control takes the form of a time switch and determines the times at which power is available. These times are usually laid down by the Electricity Authority. The charging controls or energy regulator allow sufficient heat to be put into the store to replace the charge dissipated in the previous discharge period and to build up a store of heat for the next. The anticipated discharge cannot be predicted exactly since the heating load conditions for the following period cannot be accurately determined. Various methods of control are adopted, based either on manual assessment and setting, or automatic setting controlled by prevailing weather or internal temperature conditions. The thermal inertia of the building enables these methods to obtain the required results with varying degrees of success. Any excess heat stored is likely to be wasted in units with uncontrolled output. If the output is effectively controlled the excess heat remains as a basis for the next charge.

Input control can be obtained as follows:

(i) Manual setting of the energy regulator, i.e. adjustment of the kWh charge on a variable input over the whole period of the tariff charging time.

(ii) Manual setting of a thermostat which reacts to the storage block temperature and provides a maximum charging rate immediately the tariff time switch permits.

(iii) Automatic delay of full charging, controlled by room thermostat(s).

(iv) Automatic setting of the energy regulator, i.e. kWh input varied according to outside weather conditions.

For energy conservation and closer space temperature control, storage radiators with output control are recommended. This can only be provided on heaters which do not rely solely on dissipation from the external surfaces. This requires well insulated storage heaters with an internal air path. Output control of these storage radiators is obtained by the following methods:

(i) Controlled mixing dampers to vary the temperature of outgoing air by mixing return room air with hot air leaving the store. This is a first stage.
(ii) Room thermostat control of a fan within the unit, which is the best solution.
(iii) Manual selection of fan speed in graded steps.
(iv) Variations of the above in which the fan is controlled by the thermostat but the user may select one of two speeds to give a boost facility for rapid warm-up.

(b) *Electricaire*
The tariff and charging control follow the same principles as those for conventional storage radiators. The arrangement of output controls depends upon the application. For full central heating, a room thermostat may be installed in one of the principal rooms and wired from the continuous tariff supply to control the heater fan. When the heating is to be used on a selective basis, thermostats should be installed in all the principal rooms and wired in parallel so that individual rooms can be heated as required, in conjunction with manual control of the air registers.

An alternative method, providing modulating control of the output, is to use variable-speed fans. This can be achieved by using a room thermostat of the solid-state type in conjunction with a thyristor fan control. As the room temperature approaches the set point, the fan speed is adjusted to match the heat demand.

(c) *Direct-acting appliances*
Most direct-acting appliances such as electric fires are controlled manually by a simple on/off switch. Where automatic control is required, this usually takes the form of individual room thermostats, or thermostats incorporated in the units, particularly in fan heaters.

3.5.8.2 Electric water heating

(a) *Electrode boilers*
These are relatively uncommon for HVAC systems and where used would only be employed in fully automatic situations utilising a cheap night tariff and operating into a thermal storage system. The time control would therefore be dictated by the tariff time switch although a form of optimised start control would be used to limit the period for charging the thermal storage, in accordance with the internal space temperature and external ambient conditions. Insulating shrouds around the electrodes would be automatically modulated to adjust the output in accordance with the load requirements, as dictated by an immersion temperature detector. The control system has to ensure that:

(i) The system starts only in the unloaded condition.

(ii) The time switching or optimised control may be manually overridden to 'off' (and to 'on' if there is a twenty four hour tariff available).
(iii) The boiler is shut down if the water supply fails, the three-phase system becomes unbalanced, there is an insulation failure, the water temperature exceeds preset limits at various points in the circulatory system, or excessive pressures are generated in the boiler (Ref. 2).

Electrode boiler systems are not normally used on low voltage systems or for small systems and they would have to be ranked against immersion heating for both capital costs and space requirements.

(b) *Immersion heaters*
In domestic premises these heaters are used for domestic hot water heating and tend only to be single-phase. This size is normally time switch controlled with an immersion thermostat in the storage water cylinder or tank to control the temperature. Larger sizes up to 6 kW (or 2 × 3 kW) are sometimes used, and 6 kW and above may be used for instantaneous heating of, say, showers. The larger sizes may be controlled by contactor or via a silicon controlled rectifier unit, (SCR). Positioning of the heater and thermostat is important if the storage water is all to be maintained at the desired temperature. An alternative is to use more than one heater, each mounted horizontally at different levels in the storage vessel with its own thermostat. Then different percentages of the water can be heated by the operation of a selector switch. Two part tariffs, using cheaper heating at night, should be considered.

A similar system can be used for non-domestic premises but larger systems require three-phase heaters controlled via contactors. Time switch or tariff period control would still be the primary control and the thermostatic control can vary. Where the thermal storage is for heating purposes the control may still be similar to that for domestic purposes but it would be more common to control the heating in stages according to the load as determined by comparing internal and external temperature conditions, with some limiting device on the outlet from the thermal storage vessel. The positioning of the temperature control detector may be very important in such systems.

Another method of control is the adoption of instantaneous heating controlled by a detector mounted in the outlet to the system. Whether on a large or small scale this arrangement requires very sensitive detectors and sophisticated controllers. While power is only used as and when required with this system, thus minimising standing losses, it requires very large heaters and may lead to excessive maximum demand charges. 'Burst firing' control should be avoided unless specifically approved by the Electricity Authority.

3.5.9 Control of air systems

3.5.9.1 General

The control of air systems may be considered in two parts, the first related to the main air plant and the second to the terminal units. Irrespective of the generic title given to the overall system, e.g. dual duct, variable air volume, etc., the basic controls for the main plants are very similar although certain additional requirements may vary from system to system. The most complex individual parameter to be controlled in any main plant is the dewpoint. The systems mentioned above are sophisticated air conditioning systems but there is a very wide range of air plants which do not fall into this category but still need similar controls.

A dewpoint control system, with its various options and special features, identifies a large percentage of the criteria encountered in the control of all air systems. The psychrometrics for air conditioning and air systems generally are an essential part of understanding the operation of the control system and the basic details are given below.

In energy conservation terms, dewpoint systems, where all the air is conditioned to a dewpoint in order to control the humidity, may not be the most efficient. Sequential heating and cooling, with separate humidification and dehumidification, or dewpoint control only for the fresh air supply, should be considered as alternatives. However, each system should be considered on its merits both in terms of the limitations on the control accuracy and in relation to the free cooling potential of the dewpoint plant.

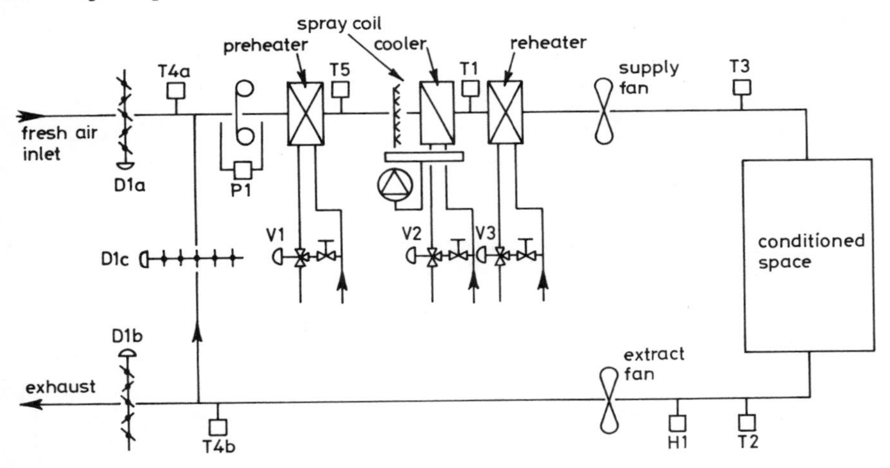

Fig. 3.5.8. *Dewpoint schematic with main reheater*

T1 Dewpoint detector
T2 Temperature detector
T3 Low limit detector
T4 Enthalpy detectors
T5 Frost protection thermostat
H1 Return air humidity detector
P1 Differential pressure switch
V1 Preheater valve
V2 Cooler valve
V3 Reheater valve
D1a Fresh air damper actuator
D1b Exhaust air damper actuator
D1c Recirculation air damper actuator

3.5.9.2 Dewpoint control

The control of dewpoint is normally associated with plants having a configuration very similar to that shown in Fig. 3.5.8. The dewpoint is controlled by T1 which sequentially modulates a pre-heater battery control valve (V1), dampers (D1a, D1b and D1c) which operate in parallel, and a cooler battery valve (V2) to maintain a constant saturated temperature condition. The reheater, which is part of many systems, but not an inherent part of the dewpoint plant, is controlled by the extract temperature detector (T2), modulating the control value (V3) to maintain a constant space temperature (a low limit detector T3 is sometimes employed in the discharge duct to override T2 and maintain the discharge temperature above a predetermined limit). Frost protection is provided by a duct thermostat (T5) which stops the supply fan and locks out on low temperature. Propotional controllers are not normally suitable for dewpoint control because the proportional band width to achieve stability gives too wide a deviation in dewpoint. Enthalpy (total heat) detectors (T4a and T4b) are used to determine when the enthalpy of the outside air exceeds that of the extract air. When this occurs it is cheaper to cool the extract air rather than the fresh air, and the dampers are therefore driven to the minimum fresh air position in such circumstances.

(a) *Psychrometry*
A typical psychrometric process for this dewpoint plant is shown in Fig. 3.5.9. The psychrometric chart defines the fixed relationship between dry bulb temperature, wet bulb temperature and, hence, relative humidity at a particular barometric

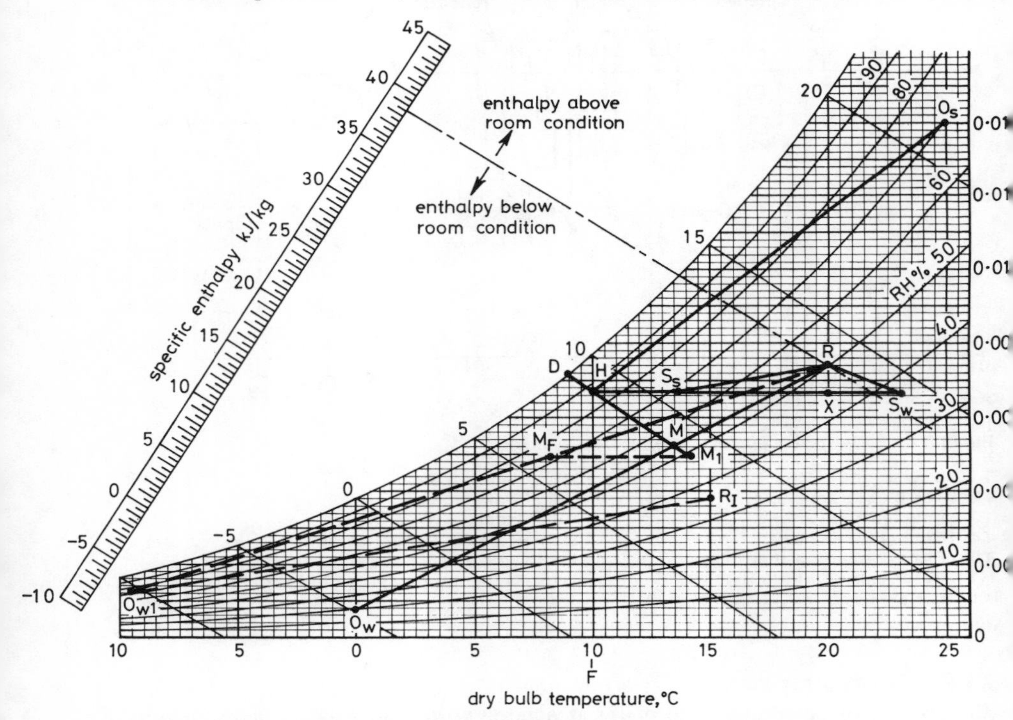

Fig. 3.5.9. *Psychrometric diagram for dewpoint control with reheat*

pressure. The total heat content of the air is also shown. The chart is used to illustrate the operation of the plant of Fig. 3.5.8.

The system in the dewpoint plant is set to provide a moisture content of H so that air is supplied to the space in a condition S, (S_W or S_s) which will permit the design room condition R to be achieved, along the lines $S-R$, when the latent gain, i.e. moisture created in the space is added and the sensible winter losses (S_W-X) or summer gains (S_s-X) are taken into account.

The line O_W-R represents the conditions achieved for different mixtures of outside air O_W and room air R obtained by modulating the dampers (D1a, D1b and D1c) and M defines a specific set of damper positions. Point O_W represents full fresh air and point R full recirculation. In winter when the incoming air is at O_W, the dampers are modulated to achieve condition M with the cooler and preheater both off. The air is then adiabatically saturated as it passes through the spray coil moving the condition point along the wet bulb line to H. If the spray coil was ideal the air would saturate to point D, where the wet and dry bulb settings are identical, but in practice the spray is not perfect and the dewpoint detector (T1), which is calibrated for dry bulb conditions, is set at F. When selecting the dewpoint, allowances are made for the inefficiency of the spray coil and the latent gains to the space. In a very cold situation, such as shown at O_{W1}, the initial room condition when the plant is started (R_I) may be too low for the mixing point M to be achieved. Alternatively the mixing condition may not be permitted because the amount of fresh air is too low to satisfy the ventilation requirements. In either case, the dampers are modulated to their minimum permissible fresh air position which creates a mixed air condition indicated by position M_F and the preheater is modulated towards the open position to reach the wet bulb line at M_1, where adiabatic saturation again takes place to move the condition point to H.

In any situation where point M can be achieved by the use of mixed fresh and recirculating air, with or without the preheater and without the cooling coil, the term 'free cooling' is used as the dewpoint can then be maintained without the assistance of mechanical cooling. In summer conditions such as O_s, the preheater is off, the dampers are modulated to full fresh air except when overriden by T4a/T4b, and the cooler valve V_2, is modulated to achieve point H.

In all the foregoing, when point H is achieved it is necessary to reheat the air to the desired discharge conditions point between S_W or S_s (although this is not part of the actual dewpoint control).

(b) *Auxiliary features of dewpoint plants*

Using the free cooling mode of control already mentioned, conditions can occur where the dampers need to be overridden. When the external temperature rises above the return air temperature (or more precisely when the enthalpy of the outside air exceeds that of the room return air) it is more economic to cool return air than outside air. Detection devices (T4a, T4b in Fig. 3.5.8) are therefore required to measure the total heat (enthalpy) or wet bulb and when the room total heat is exceeded by that of the outside air, a signal from the devices drives the dampers to the minimum fresh air position.

In rare cases a humidity detector (H1) mounted in the extract duct from the conditioned space is provided to monitor any excessive or reduced latent gains in the space. It then resets the dewpoint detector (T1) setting either down or up, respectively, to compensate for this.

A differential pressure detector (P1) fitted across the plant filter is a standard control item to provide a warning of high pressure across the filter for both maintenance and energy conservation purposes. Other safety and limit devices are sometimes required for specific purposes.

For fire defence it is becoming standard practice, sometimes mandatory, to ensure in the event of smoke or fire that the plant shuts down and that the firemen have the facility to start the extract fan independently of the supply fan, with the dampers run out of sequence. A frequent requirement is for the exhaust damper to be open and the fresh air and recirculation dampers to be fully closed to facilitate smoke exhaust.

Air conditioned plants normally use dewpoint control irrespective of the type of terminal arrangement which gives the system its generic title. In the present era of energy conservation practices the use of dewpoint control may be queried and other forms of plant substituted (Section 3.5.9.1). This should only be done however after careful consideration and with the knowledge that some of the alternatives may not comply with what is generally regarded as "air conditioning", i.e. the heating, cooling, cleaning, humidification and dehumidification of air.

The following sections cover some of the more common systems and the principles identified can often be applied to other systems not covered here. The selection of suitable controllers, detectors and valves should be based on the criteria laid down elsewhere in this chapter and on the environmental limits which are specified.

3.5.9.3 Single duct constant volume

This system has effectively been covered in the previous section. Basically, there is a dewpoint plant or plants which serve one or more reheaters, each controlled in the manner described for Fig. 3.5.8. Depending on the area served by each reheater and the occupation pattern, the control detector (T2) may be mounted in the space or the extract ductwork. Where wide limits of temperature are permissible, proportional control of reheaters is acceptable.

3.5.9.4 Dual duct and multi-zone units

These systems permit close temperature control, but do not normally provide low energy systems as there is continuous mixing of hot and cold air streams to each space. There are many plant variants but one basic arrangement is shown in Fig. 3.5.10. The preheater valve (V1) and dampers (D1a, D1b, and D1c) are controlled in sequence by the mixed air detector (T1). The hot deck temperature is controlled by detectors (T2 and T4) modulating the hot deck coil valve (V2) to achieve a compensated temperature characteristic. The cold deck temperature is contolled by a detector (T3) modulating the cold deck coil valve (V3). Most modes of single and two term controller are acceptable for all three loops, but avoid proportional control.

The dual duct system then operates through mixing boxes as shown in scheme A and each is controlled by a temperature detector which mixes the air streams to achieve the correct space temperature. Multi-zone units use the system of scheme B, where several sets of dampers are controlled as shown, achieving broadly the same effect as the mixing boxes.

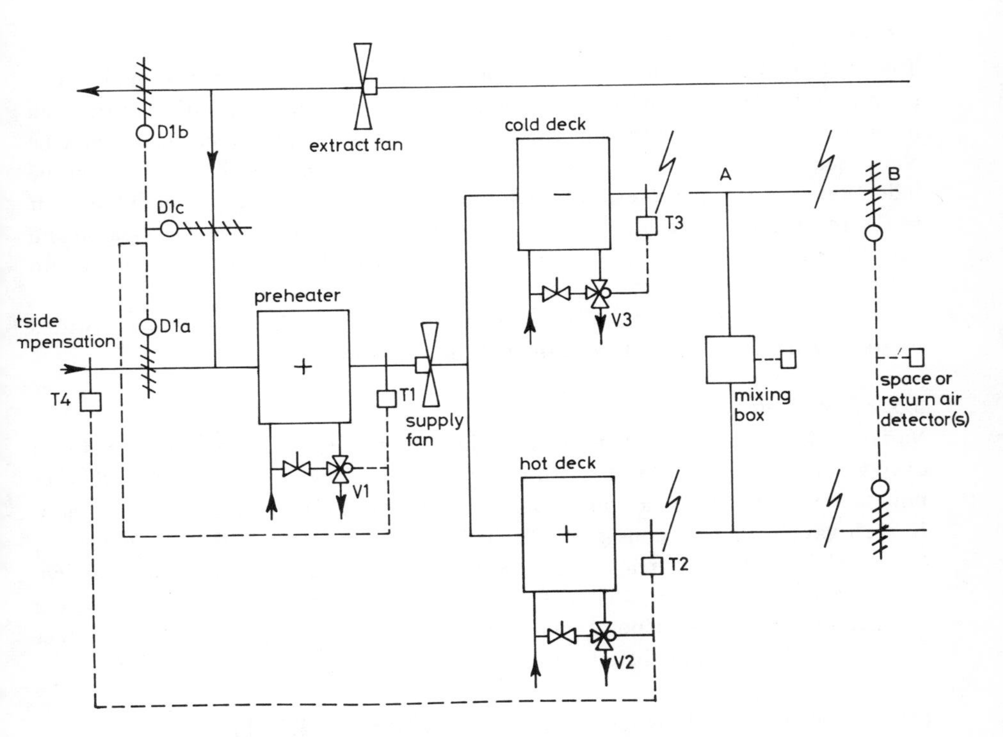

Fig. 3.5.10. *Basic schematic for dual duct or multi-zone system*

3.5.9.5 Induction units

Many induction unit systems are in operation using two pipe changeover or non-changeover systems which would not be acceptable if designed now, because they use heating and cooling simultaneously to achieve the desired conditions. The use of induction units in temperate climates today would normally be confined to four pipe systems. In these systems the central air plant operates generally as described for dewpoint control and distributes high velocity air to the individual units which each contain heating and cooling coils. Each unit is then fitted with either two control valves, one for the heating coil and one for the cooling coil (a single multiple ported valve may also be used as an alternative), or with a damper arrangement to provide the same effect.

Temperature sensors located in the space, or the return air to the units, sequence the valves or modulate the dampers to maintain the correct temperature. It is not necessary and sometimes not desirable to use one temperature sensor for each unit. Units should be grouped so that one sensor is used to control the valves or dampers on all the units serving a defined space. With certain equipment the motive power for the control of the dampers is achieved from the primary air pressure.

3.5.9.6 Fan coil units

The central plant for such systems normally comprises a dewpoint plant which provides the fresh air component of the air change rate. This air is either distributed independently or ducted to units each with heating and cooling coils, which may be controlled in sequence by temperature sensors in the same manner as those on the induction unit systems previously described. The motive power for circulating air in the space is provided by a fan in each unit. The fans have to be switched on and off either as part of the overall plant switching or by local control, depending on usage.

During periods of plant shutdown frost protection would normally be provided by starting the unit fans and using the unit heating coils.

3.5.9.7 Variable air volume

Variable air volume (VAV) systems are in common use because of their reduced energy consumption compared with other systems. They are particularly suited to buildings where there is a continuous cooling load during periods of occupation. In their basic form they consist of a dewpoint plant, or plants, with variable volume fans serving the treated area via thermostatically controlled terminal units as shown in Fig. 3.5.11. The essential control requirements are quite simple but there are a number of consequential points which need to be considered because they affect the controls and these are listed below:

(a) The positioning of the fan pressure sensor (P1 in Fig. 3.5.11).

(b) The use of air balancing dampers in supply and extract systems to ensure that the automatic controls can perform satisfactorily over the total range of loads.

(c) The control of the extract fan so that it matches the variable output of the supply fan.

(d) System stability at the air volumes required on low loads.

(e) The maintenance of the design minimum fresh air quantities under low load.

(f) The choice of terminal units with or without fixed minimum air regulation.

(g) Methods of plant start-up and early morning boost (VAV systems are basically 'cooling only' systems).

(h) Basic fan selection which has to cover suitably stable fan characteristics over a wide range of volumes and fan total pressures.

(j) Means of controlling fan output volume which may be by air restriction devices in the ductwork adjacent to the fan, fan blade pitch control or motor speed control which may be:

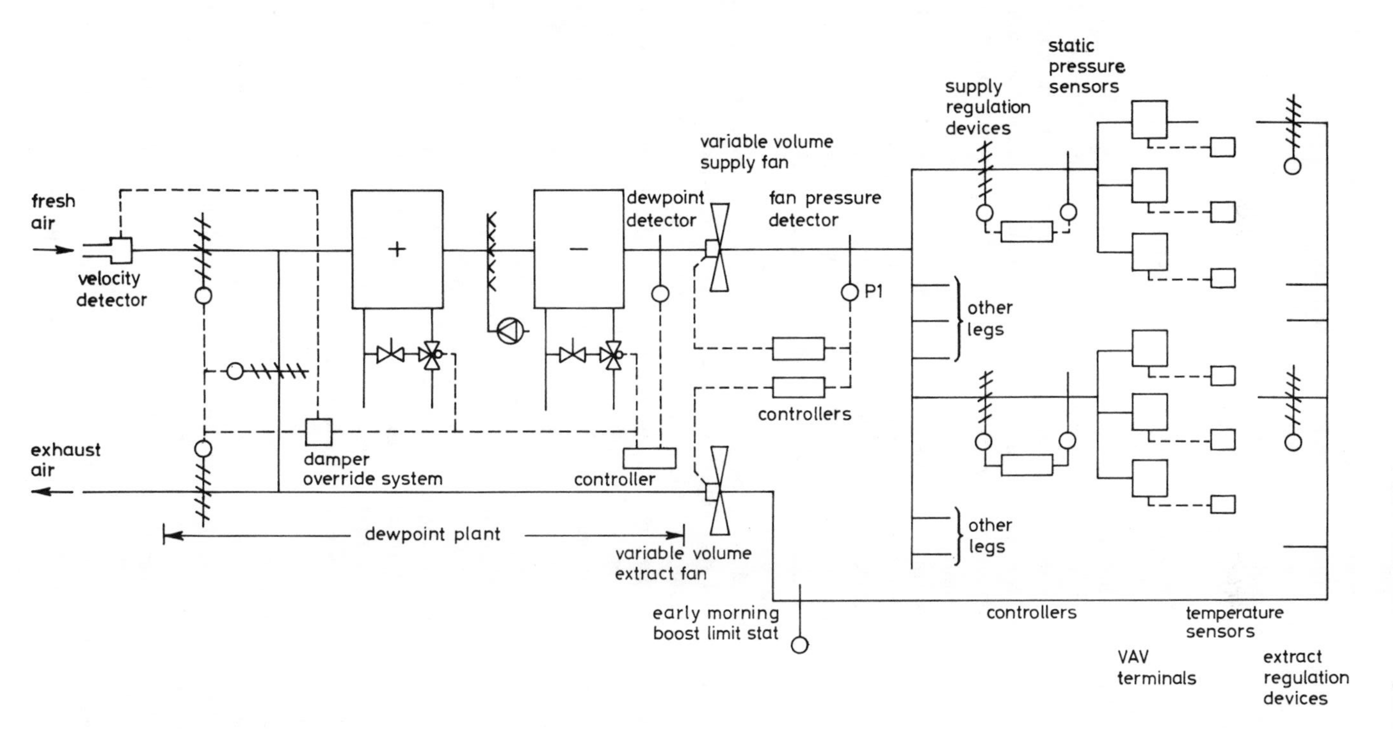

Fig. 3.5.11 *Schematic of variable air volume system and controls*

(i) Thyristor convertor with d.c. motor.
(ii) Slip ring induction motor with variable rotor resistance.
(iii) Ordinary induction motor with variable voltage.
(iv) Ordinary induction motor with variable frequency.
(v) Eddy current couplings.
(vi) Fluid coupling.

The systems most commonly used for HVAC are (i) (v) and (vi)

3.5.9.8 Heat pumps (See also Chapter 4.6)

The use of heat pumps is becoming more and more prevalent as fuel costs continue to rise and the need to conserve energy becomes more imperative. The range of heat pump applications and the availability of suitable models is increasing rapidly and the control arrangements are normally included as part of the manufacturer's package. The most common form of heat pump incorporates a refrigerant compressor unit with evaporator and condenser where the functions of the latter two elements may be reversed, dependent on whether a heating or cooling cycle is required. (Fig. 4.6.1). The basic control requirement for the changeover systems is a thermostatic device which selects either the cooling or heating mode of operation according to load. The other controls are effectively those which would normally be provided with chillers and condensers.

The changeover system has been used over a period of years in air conditioned buildings where a series of such units, with individual air circulation fans, has been coupled to a water circulating system. The water is supplied to all the units at a constant temperature. Heat is then extracted or added to the water by each of the units depending on whether they are on the heating or cooling cycle. Each of the individual units is controlled by specialised two step thermostats which call for either the heating or cooling mode according to the space temperature. There is a dead zone between the two temperature settings. The changeover of the refrigerant circuit from heating to cooling is accomplished by one or other of the thermostat switches and the compressor does not operate in the dead zone.

The water temperature to the units is maintained at the constant level by means of a cooling tower or heat source in the main plant which operates in sequence according to the overall heat input or rejection, summed for all the individual units. The use of the safety devices is critical if unnecessary lockout conditions are to be avoided on the units.

Heat pumps are now also being used more frequently, purely for heating applications, but whether in this mode or as reversible units they may be found in air to air, water to water and air to water heat transfer situations. Each arrangement has its own control requirements related to the initiation temperatures at which the heat pump will operate satisfactorily and these should be defined for each application.

In some heating applications, particularly where heat is being extracted from outside air, the external coil acting as the evaporator will tend to ice up and a defrost control system must be used. This requires a thermostatic and/or timing device which is associated with the refrigerant reversing valve, allowing hot gas to be passed through the coil for a short period. Alternatively, separate electric heaters may be used. All such systems should be installed only in collaboration with the equipment suppliers.

The majority of heat pumps are normally electrically powered but engine driven pumps are possible alternatives which are being examined in depth. The latter may use a variety of fuels for driving the engine, the most common being gas fired. Such heat pumps can be more efficient than the electrically driven versions but they are more complex and costly.

3.5.10 Control panels and motor control centres

Most projects outside the domestic sector now incorporate control and starter panels. Because of their importance in comprehensive control systems some features which may affect the controls are detailed below. The list is not exhaustive but should ensure that the necessary interfacing takes place between the various parties directly and indirectly involved in producing the complete operational system.

3.5.10.1 Type and suitability

Panels may be floor or wall mounted, the latter being normally used only for small plants with few controls. They may be of three basic types – wardrobe, cupboard and cubicle. For the purpose of this brief discussion, the first two may be consiered as being similar in that the doors open as for cupboards or wardrobes. One common arrangement used relates to situations when the shut down of a total plant is acceptable, or where the failure of one item in the panel renders the remainder of the plant ineffective. The door opening mechanism is interlocked with the main incoming supply to the panel, so that all equipment is de-energised when the doors are opened. Where the predominant equipment is starters, this type of panel is often referred to as a multi-motor panel.

An alternative arrangement is used where access to specific items of equipment may be necessary without a complete shutdown of the panel. It is of particular use where several plants are started and controlled from the same panel section. The doors are lockable but not interlocked with the main incoming supply. In this case all the equipment is shrouded and individual isolation is provided for those items which may require routine servicing and maintenance.

In the cubicle type panel each major item is mounted in its own isolatable section. There may be up to ten openable doors in a single vertical section of panel each of which is interlocked to isolate everything in the cubicle when the door is open. Such panels are very useful when maintenance or repair is required during periods of plant operation.

3.5.10.2 Equipment and wiring

The choice of electric or pneumatic controls may affect who does what within the panel. Pneumatic piping is often done by the controls supplier and there can be confusion as to who will supply the interlocking items – relays, timers, etc.

Serious problems are often encountered which relate to starter data. It is essential to identify power ratings at which changeover from direct on-line to star-delta, etc., takes place and this information is also necessary for designing the electrical distribution and purchasing. Any special features must be stipulated, e.g. back contacts on overloads for alarm purposes, closed transition on star-delta starters and run-up times on large drives.

Fuse or circuit breaker characteristics must be specified to suit applications, i.e. motors, immersion heaters, SCR controllers, etc. all require different types. Isolators need to be specified as on-load or off-load devices. For switches, types and method of operation are important for control, e.g. a three position switch for selection of run and standby plant should have a positive off position between the two operational positions. Ammeters are necessary for all but the smallest motor drives. They permit checks on performance to be carried out on all fans and motors against their published data and are a testing and commissioning aid. Where relays and contactors are used, suitable circuitry and performance criteria should be detailed, e.g. coil voltages, in-rush currents and acceptable numbers and types of contacts.

Wiring standards are important. The type of wiring to be used and its form, e.g. loomed or carried in trunking, must be specified, and the means of identifying each connection uniquely and on co-ordinated drawings shown in detail. The terminations to be used both for the incoming and outgoing cables and for interconnections in the panel should be detailed. Identify whether the cable entries are into the top or bottom of the panel – the main incoming feed may differ from the other cables.

3.5.10.3 Mounting requirements

It is necessary to schedule which equipment is to be mounted together or apart, e.g. thermostatic controllers should always be mounted in a section independent of the power sections.

The necessary spares, e.g. fuses, for site maintenance, must be included and some flexibility in terms of additional space allowed for future modifications.

3.5.10.4 Testing

Testing is a vital element in ensuring a workable control system and the panel testing is one stage of the total testing and commissioning procedures. All functional, operational and safety sequences should be simulated and checked before panels are accepted at works, also covering compliance with any regulations in force.

On site, all connections into the panel should be checked before any power is switched on and the functional operational and safety sequences should be rechecked before the plant is operated.

3.5.11 Interlocking and functional co-ordination

Interlocking refers to the functional requirements which are satisfied by logical operation and sequencing of various components in a control system, items of plant and equipment systems. The logic and subsequent interlocking are prime elements in the design process and require a marked degree of integration between the different design disciplines. The interlocking logic is critical for the proper operation and protection of the control system and plant. The functional sequences should include all the requirements for control loops as described elsewhere and all interface conditions between items of equipment and plants, e.g. frost protection devices which operate air plants should be interlocked so that associated boilers are started and the water temperature is up to a suitable level before the fans are permitted to function.

It is important to ensure that all safety and limit devices to protect plant and satisfy any statutory regulations are included in the logic sequences. All the necessary visual and audible alarms to indicate the operation of these devices must be included, and their situations specified.

It is now possible to provide interlocking by means of hardware or software. At an early stage in the design a decision is needed on whether the interlocking sequences are to be carried out using conventional relays or programmable controllers (which also include building automation systems). In the latter case the software facility of the controllers may be used to set up the logic sequences and control panels may be purchased with starters only, with their coils connected directly to outgoing terminals.

The satisfactory supply and performance of controls and control panels depends on the co-ordination of an extremely large number of interfaces between equipment, equipment suppliers and designers. The choice of panel supplier is important. The most likely alternatives are the controls supplier, a specialist panel manufacturer, the HVAC sub-contractor, the electrical sub-contractor or the switchgear supplier. The first causes the least interface problems, even if the panels are then sub-contracted.

The wiring and possible pneumatic pipework in panels creates a number of confusing situations, which must be clarified. The pipework is normally carried out by the controls supplier within, and external to, the panel. The wiring in the panel is always carried out by the panel manufacturer, with the exception of connecting the incoming cables. The external wiring to the panel may be by the electrical sub-contractor and/or the HVAC sub-contractor. It is often advisable to make a particular sub-contractor responsible for the co-ordination even if the work is carried out by others.

Panel diagrams are always composed of a number of different suppliers' drawings. The final drawings are normally prepared by the panel manufacturers but they are not in a position of responsibility in terms of obtaining information from others. This responsibility, together with the co-ordination of suppliers' drawings and in particular the interfaces between one set and the next should be specified as one sub-contractor's function. Drawings finally incorporated into panel diagrams will include those from:

Controls supplier
Boiler supplier
Chiller supplier
Cooling tower supplier
Starter supplier
Electrical sub-contractor
HVAC sub-contractor

3.5.12 Testing and commissioning (See also chapter 3.6)

Modern control systems are a critical sector of the overall plant and often represent the greatest proportion of the T & C element during the construction period, particularly, prior to practical completion. In order that this work is satisfactorily carried out it must be included specifically as part of the overall construction programme and planned as part of the overall design process. Ideally the final T & C of the control system should be carried out when the building and plant have been finally completed and put to work and the building is otherwise ready for occupation.

Some guidelines are useful to ensure that this element of the design and building process can be performed efficiently and successfully. These requirements and T & C have become both more complex and understood in the last 15 to 20 years. Thus there are well defined standards and codes of practice for much of what is required, and specialists to carry it out, although the latter are still fairly rare. Virtually all members of the design team have a contribution to make towards the proper T & C of control systems and plant. The following list indicates matters which need to be considered:

(a) Detailed specification of T & C for any project, using the CIBS Commissioning Code C 'Automatic Controls' (Ref. 3) as a basis, and providing all environmental conditions and limits for plant operation and occupied areas.
(b) The use of properly qualified staff to carry out the work, which should be specified as part of the tender documents.
(c) The inclusion of specialist site supervision during the construction phase of the control system.
(d) Planning the site programme so that all items of plant related to the controls are completed and functional, prior to the controls T & C.
(e) Provision of suitable access to main plant items and controls, with recognition that access will be necessary regularly during the life of the building and services. This latter point has particular relevance to equipment and controls above false ceilings.
(f) Integration and co-ordination of drawings from different suppliers. This should

not be underestimated in terms of either time or cost. The effort needed is indicated in Fig. 3.5.12 which does not include fire, security or the designer's and main contractor's involvement.
(g) The recording of all T & C results and settings for inclusion in the operating and maintenance manual.
(h) The inclusion of some maintenance and servicing element for the control system during the defects liability period (this is a precaution against unskilled or uninformed on-site servicing during this period).

3.5.13 Building automation systems

3.5.13.1 General

The use and selection of a building automation system (BAS) for the functional control and supervision of the services within the building complex is dependent on a number of factors. These include the level of facilities required by the client, the staffing policy for operating and maintaining the building, the effect on the design and contract programming of selecting the system and the cost effectiveness of the system.

Building automation systems are the generic name for energy management systems, building management systems and a host of derivative titles. Started some twenty to thirty years ago, mainly as data loggers with some switching and visual display capability, they were based on electromechanical devices. Since that time they have progressed through various generations of electronics to fully computer based systems with a host of functional facilities. The latest generation of systems is based on the use of microprocessors, which has considerably reduced the overall cost and extended the market for the application of the equipment. Prior to the oil crisis of 1974 the energy management facility of the systems was considered of secondary importance to the improvements in functional operation offered by their use. Nowadays the energy management features are the most commonly emphasised, but they are in fact one facet of the overall system, albeit very important.

3.5.13.2 Operations staff

Possibly the single most important criterion when selecting a suitable system is the relationship between system complexity and the staff appointed to operate it. In the not too distant past very sophisticated arrangements have been installed where the software has required highly qualified operators of a type rarely found in the building operations field. Nowadays, the use of the high level language interactive software has alleviated this problem but it is still essential to provide suitable technical and back-up staff to optimise the undoubted advantages of these systems.

This particular requirement must be acceptable to the client before the other technical and financial criteria are examined.

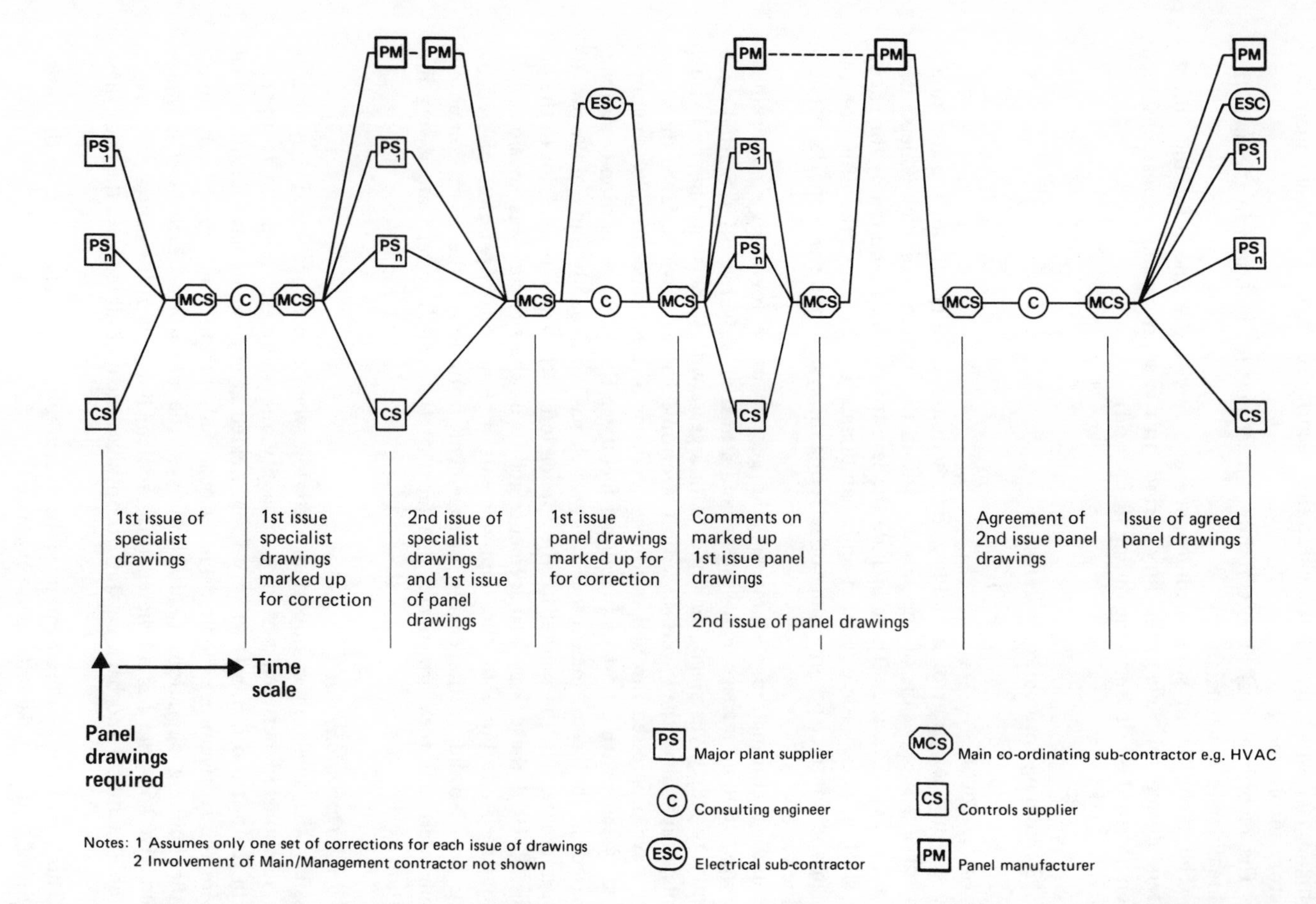

Fig. 3.5.12. *Basic control panel wiring diagram programme*

3.5.13.3 Facilities available

Commonly available features provided by the modern systems are:

(a) HVAC and equipment control:
(i) Functional operation, alarms and limiting conditions
(ii) Optimised start/stop
(iii) Energy management
(iv) Individual loop control, e.g. temperature control by means of digital software, known as direct digital control. (DDC).

(b) Lighting control and remote switching of other plant items.
(c) Energy metering (and billing if necessary).
(d) Panel interlocking logic.
(e) Security monitoring.
(f) Fire monitoring.
(g) Planned maintenance.
(h) Intercommunication.

If a BAS is selected based on one or more of the facilities listed above it is then also reasonable to consider its use for other purposes. These include:

(a) Lift monitoring.
(b) Closed circuit television (CCTV) control and monitoring.
(c) The use of the BAS as a testing and commissioning tool.

The configuration of BAS varies according to the supplier and the particular generation of equipment. While it is feasible to carry out all the temperature loop control from the central processor this is rare because of dependence on a single unit for all control loops and the tradition of supplying individual controllers adjacent to the loop being controlled. The most common present method of approach is to use intelligent or semi-intelligent outstations and individual electronic loop controllers. Such a system is shown in Fig. 3.5.13.

The software power of the outstations enables the systems to remain operational even if there is a total failure at the central processor unit (CPU) or in the data transmission loop. This increasing capability and development is producing outstations which perform the control functions of the local individual loop controllers by means of DDC. Such an outstation is shown in Fig. 3.5.13. The form of data transmission loop can also be modified so that signals from the CPU or outstations may be carried on the normal power wiring to equipment or plant containing uniquely addressable microprocessors.

3.5.13.4 Effect on programme and design

The choice of facilities may govern the planning and programming of the project. Where the features are directly involved in the overall functional operation of the building, then the BAS must be completed and commissioned prior to the final testing, commissioning and handover of the remaining plant and systems. Facilities which fall into this category include HVAC and equipment switching, individual loop control, panel interlocking logic and fire monitoring. In all these cases a clean area (sealed against construction site dust and probably air conditioned) for housing the BAS and power supplies together with the communications network to the relevant remote equipment must be complete well before the main body of the project.

In order to accomplish the necessary planning, design, supply and installation for this specific form of phased completion, an early decision is essential on the form of BAS and the facilities required.

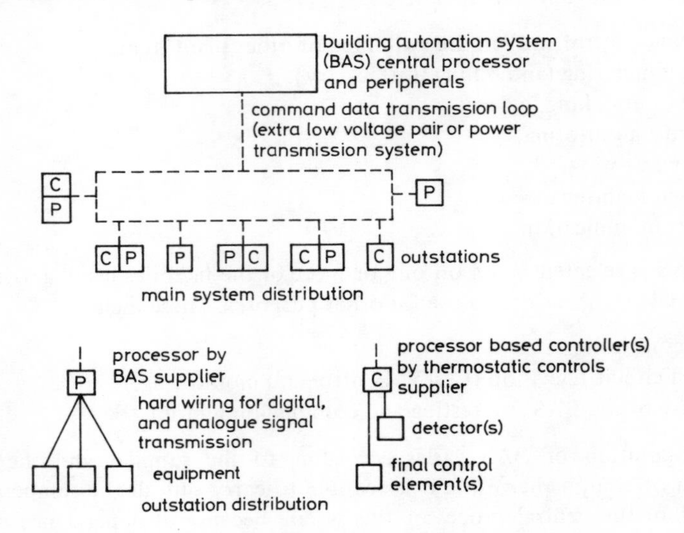

Fig. 3.5.13. *Block diagram of typical Building Automation System* (JIEE) Jan. 81

3.5.13.5 Hardware

The basic hardware for the BAS comprises the CPU, keyboard, visual display unit (VDU), printer(s) and the remote outstations. The VDU for computer based systems is normally a television type display of either alphanumeric data or graphics, in either black or white, or colour. Other visual devices are also employed normally as supplements to the screen display and these include mimic diagrams and annuciator panels of various types. Wiring systems normally consist of hard wiring (conventional cabling) from the elements of plant and detectors, back to the outstations, and on extra low voltage ring or radial two wire or matrix systems from outstations to the CPU. It is important to assess and provide specific back up features against particular failures. These range from back-up power supplies, through to a duplicate CPU and/or adequate spares.

3.5.13.6 Software and systems suppliers

It is vitally important that the majority of software necessary for the correct operation of any of the selected features is both available and validated. Software which has to be written for any particular project is likely to be costly and require independent validation. Commonly available software covers:

(a) Alarm priorities.
(b) Alarm inhibition.
(c) Analogue alarms.
(d) Integration e.g. energy consumption.
(e) Totalisation i.e. summation of motor run times, etc.
(f) Time switching, including optimised start and multi-channel control.
(g) Event initiated sequences, e.g. an alarm which initiates a specific sequence of operations.
(h) Load shedding.
(j) Load cycling for energy conservation.
(k) Restart after power failure: prevents electrical overload on restart.
(l) Process control i.e. the use of the system outstations as the controllers for individual loops.
(m) Optimum damper control – free cooling cycle.
(n) Security, i.e. patrol tours and card entry.
(o) Interlocking, i.e. the use of software in place of conventional relays and timers, etc.
(p) Fire, i.e. alarms and specific event initiated sequences.
(q) Programmed maintenance, i.e. the use of stored data to produce a work schedule for maintenance and servicing.

Suppliers of suitable hardware and software fall into two categories. The first consists of companies whose background includes the provision of commercial thermostatic control systems from which they have developed suitable BAS using their knowledge of controls and building services operation to write suitable software.

The second category of supplier is normally one with a computer hardware and software capability which has been successfully employed in a related area of activity, e.g. fire, security or process control, without the commercial controls experience. In such cases it is often more difficult to ascertain whether the declared software capability is sufficient, to produce the programs necessary for the full range of BAS facilities. Proof of software operation in practice is essential for both categories.

3.5.13.7 Costs and cost effectiveness

To obtain the maximum effectiveness from a BAS it should be included at the concept stage of the project and selected in a manner which minimises the duplication of equipment. A simple example concerns sophisticated fire or security systems which normally require their own central monitoring consoles. These consoles may be redundant if a BAS is supplied, with a consequential cost saving. If dedicated printers are required for fire and security control purposes they may be supplied as additional peripherals to the BAS.

The costs and cost effectiveness must be properly evaluated and include the following, where relevant to the particular system selected:

(a) Capital cost of system, including outstations, detectors, instrumentation, modified plant, standard software and wiring, less any saving for equipment which it replaces.
(b) Value of energy savings which the system itself will provide.
(c) Cost of additional staff required to fully utilise the system, less the saving on those maintenance staff who will be replaced by the unit.
(d) Savings achieved by using the system software capability to replace interlocking relays in control and motor starter panels.
(e) Annual cost of maintaining the building automation system and interest on capital cost.
(f) A substantial capital sum to cover the cost of collecting data from the building during the first one to three years of operation and producing software for specifically optimising the energy use in the building thereafter, e.g. automatically re-setting the control point of the chilled water temperature in accordance with the load.
(g) Savings from using programmed maintenance detailed by the system. These should include value of increased plant life, less the actual cost of preparing such a programme on the system.

The use of a BAS should be considered at the initial stages of design or refurbishment in the context of all the previous points in this section.

3.5.14 Fire defence and intruder security systems. (See also chapter 4.14)

These two elements of engineering services are becoming more and more common in buildings and are the final systems which should be included in the normal consideration of automatic controls. The principles behind both types of system are simple – the provision of alarms under particular circumstances – but some of the systems can be very sophisticated.

Fire and security systems both differ from other control systems in one vital respect. The other systems function regularly and go into alarm only due to some failure, whereas fire and security systems are initiated very infrequently – hopefully never – but must give a guaranteed alarm when they are required to operate. Large fire defence systems often utilise a computer based centralised control which may be stand alone or part of the BAS mentioned earlier.

In control terms, however complex the system, the basic element is a digital signal or signals which are used to initiate alarms and associated actions. These actions are an important element of the overall control system but building regulations and insurance needs may markedly affect the detailed requirements.

Intruder security systems operate very similarly to fire defence systems in respect of their control signals and here too the interlocks with other elements of building services are important. The use of card access systems and electrically controlled door locks for example may have a bearing on the operation of other services. The use of a BAS or its security equivalent is often considered on highly serviced and/or security risk buildings and the control of the security system may need physical separation from other services even when a common centralised BAS is being employed. This is achieved by the use of multiple peripherals, suitably sited and dedicated to particular services such as fire and/or security.

3.5.15 References

3.5.15.1 References in text

1. CIBS Guide Section B11 'Automatic Control'.
2. SAY, M. G: Electrical Engineers Reference Book, (Butterworth)
3. CIBS Commissioning Code C 'Automatic Controls'.

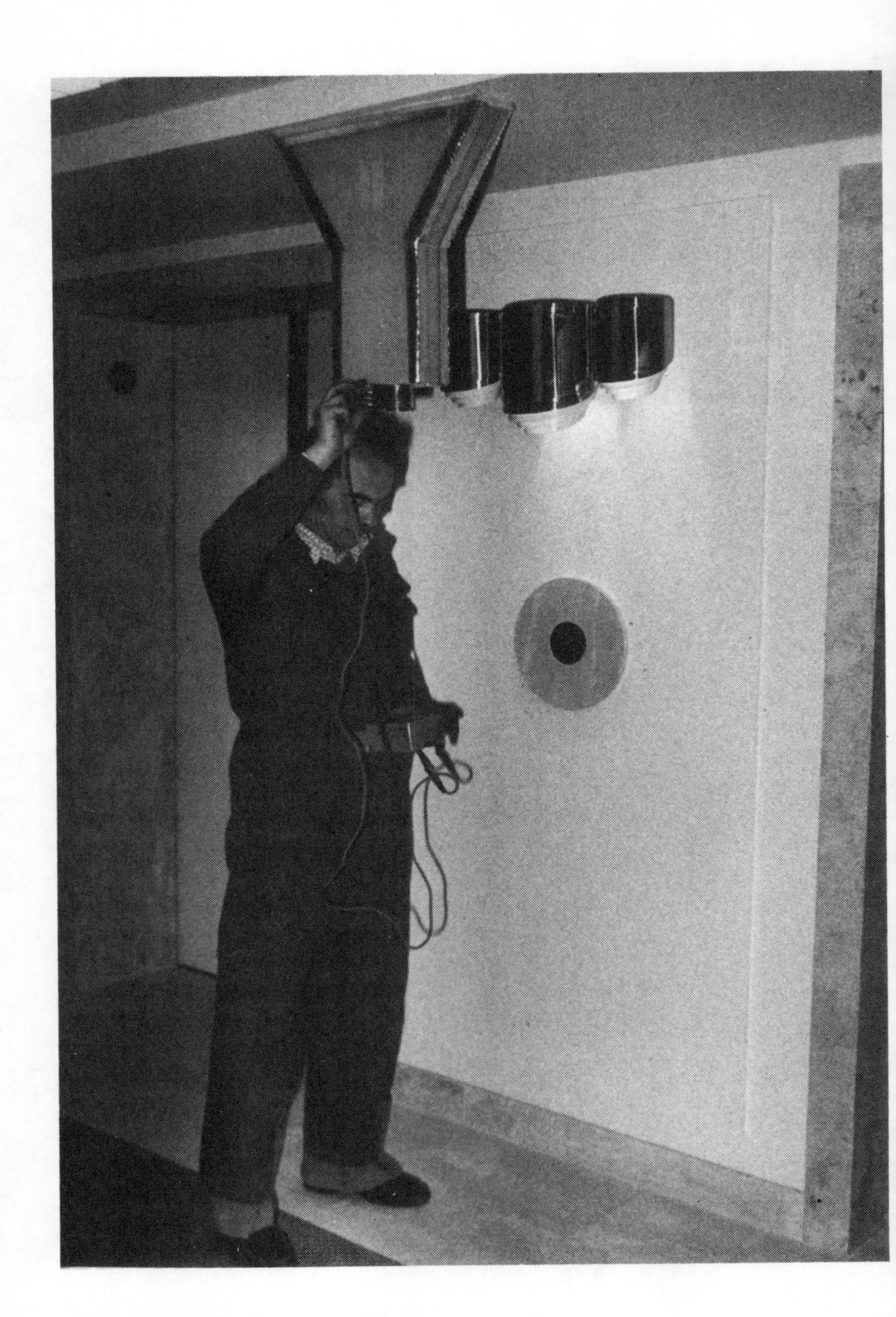

Test hood in use for air measurement

Chapter 3.6

Commissioning

J. Pascoe, A.M.I.E.E., F.C.I.B.S.
Manager, Control Engineering and Commissioning Departments, Haden Young Limited

3.6.1 Introduction: The importance of commissioning

The commissioning of a building services installation should be a planned operation involving both the installation designer and the project management team. This is essential if the commissioning tasks are to be carried out on time and with the effective use of manpower. On a services installation time must be allowed for attending to the difficulties which inevitably occur when the installation is tested and set to work for the first time. It is during the commissioning period that any failure due to design, equipment, communications, installation or operation are likely to be identified. This is an unrecognised function of commissioning which is not often seen or welcomed by the services contractor. Building owners, however, give increasing recognition to the value of witnessing the commissioning function as one of the few forms of quality control possible on a services installation.

With few exceptions every building service installation is a unique combination of mechanical and electrical plant installed to provide a specified performance. Such installations are the result of work by very many people including Architects, Consultants, Manufacturers, Contractors and Sub-Contractors. To ensure that all the equipment works satisfactorily, and provides the desired environmental conditions, the completed installation must be subjected to routines for testing, setting to work and commissioning. Often further independent checks need to be witnessed by the client or his representative as a part of the handover arrangement.

Commissioning therefore becomes one of the most important functions within the project completion sequence. Commissioning routines need to include checks on the individual items of plant to ensure their satisfactory operation. Once this has been established complete systems can be set to work and adjusted. The latter operation can be a lengthy procedure for air and water systems and for the final environmental checks. It is during these latter stages that any design or equipment selection failures will become apparent. For example air leaks on ductwork, or incorrect ductwork system resistance, will often lead to changes in the fan duty. If critically sized, the fan, motor, starter, wiring and sections of the control panel will need to be changed. Without formal commissioning the plant could be allowed to run at whatever output level available with associated loss of environmental performance.

The following discussion on commissioning is directed towards the management of the commissioning operation in a logical sequence, the objectives being to identify potential difficulties in order to maintain the commissioning programme in the most effective manner with regard to the use of manpower and costs. Lastly, it is emphasised that final commissioning must take place of the installation as a whole, and not only of the constituent parts individually.

3.6.2 Objectives of commissioning

Commissioning of a Building Services Mechanical and Electrical Installation calls for sound planning and co-ordination by the project management team if the commissioning objectives are to be achieved. Such objectives include making the installation achieve the design intent, meeting the programme dates and conserving scarce manpower commissioning resources; all within an acceptable cost budget. It is intended here to indicate management responsibilities throughout the commissioning sequence. These are summarised in Table 3.6.1.

3.6.3 Responsibility for commissioning

3.6.3.1 The designer's role

The functions required for commissioning together with the need for subsequent maintenance should be a consideration of the designer at the strategic outline stage. Any savings in floor space for instance may be outweighed by the difficulties caused by placing operational plant above ceilings or in other locations having difficult access. It is the designer's responsibility to write the commissioning specification and then to ensure that the key commissioning operations are possible by the provision of the necessary access and measuring facilities, particularly those for air and water systems.

The designer has a responsibility for providing the commissioning brief. This brief will include the design information against which the installation can be balanced and controls set. It is important also that this brief should include the tolerances associated with measurements taken and also provide a clear statement regarding the degree of witnessed testing required. The latter factor is important to the contractor since both the commissioning time and cost can be considerably extended as a result of witnessing procedures.

Table 3.6.1 *Responsibilities for Commissioning Operations*

System Designer	Checks to ensure that controls are specified and correctly located and installed.
Client	Overall performance of installation. There will often be special requirements associated with controls since these are the client's effective interface with the system operation. It may be necessary to carry out environmental control checks after the client's occupation, possibly dependent upon weather conditions. The need for such checks should be discussed with the client. Often such work is regarded as remedial if the problem is not understood by the client.
Electrical Contractor	Checks on the wiring which will confirm insulation, earthing of equipment and cables, and correct point to point wiring. Such checks may need to be made alongside the controls manufacturer when advanced technology electronic equipment is installed, or interfacing is required to microprocessor equipment. All interlocks associated with controls, particularly those required for safety, require checking and documenting.
Mechanical Contractor	Checks on correct location and part identification of control valves. Checks on flow switches and other system interlocks. Linkage checks on motorised dampers. Correct labels and identification on plant. Functional checks on completed installation. Environmental checks for client and possible formal demonstration. Balancing and flow measurement checks of air and water system. Operational checks on main plant such as boilers or refrigeration machines.

Table 3.6.1 (cont.)

Controls Manufacturers	Checks for proper controls installation. Adjustment of valves and actuators from control system. Identification of operational problems such as pick-up on cables.
Specialist Manufacturers	Fire, security and other specialists may have provided systems which require similar routines for the co-ordination of commissioning.

3.6.3.2 The project manager's role

The project manager's participation in the commissioning operation is vital. He must ensure that the commissioning activities are included in the initial job planning; he must provide the space and accommodation for the commissioning team where drawings may be laid out and instruments left secure; he must be satisfied that any necessary commissioning priorities are given to the commissioning and testing team and that any defects which they report are attended to.

3.6.3.3 Planning for commissioning

Network planning, carried out by a skilled planner and supported by an experienced commissioning engineer, will result in a logical presentation of information which shows how highly interrelated are the constructional and commissioning activities. Within the construction industry many forms of planning are employed and network planning is not universal. Project engineers are well advised to carry out at least a few sample exercises of network planning for commissioning and constructional relationship.

For large or complex installations such a form of logical planning is essential. This will possibly highlight the following:

(a) That the initial time allowed is unrealistic.

(b) That the builder's programme of completion, based on occupied areas, is not always compatible with the commissioning need for completed air and water systems.

(c) That peaks will occur in manpower requirements on such occasions as when the electrical power or fuel supply becomes available. Some temporary electrical work and possibly temporary power supply will be called for if these peaks are to be reduced.

The rearrangement of some constructional activities will enable the commissioning work to be started earlier. This may be necessary if manpower peaks are to be reduced and the contract is to be completed on time.

The lack of a suitable load for testing may cause some commissioning work to over-run into the occupational dates agreed with the client. For example environmental load testing may have to be delayed until the outside weather conditions are suitable. In these circumstances early agreement with the client on the extent of the commissioning work to be carried out after building occupation is essential. The occupier's maximum co-operation will be more likely and the contractor will be relieved from unfair accusations of late completion.

Commissioning operations on sites suffer interruptions which make rigid adherence to a previously determined plan almost impossible. The greatest advantage of the planning operation, therefore, lies in the initial exercise which identifies potential problems and which co-ordinates the activities of construction and commissioning.

Simplified presentation of the initial planning information in the form of bar charts is generally adequate if they are designed in a manner which also records the actual work done.

Factors outside the control of the commissioning team may cause delays or changes to the programme on a short term basis. There will be an element of this on every project and the skilful re-deployment of manpower can often accommodate such short-term changes without any serious alteration to the overall programme.

3.6.3.4 Pre-commissioning visits

The main concern of the project manager is to meet the constructional programme, at the same time making the best use of his resources. An independent visit to the site by an experienced commissioning engineer in order to advise on commissioning matters can be invaluable. The commissioning engineer will be looking ahead to the possible difficulties of commissioning and the manner in which any potential problems can be avoided. On the air systems, for instance, he will look at ductwork constructional details to ensure the minimum of air leakage, the placing of access doors for fire dampers, grill terminations, adequate dampers for balancing and proper linkages on control dampers. Similar checks on the hydraulic and electrical equipment are likely to show a number of faults which occur regularly on new installations. The ability to identify trouble spots early will enable later remedial work to be carried out at minimum cost and delay. For instance the addition of a flow measuring point in pipework while the fitters are working in a plantroom is easier than carrying out the same job after the pipes have been insulated and the system filled.

A 'snagging' report (i.e. one detailing defects or incomplete work) following the pre-commissioning visit should have an action column and should be treated seriously by the project team. The matters raised do not disappear with time and may later be the cause of delays and embarrassment.

3.6.4 Commissioning operations

3.6.4.1 Major tasks

Where the responsibilities for construction and commissioning are divided the concept of 'static completion' can be useful in order to create an arbitrary stage where changeover of responsibilities can occur. At this point it is assumed that the installation is complete, that the constructional testing routines have been carried out and that the state of the building is suitable for the plant to run. Until formal handover it is important to realise that a contractor can be the statutory occupier of the building, and may be liable for breaches of the Factory Acts and the Health and Safety Regulations. These may have particular application in the use of electrical installations and equipment. For a building services installation the main commissioning tasks will include:

(a) The commissioning of the electrical power supply installation.
(b) The electrical plant and motor control panel commissioning.
(c) The control system and commissioning.
(d) Millwrighting checks on rotating machinery.
(e) Setting to work pumps and air handling systems.
(f) Balancing water systems.
(g) Balancing air systems.
(h) Setting to work boiler installations.
(j) Setting to work refrigeration plant.
(k) Commissioning supervisory controls, fire and security systems.
(l) Environmental checking of completed installations.

3.6.4.2 Electrical installations

Established test and inspection routines observed as a normal activity during the installation of cables and electrical equipment reduce considerably the need for an independent commissioning operation. Building services main electrical installations normally contain:—

(a) The incoming power switchgear, transformers and distribution equipment.
(b) Cables, wiring and accessories.
(c) Motor control switchgear and rotating plant.
(d) Lighting and small power services, including fire and security systems.

It is of course necessary for the relevant electrical installation to be completed before commissioning can commence.

3.6.4.3 Switchgear and cables

Commissioning responsbilities for the main high voltage switchboards and transformers tend to lie with the electrical supply authorities who own the equipment. Where the client assumes responsibility, all the high voltage commissioning routines must be observed and carried out under the direction of a properly Authorised Person.

Heavy switchgear commissioning tends to be carried out by manufacturers' representatives where the contractor responsible does not employ adequately trained staff. When contractors' commissioning technicians carry out this work it is recommended that attendance at works testing is regarded as a part of the commissioning operation. This will ensure a degree of familiarity with the equipment.

Site work begins with visual inspection followed by insulation tests, earth checks, circuit testing and polarity checks. Electrical clearances and the tightness of electrical connections must be regarded as one of the most important checks made.

Commissioning and inspection routines are covered in the IEE Regulations, Part 6, "Inspection and Testing".

3.6.4.4 Motor control switchboards

Electrical equipment must be commissioned and set into operation before any mechanical plant can be commissioned. Power supplies may not be available at an early date and it may become necessary to carry out some commissioning checks before operation is required. The checks suggested are therefore divided to allow for this:–

(a) *Before power is available*

Panels and switchgear clean and dry.
Equipment properly identified throughout.
Incoming connections shrouded.
Fuse sizes correct for loads.
Overloads correct with nominal settings.
Insulation check of cables and motors acceptable.
Packing removed from contactors and relays.
Busbar connections tight and covers fitted.
Internal links on starters correct.
No mechanical damage.
Power connections to board, correctly protected by fuses or circuit breakers.
Provisional settings on timers and controls.

(b) *With power available*

Hang Safety Notices where necessary.
Remove two phase fuses leaving only control fuses. (Assuming panel correctly designed, with all control circuits on one phase to neutral).

Check control circuit operation including safety circuits, timers, interlocks and signal connections.

Replace power fuses with all loads switched off. Start each motor in sequence and check rotation. It is important that this is only done after millwrighting alignments, and the load has been cleared to run by the person responsible.

Check current on all phases for each load.
Adjust starting timers and overloads as necessary.
Complete test sheets and schedules.

It is possible that the boards will be shut down at this stage until the controlled installation is commissioned and operated. Make certain that doors and covers are fitted. During the running of fans for the first time the co-operation of the mechanical services engineer is desirable. A fan may overload due to damper position allowing too much air to be handled. The system may not have been cleaned out and plantroom doors may not be fitted or locked.

3.6.4.5 Control systems

In order to commission a controls installation it is necessary for the commissioning engineer to understand:

(a) The operational requirements of the controlled system.
(b) How the controls operate and how they can be adjusted.
(c) The effects of any failure to maintain the control conditions within safe parameters.

For any given type of process or commercial building installation, the choice of suitable skilled personnel to carry out the control and instrument commissioning is very limited. Often a controls technician and an engineer having system knowledge, jointly have to carry out the commissioning operation. In process and manufacturing companies the question of security relating to the manufacturing processes will add a further limit on the possible choice of the commissioning team. In such instances the final programming of process equipment will often be carried out by the company's own staff.

When planning for control and instrument commissioning attention must be given to the following:

(a) The installation must be complete and ready to run.
(b) Checks will be required at the interface points of controls and plant to ensure the correct physical matching.
(c) The centralised control and instrument setting to work will probably be carried out by a specialist.
(d) Support will probably be required to the Testing and Commissioning technician in order to operate the plant, etc., which is critical to commissioning but outside the control supplier's responsibility.
(e) The initial controls work will be in proving the operation of sensors, controllers, actuators and monitoring equipment. The performance under dynamic conditions may have to be proved at a later date. The fine tuning of an installation is often considered to be part of the final environmental testing of the installation.
(f) CIBS Commissioning Code C 'Automatic Controls' describes commissioning procedures for control systems. It does not however identify the responsibilities of suppliers and contractors. Such matters have to be predetermined by the parties involved.
(g) Control and instrument commissioning is highly dependent upon the mechanical and electrical installation completion. The system must be freely available for reasonable periods for the commissioning engineer to work without interference. Abortive visits caused by a failure to observe these conditions are likely to lead to commercial implications.

3.6.4.6 Millwrighting

The life of rotating machines depends very much upon the treatment they receive on site, their installation and in the commissioning procedures adopted. Ball and roller bearings suffer badly when subjected to shock or vibration and severe damage can be caused even when the machine itself is stationary.

Any lack of care therefore during the delivery or storage of machinery can lead to bearing failures at an early date. Often such failures are identified during the commissioning period.

Commissioning checks on rotating machines include examination and adjustment of anti-vibration fittings, the alignment of motors and drives, and setting to work under conditions recommended by the manufacturer. The aim should be to set the machine to work with closer tolerances than the worst called for by the equipment supplier. The better the alignment the less chance of stress being imposed on the equipment and consequential improvement in the running life of the machine.

Direct coupled drives on large or fast running machines require skilled attention. Accurate levelling of motors and the driven machine combined with alignment check made by dial gauges are essential. Records should be maintained of axial and radial final measured values in order to provide base information for future maintenance.

Pumps require special attention to ensure freedom from gland trouble. Packed glands need to be adjusted for the drip rate recommended by the manufacturer. Pumps having mechanical seals must only be rotated under clean water conditions. Dry running of a pump can quickly wreck the glands. The pump body must be free from stress since pump impellers can be damaged by stresses on the pump bodies or by axial thrust caused by misalignment. Body stresses can be caused by inadequately supported pipework coupled to the pump or by poor alignment. A summary of the commissioning operation on a pump installation is illustrated in Fig. 3.6.1.

Fans require special attention to the anti-vibration unit mounting and their adjustment. Often the motor and the fan are mounted on a common frame where their loading is anything but equally distributed on the four corners. The selection of anti-vibration mountings and their placing should overcome this. Failure to understand such matters during the installation can lead to anti-vibration mountings being incorrectly placed and adjusted.

Switching electric motors 'direct on line' produces a high starting torque which can affect belt drives if they are not properly adjusted. Pulleys or couplings may rotate on the motor or driven shaft if they are incorrectly fitted. It is never wrong to align the shaft and the couplings by the use of an accurately fitted key.

The fitting of guards on machinery at the end of a commissioning operation is essential. It is surprising how often it is found that the guards have not been properly designed or installed in the first place.

3.6.4.7 Air systems

Before setting a fan to work, the complete connected installation, including the fan chamber, must be checked for cleanliness and safety. All grills and dampers need to be set in the open position. Special points to check include access to reset fire dampers and details of the linkage system on the control dampers. Some difficulties can always be expected with these items.

Builders' work in the ventilated areas must be completed and easy access through the building made possible, since the balancing procedures are based on using one air terminal as a reference.

On a vertical air distribution system in a building, where the lifts are not working, this can lead to unneccesary exertion and loss of time by the commissioning engineers.

The procedures for balancing air systems are extremely well documented in the CIBS Commissioning Code A 'Air Distribution' and the practical explanation together with details of their use are covered in the BSRIA supporting publication. These two documents have now become a standard reference for the Building Services Industry ventilation systems balancing.

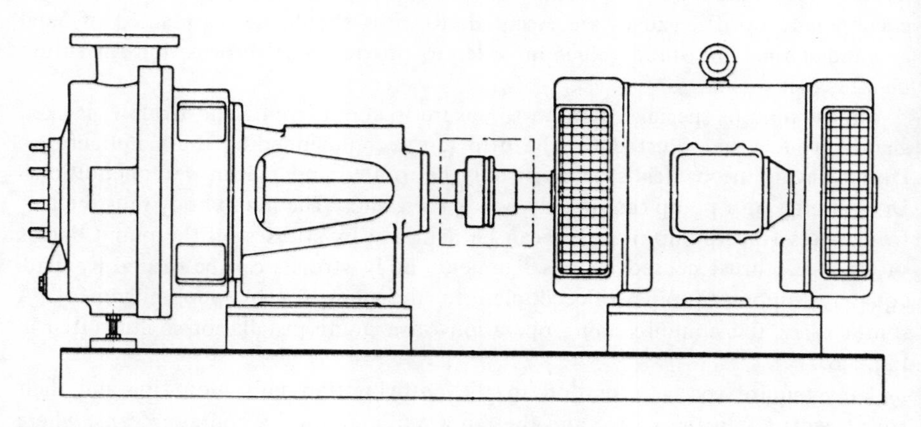

Electrical
- Wiring complete
- Correct voltage
- Supply available
- Correct starter
- Correct control interlocks
- Correct safety interlocks
- Correct fuses
- Motor & starter connections correct
- Timer settings
- Overload settings
- Electric current check
- Insulation check
- Remote Monitoring tests

Installation
- Correct duty
- No strain from pipework
- Antivibration mountings correctly installed
- Unit clean
- Drains fitted
- Gland checks
- Safety guards fitted
- Works tests and curves available

System
- System cleaned & flushed
- Air venting of system
- Noise checks
- Vibration checks
- Flow checks
- Alignment checks
- Bearing checks

Fig. 3.6.1. *Commissioning operations: pumps*

3.6.4.8 Hydraulic systems

The initial cleaning and flushing of a hydraulic system is not regarded generally as a commissioning operation. This work however must be done thoroughly. Filling the system and allowing it to drain is inadequate and can lead to the blockage of small pipework and control valves at a later date.

Advice should be sought from commissioning engineers and will probably include:

(a) Bypassing of terminal units and small control valves before any flushing operation takes place.
(b) Circulating water at the maximum possible velocity. If possible the water should be discharged and refilled at a high rate.
(c) Filling the system from the bottom rather than filling from the cold water supply tanks in order to reduce the likelihood of air locks.
(d) The use of commissioning filters, chemicals or magnetic separators for the removal of deposits within the system.

The hydraulic system will require balancing to ensure the correct maximum flow rates through heat exchangers. On constant volume circuits this can be achieved by measuring the pressure drops across the exchangers or across associated control valves. Line and bypass valves, correctly selected and fitted in appropriate positions, must be adjusted to achieve the desired balance.

Systems using variable flow rates are often favoured due to the reduced commissioning effort required and because of the energy saving in pumping when the loads are reduced. Variable volume systems cannot be simply balanced by flow measurement. A good designer will employ calibrated regulating valves in appropriate locations and state the settings required. Flow measurements need only then be taken to prove pumping duty unless some operational difficulty is encountered. System designs must always allow for water flow through boilers and the evaporators on refrigerating systems to be at constant flow rates. The flow rates must be proved by the commissioning engineer before such equipment is brought into operation.

The routine for water system balancing is well described in CIBS Commissioning Code W, 'Water Distribution Systems', and BSRIA have again produced a supporting field manual which includes details of suitable instruments and methods of taking measurements.

3.6.4.9 Boilers and associated plant

Many potential boiler commissioning problems have been overcome by the practice of supplying boilers complete with the matched combustion equipment. Thus the most frequently used packaged boiler units will have their combustion spaces, air supplies and gas or oil burners matched to the boiler. The commissioning of boilers however cannot be considered in isolation from the installation which the boiler serves. All ancillary plant must be available for operation after having already been through the commissioning phase. Statutory Regulations for plantroom ventilation and for fire precautions must be complied with before start up and a load must also be available from the connected system in order to enable the performance checks on the boiler installation to be completed.

It is very easy to overlook minor details during the start up of the boiler and the associated plant and check lists are required by anyone who is not a specialist in this field. The manufacturers' Operation and Maintenance manuals together with the CIBS Commissioning Code B 'Boiler Plant' becomes essential reading for anyone who is not familiar with the problems of starting up boiler plants and gradually bringing it up to a fully operational condition.

The special interests of the boiler insurance company covering the boiler must be considered. An inspector may require to witness and carry out his own inspections as a preliminary to the commissioning sequence. Other equipment such as water treatment, pressurisation and installation details such as boiler flues may also fall under the insurance agreements.

The combustion performance analysis will require instruments for measuring flue conditions and carrying out gas analysis of the flue gas. The statutory requirements for limiting the density of smoke discharge from the chimney must also be observed. The fuel consumption needs to be accurately measured and the system should be provided with suitable metering equipment which will allow for measurement of fuel consumed and the output of the boilers.

Water treatment is important from the time that the system is filled, cleaned and flushed. If this is not the subject of an agreement with a specialist water treatment company, samples should be taken of the water in the system and analysed by an independent authority. Since the condition of the originally treated water will change, frequent tests should be made during the early life of the installation if early boiler and system failures are to be avoided.

3.6.4.10 Refrigeration systems

Whilst the basic refrigeration cycle is easy to follow, the practical complications of machine design and support system refinements result in a wide variety of machine types and components which call for attention by properly trained personnel at commissioning stage. Refrigeration equipment manufacturers will, in most instances be responsible for the charging and setting to work of the machines which they have provided. Apart from the specialist skills required, this is desirable in order to maintain the manufacturers' warranty which may be dependent upon approved commissioning. (Fig. 3.6.2).

3.6.4.11 Specialist systems

Fire security and building services monitoring installations have become increasingly sophisticated and are often the subject of a complete supply install and commission subcontract. In such instances electrical power supplies and the necessary access to the building will need to be included in the arrangements necessary before the specialist commissioning can take place. Commissioning support may be required from the services contractor who will probably also be required to organise the witnessing of the specialist commissioning.

Fig. 3.6.2. ***Refrigeration machine commissioning***
There are many safety devices and timers to be set on a refrigeration machine. Each one has to be checked in operation.

Security installations have very little relationship to any of the mechanical services installation. The very nature of security systems is such that the briefing of the supplier is often carried out direct by the building owner in order to reduce the number of people having a knowledge of the installation.

Fire protection and detection installations have to comply with a number of Statutory Regulations. The local Fire Officer may wish to inspect and check the completed installation before the building can be occupied.

Building services monitoring installations will be heavily interfaced with the controlled plant and a programme of combined checking and commissioning is essential. Before accepting a monitoring installation it is necessary for comprehensive schedules to be prepared identifying all the functions to be carried out from the central equipment. Every function needs independently proving before the system can be accepted.

Failure to do this will reflect heavily upon both the monitoring system supplier and the contractors responsible.

3.6.4.12 Environmental proving of installations

One of the important objectives of a services installation designer will be to create a suitable environment for the people who live and work within the building. The installation will be commissioned to achieve the design air and water flow rates and temperatures. Further checks will be required to ensure that the completed installation will achieve the designer's objectives.

All constructional delays affect the final proving dates. This fact, combined with the certainty that outdoor conditions will not drive the plant to maximum summer or winter conditions, leads to consideration of environmental testing as being a delayed operation, possibly taking place to some extent during the initial occupation. Recognition of this is important and a suitable programme agreed with the client.

The designer may wish to participate in this last stage of the commissioning operation and special recorders etc. may have to be organised for the test period. Probably the ideal arrangement would be the detailing of environmental tests required in the design specification.

3.6.5 The commissioning team

3.6.5.1 Establishing the team

An experienced commissioning engineer should be appointed to lead the comissioning operation. Such an appointment should be made at an early date to enable designers and contract staff to obtain advice at a time when it is most appropriate. For instance it is easier to provide tappings and bypass arrangements around valves during the initial design than it is to carry out such operations on a completed installation. Lead commission and test engineers can participate in planning and in works testing. Visits to site can ensure that constructional details affecting commissioning are properly attended to. Participation at this stage may probably only be on a part-time basis.

The development of the commissioning team will depend upon the nature of the tasks to be completed and the resources available. An industrial project may call for a strong team of technical specialists while an office block may have a call for specialists working in the plant room supported by a number of lesser skilled operatives for tasks such as air and water balancing.

3.6.5.2 Man-power resources

Late starts to the commissioning operation often occur due to inadequate manpower planning. The resources available need to be examined at an early date. Very good arguments exist for using the job project engineers to carry out many commissioning tasks within their practical capabilities. Of these the provision of feedback related to operational problems must be considered to be of future value. Junior engineers should be encouraged to work alongside experienced commissioning engineers as a normal part of their practical training. Recognition should be paid to the possible difficulties which may arise at the later stages of the constructional sequence due to the transfer of senior staff to new work or to matters associated with clearing up record information in order to complete the contract. One result of this is that the project staff cease to become available for commissioning. This possibility must be recognised and alternative resources considered to complete the essential commissioning tasks. The following possibilities are worthy of examination:

3.6.5.3 In-house commissioning unit

Any services contracting organisation with a reasonable turnover will have a continuous call for commissioning. A possibility therefore exists to justify the fulltime employment of an engineer having suitable experience for commissioning work. A sound knowledge of electrical commissioning allied to an ability to understand and operate complete services installation would probably be the first qualities to look for. A choice of an electrical background at this stage is mainly because the electrical skills of mechanical contractors and designers is often a weak point. All installations have a high dependency upon the satisfactory operation of electrical equipment which must be operational before anything else can work. This is best dealt with by an engineer with a suitable background who can represent the company's interests rather than to use external hired staff.

The development of the in-house commissioning team will be a process of adding additional necessary skills, at craftsman level, with technicians who are able to work at a high technical level and have a reasonable management ability. Good all-round commissioning engineers cannot be found easily. The development programme to be adopted should be one of identifying suitable talent and over a period of time investing in their training.

3.6.5.4 Use of project engineers

Project engineers already on site can make a valuable contribution to the commissioning operation. Their better knowledge of the site and plant, and often better management ability combined with planning experience, makes their employment attractive. The availability of project engineers however, at the time when they are required, seems to be the major problem.

3.6.5.5 Hired support

Specialist commissioning organisations exist and operate at a number of varying technical and management levels. Some provide full commissioning consultancies whilst others specialise in air and water balancing using staff trained only for this work. Selection of the most suitable organisation to work with must be therefore carried out with care and consideration for the tasks to be completed. Remember commissioning concerns the final performance of an installation upon which the reputation of the contracting organisation may be dependent. The choice therefore of a commissioning partner based on the lowest initial quotations may not achieve the desired result. The best arrangements tend to be obtained by joint working on a number of projects with a limited number of commissioning companies.

3.6.5.6 Manufacturers commissioning

It is sometimes suggested that there is no need for special or commissioning skills if the manufacturers are employed to commission their own equipment. This is a fallacy. Manufacturers are mainly concerned in the proving of terminal performance of plant or of control systems for which they are responsible. Typically a refrigeration machine manufacturer would be able to set his machine to work only after the correct water quantities through condensers and evaporators had been established and after ancilliary equipment such as cooling towers had been properly commissioned. The electrical installations for both power and control electrical interlocks must all be proved before the manufacturer can carry out his specialist charging and commissioning operation. Other examples can be found to show that the use of manufacturers, without overall management and support, will produce an installation which has varying qualities regarding commissioning and operations.

3.6.5.7 Commissioning co-ordination

The appointment of a commissioning co-ordinator on a major project is desirable. An examination of the many information exchanges between all parties concerned with commissioning on a complex or large installation will identify a role for a co-ordinator. Such a person will provide up-to-date priorities for the commissioning operation, expedite suppliers problems, liaise with the builder and generally ensure that action follows any snagging reports made by the commissioning team. The commissioning co-ordinator need not be a senior engineer. The choice may be for someone with enthusiasm for the job, who knows the company systems and has the right personality.

The appointment of a commissioning co-ordinator should not in any way block the access of the lead commissioning engineer to the project manager. There is a danger of this occurring because it is convenient to the project manager and because the co-ordinator is able to build up a very good knowledge of both the job requirements and the commissioning operations.

3.6.6 Safety

3.6.6.1 Safety legislation

The effects of Acts such as the Health & Safety at Work etc. Act places an additional responsibility on everyone concerned with the installation, from the client who will own and operate it, through the design and construction team, to the operatives who carry out the practical work on site. These responsibilities are not limited by time and unidentified problems can show-up later at any time. It is also important to be aware of the implications arising from the fact that a construction site falls within the scope of the 1961 Factories Act. Upon completion, the use of the building may relieve the occupier of this responsibility.

There are often major constraints which apply to the Testing and Commissioning team and which in turn may prevent those involved from identifying safety related problems. These constraints include:

(a) Time available between constructional completion and occupation by client.
(b) Limited brief and responsibility due to contractual divisions of mechanical and electrical installation work.
(c) Financial restraints which lead to a limited commissioning operation. Often such constraints are applied on behalf of the building owner by those responsible for cost control who do not personally have any practical responsibility for the installation.

3.6.6.2 Safety during commissioning
Commissioning operations are mainly concerned with energising electrical equipment and operating plant for the first time. This is a period when new and dangerous situations arise and where special precautions need to be taken if accidents are to be avoided. The management responsibilities for safety include the co-ordination of safety procedures with the client, builder, and sub-contractors. The commissioning engineer also needs to be aware of his special responsibilities and must comply with the rules agreed for the site. It should not be his responsibility to set up and operate safety procedures.

3.6.6.3 Electrical safety checks
Safe working considerations should be included on any pre-commissioning check lists and other operation or maintenance documentation. Initial checks should be made to ensure that equipment is installed and identified as laid down in the design. Equipment should be clean, covers in place and all switches and control valves in the appropriate start-up position. Electrical terminals must be tight, covers for access fitted and no live unterminated wiring exposed. Before energising any part of the installation, appropriate tests must be carried out with instruments.

Adequate warning must be given to personnel in operational areas that the system will be energised. Where entry is unrestricted to the area containing the electrical plant suitable warning notices must be posted. Plant under test must be physically isolated and placed under the control of an Authorised Person.

Safety is mainly a matter of common sense and good judgement. Safety training and company disciplines improve safety. No clear rules exist which cover adequately safe working procedures for all the situations which arise during commissioning. Probably the most important legislation that can be used as a guideline lies in the Factories Act. A building site under construction falls within the scope of these acts up to the time of handover to the client. At this stage it appears that the nature of the building will determine whether or not the Act continues to apply.

It is essential that correct tools and instruments are used for all tasks. Made-up test equipment and badly fitting spanners are a frequent cause of minor accidents and should be the subject of checks by the project manager and others responsible for safe working. A completely safe system of work should be the objective.

3.6.7 Documentation

3.6.7.1 Commissioning documentation
There is a tendency for the time and effort associated with commissioning documentation to be underestimated. The breakdown of written communications, directly associated with commissioning, for a mechanical services installation would include:

Completed before commissioning

(a) The Commissioning Specifications.

(b) The Commissioning Brief.
(c) Planning Information (already discussed).

Completed During Commissioning

(d) Pre-commissioning Check Lists.
(e) Commissioning Codes.
(f) Commissioning Test Sheets.
(g) Commissioning Reports and Records (Fig. 3.6.3).
(h) Cost Control Records.
(i) Marked up Drawings and Wiring Diagrams.

Whilst it would be easy to extend this list efforts at reducing the documentation should be directed to easing the efforts required by site staff rather than limiting the information to the commissioning team.

3.6.7.2 Commissioning specifications

The references to commissioning and testing can be the subject of differing interpretations over a wide spectrum. It is therefore important that the scope of commissioning should be properly described by a consultant to a contractor or by a contractor sending enquiries to any specialist commissioning company.

Specifications need to include the criteria against which the performance of the T & C operation can be considered acceptable and a statement of the extent of any witnessing required. The latter can be very expensive if carried out in any detail due to the duplicated effort by the contractor or manufacturer in completing his own tests before repeating them for demonstration and in the cost of making available adequately trained staff to carry out the acceptance.

3.6.7.3 The commissioning brief

The importance of the commissioning brief – preferably drawn up by the system designer – is often underestimated. A sound brief which provides the necessary information and defines the responsibilities of the commissioning team will enable the operation to be properly planned and staffed. Failure to provide an adequate brief can lead to abortive work, overrun of commissioning costs and failure to meet commissioning programmes.

A commissioning brief will need to include:–

(a) Copies of relevent drawings and schedules covering the plant to be commissioned. Schematic diagrams are particularly valuable in providing an introduction to the installation.

(b) Copies of the specifications, where appropriate, codes applying to commissioning and testing and any standards relevant to the commissioning operation.

(c) Manufacturer's instruction and technical data covering both the installation and commissioning of equipment.

(d) Wiring diagrams and supporting technical information necessary for setting up all the switch gear and control equipment. Setting values for protective relays and controls should be provided by the designer.

Commissioning records: *Electrical motors and controls*

Job . . . . Control Panel Ref. . . . .

	Plant Item and Ref. No.	kW	phase	Fuse Rating A	Full Load current A	Running A	Starter Ref.	Starter Make	Coil V	Overload Range A	Overload Setting A	Control Panel Check	Type of Starter	Comments

Date Test Began. . . . . Date Completed. . . . .
Readings Taken By . . . . Approved By . . . .
Instruments Used . . . . Date . . . .

Fig. 3.6.3. *Typical Electrical test record*

(e) Basic job information including programme site organisation and key people associated with the commissioning operation. The procedure for obtaining the client's approval should be confirmed at this stage.
(f) The provisions made for the accommodation of the commissioning team on site. This will be required for instrument storage, the accommodation of records and space to lay out drawings.
(g) On major or complex projects the brief will need to be developed with the assistance of an experienced commissioning consultant or commissioning engineer. The result may be presented in the form of a commissioning method statement and examples of the test sheets to be completed.

3.6.7.4 Pre-commissioning checks

Whilst an installation may appear to be completed, a closer examination may identify many small details which will prevent the installation from being commissioned in a straightforward manner. Pre-commissioning visits by an experienced commissioning engineer will assist in clearing up trouble spots at an early date. Often the introduction of suitable pre-commissioning check sheets to the site at this time will enable project staff to spot the faults at an appropriate time.

An example of such a check list is provided here. Others can be developed for most of the important plant and systems. A good example of an air balancing check list is given in the appropriate BSRIA manual.

3.6.7.5 Commissioning codes

The benefits of industry codes for commissioning have been recognised and the CIBS and BSRIA have produced a number of important codes for services commissioning. The IEE Regulations now include commissioning recommendations.

3.6.7.6 Commissioning test sheets

The use of well designed test sheets is essential if the results of the commissioning operation are to be properly recorded. Test sheets provide the basic documentation for witnessed testing and for records of settings of overloads, protective relays and valves, which later become the basis of maintenance records.

3.6.7.7 Commissioning reports

Commissioning engineers do not generally like or see the need for extensive reporting which can be time consuming during the period when an all out effort is being made to get the installation operational. Therefore, reporting procedures should be simple and frequent. Tying up report forms with time sheets for instance ensures regular reporting. It is important that reporting systems should avoid duplication of information already given by test sheets and that a column is provided for stating the action required by others to keep the commissioning going. Specialist subject reporting should be encouraged. Often commissioning engineers will see faults repeated in a number of situations, and not bother to report them.

3.6.8 Conclusion

In this chapter, emphasis has been given to management aspects of commissioning rather than to descriptions of commissioning tasks. Failure to achieve commissioning objectives in terms of time, cost or technical detail are far more likely to occur due to poor planning, poor briefing or poor management than for any other cause. There are many opportunities for the designer, contractor and client to use the commissioning place of a project as a testbed for learning how to operate the installation in the future and lay the foundation for improved design.

3.6.9 References

3.6.9.1 Legislation (See also Appendix 6.1)

Factories Act 1961
Health and Safety at Work etc. Act 1974
Memorandum on the Electricity Regulations

3.6.9.2 Bibliography

BSIRA Application Guide 1/75 'Manual for Regulating Air Conditioning Installations'
BSRIA Application Guide 1/77 'Documents for Air System Regulation'
BSRIA Application Guide 1/79 'Manual for Regulating Water Systems'
Published by Building Services Research and Information Association (BSIRA), Old Bracknell Lane, Bracknell, Berkshire RG12 4AH
CIBS Guide Volume B 'Installation and Equipment Data'
CIBS Commissioning Codes A 'Air Distribution', B 'Boiler Plant', C 'Automatic Controls, R 'Refrigeration Systems', W 'Water Distribution Systems'.
CIBS Proceedings of Symposium 'Testing and Commissioning of Building Services Installations'. ('TESCOM 77') Published by Chartered Institution of Building Services.
'Arrow Diagram Planning'. Published by Construction Industry Training Board (CITB), Radnor House, London Road, Norbury, London SW16 4EL.
Regulations for Electrical Installations (Institution of Electrical Engineers)
IEE Proceedings of Seminar 'Building Engineering Services: Testing and Commissioning of Sophisticated Plant and Installation'. October 1980.

Chapter 3.7

Special considerations for construction sites

J. W. Sutton, Dip.Tech.(Eng.)
Chief Engineer's Department, Southern Electricity Board

3.7.1 General (See also section 3.1.13.2)

A consideration of paramount importance when planning a new project is to ensure that a supply of electricity will be available at the commencement of the construction stage to meet the demands of the electrical services. Because of the timescale involved, particularly if a substation is required, this is only possible with close co-operation at the planning stage between all those responsible for the building, and the local Electricity Authority. The availability of an electricity supply is vital since it can be used on site to provide light, heat and power to increase productivity and make best use of the labour force. The load involved at the construction stage often exceeds that required for the permanent building, but to avoid duplication of effort, it is desirable to consider both demands jointly. By early liaison with the parties concerned, economic advantage may be obtained by utilising part of the proposed permanent supply to provide the construction site supply.

The stringent precautions for safety demanded in the UK by the Health and Safety at Work Act have moved construction site installations outside the sphere of operations of the main contractor's handyman. Present day electrical supplies on construction sites require the same careful planning and consideration as permanent installations. The aim must be to provide a supply and service which is safe to use, efficient in operation, not liable to avoidable interruptions, flexible to take into account changes as work proceeds and economic with a possible high level of equipment recovery on completion of the project.

3.7.2 Equipment operating voltages

In the United Kingdom, electricity is available from Electricity Boards at either 415 V three-phase 50 Hz or 240 V single-phase 50 Hz. Such voltages can be lethal and should be transformed down to lower voltages for hand held lighting fittings, portable tools and other equipment. For normal construction and repair work which involves the use of hand held devices, the use of 110 V single-phase supply fed via a double wound, centre tapped transformer is recommended. With the centre tap of the 110 V side of a single-phase transformer connected to earth, the danger of serious shock is greatly diminished since the maximum voltage to earth of the secondary winding is limited to 55 V. Where a three-phase transformer is employed, the voltage to earth is approximately 65 V.

In hazardous situations, such as abnormally wet conditions, or when working inside earthed enclosures (e.g. metal shells), it is preferable to employ even lower voltages. In such circumstances, hand tools should derive their supply from a 50 V transformer (centre tapped to give a maximum voltage to earth of 25 V) whilst portable lighting, which tends to be more vulnerable, should operate from a single-phase 25 V supply. In the latter case the earth connection on the 25 V winding should be omitted and reliance placed on the integrity of the system and its low voltage for operator safety. Lampholders should be selected to ensure that 110 V and 240 V lamps cannot be inadvertently interchanged, but tungsten filament lamps for use on 25 V systems must be of the three pin bayonet cap type to ensure that they cannot be fitted into holders on higher voltage systems. The Electricity Authority will advise on step down voltage transformers or generators if required, but the means of earthing and safety are finally the responsibility of the contractor.

Recommended voltages for various applications are summarised below:

(a) Fixed plant and mobile plant fed via trailing cable: three-phase mains voltage.
(b) Site offices, stores, drying rooms and fixed floodlights: single-phase mains voltage.
(c) Portable and hand held tools: 110 V single or three-phase.
(d) Portable site lighting: 110 V single or three-phase.
(e) Hand tools in hazardous situations: 50 V single-phase.
(f) Hand lamps: 25 V single-phase.

3.7.3 Source and arrangement of supply

The most convenient and, usually, the most economical source of supply is from the Electricity Authority. For short term or emergency work, or where a public supply would not be feasible because of the remoteness of the site, motor-generator sets may be used. Specifically sound-proofed models are now available for situations where inconvenience may be caused by excessive noise, e.g. in urban areas.

A public supply can generally be provided wherever it is needed, but it cannot always be arranged at short notice. As soon as a future building development is considered and certainly not later than the planning application stage, it is essential that the local office of the Electricity Authority is approached. They will need to know precisely when and where the supply will be required, the maximum demand and nature (i.e. number and size of motors, heating and lighting loads, etc.) of the load which will be required for construction purposes and the expected maximum demand of the developed site. It may be that, by careful planning, much of the equipment installed for the initial site supply can be used for the final supply, and this is particularly significant when a substation is required.

It would be advantageous to establish the supply characteristics at this stage to facilitate the design of the site distribution network (i.e. to calculate the prospective short circuit current and earth fault loop impedance). A further matter for discussion at an early stage is the identification and location of existing electrical services. These may be overhead or underground and may require re-siting or removal prior to commencement of work. Precautions will need to be taken to avoid damage to or accidental contact with any services which remain on site.

Topics to be covered in the initial discussions with the Electricity Authority are summarised below:

(a) Nature and size of loads for building purposes and final supply.
(b) Can initial supply be used wholly or in part for final development, paying particular attention to supply intake?
(c) Expected connection date.
(d) Establish characteristics of supply.
(e) Metering requirements.
(f) Establish possibility of provision of earth terminal by Electricity Authority
(g) Establish precautions to be taken with regard to existing services on site.

3.7.4 Distribution and wiring

The distribution of electricity on a site is necessarily quite different from that of a permanent installation. As work proceeds, the type of equipment used tends to change and there is a need for convenient means of connecting plant which operates on a variety of voltages, phases and currents. Wiring problems arise because runs require re-routing and the control gear must remain portable.

In new work, the Electricity Authority's meter and fuses, and the main switchgear will be contained in a cubicle, fully weatherproofed and often situated at the edge of the work area or site. Where transformers or switchgear are required, there must be full access to the site to deliver and install equipment. The routes of any underground cables to be laid must be kept clear of obstructions, electricity supply cables being buried at a minimum depth of 450 mm. Where the cable route coincides with or crosses a heavy traffic route, the cables should be buried at a depth of 600 mm and further protected by encasing in steel tubes, or stoneware, or pitch fibre pipes, each end of a road crossing being prominently identified by a cable marker.

Cables used for connections between distribution units and for connecting fixed equipment should be installed wherever possible around the perimeter of the site, avoiding road crossings. These overground cables should be supported on hangers from an independent wire suspended between properly designed poles or attachments, fixings to fencing etc., being deprecated. Table 11B of the IEE Regulations gives details of minimum heights above ground for different cables in various situations. Routes where cranes or mobile plant are likely to pass must be erected so that there is a minimum clear height of 5·8 m; the passageway should be clearly marked with protective barriers and 'goal posts'. To make these overhead cables more conspicuous to operatives, the cables can be bound with black and white tape, or red and white bunting attached to posts each side of the cables and parallel to its route. (Fig. 3.7.1).

Fig. 3.7.1. *Sites where plant will pass under the line. Example of rigid goal posts and barriers (Health and Safety Executive)*

If cables on the site are buried, this must be done under the same conditions as outlines above for Electricity Authority cables. Where cables are allowed to lie on the ground, even for short periods, they must be provided with appropriate additional protection.

Cables operating on the mains voltage system should be armoured with p.v.c. insulation and for fixed equipment comply with BS 6346. For connections to moveable plant, flexible armoured cables complying with BS 6116 are recommended.

Where electric welding is being utilised, the cables to the electrodes should be to BS 638, part 4. Flexible cords for connection of portable tools and hand lamps need to be mechanically robust, requiring a cross section of not less than 1 mm^2. The sheaths of all cables should be durable to resist the harsh site conditions, i.e. p.v.c., p.c.p. or h.o.f.r., and be black in colour to resist the effect of sunlight.

BS 4363 'Distribution Units for Electricity Supplies for Construction and Building Sites' sets out the essential requirements for the control and distribution of electricity from a three-phase, four wire, a.c. system with a declared voltage of 415/240 V. The standard deals specifically with supplies with a maximum capacity of 300 A per phase, but states that for supplies of greater capacity, the specification shall be regarded as generally applicable. There would, of course, be a requirement for greater space to terminate such a supply and this would be the subject of discussion between the Electricity Authority and the contractor. The recommended distribution system gives maximum flexibility and affords protection by sensitive circuit breakers to the 415 V equipment and provides reduced voltage for portable tools and lighting. It consists of five units (supply, incoming unit, main distri-

Fig. 3.7.2. *Distribution unit on construction site* *(Tripower Ltd)*

bution unit, transformer outlet and extension outlet units) supplying 110 V single-phase (55 V to earth) with interconnecting cables. The transformer unit should be situated as near as possible to the incoming supply to reduce cable lengths at mains voltage to a minimum. Long trailing cables from hand equipment should also be avoided by planning the distribution system to bring socket outlets near to the working area. Equipment on the lines of BS 4363 is now available from several manufacturers. It is strongly recommended that this system be adopted for all site work and that a clause requiring its use be included in the contract specifications. (Fig. 3.7.2).

3.7.5 Earthing and protection

The distribution system and all appliances connected to it must be efficiently earthed in accordance with BS CP 1013. If the supply is provided either from a transformer on the site or from a low voltage network which has separate neutral and protective conductors, then an earth terminal may be provided. The circuit protective conductors of the installation could then be bonded to the main earth terminal and this would be a TN–S system (see Section 3.1.6.2), as defined in the IEE Regulations. However, if the Electricity Authority is operating a PME network, it may not be possible for an earth terminal to be provided. The alternative to an earth terminal from the supply system is a site earth electrode using driven rods or tubes, buried plates, metal strip or bare stranded cable.

For a TT system the IEE Regulations additionally recommend the use of a high sensitivity (30 mA) residual current device (r.c.d.) for the protection of circuits supplying socket outlets. To use only one such device to control all the circuits would have the disadvantage that an earth fault anywhere on the installation would result in a total disconnection of the supply. This would be inconvenient or even dangerous, so the circuits should be divided and protected by separate residual current devices whose sensitivity would be related to the circuit use, e.g. 100 mA or 500 mA r.c.d. for fixed equipment.

The use of overcurrent protection devices in conjunction with an earth electrode for earth fault protection requires special consideration, as outlined in the IEE Regulations, not least of which is a very low earth electrode resistance which may be difficult to achieve economically.

Excess current protection can be provided by rewireable fuses, cartridge fuses or miniature circuit breakers: BS 4363, however, specifies m.c.b. Rewireable fuses are open to misuse by operatives who can replace the elements with any piece of fusewire available. Cartridge fuses are expensive and, again, unless a spare is readily available, any piece of wire can be put across the terminals. Miniature circuit breakers, while relatively expensive to install, are virtually foolproof and offer satisfactory protection against the types of fault usually encountered in this type of installation. It will be necessary, however, to ensure that the proposed protective devices are capable of withstanding the prospective short circuit current at their point of installation.

3.7.6 Safety

A temporary site installation should be in the charge of a competent person who is s responsible for the safety of the installation, its use and any alteration or extension thereto. The name and designation of the nominated person should be prominently displayed close to the main switch or circuit breaker of the installation.

All accessories and wiring should comply with the IEE Regulations. Plugs and socket outlets should comply with BS 4343 and with the variety of voltages available on the site, it is essential that they are colour coded and the earth pin position correctly located so that equipment operating at one voltage cannot be plugged into the wrong supply.

The following standard colour coding for plugs and sockets should be adopted:–

Operating Voltage	*Colour*
25 V	Violet
50 V	White
110 V–130 V	Yellow
220 V–240 V	Blue
380 V–415 V	Red
500 V–750 V	Black

Because the electrical skills of the operatives utilising the equipment will vary widely, it is essential that circuits are correctly labelled, danger and warning notices are prominently displayed and diagrams and instructions are readily understandable. Periodic inspection and tests of the installation and equipment should be undertaken at least every three months and a record kept of the results. Periodic maintenance of plant is essential to keep the risk of accidents and equipment downtime to a minimum.

Particular attention should be paid to the siting of electrical plant and to its supply leads. Heavy fixed plant, tower cranes, hoists and the like should be sited so that they can remain in one position throughout the job and their supply cables can be routed clear of construction work. Heavy transportable electrical plant should be handled carefully so that the supply cables do not become damaged. Care must be taken in handling portable tools, and long trailing supply leads must be protected from damage. Tools should always be disconnected before any adjustment or changes of attachment are made. Where double-insulated and all-insulated tools are used without earth connection on premises covered by the Factories Acts, (such as building sites), the effect of present legislation is to require them to carry the certification mark of an approved, testing organisation, e.g. the BSI kitemark, indicating conformity with BS 2769. Provided the installation complies with the provisions of BS CP 1017, using distribution units to BS 4363, it will, in general, meet the various legal requirements, but where special conditions arise, advice should be sought from the Heath and Safety Executive. The main statutory provisions applying to construction sites, which must be complied with, are:–

Electricity (Factories Act) Special Regulations 1980 and 1944

Construction (General Provisions) Regulations 1961

Health and Safety at Work etc. Act 1974

Under the terms of this legislation, employers have a legal obligation to prevent danger to persons from live overhead and underground cables. It is, therefore, essential that the Electricity Authority's engineers be approached before work begins so that the location of all cables and safe working clearances from overhead lines can be indicated. Guidance on the correct procedures to be adopted are contained in two documents entitled 'Avoidance of Danger from Overhead

Electric Lines' which is Guidance Note GS6 from the Health and Safety Executive (Ref. 1) and 'Recommendations on the Avoidance of Danger from Underground Electricity Cables' produced by the National Joint Utilities Group (Ref. 2). Damage to Electricity Authority equipment due to a contractor's negligence will have to be paid for by him and may prove costly.

3.7.7 References

3.7.7.1 Legislation (See also Appendix 6.1)

Electricity (Factories Act) Special Regulations, 1908 and 1944
Construction (General Provisions) Regulations, 1961
Health and Safety at Work etc., Act, 1974
Electricity Supply Regulations, 1937

3.7.7.2 British Standards. (See also Appendix 6.2)

BS 638 Part 4 deals with arc-welding equipment, BS 2769 with portable tools, BS 4343 with industrial plugs and sockets and BS 4363 with distribution units for building sites. BS 6116 relates to flexible cables and BS 6346 to p.v.c-insulated cables. BS CP 1013 covers earthing, and BS CP 1017, distribution of electricity on building sites.

3.7.7.3 Bibliography

(Ref. 1) Avoidance of Danger from Overhead Electric Lines (Guidance Note GS6, Health and Safety Executive, Baynards House, 1 Chepstow Place, London W2 4TF).
(Ref. 2) Recommendations on the Avoidance of Danger from Underground Electricity Cables. (The National Joint Utilities Group, 30 Millbank London SW1P 4RD).
Regulations for Electrical Installations. (Institution of Electrical Engineers)

Installation in Desert Conditions

(Ewbank Design Partnership)

Chapter 3.8

Special precautions in hot climates

J.M. Acton, B.Sc.(Eng.), C.Eng., F.I.E.E.
Managing Director, Ewbank Preece Design Partnership

3.8.1 Introduction

Most people reading this chapter will be familiar with the Codes of Practice, Standards and Regulations, which generally relate to the installation practices in countries having cool or temperate climates. Historically, these are the countries in which the electrical installation practices are well developed and prescribed. Engineers from these countries were almost invariably associated with the design and construction of the early electrical installations in those territories having predominately hot climates. In many instances they merely transferred their home country technology to the overseas country for which they were now designing. By and large, this has been generally satisfactory but there are several instances where there could have been improvements by the adoption of straightforward but special precautions.

In general, the main factors which will concern the electrical engineer in countries having a hot climate include:

(a) Availability of Codes of Practice, Standards and Regulations.
(b) Supply conditions.
(c) Established custom and practice.
(d) Equipment suitable for the specified country.
(e) Temperature and humidity
(f) Corrosion and other factors likely to cause damage or maloperation.
(g) Availability of materials, standardisation and other external factors.

There will be certain additional factors which affect the installation practice in each country, but, by and large, the above list covers most of the main items. Of these, temperature, humidity and corrosion are going to be the main concern of the engineer and particular care must be taken when selecting materials, equipment and designing the installation so as to overcome these problems.

3.8.2 Regulations, Codes of Practice and Standards

Most countries originally adopted the Standards and design practices of the country of origin of the engineers who first designed the electrical supply and distribution systems. This has, inevitably, meant a proliferation of different standards, although the British and American are the most prevalent. A detailed knowledge of the appropriate British and American Standards, Codes of Practice and Regulations for Electrical Installations, although not mandatory, will certainly enable the electrical engineer to be at home in most countries. However, the engineer should be alerted to the fact that many of the countries which we are here considering now have their own Statutory Regulations. Local wiring installation Regulations are also appearing in a large number of them. Many of these "new" Regulations contain the distilled knowledge and experience of electrical engineers who have many years of practical experience in hot climates. Reference should always be made to these in the first instance.

3.8.3 Supply conditions

The electrical engineer will first wish to establish the details of the system for the particular country under consideration. Published data is readily available scheduling information about voltage, frequency and system parameters. However, due to the way in which these systems have developed it is often found that discrepancies exist between published and actual site details. Further, no information is given concerning the stability of the supply and it will be found that outages or disconnections are often a matter of everyday life. It must also be remembered that the peak demand is often encountered at the time of highest temperatures due to the wide adoption of air conditioning in both homes and places of work. The capacity of the electrical equipment to meet these peak demands is reduced by the high ambient temperatures, leading to automatic disconnections and loss of supply.

Dependent on the type of installation will be the need to provide standby generation and reserve electrical capacity. Inevitably, these too must be sized to permit operation at elevated temperatures. It is therefore important, when considering electrical installations in hot climates, to research, preferably at first hand, accurate information about the local conditions relating to the supply system and its operating characteristics.

3.8.4 Established customs and practice

Many countries experiencing a hot climate have also enjoyed a rapid development of their electrical distribution systems and building installations. Others have a long history of electrical installation work. In both cases the installation practice will vary from that found in more temperate climates due to its adaptation to suit the different installation conditions, installers' skills, and measures necessary to overcome the conditions of high temperature and humidity. Each particular country will have developed its own custom and practice to meet these requirements.

It is therefore important that a knowledge of these customs and practices should be known to the engineer and designer so as to ensure compatibility with existing work. Failure to do so will result in unfamiliarity by the local operation and maintenance staff with the possible risk of danger. This is particularly so when the local staff is contemplating any extension to a completed project.

3.8.5 Equipment suitable for the country

3.8.5.1 Need for adequate spare parts

Operating an electrical system in a hot climate requires a larger amount of spare parts than would be required for a similar installation in a more temperate climate. This is because wearing parts deteriorate more quickly, temperature sensitive devices expire more readily and safety devices operate more frequently. To allow for this a higher degree of maintenance is required. Unfortunately, this is one aspect in the life of an electrical installation which is sadly neglected. Electrical equipment must therefore be chosen so as to give the longest possible life with the minimum of maintenance. Further, should replacement parts be required, then they must be readily available from the local suppliers. Much valuable research can be undertaken by the engineer spending time browsing amongst the shelves of the electrical wholesalers who are operating in the particular country.

3.8.5.2 Appropriate technology

There is also a tendency by designers to transfer new but inappropriate technology onto inexperienced clients. Latest technology is often sensitive to temperature and supply conditions and may be quite unsuitable for installation in a hot climate. Well proven technology appropriate for the particular country employing 'solid' construction techniques is generally preferable to the 'state of the art' designs which are so popular with temperate climate designers.

If a 'technology transfer' is taking place in the design of the electrical installation, then it is preferable to adopt a distributed type system rather than a centralised one. By having several units distributed throughout the facility, the installation will still be able to function after the failure of one or maybe more units, albeit at a reduced level of performance.

3.8.5.3 Solar generation of heat

Long hours of sunshine will make solar generation a better prospect than is the case in temperate climates, particularly for water heating and providing cooling in air conditioning systems. However, the limitations of solar heating must be taken into account in practical applications, particularly in conversion to useful thermal energy. (See Section 2.2.3.7).

3.8.6 Effects of temperature and humidity

3.8.6.1 Availability of data

As has already been stated, the major limiting factor for any electrical installation in a hot climate is the effect of temperature and humidity. Reference to published data will give reasonable guidance on the highest temperature and humidity condition likely to be encountered in any particular country. Meteorological records are now more readily available for specific countries and even specific areas of each country. Reference should be made to these, if at all possible, so as to ensure the accuracy of the information being used as a basis for design.

Reliable meteorological records are kept at most airports and this data is in a standardised International format which usually includes the following on a daily and averaged monthly basis:

Dry bulb temperature – 24 hour maximum and minimum
Wet bulb temperature – 24 hour maximum and minimum
% Relative humidity – 24 hour maximum and minimum
Wind velocity and direction
Dust/obscuration factors
Barometric pressure.

As has been stated above, Codes of Practice, Standards and statutory Regulations may now be available and custom and practice will also provide guidance on how to meet the requirements in both hot and other climates. In many hot countries, it is possible to have periods of high humidity coincident with high temperature. Meteorological data will again confirm this information.

3.8.6.2 Overheating

The key criterion for electrical systems in hot climates is the upper limiting temperature at which it is safe to operate. Protection from overheating of both equipment and wiring is still the major safeguard to prevent danger and loss. In general, most electrical equipment and wiring systems dissipate heat generated whilst carrying current or whilst doing mechanical work. Cooling is normally achieved by allowing the heat to dissipate into the surrounding air. High ambient temperatures reduce the ability for the heat to be dissipated and hence most electrical equipment used in hot climates has to be derated for safe operation. Overheating leads to premature failure. Such failure affects the whole range of low and high voltage equipment normally found in buildings, including transformers, switchgear and lighting and small power services.

The normal failure is the breakdown of the insulation, often causing secondary failures. The rupturing of chokes and ballasts forming part of modern lighting control gear is a typical example. Overheating also causes cable insulation failure and can be even more dramatic with toxic fume release and subsequent fire hazard.

Overheating is a particular problem when cables are buried in the ground and whenever possible, this should be avoided. Any buried cable will dissipate less heat at the period of peak demand than one in air. In order to arrive at a reliable derating factor for a buried cable or group of cables, the following information is essential:

(a) The 'soil' absolute maximum temperature (which can be above the air temperature).
(b) The depth at which cables will be buried and the 'soil' temperature at that level.
(c) The 'soil' emissivity and resistivity.

In addition to these, a grouping factor must be applied to take into account the actual loads to be taken by the cables (equal loads should not be assumed.)

Even cables run within electrical trunking or builders work ducts must be reviewed to provide for the detrimental affects which might arise from inadequate ventilation of the closed space within which the cables are run. Grouping factors related to physical spacing, cable size and load, must also be analysed for trunking and ducted cable routes.

3.8.6.3 Condensation

Condensation caused when the temperature of the metal of the electrical installation falls below the surrounding air dew point temperature, can cause similar failures. Typical are tracking, insulation failure, oil contamination and accelerated corrosion. Examination of the external environmental data is therefore essential to any designer for the assessment of the conditions which are likely to affect the electrical installation.

The daily cycle of temperature and humidity change between night and day causes major changes in the ambient air conditions affecting the electrical installation. It is possible for condensation to form upon open terminal connections and other electrically insulated parts even in what is normally considered to be a dry desert environment. Figure 3.8.1 illustrates the 'high condensation' risk periods which occur under these conditions.

3.8.6.4 High ambient temperatures

In general, most electrical equipment is designed to operate in an ambient dry bulb temperature of up to 40°C. Higher ambient temperatures can be encountered but few places in the world have an outside ambient temperature much above 50°C for more than short periods, usually during the early afternoon. Electrical equipment, suitably derated, can operate at these elevated temperatures. The major problem which arises in practice, however, is where the electrical services are either exposed to direct solar gain or are installed in a building, where the external high ambient temperature coupled with the internal heat gains cause the electrical equipment to be exposed to temperatures well above the 50°C level. A typical example of such a condition occurs at the high level roof area of a power station operating in a hot climate.

Further derating of the equipment so that it is suitable for ambient temperatures of up to 60°C is possible but the output is so reduced as to make this an expensive

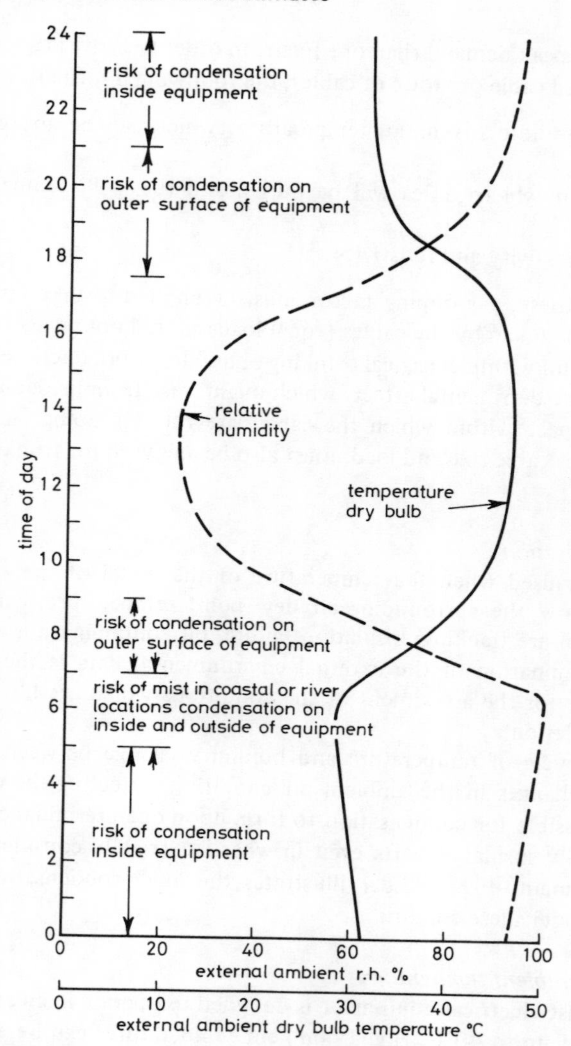

Fig. 3.8.1. *Typical cycle of temperature and humidity in middle Arabian Gulf area.*

proposition. It is then generally preferable to use higher standards of insulation, enhanced heat dissipation techniques or artificial cooling of the affected installation area. It must also be remembered that the electrical protection equipment and relays are often located in air conditioned areas which are generally maintained at lower temperatures than the equipment being protected. Special consideration should be given to the use of embedded temperature detectors or thermistors to monitor the temperature of the exposed electrical equipment.

Electrical equipment installed in air conditioned environments are often sized on the basis of the specified temperature and humidity being continuously maintained. Failure of the air conditioning equipment causes an additional problem. The temperature often rapidly rises and overheating of the electrical equipment results. Although immediate failure may not occur, it is to be anticipated that the life expectancy of the equipment will be much reduced. Therefore, plant which is required to operate continuously or during emergency conditions, should be selected for operation in the peak temperature conditions which may result on the failure of the air conditioning equipment. For this reason, a higher safety factor should be employed when selecting components for a system supplying emergency, back-up or essential services.

Fig. 3.8.2. *Example of disparity between design intent and installed result*

3.8.6.5 Location of equipment

Much can be done to mitigate the affect of the hot climate by carefully considering the location of the component parts of the electrical installation. For example, the highest temperatures are experienced at the top of the space. By mounting the equipment lower down, it is possible to operate the installation at more favourable temperatures, often within the influence of the air conditioning systems. As a general rule, it is preferable to keep the equipment away from the inside of external walls and roofs and an 'island' plant layout philosophy is to be recommended.

Finally, it is worthwhile considering the location of externally mounted equipment with regard to the shading provided by the buildings or other items of plant. Solar radiation not only raises the temperature of the electrical equipment but the ultraviolet radiation also causes considerable damage to plastic and other synthetic materials. If shading is not available, then consideration should be given to the provision of durable sun shades. Modification of the installation techniques can also provide a degree of protection particularly from ultraviolet radiation. For example, the use of an inverted cable tray installation can greatly extend the life of p.v.c. sheathed cables.

Fig. 3.8.3. *Severe corrosion caused by condensation and salt laden moisture.*

3.8.6.6 Intermittent operation

Frequent switching and operation of electrical equipment causes overheating problems wherever the electrical equipment is installed. Special electrical protection is required and it is often necessary to select motors, switches, contactors and cables to a higher quality to withstand this type of operation. This problem will be further accentuated if the equipment is installed in a hot climate. The equipment will have to be specially selected to make it suitable for operating in this mode.

3.8.7 Corrosion and other external factors

Other external factors affect the life of electrical equipment installed in hot climates. For example, corrosion damage due to rusting can be much accelerated and saline atmospheric attack is often more severe. Better paint systems and the greater use of galvanizing is to be recommended.

Strong winds, dust and sand storms are often features of a hot climate. External equipment must therefore be firmly fixed and all external openings designed to prevent the ingress of dust particles. The sand storms have a grit blasting affect on external surfaces and the protective coatings must be resistant to this type of erosion. Sand collecting around electrical equipment causes overheating problems. It is often desirable to locate equipment such as transformers in sand-storm resistant enclosures.

Soil conditions are also likely to be aggresive to buried equipment and may contain insects and termites with an appetite for plastic and other insulating materials. For example, the subkha (soil) of North Africa is highly corrosive to buried metal systems, and therefore the integrity of any external sheathing material must be ensured.

Besides the aggresive properties of the soils found in these locations, it must be remembered that additional problems can result from the wide variations of thermal and electrical resistivity. The assessment of current ratings of buried cables, high ohmic values for buried earth electrode systems and low conductivity of earth return paths, are typical. Further, the instability of the soil conditions, for example in desert regions, can cause additional problems with regard to buried services and particularly any buried earth electrode system.

In areas of high sunlight, problems from ultraviolet radiation attack can occur. Similarly, ozone attack, particularly in tropical sea-board applications, can significantly reduce the life of exposed insulants.

Finally, electrical equipment makes an excellent home for rodents, snakes and other animals and insects. Insulation can be stripped off to make nest and bedding material. Precautions must therefore be taken to prevent the entry of these "predators" into buildings and also into the electrical equipment. All deliberate openings must be adequately screened and all doors and covers properly gasketted.

3.8.8 Materials, standardisation and other local factors

Although most types of electrical equipment and installation materials are available in the countries which we are considering, it should be noted that many countries have financial difficulties, trade embargoes, import licensing and long shipping periods. All of these factors can severely affect the implementation of the designer's intentions. Again, research amongst the local wholesalers and import agents can be most rewarding. This research will enable the designer to select materials which are in common use and thus make the new design compatible with existing installations. This attempt at standardisation will be viewed as a courtesy by the recipient country's electrical engineers. Thus, to find a 240 V 13 A ring main socket outlet connected to a 110 V 60 Hz system should not come as a surprise!

Certain other local factors may well affect the ultimate success of the completed installation. Amongst these, the later substitution of cheaper and inferior products by the installing contractor and the wish of the owner to incorporate products of which he has the sole import or manufacturing licence, must be viewed as typical. Many more variations of this type of difficulty should be expected and will inevitably be encountered.

In conclusion, it will be seen that electrical installations in hot climates do require special precautions. Although most of these are of a normal engineering type, others are more difficult to predict since they will be particular for each country under consideration.

3.8.9 References

3.8.9.1 British Standards (See also Appendix 6.2)

British Standards relating to cables (e.g. BS 5467, BS 5468, BS 6004 etc) are of importance; BS CP 1014 gives guidance in the protection of elastic proven equipment against climatic conditions.

3.8.9.2 Bibliography

Regulations for Electrical Installations, (Institution of Electrical Engineers)
BICC (Wiring and General Cables) Ltd. Cable Materials: Publication No. 766.
AEI (Cables) Ltd: Publication RPD/5/M.
Property Services Agency: Technical Publications (M & E) Series.
CIBS Technical Memoranda 4: CIBS Design Notes for Middle East.
State of Qatar, Electricity Department Regulations.

Part 4
Environmental principles and technology

Grampian Regional Council Offices, Aberdeen

Chapter 4.1

Environmental control

Professor A.C. Hardy, M.A., B.Arch., Dip.T.P., A.R.I.B.A., M.R.T.P.I., C.C.I.B.S.
Professor of Building Science.
B. Warren, B.Sc.(Eng.), C.Eng., M.R.Ae.S., M.C.I.B.S. Lecturer.
T.J. Wiltshire, B.Eng.(Tech.), Ph.D., M.C.I.B.S. Lecturer

Building Science Section, School of Architecture, University of Newcastle upon Tyne

4.1.1 Introduction

Any building, from an energy point of view, is a complex system and the stages in this system can be divided into a number of interrelated parts. The first is the exposure of the building to the external environment, the microclimate of the site. This is not only determined by its geographic location but also by ground conditions, exposure and height.

The aim in the design of the building enclosure is to ensure that this is capable of modifying the external conditions so that the energy required to maintain an acceptable internal climate is minimised. While in the past consideration was usually given only to the energy needed in winter, today we must also look at the acceptability of the summer conditions, as overheating by either internal or solar gains or both can increase energy consumption for air conditioning or fan power. Not only has building shape and form to be considered in the context of external exposed surfaces relative to the enclosed volume or floor area, but also orientation, glazing area and location must be taken into account.

Following on the consideration of the three dimensional building form comes the specification of performance of the building enclosure, including such factors as thermal insulation, thermal time lag, the temperature conductivity of internal surfaces, solar gain and glazing area and the airtightness of the construction. It must be remembered that in certain circumstances it is possible to over-insulate as well as to over-glaze. At this stage of the design checks have to be made on the risks of interstitial condensation.

Although work can be undertaken to produce a thermally efficient building enclosure, all the advantages of this can be lost if the environmental services performance is not matched to the building thermal response, the requirements of thermal comfort and the pattern of occupation of the proposed building. At this stage energy choice is an important decision as this can affect the basic planning of the building, the space required for plant rooms, service distribution and access for service maintenance. In an elementary way it has been found that space can be saved if energy is distributed vertically in liquids and horizontally by air.

As building services maintenance is usually very inadequate it is important that all plant is readily accessible and that sections of plant can be easily removed and replaced. Often plant malfunctions which affect energy are not discovered unless there is thermal discomfort. It is important therefore that monitoring systems are installed for early identification of malfunction.

Even if all these measures are taken by the designers, the occupants of the building can still overcome all its advantages by misuse of controls, not realising their effects on plant operation. It is important therefore that controls are not accessible to inexperienced personnel, but only to qualified engineers. It is equally important that all new building installations are properly commissioned. Often commissioning is at fault in that it may only reveal that a control is working but not necessarily correctly. Controls have often been incorrectly wired up and motorised valves and fans operating in reverse.

Unless great care is taken at all stages in design installation and plant operation the building and its environmental system can never operate to achieve its predicted performance specification.

4.1.2 Design approach

4.1.2.1 Building construction

Traditional buildings constructed of indigenous materials usually provided adequate elementary climatic protection in that they kept out precipitation and provided shelter from the wind. The relatively poor environmental conditions at this time were overcome by the adaptation of the user. For example, the low internal temperatures were offset to a large degree by the much higher insulation value of the clothing worn indoors at that time.

In this century we have seen great changes in building design (Ref. 1), as a result of developments in construction and methods and materials, and the rising standards of the internal environmental conditions considered as being acceptable by the occupants. In the latter part of the 19th century the masonry and timber loadbearing wall construction was rapidly being replaced, first by cast iron frames, then by both concrete and steel frames in the larger buildings. This resulted in the loss of the thick loadbearing wall and limited window areas due to the structural limitations on spanning openings in the wall. The invention of the elevator made possible high rise framed buildings. The results of these developments brought about larger glazed areas as the external walls were non-loadbearing, lower thermal insulation standards because of thinner external cladding, and loss of thermal time lag. High rise buildings were also exposed to a more rigorous climate. The majority of these factors resulted in higher energy consumption for both heating and cooling, but this loss in the performance of the building envelope was not considered to be an important factor in building design.

It was in the early 1950's when problems first arose. The large frame structures which, before 1940, had often been clad in traditional heavyweight materials such as brick, stone or concrete, were now predominantly clad in glass and opaque external cladding panels with the minimum of thermal insulation and time lag (Ref. 2). As these frames were no longer clad in monolithic wet forms of construction but in prefabricated cladding with joints filled with mastic or gaskets, their ability to resist wind penetration was much reduced. In any case the life of mastic or gaskets was often less than 10 years, but these were not often replaced if rain did not penetrate, although the air infiltration rate became much greater.

There was an increasing number of building designs in which the internal environment was becoming more and more difficult to control. The servicing of these buildings became costly, both to provide and to operate, and the rising cost of fuel led to increasing concern. It was realised that the existing design process, although able to cope with construction and aesthetics, was inadequate in terms of building performance, since the relationship between the performance of the building enclosure and the internal environment had largely been neglected.

This situation arose as buildings were designed by the traditional fragmented design process. The architect designed a sketch scheme to solve a three-dimensional spatial problem which was then passed on to a structural engineer to solve a structural problem; afterwards these developed schemes were handed to a heating, ventilating and air conditioning engineer to solve a thermal problem. By this stage in the design process it was not possible to alter either the thermal performance of the building or the structural system, that often causes obstruction to the thermal distribution system. The architect, at the commencement of the project, had not set out to design a specific building type in a thermal sense, but the decision on the necessary environmental system was taken by the heating, ventilating and air conditioning engineer at a later stage in the design process (Ref. 3).

4.1.2.2 Integrated design

In an attempt to rectify the fragmented approach to design which was leading to reduced standards of performance an 'Integrated Design' philosophy was introduced during the late 1960's. Central to this approach was the idea that the thermal performance and cost of the building and its associated services should be considered together. In practice this meant that architects, engineers and quantity surveyors formed a team, the disparate skills of which were used to manipulate certain aspects of design to ensure that they were considered within a design framework which enabled a solution to be produced based on an agreed set of priorities. Because of the agreed priorities, the building forms produced had a high

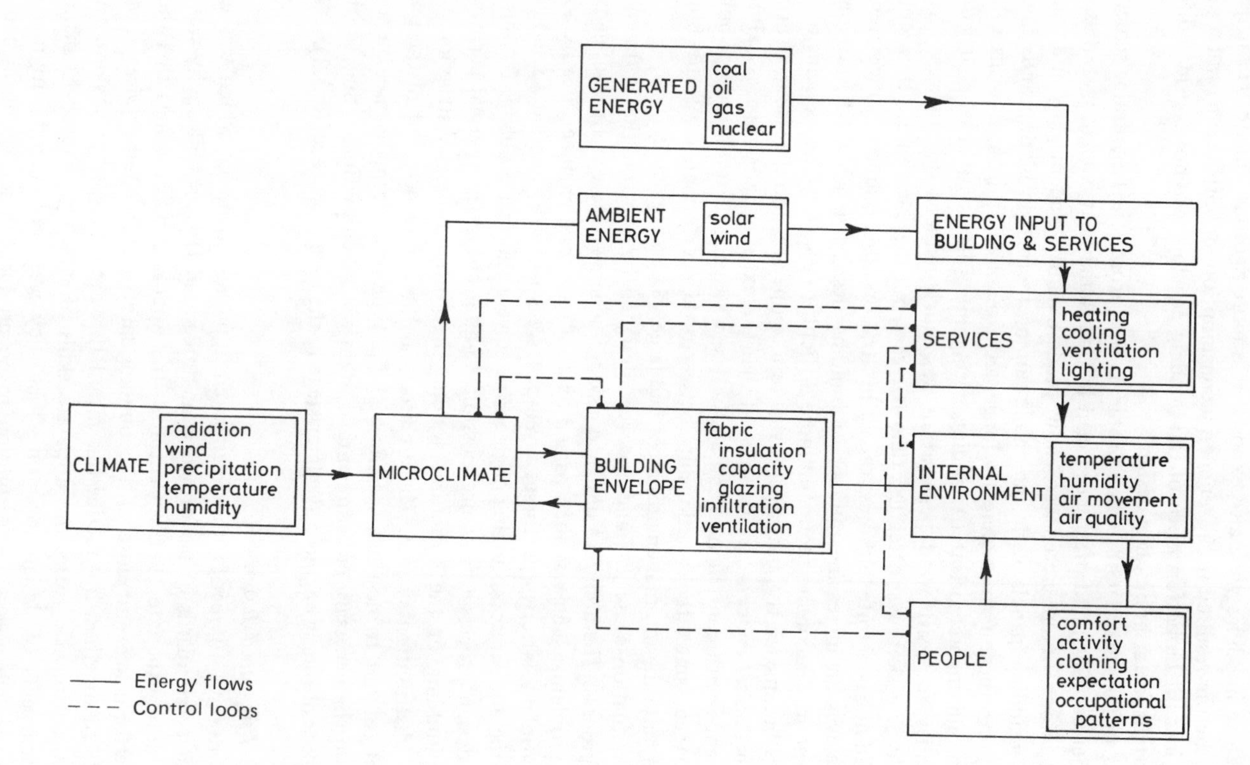

Fig. 4.4.1. *Diagram of building energy system*

degree of climatic modification with sophisticated services, often with heat recovery, producing a closely controlled internal environment. Since then, considerable effort and research has been put into examining the performance relationships between the various aspects of building design, and designers have been encouraged to adopt a design philosophy embracing the total system. Fig. 4.1.1 is one representation of such a system and includes not only climate, building and services but also people, interactions, and feedback loops within the system.

In some building types it may be possible to change the standards of the internal environment and let the occupants adjust to the conditions which may occur by, for example, adjusting their clothing, a means of 'control' that tends to be neglected in many modern buildings where the occupants have become accustomed to fairly rigid environmental standards. To allow temperatures to rise in summer and fall in winter, energy may often be saved and the load on the building/services combination eased. Whilst the needs of the user in terms of his expectations have to be taken into account, to implement such an approach requires a questioning of environmental standards, a move away from a fixed optimum to an appreciation that there is a range of conditions under which users will not suffer discomfort providing that the rate of change is within acceptable limits. It is also presupposed that there are control systems which can be employed to achieve this situation.

4.1.3 Climate

4.1.3.1 Climatic data

In order to achieve acceptable internal conditions the building and its services must be designed to cope with the external conditions to which they will be subjected, and to this end a knowledge of the climate is required. It is also becoming more and more necessary, because of rising fuel costs, to be able to predict the energy consumption of buildings and to take as much advantage as possible of available ambient energy. It is first necessary to obtain a broad appreciation of climatic conditions.

In the UK, although the design temperature is often taken as $-1°C$, absolute minimum temperatures as low as $-17{\cdot}5°C$ have been recorded for short periods around dawn in inland areas far removed from water masses. If the average annual frequency of days when the shade air temperature does not rise above 0°C is studied it will be found that this varies from 1 day per year on the South Coast up to 5 days per year on high ground in inland areas in the North of England and Scotland. Coastal areas usually do not have more than 2 days per year with shade air temperatures not exceeding 0°C. The inland areas of the South East of England have the highest number of days when the shade air temperature exceeds 26°C, being 10 in number, while in other areas this temperature is reached for rarely more than one day per year.

Average annual wind speeds vary widely in relation to geographic location. The lowest average wind speeds are in the low altitude plain areas of Central England which have average annual wind speeds of less than 16 km/h (4.4 m/s). The next lowest average annual wind speed is on the South Coast of England, 20 km/h (5.6 m/s). The East and West Coasts of England have average annual wind speeds of 24 km/h (6.7 m/s) and the highest average wind speeds of 28 km/h (7.8 m/s) are in the North West of Scotland. Wind speed also varies with height. Average annual wind speeds of up to 40 km/h (11·1 m/s) can occur on sites of 150 m altitude and up to 44 km/h (12.2 m/s) on sites at 300 m altitude.

Information on the direction of the prevailing wind and winds of highest velocity can be obtained from local meteorological wind rose diagrams as these vary considerably in different parts of the country.

Data on the Driving Rain Index is published by the Building Research Establishment (Ref. 4). The Driving Rain Index is a unit calculated from the annual rainfall in millimetres multiplied by the average wind speed in m/s divided by 1000, and applies to facades facing the wind direction. The index ranges numerically from 3 to higher than 10. For a Driving Rain Index of 3 or below, which only occurs in South East England away from the coast, the exposure is described as Sheltered. For a Driving Rain Index of between 3 and 7 the exposure is Moderate, except in areas within 8 km of a coastline or estuary where the description Moderate applies only to an Index of between 3 and 5. The description Severe applies to an Index of 7 or more, or 5 or more in areas within 8 km of a coastline or estuary.

The Driving Rain Index map of the UK shows that, in general, the least driving rain is in the South East of the Country and the highest in the West and North West. It should be noted, however, that for buildings on open high ground, higher than their surroundings in built-up areas, the Driving Rain Index should be taken as one grade more severe than the general area.

The average annual mean of percentage of possible bright sunshine varies from 40% in the South East and South Coasts to 35% on the South West Coast, 30% on Central and North and West Coasts of England, and 25% in North West Coasts of Scotland. The interior areas of England receive between 25% to 30% and the interior of Scotland 20%. The average annual number of days with more than nine hours of bright sunshine is similarly distributed, with between 60 and 70 days in the South and South East Coasts reducing North Westwards to less than 30 days in North West Scotland.

The highest intensity of solar radiation is on the vertical facades of a building when the sun is at an altitude of between 30–38° above the horizon, with an intensity of some 600 W/m^2. This maximum solar gain occurs in the months of March and September when the sun has an azimuth of between 144° to 217°.

As the UK has a Temperate Maritime Climate it has a high relative humidity throughout the year. Relative humidity, however, has to be related to temperature as for a given air moisture content the relative humidity varies in relation to air temperature. The higher the air temperature the lower the relative humidity for a given moisture content. Published data is usually related to the relative humidity at midday when the air temperatures are high and the relative humidity lowest. On this basis the annual average relative humidity in the UK is 80% for coastal areas and 70% for central inland areas.

While there is a large amount of meteorological data available in published form, this is usually collected for the specific purpose of weather forecasting and therefore relates to the climatic conditions in the free air mass high above the ground level. The actual climatic conditions experienced near to the ground are considerably modified by the physical properties of the ground, geographic location, local topography and vegetation, and the built environment. Local climatic conditions are known as microclimate when related to a specific site. The environment in which buildings are built is therefore one of microclimate. T.R. Oke (Ref. 5) recognises this area as the Turbulent Surface layer which is characterised by small scale turbulence generated by the surface roughness and convection. This layer extends, depending on climatic conditions and time of day, for a distance between approximately 1 and 10 m above the earth's surface.

4.1.3.2 Microclimatic effects

The effect of such influences as geographic location, local topography and vegetation, and the built environment produces a wide range of microclimatic conditions which cannot be described by normally available meteorological data. The total range of effects cannot be covered here but typical well-known examples are the funnelling effect on winds produced by valleys and the diurnal changes in local winds brought about by convection currents set up due to differences in the thermal properties of adjacent surfaces. Typical of the latter are the onshore and offshore breezes resulting from the different properties of the land and the sea. With particular reference to buildings the surroundings considerably influence the amount of solar radiation received and the longwave radiation losses from the building itself. Surrounding buildings may be seen to act as heat generators which can produce measurable local temperature changes. This is the so-called 'heat island' effect produced by large conurbations.

4.1.3.3 Use of climatic data

The way in which buildings and services designs have developed, the expectations of their occupants, and the increasing interest in energy conservation, has led to a considerable change in the type of weather information required. Taking the U.K. as an example, the information required can be listed as follows, in terms of chronological development:

(a) *Winter design*
Information in this category is needed to enable heating systems to be designed to cope with the worst winter conditions normally expected whilst at the same time ensuring that systems are not oversized. The majority of designers use the CIBS Guide (Ref. 6) as their source of weather information which provides some basic cold weather frequency data for a limited number of geographical locations. This enables the designer to select the external design temperature most suitable to his particular case. The influence of solar radiation is usually neglected. Information concerning external relative humidity may be necessary to determine winter humidification requirements.

(b) *Summer design*

Warm weather data is required to enable estimates of heat gains to be made for the calculation of air conditioning loads. In non-air conditioned buildings it may also be necessary to predict the peak temperatures likely to occur inside a building. The information required is more complex than for the Winter Design requiring a knowledge not only of external temperatures and how they vary but also of solar radiation. In the latter case, due to the unpredictable nature of, amongst other things, cloud cover, recourse must normally be made to tabulated theoretical data (Ref. 6). The calculation of heat flow through opaque building elements is facilitated by use of the concept of 'sol-air temperature' which is derived from the combined effect of air temperature and solar radiation and takes into account the absorptivity, emissivity and surface resistance of the building element under consideration. (Section 4.4.2.3)

Data on sun position in terms of azimuth and altitude for different locations, seasons, and times of day may also be required for the design of particular building elements such as windows and shading devices. This information is readily available either from Sunpath diagrams (Ref. 7) or as tabulated data (Ref. 6).

In the design of air conditioning systems a knowledge of external relative humidity is necessary for the calculation of humidification and dehumidification requirements.

4.1.3.4 Energy consumption

In order to be able to predict the energy consumption of buildings, more factual data is required, and information on extreme conditions only is no longer appropriate. The concept of degree days provides a measure of the severity of cold weather or a month by month basis which can be used to predict the heating consumption of buildings and more recently the CIBS Example Weather Year (Ref. 8) has been introduced. This comprehensive compilation of temperature data is based on Kew for the period 1st October, 1964, to 30th September, 1965. This 'year' can be used as a reference year for the purpose of facilitating comparative predictions of energy consumption. The tabulated information currently available only covers dry bulb temperatures but it is expected that information on wet bulb temperatures, solar radiation, wind speed and direction, and sol-air temperature will soon be available. This additional data will enable comparative cooling energy consumption estimates to be made.

4.1.3.5 Availability of ambient energy

Energy from the sun is increasingly being used to complement the more conventional fossil fuel sources, and for designers to take full advantage of this a comprehensive knowledge of the intensity and availability of solar radiation is required. To provide detailed microclimatic information for the design of buildings is not practically possible and one must therefore depend on the information produced from weather stations. The needs of building design are however producing a demand for more sophisticated information.

4.1.4 Building enclosure

4.1.4.1 Building enclosure. Climatic modification

The building enclosure performs a variety of different functions, chief amongst which are to provide security for the occupants and a barrier between the internal environment and the exterior. In thermal terms a perfect barrier cannot be provided and in reality the building serves to modify the effects of the external climate with respect to the internal environment. Because of this the thermal function of the building enclosure is often described in terms of its 'climatic modification'. One of the major problems facing a building designer is to provide a high degree of climatic modification, whilst at the same time ensuring that the building is aesthetically acceptable.

The building enclosure modifies the effect of the external climate mainly by virtue of its thermal insulation, which controls the amount of heat transmitted through the structure and also because it provides a time delay to changes in the

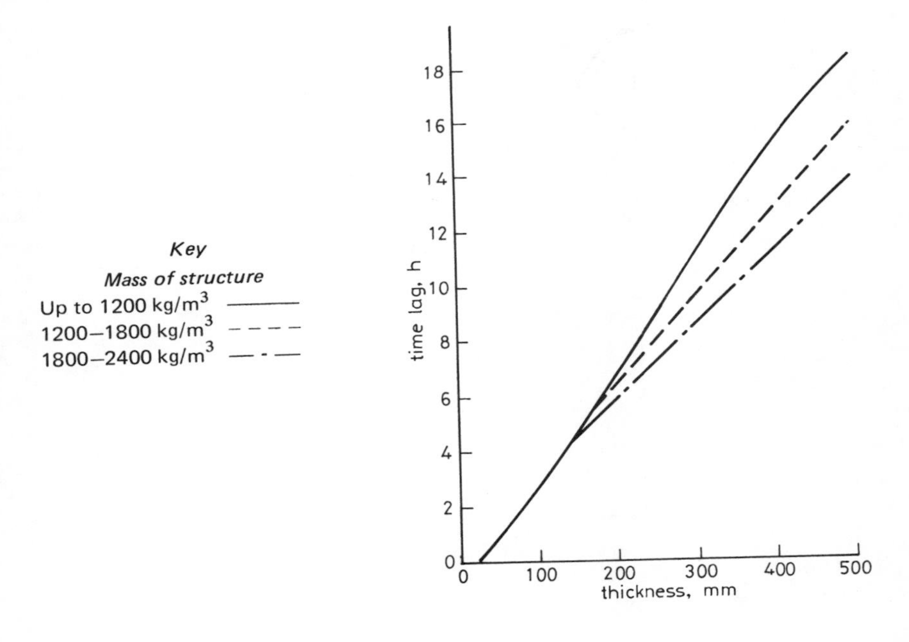

Fig. 4.1.2. *Thermal time lag*

external conditions. This delay is often known as 'time lag' and is a function of the building materials used, their thermal properties and the thickness of the construction. Heavyweight materials such as masonry transmit temperature changes more rapidly than lightweight materials such as insulation, and for constructions of the same thickness the time lag for a heavyweight construction is less than that for a lightweight construction. In practice, however, heavyweight constructions are considerably thicker than lightweight and therefore usually have a longer time lag. Fig. 4.1.2 shows how time lag typically varies for different thicknesses of masonry construction.

A further climatic modification aspect is that when a building element, such as a wall, is subject to varying external temperature the temperature changes are reduced in magnitude when they penetrate to the internal surface. This reduction is described by the Decrement Factor which again mainly depends on the thickness of the element. Fig. 4.1.3 gives typical decrement factors for different element thicknesses. (See also section 4.4.2.3)

Since building elements are often not homogeneous constructions but are more likely comprised of 'layers' of different materials having different thicknesses and thermal properties their dynamic performance is complex and can normally only be solved by the use of mathematical models and the application of computers.

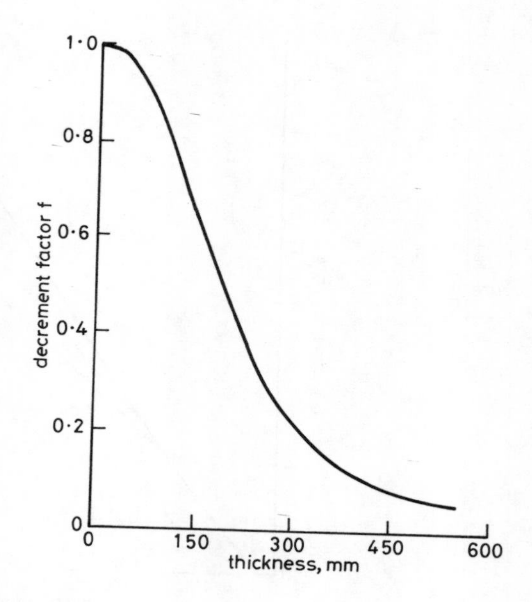

Fig. 4.1.3. *Decrement factor* (CIBS)

4.1.4.2 Thermal storage

The building fabric, by virtue of its mass and specific heat, also acts as an energy store and this property can be utilized by the designer. In general, buildings of heavyweight construction, when they are heated, store large amounts of energy which may be released into the interior to offset the fall in overnight temperatures. When lightweight constructions are used the energy stored will be small and thus these buildings will experience lower overnight temperatures when intermittent heating is used. In the design of some solar heated buildings the storage effect is used as a way of absorbing solar energy during the day and releasing it when required.

This explanation of thermal storage is, of course, much simplified and is considerably influenced by the amount and position of insulation in the structure. In general terms, however, the building fabric may be likened to a 'thermal flywheel' which evens out energy fluctuations resulting from changing external and internal conditions.

4.1.4.3 Room response

The response of room temperature to variations in internal energy input is largely determined by the materials used on internal linings. Lightweight (insulating) linings will heat up quickly and allow both air temperature and mean radiant temperature to rapidly meet comfort requirements. In the summer, however, this means that incidental energy inputs, from the sun for example, can produce overheating. The way in which the room surfaces respond to changes in energy input is described by their 'Admittance'.

For more detailed descriptions of the building envelope performance the reader is referred to Chapter 4.2, and to Sections A3, A5 and A8 of the CIBS Guide.

4.1.4.4 Design aspects

(a) *Opaque building elements*

As the majority of building types use the greatest proportion of their energy requirements for space heating, the higher the level of thermal insulation the lower will the energy requirement be. The insulation requirements for buildings are covered by the Building Regulations, Parts F and FF, Part F applying to domestic buildings only. (Ref. 9) As a general rule the walls, roofs and floors of buildings designed to Part FF must have a maximum 'U' value, the thermal transmittance, of 0·6 $W/m^2 \,^{\circ}C$. There are, however, certain exceptions. Dwellings, covered by Part F, have different standards and Part F now requires insulation values of 0·6 $W/m^2 \,^{\circ}C$ for external walls and 0·35 $W/m^2 \,^{\circ}C$ for roofs and ceilings. No regulations cover the other aspects of thermal performance. (See also section 4.2.2.5)

(b) *Provision of insulation*

A wide variety of insulating materials and methods of application is used in building. The most common materials are mineral fibres and cellular plastics and they occur in a variety of forms ranging from loose fill types to rigid slabs. Some plastic materials such as ureaformaldehyde may be foamed in situ.

Walls may be insulated either within their thickness using, for example, cavity fill materials or at the inner or outer surface. The method used will affect the thermal performance of the wall differently. On new buildings it is usually cheapest and most effective to provide cavity insulation. Roofs may be insulated similarly although in pitched roof designs it is often cheaper and more effective to provide the insulation directly over the ceiling rather than on the underface of the sloping portion. Ground floors, by virtue of the ground beneath them often provide relatively good insulation if they are large in area and do not have a high perimeter to area ratio. Where floors need to be insulated, this is often achieved by treatment of the edges only, using vertically placed slab material, as this is the area of highest heat loss.

With high levels of insulation especially, extra care must be taken to ensure that condensation is avoided. The need to reduce energy consumption and the consequent need for higher insulation levels may require considerable re-appraisal of methods of building construction.

The detail design of buildings must be given careful attention since although different building elements may perform well thermally, the way in which they are integrated into the building can cause problems. One such problem is that of 'cold bridging' which is often caused by local structural elements, such as concrete lintels, with poor thermal insulation values. These elements may form a high heat loss 'bridge' directly connecting the inside of the building to the outside. Cold bridges can give rise to local condensation as well as reducing the overall level of insulation of the building. Also, it is particularly important to pay attention to the detail design of joints and openings in the building envelope to ensure that air leakage (infiltration) is reduced to a minimum. Any ventilation over and above that normally required for the operation of the building and the well being of its occupants results in unwanted energy consumption.

(c) *Windows*

Since windows generally constitute the elements of a building having the highest 'U' value, $5{\cdot}7\ W/m^2\ {}^\circ C$ in the case of single glazing, a great deal of attention must be paid to their design and the areas of glazing used.

The window is important because its functional requirements of letting in light and air and providing a view conflict with its poor thermal performance. It does, however, have the merit of admitting solar radiation which can offset the winter heat losses. In certain circumstances this may result in the window becoming a net provider of heat energy, this aspect being taken advantage of by the provision of large areas of south facing glazing in some 'solar' building designs. The seasonal heat balance of a window is, however, difficult to determine and mistakes may easily be made since a large number of factors have to be taken into account.

As far as Building Regulations are concerned the high heat loss characteristics of windows are normally offset by limiting the glazed areas, although some provision is made for trading off window area against improved 'U' values if it can be shown that similar thermal performance can be achieved.

Although the window is traditionally used for providing ventilation it has the shortcomings that it is often not easily adjustable over the full range of ventilation requirements. Ventilation is required at a high rate to control temperatures in the summer but at a very much lower rate to combat condensation in the winter. In houses especially there is a trend towards the Scandinavian practice of providing a well fitting window that can be kept shut in the winter, and using a separate, finely controllable, ventilator for condensation control purposes. As far as traditional windows are concerned the vertical sliding sash type provides better ventilation control than, for example, the horizontal centre pivot type.

4.1.4.5 Interactions

The performance of the building envelope and its ultimate effect on the internal environment and services may be considerably influenced by the actions of the occupants. They may be allowed to control window and ventilator openings and provide a measure of solar control by adjusting blinds and curtains. Depending upon conditions these actions may result in either an increase or a decrease in the energy requirements of the environmental services since the people will generally only make adjustments to suit their own comfort requirements. From the designer's point of view a decision may have to be made therefore on the degree of control exercised by the occupants.

4.1.5 User needs

4.1.5.1 General

The users of a building will have particular requirements in terms of the internal environment of which the designer must be aware since they can influence, amongst other things, the design of the building envelope. User needs, as considered here, are those requirements of the internal environment that enable the occupants of a building to carry out their function in a comfortable and efficient manner though these two requirements may, in certain cases, conflict. It must also be borne in mind that user needs with respect to the building function may entail the provision of particular environments, as for example, that of a cold store, which may conflict with normal personal comfort standards.

The range of environments required in buildings is extremely wide and depends not only on the function of the building, but the expectations of the user. The environment in a discotheque is usually extremely different from that of a concert hall and neither would be acceptable in an office. The user of a building not only has his own interpretation of when he is comfortable, but also has certain expectations regarding the type of building he is using. The occupants of an automatically controlled air conditioned building may be much more critical of conditions over which they have no control than the occupants of a naturally ventilated heated only building where perhaps some degree of personal control over the environment is possible by adjusting radiators or windows.

Comfort has been defined as 'that state of mind that expresses satisfaction with the environment' (Fanger) (Ref. 10) and as such varies to a certain extent from one individual to another.

The designer has, in effect, the task of producing a physical interpretation of the expectation of the building user. To do this he must have a knowledge of the physical conditions which are generally accepted as producing comfort. Individuals are, of course, able to adjust their own comfort conditions within a given environment, to a certain degree. In the case of thermal comfort, for example, adjustments to clothing may be made so that a number of individuals may feel comfortable in an environment in which, if they were all dressed alike, only one or two would be satisfied.

4.1.5.2 Thermal comfort

The major aspects of the internal environment which the designer must consider are those relating to thermal comfort, including ventilation, lighting and acoustics.

All human beings produce heat, the amount depending on the degree of physical activity and a basic requirement is that the heat produced by the body is balanced by the heat lost. If the rate of heat production exceeds the rate of heat loss then the body temperature will rise until, in the extreme case, death results. On the other hand, if the body loses heat at a greater rate then it can be produced, the body temperature will fall and again can finally cause death. Between these extremes the human being survives under varying degrees of discomfort, from being too hot to being too cold. In order to be comfortable not only must there be a heat loss/heat gain balance but the various mechanisms by which the body loses heat must also be in a favourable relationship.

Sensible heat loss from the body, that which depends on the difference between skin temperature and the temperature of the surroundings, takes place in three ways:

(a) By direct conduction to surfaces in which it is in contact, e.g., from the feet to a cold concrete floor.
(b) By conduction through the skin and clothing to the outer surfaces and thence by convection to the surrounding air.
(c) By radiation from the body surfaces to surrounding objects.

In this case exposed skin surfaces will be most sensitive to radiation losses. Latent heat loss is a result of moisture being evaporated by body heat and rejected by the body. Under normal conditions latent heat is rejected mainly as moisture in exhaled air but under more extreme conditions sweating takes place. The rate at which heat is lost by this means will depend also on the humidity of the surrounding air and its rate of movement. The body is able to control its rate of heat losses within certain limits by several mechanisms. The blood vessels near the skin surface may be constricted or dilated to reduce or increase the rate of heat transfer, the hairs on the skin surface may be raised (goose pimples) or lowered to reduce or increase its conductivity and the rate of moisture transpiration may be changed. These mechanisms are involuntary in nature and any further control of heat loss must be provided by positive action on the part of the individual. He can either change his activity, change his clothing or change his environment.

Under normal, comfortable conditions about 115 W of heat is liberated by the body, of which approximately 75% is by convection and radiation and 25% by evaporation. Conduction is usually only a small quantity since generally only the feet are in contact with uninsulated surfaces.

The major factors upon which thermal comfort depends are therefore:

(a) The activity level
(b) The type and quantity of clothing
(c) The temperature of the air
(d) The rate of air movement over the body
(e) The relative humidity of the air
(f) The temperatures of the surrounding surfaces (the 'mean radiant' temperature)

Of the above factors, the first two are effectively under the control, to a certain degree, of the individual, whilst the remainder may be the result of design by the architect and services engineer. Air temperature may, under certain circumstances, be controlled by the individual by, for example, adjusting a thermostat, although the means of control would be provided by the engineer. (Relative humidity is the ratio of actual moisture vapour pressure to the moisture vapour pressure when the air is saturated at the same temperature. Percentage relative humidity is sometimes quoted but this is a meaningless term without reference to air temperature.) The relationship between the above factors is complex but Fanger (Ref. 10) has derived a Comfort Equation with which it is possible for selected clothing insulation and activity values to calculate the combinations of air temperature, mean radiant temperature, humidity and air velocity conducive to comfort.

Since one's state of comfort is a subjective response to the physical environment, actual values of the various environmental parameters concerned can only be obtained by evaluating the response of test subjects under a wide variety of conditions.

4.1.5.3 Resultant temperature

Various attempts have been made to produce a single number measurement of the internal environment to describe its acceptability in terms of comfort. Of these comfort indices the Resultant Temperature is that recommended for use in the UK and is given by:

$$t_{res} = \frac{t_r + t_{ai}\sqrt{10v}}{1 + \sqrt{10v}} \qquad (4.1.1)$$

where

t_{ai} = inside air temperature (°C)

t_r = mean radiant temperature (°C)

t_{res} = resultant temperature (°C)

v = air velocity (m/s)

The resultant temperature is the temperature measured at the centre of a blackened globe 100 mm in diameter. It takes no account of humidity, which has only a small effect on comfort as long as it lies between about 40% and 70% RH. At low air

Table 4.1.1 *Resultant Temperature °C*

Building Type	
Assembly Halls, Lecture Theatres, Bars, Churches, Chapels	18
Offices	20
Living Rooms	21
Swimming Pools	26

(CIBS)

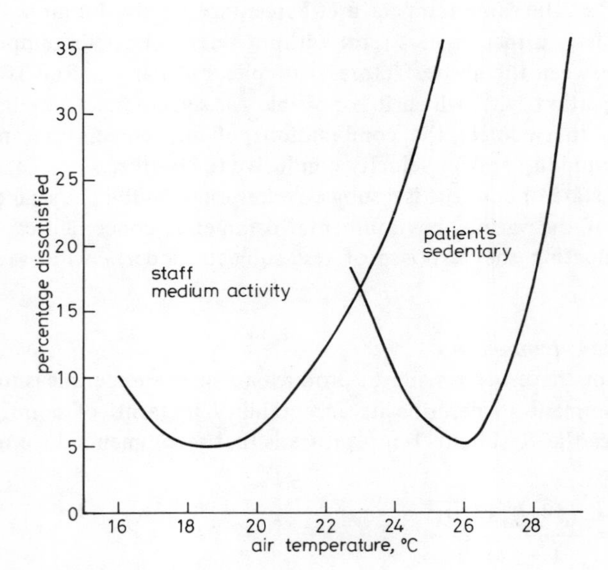

Fig. 4.1.4. *Comfort in a geriatric ward*

speeds when $v = 0{\cdot}1$ m/s the equation simplifies to

$$t_{\text{res}} = \tfrac{1}{2}t_r + \tfrac{1}{2}t_{ai} \qquad (4.1.2)$$

Table 4.1.1 gives some examples from Section A1 of the CIBS Guide of values of resultant temperature for a range of different conditions.

As the mean radiant temperature depends on such factors as the wall construction, area of glazing and carpeting of a building, the architect will have an influence on the way a space performs with respect to comfort.

Particular care must also be taken when designing spaces in which people are engaged in different activities, since their comfort requirements may differ widely. Fig. 4.1.4 shows the theoretical comfort requirements for a geriatric ward where the designer is concerned with both the comfort of the patients and the nursing staff.

Even though the designer may provide acceptable conditions overall, people may still experience discomfort if asymmetric conditions exist, as, for example, in the case of a large temperature difference between foot and head level or if a person is seated adjacent to a cold window.

For a full discussion of all aspects of comfort the reader is referred to the CIBS Guide. (Ref. 11).

4.1.5.4 Ventilation

All buildings need to be ventilated, either naturally or mechanically, in order to provide a safe and acceptable environment. The amount of air required to meet

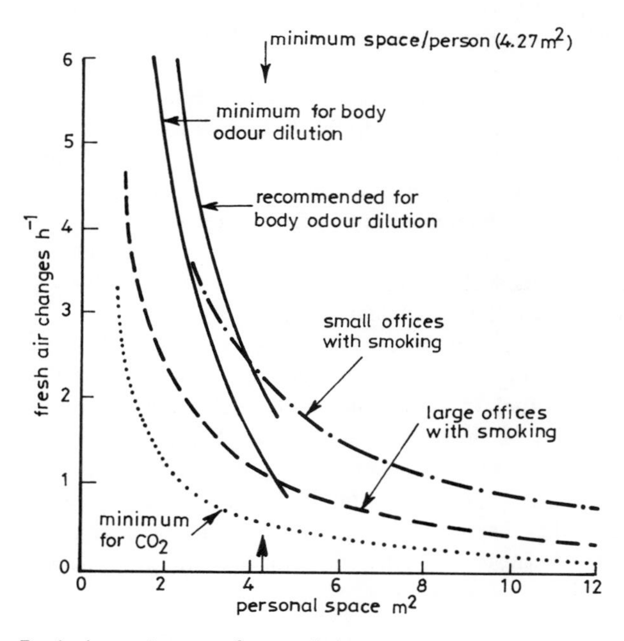

Fig. 4.1.5. *Fresh air requirements for people in a room* (CIBS)

oxygen requirements is very small and ventilation is generally required to remove contaminants. In buildings such as offices and dwellings the main contaminants are odours produced by the occupants themselves, either from the body or, for example, when smoking or cooking. The ventilation rate for odour control depends not only on the number of people occupying a given space, but also on the space occupied per person and the activity carried out. As the provision of ventilation entails the use of energy either to heat the incoming air or to provide fan power it is most important that no more ventilation is supplied than is necessary for its particular function.

Fig. 4.1.5 gives the basic ventilation requirements related to personal space for a lightly active person. (See also section 4.3.1.1)

4.1.6 Services and energy

4.1.6.1 Energy requirements of buildings

The mechanical and electrical services provided in buildings, although widely varying in type and complexity, have one thing in common, that is they use or provide the means for using energy. The environmental services are, in the majority of buildings, the most important as not only do they make the largest contribution to the capital and running costs but they are also related to, and should be designed complementary to, the performance of the building. Over half of the UK energy consumption is attributable to heating, lighting and other environmental services in buildings.

In many cases a choice exists between investing capital in the building or in the services to achieve the same end result; but assuming that the designer has made this choice he is faced with a further set of decisions, namely, that relating the capital cost of the services, their energy consumption, and running costs, to arrive at an overall cost in use. Probably the most important decision is that of choosing the fuel for heating and domestic hot water. This choice will not only depend on the more obvious aspects such as cost per unit of energy, convenience in use, space requirements, etc., but on the actual heating energy required.

A situation of changing fuel prices does, however, mean that the designer has to make long term predictions based on very inadequate data, especially uncertainty over long term costs of fuel. It is becoming increasingly necessary to ensure that the least amount of energy as possible is used within buildings, and it is efficiently utilized. This approach inevitably means that more money must be spent on providing efficient systems. In many existing buildings large quantities of energy are wasted as emphasis has been put on providing environmental services at a low capital cost and largely neglecting efficiency since, at the time of design, fuel costs were regarded as of lesser consequence.

4.1.6.2 Building performance specification

Before commencing the design of the environmental services the engineer must determine the requirements of the building and its user in order to prepare a performance specification. Heat gains and losses must be established and the internal environmental conditions required. It may also be necessary to establish the pattern of heat gains and losses as this can influence the capacity of the plant and its energy consumption. In air conditioned office buildings, for example, the maximum cooling load may not occur until late afternoon and there may be no necessity to provide plant to meet this condition since the occupants will be leaving the building anyway at the end of the working day. Failure to appreciate aspects such as this can lead to oversized plant which will not only cost more but in all probability will be inefficient to run.

4.1.6.3 Incidental energy gains

Virtually all buildings will have incidental energy gains from a variety of sources. The most important are usually the gains from solar radiation, the heat given out by people, and that given out by artificial lighting. An estimate must also be made of the energy usage of items of plant such as fans and pumps as well as that of office machinery which may appear as heat gains within the building. With a knowledge of the energy gains and losses the designer is able to predict the performance of his design and ensure that energy gains to the building are utilized efficiently, the aim being to ensure that no energy is rejected from the building as a whole unless absolutely necessary.

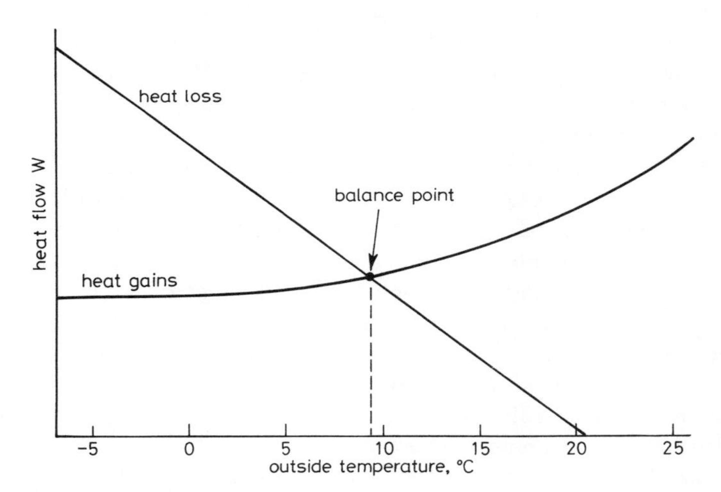

Fig. 4.1.6. ***Heating requirement of a building***

Fig. 4.1.6 is a simple diagram showing the relationship between the steady state heat loss of a building and its incidental energy gains from which it is seen that by utilizing incidental gains the heating requirement of a building may be reduced.

In many buildings situations exist at certain times of the year when some zones may require heating at the same time that other areas require cooling and the designer must endeavour to ensure that his system can transfer energy from one zone to another rather than treating them separately. A strategy may thus be determined as to how the energy flows to and from the various parts of the building can be utilized most effectively. Having determined this strategy the designer is then able to formulate the type of system most suitable to his purpose, always bearing in mind such other requirements as space and capital cost.

4.1.6.4 Heat transfer systems

A wide variety of system types and combinations of types exist which have been developed over the years, often to meet specific requirements. Some types may be more prone to energy wastage than others and must be designed very carefully if losses are not to be incurred. The dual duct air conditioning system for example produces air at a desired temperature by mixing hot and cold air supplies and an infinite combination of hot and cold air streams may achieve the same desired result. From an efficiency point of view it is clearly better to mix moderately hot air with moderately cold air rather than very hot with very cold. In general, it is desirable for the air in an air conditioning system to be as near to the desired room temperature as possible though, for a variety of reasons, this is not normally a practical proposition. Extremes of temperature however will mean that heat gains and losses from ducts and pipes are increased and should therefore be avoided. All duct and pipework carrying hot or cold fluids should be insulated not only to directly reduce energy losses but also because they often provide uncontrolled heat losses or gains to the spaces through which they pass. This is especially important in well insulated buildings where large temperature changes can be produced by relatively small energy inputs.

Insulation is also required to reduce the losses in domestic hot water systems especially where storage calorifiers are used or long runs of pipework exist. In the past it has often been the practice to provide domestic hot water using the main boiler plant even when only small water usage is required. Considerable economies can often be made by generating hot water at its point of use when the savings in standing losses may more than offset the use of a more expensive fuel.

As has been previously mentioned pumps and fans contribute to the energy consumed by the services which may amount to some 20–30% of the overall electricity used in a large air conditioned building. The power required to transport a fluid depends on the amount flowing and the pressure losses in the system, both of which should be kept low if energy is to be saved. Duct and pipe design should therefore be such as to permit the use of low fluid velocities with minimal restrictions to flow. This can only be achieved by giving considerable attention to the detail design of ducts and pipework even though its capital cost may increase. The CIBS Building Energy Code, (Ref. 12), gives guidance on the design of ductwork systems making use of the concept of Air Transport Factor, which is defined as the energy transported by the air divided by the fan power required.

4.1.6.5 Controls

The controls associated with environmental systems may be very sophisticated and often the design of plant components is crude by comparison. In particular the precise control of fresh air flow, which may represent a large component of energy consumption, is often negated by the use of badly fitting control dampers and 'negative pressure' plant rooms which permit considerable uncontrolled leakage to occur.

4.1.6.6 Lighting

Because the mechanical systems in building tend to have more complex plant we may take for granted the energy consumed by lighting installations. In a large modern office building the installed lighting load may be of the order of 20–25 watts per square metre of floor area. The design and operation of lighting systems may therefore have a considerable impact on the operating costs of a building. The decision as to whether a building will be predominantly artificially or naturally lit is one of the first decisions to be made during the design of a building since it can considerably affect the building design in terms of type and area of glazing, with important consequences for the thermal performance of the building envelope. Levels of illumination should be no more than the task requires as also should be the standards of colour rendering in order to maintain high efficacies and consequently lower installed lighting loads.

4.1.6.7 Commissioning and maintenance

The importance of correct commissioning and maintenance of systems cannot be overemphasized. It is quite possible for some systems to produce acceptable results in terms of the environment but to do so in an inefficient manner due to poor setting up or maintenance of the system. Like car engines, systems may need tuning to provide optimum performance.

Finally, having designed and installed an efficient system one is faced with the task of operating it in an efficient manner, managing its energy. There are many levels of energy management which may range from the individual setting of a thermostat to complex computer controlled systems. Whatever level is used for a particular building there is nearly always an element of personal control such as switching lighting which can considerably affect the energy used, and the users of buildings must be made aware of how their actions may influence annual running costs.

Obviously it is only possible here to touch briefly on some of those aspects affecting energy consumption and building services, and for further information it is suggested that the reader also obtains the CIBS publication 'Building Energy Code', Part 1, "Guidance Towards Energy Conserving Design of Buildings and Services" (Ref. 12), as well as referring to other chapters in this book.

4.1.7 References

(1) GIEDION, S. 'Space, Time and Architecture' Oxford University Press, 1967
(2) ROSTRON, M. R. 'Light Cladding of Buildings.' The Architectural Press, 1964.
(3) HARDY, A. C., 'Environment Performance and the Design Process. Internation Sym-

posium on the Environment in Buildings.' Loughborough University 1972
(4) LACEY, R. E. 'An Index of Exposure to Driving Rain' BRE Digest 127, 1971 (Building Research Establishment Building Research Station Bucknalls Lane Garston Watford WD2 7JR)
(5) OKE, T. R. 'Boundary Layer Climates.' Methuen, London, 1978
(6) CIBS Guide Section A2: 'Weather and Solar Data 1982'
(7) PETHERBRIDGE, P. 'Sunpath Diagrams and Overlays for Solar Heat Gain Calculations' BRE CP Research Series 39, Supplement 1. (Building Research Establishment)
(8) Report on the Example Weather Year Task Group. CIBS, 1979.
LETHERMAN, K. M. and WAI, F. M. Condensed Statistics on the CIBS Example Weather Year – Kew. Building Services Engineering Research & Technology (BSER & T). Vol. 1, No. 3, 1980
(9) The Building (First Amendment) Regulations 1978 Part F 'Conservation of fuel and power in dwellings'. Part FF, 'Buildings other than dwellings'.
(10) FANGER, P. O. 'Thermal Comfort. Analysis and Applications in Environmental Engineering.' Danish Technical Press, Copenhagen 1970
(11) CIBS Guide Section A1: 'Environment Criteria for Design, 1978'.
(12) CIBS Building Energy Code Part I. 'Guidance towards Energy Conserving Design of Buildings and Services'.

Chapter 4.2

Principles of heating, cooling and air circulation

W.P. Jones, M.Sc., C.Eng., F.Inst.E., F.C.I.B.S., M.A.S.H.R.A.E.
Air Conditioning Consultant, Haden Young Limited

4.2.1 Temperature and heat

Energy is a fundamental property of the material world and, although it can neither be created nor destroyed, it can be transmitted from one substance to another. It can also appear in different forms, for example as thermal, electrical, chemical or mechanical energy, but here we are primarily concerned with heat and the way it can be put to good use.

Temperature, on the other hand, is an aspect of thermal energy indicating its intensity, the difference in temperature between two bodies representing the driving force that promotes a flow of heat from a hotter to a colder body. Heat and temperature are clearly very different and this difference is reflected in the units adopted for their quantitative expression. Because energy may be apparent in different forms its units must be interchangeable in a consistent fashion, according to the aspect of energy considered. This is most clearly exemplified by the triple equation relating the thermal, mechanical and electrical units of energy:

$$1 \text{ joule (J)} = 1 \text{ newton metre (Nm)} = 1 \text{ watt second (Ws)} \tag{4.2.1}$$

As a convenience, the kilowatt hour (kWh) is commonly adopted for the expression of electrical energy because it is easily evaluated as the product of the power of an appliance and the number of hours that it runs. We can see that

$$1 \text{ kWh} = 3.6 \times 10^6 \text{ Ws} = 3.6 \times 10^6 \text{ J}. \tag{4.2.2}$$

Temperature is expressed relative to a conveniently chosen zero and different scales are in use. The modern scale that is systematically displacing the others, in the process of worldwide metrication, uses the degree Celsius (°C, sometimes called the degree Centigrade), in values related to the freezing point of ice at 0°C and the boiling point of water at 100°C, for a standard atmospheric pressure of 101·325 kilopascal (kPa).

4.2.2 Heat transfer

Thermal energy may be transferred from one substance to another by four processes: conduction, convection, radiation and evaporation. The first three of these involve the transmission of sensible heat, that is, the passage of heat from a hotter body to a colder one by virtue of the temperature difference between them, without any change of phase. An evaporative process is rather different, energy flowing because of a phase change in the substance, for example from liquid to vapour when water boils. Such a change occurs at constant temperature and pressure and is termed a latent process.

4.2.2.1 Conduction

When the flow of heat through a body has reached a stable condition, that is, when the temperature in any given place is not changing with respect to time, the heat transfer is described as 'steady-state'. On the other hand, during the heating up or cooling down periods before or after the stable condition exists, temperatures are altering with respect to time and the heat flow is described as 'unsteady-state'.

Steady-state heat transmission in one direction (e.g. between the inner, warm face of a wall to its outer, cold face) is expressed by the following equation:

$$q_c = kA(t_1 - t_2) \tag{4.2.3}$$

wherein q_c is the rate of heat flow in watts, A is the cross-sectional area of the body at right angles to the direction of heat flow in m^2, t_1 is the temperature of one section of the body and t_2 that of another in °C. The thermal conductivity of the material, denoted by k and expressed in W/m^2 °C is an indication of the ability of the substance to transfer heat in relation to a specified standard condition (Fig. 4.2.1), namely through a one metre cube. Different materials have different values of thermal conductivities, defined by

$$k = x \text{ Jm/s m}^2 \text{°C} = x \text{ W/m°C} \tag{4.2.4}$$

which means that if x joules of thermal energy flow each second through a metre cube of material, for each degree of temperature difference across its faces, the value of k is x W/m°C, as Fig. 4.2.1 shows.

For the case of unsteady-state heat flow the picture is more complicated and although the details are not discussed here it is an important subject because the unsteady-state heat flow that occurs when a building warms up or cools down as its heating system is cycled on-off influences the quantity of energy used and so the operating cost. The further implications of this are touched upon in section 4.2.5.

4.2.2.2 Convection

If air comes in contact with a warmer surface it acquires heat by contact (conduction) and its temperature rises. Since warm air is less dense than cold air it rises up the surface, its former place being occupied by colder air, and the process continues, an upward convection current of warmed air becoming established. This process is termed 'natural convection' and it plays a significant part in the emission of thermal energy from heating appliances in buildings and the loss of heat through their walls to outside. Heat transfer in watts, by natural convection is expressed by:

$$q_v = AC(t_s - t_a)^n \tag{4.2.5}$$

where A is the area of the surface in m^2, t_s is its temperature and t_a is the ambient air temperature, both in °C, and n has a value of 1·25. C is a constant that depends on the shape and attitude of the heat-emitting surface: for horizontal surfaces looking up C is 1·9, for horizontal surfaces looking downwards it is 1·3 and for vertical surfaces 2·5.

Airflow over a surface may be artificially increased by using a fan, producing a greater rate of heat emission by a process called 'forced convection'. This process cannot be described by an equation as simple as 4.2.5.

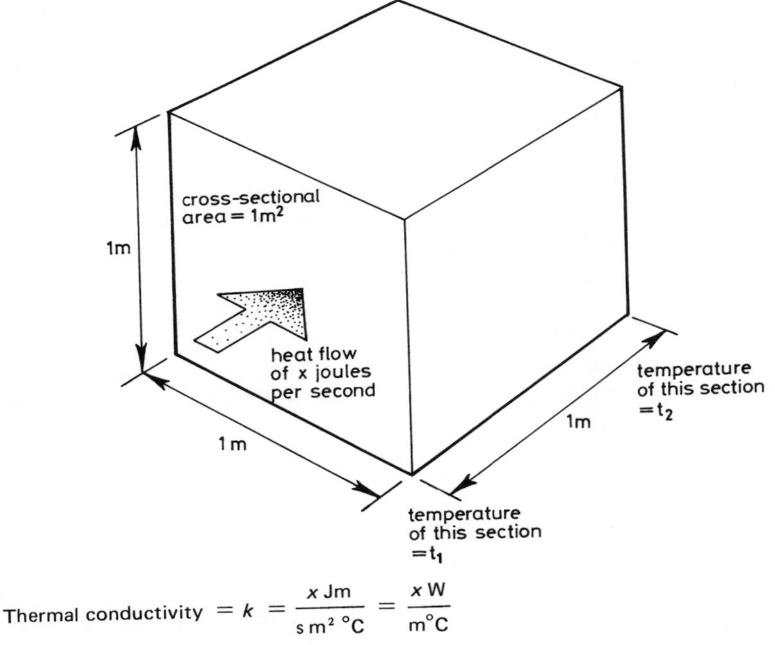

Fig. 4.2.1. *Definition of thermal conductivity*

4.2.2.3 Radiation

Thermal or infra-red radiant energy with a wavelength in the range from 800 to 400 000 nm is emitted by all surfaces having a temperature greater than −273·15°C, the so-called absolute zero. If an absolute scale of temperature is adopted, having values equal to the temperature in °C plus 273.15, we can say that thermal radiation from a surface is a function of absolute temperature, denoted by T and expressed in units termed kelvin (K). In fact the emission is proportional to T^4 and is further complicated by the nature of the emitting surface: matt black surfaces have a high ability to emit thermal radiation (emissivity) and polished, metallic surfaces a low ability. At room temperatures most building materials have emissivities (denoted by ϵ) in the range 0·8 to 0·95 whereas polished aluminium has an emissivity of 0·05. A usable expression for the radiant heat transfer in W between two surfaces at absolute temperatures T_1 and T_2 is:

$$q_r = 5.67 \times \epsilon \times A \left[\left(\frac{T_1}{100}\right)^4 - \left(\frac{T_2}{100}\right)^4\right] \quad (4.2.6)$$

4.2.2.4 Evaporation

There are two essentials for evaporation from a water surface to occur. First, the ambient air must not be saturated and, secondly, heat must be provided to effect the change of phase from liquid to vapour. This heat energy is needed because the molecules of liquid possess less kinetic energy of movement than do those of a gas. When evaporation occurs from a surface the rapidly moving molecules in the vapour have acquired their energy at the expense of those left behind in the liquid. Since the temperature of the liquid is an outward indication of the inward kinetic energy of its molecules its temperature will fall as evaporation takes place, unless there is a continuous input of heat from outside to the liquid in order to maintain the evaporation at a constant temperature, as in a boiler for raising steam. It follows that there are two useful processes involved: the evaporative cooling of water by blowing a stream of unsaturated air across it and the humidification of the air-stream as this occurs.

4.2.2.5 Thermal transmittance coefficient (U value)

When heat flows between two fluids across a solid barrier separating them, the transfer from the fluids to the surfaces must be considered separately from conduction through the solid material. Because heat is convected at a surface there must be a temperature difference across the film of gas next to the surface. Furthermore, the surface loses or gains heat by radiation through the surrounding gas to the more distant surfaces. Figure 4.2.2 illustrates the sort of temperature gradients that prevail. It is customary to speak of a heat transfer coefficient, h_c, to describe the convective process at the film and another, h_r, to express the radiant exchange. The combined coefficient, h_s, to define the heat flow through the surface film is then given by $h_s = h_c + h_r$. Additional subscripts o and i are added to denote the outside and inside surface coefficients, h_{so} and h_{si}, both quoted in W/m^2°C, the temperature difference being that between the air and the surface.

The overall (air-to-air) resistance to heat flow, Σr, equals the sum of the thermal resistances of the individual elements in series. In a solid structure such elemental resistances are defined as L/k, where L is the thickness of the component and k its thermal conductivity. When an unventilated air gap appears in a structure its resistance is established experimentally but is approximately the sum of two inside surface resistances. Denoting this by r_a we can write the overall resistance to heat flow for a cavity wall as

$$\Sigma r = r_{so} + L_{w1}/k_{w1} + r_a + L_{w2}/k_{w2} + r_{si} \quad (4.2.7)$$

wherein r_{so} and r_{si} are the reciprocals of h_{so} and h_{si}, respectively.

The U value of a building element is defined as the reciprocal of the sum of the component resistances and has units of $W/m^2\,°C$, the temperature difference referring to the air temperatures on each side. The U value is then used to calculate the heat flow through a wall, window, roof or exposed floor with an air temperature t_r, to the outside air at temperature t_o, by the equation:

$$Q = AU(t_r - t_o) \quad (4.2.8)$$

U values are also adopted to calculate the performance of boilers, heat exchangers, etc and in these cases the temperature difference used is that of the fluids on each side of the solid material separating them.

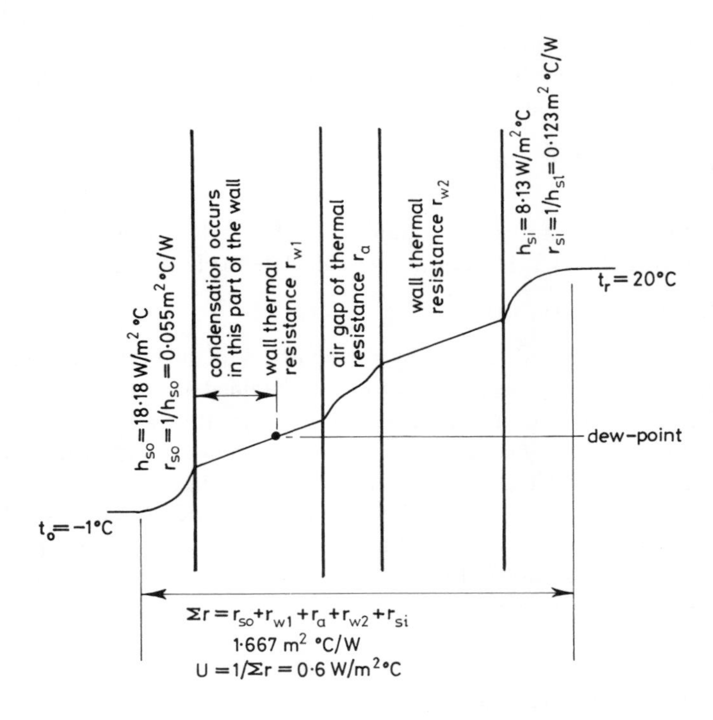

Fig. 4.2.2. *Heat flow through a wall*

4.2.3 Heat storage and specific heat capacity

When any substance, gas, fluid or solid, is warmed from one temperature to another heat is stored in it. The amount of heat stored is different for different materials because of their chemical compositions and physical structures. This varying ability to store heat is called 'specific heat capacity' and is expressed in kJ/kg°C. Thus 4·186 kJ of heat must be supplied to one kg of water to change its temperature by 1°C. That is, its specific heat capacity is 4·186 kJ/kg°C. On the other hand the specific heat capacity of air is 1·026 kJ/kg°C. Specific heat capacities are temperature-dependent.

4.2.4 Natural infiltration

No practical building is literally airtight. Consequently cold air from outside will enter any building because of wind pressures and, if the building exceeds about 10 m in height, the pressure set up by stack effect (arising from the difference of air temperature inside to outside). This infiltrating air must be warmed from the outside air temperature to that maintained within the building by its heating system. Supposing the volume V of a room is changed n times per hour by the natural infiltration of air having a specific heat capacity of 1026 J/kg°C and a density of 1·20 kg/m^3, the heat needed to warm this through 1°C is given by

$$Q = \frac{nV}{3600} \times 1.2 \times 1026 = \frac{nV}{2.9} = \frac{nV}{3} \text{ J/s} \qquad (4.2.9)$$

If we calculate the sum of the products AU for each element of the building envelope and write this as ΣAU we can then calculate the heat loss as:

$$Q = (\Sigma AU + nV/3)(t_r - t_o) \qquad (4.2.10)$$

The heat loss must be made good by the emission of the heating system within the building if a steady temperature is to be maintained at t_r inside when it is t_o outside. The difficulty in using eqn. (4.2.10) is in allocating a suitable value to n. The CIBS Guide (Ref. 1) gives a table of empirical values of air changes for infiltration to be used in calculating winter heat loss and these vary from 0.5 to 5.0. In practice a value of 1.0 is often taken for an office and as much as 4.0 for an entrance hall, when heat losses are estimated. The uncertainty in this part of the calculation of heat loss implies that excessive refinement in the determination of ΣAU may be misdirected.

4.2.5 Thermal response of buildings

The admittance of a surface (symbol Y) is its ability to receive and store thermal energy. It follows that the surfaces within a building will smooth out air temperature fluctuations and their facility in doing this will depend upon their mass and upon the presence of any insulating layers. Thus a heavy concrete floor slab has a high admittance of about 6·0 W/m^2°C but the presence of a carpet will reduce this to about 3·0 W/m^2°C because of its insulating effect. Similar considerations apply to walls and ceilings. A thermally transparent surface, such as a window, has an admittance equal to its *U*-value. The response factor, f_r, of a building can then be defined by:

$$f_r = \frac{\Sigma(AY) + nV/3}{\Sigma(AU) + nV/3} \quad (4.2.11)$$

in which $\Sigma(AY)$ is the area-weighted sum of the admittances of all surfaces exposed to the heated space, both sides of the surface being used when both are in the building. (Ref. 2)

The relevance of the response factor is in determining the amount of pre-heating needed before occupancy starts, if both the air temperature and the building surfaces are to be comfortably warm when people first enter. Figure 4.2.3 shows that a very light-weight structure cools down and heats up almost instantaneously and, because the mean room temperature is comparatively low over a period of 24 hours, offers considerable opportunity for the conservation of thermal energy by intermittent system operation. As the building structure gets heavier the pro-

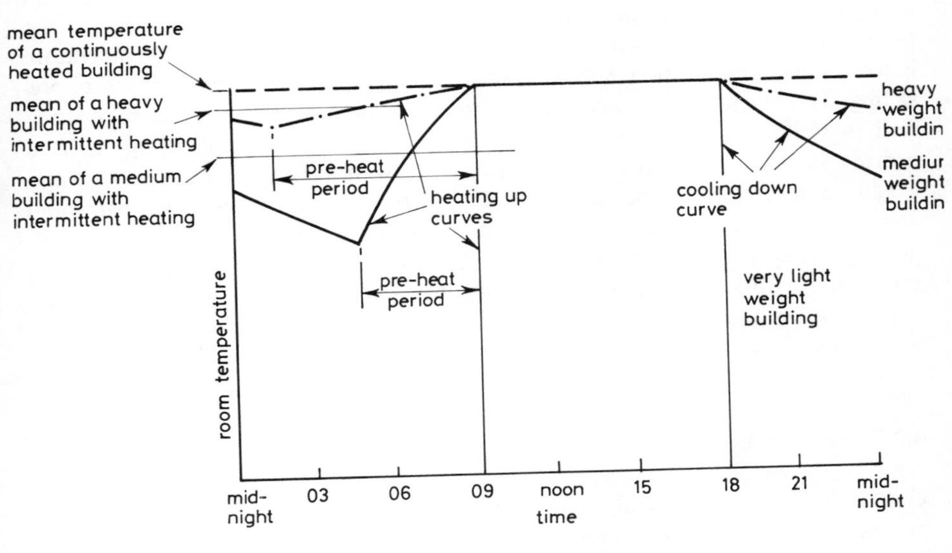

Fig. 4.2.3. *Intermittent heating system operation*

cesses of cooling down and heating up take longer and the mean room temperature gets higher. Eventually, with a very heavy building, there are no benefits to be obtained with intermittent heating and the system might just as well run continuously. Heavier buildings require a longer pre-heating time and the calculation of the response factor will indicate this: for values of f_r less than 2.5 only two hours pre-heat is needed but when f_r exceeds 10, five or six hours are necessary. As an indication (ref. 2), a typical office block, 86·4 m long × 13·5 m wide × 12 storeys high, of concrete construction and with partitioned offices would have a response factor of about 6, requiring about four hours preheating.

4.2.6 Condensation

The quantity of moisture present in the air is determined by its percentage saturation or relative humidity, for a given temperature. If the air is cooled its temperature decreases and its relative humidity increases until, at last, the air is saturated and any further attempt to cool it will cause some of the water vapour present to condense into liquid. The temperature at which this occurs is termed the dew-point and it is higher if the air has a higher initial moisture content. If surface temperatures in a room are at a temperature below the dew-point (because of inadequate heating, say), condensation on them will occur. Figure 4.2.2 shows that the temperature within the material of a wall reduces progressively from the warm side to the cold face. Clearly, even if there is no condensation on the room side of a wall it is possible for it to occur within the depth of the wall, if the water vapour in the room can penetrate the surface and migrate to those parts where the temperature is less than the saturation temperature corresponding to the vapour pressure prevailing. To prevent this it would be necessary to put a finish on the surface of the wall in the room that was impervious to vapour flow. It is not always easy to provide such a vapour barrier. In dwellings, in winter, the major source of water vapour is from the occupants themselves and from the activities in the bathroom and kitchen. The problem of preventing condensation is best solved by enough heating to keep the surface temperatures above the dew-point and by enough ventilation with air from outside to dilute the moisture content in the room air to a lower value and hence a lower dew-point. This is possible because fresh air in winter has a lower moisture content.

4.2.7 Forms of heating

Central heating is commonly provided in modern buildings in the UK by the pumped circulation of low temperature hot water (LTHW) from a boiler, through steel or copper pipes, to so-called radiators, located throughout the building. These radiators provide most of their heat output (about 50 to 80%) by natural convection, rather than by radiation, and they are best situated around the perimeter of the building beneath window cills, so that they may combat the uncomfortable effects of cold surfaces and infiltration from outside. The boiler produces LTHW at about 85°C, the temperature of which falls progressively to about 65°C as heat is given up at the radiators served. One or two pipes can be used for distribution. The former distributes hot water to each radiator and receives cooler water from it into the same pipe; thus water received by radiators remote from the boiler is less hot than by those near to it and distant radiators must be larger if they are to emit the same amount of heat. A two-pipe system uses separate flow and return pipes and radiator sizing is simpler. It is desirable to compensate the flow temperature of the LTHW downwards as the outside air temperature rises to give an overall reduction in heating output from the radiators as the weather gets milder. With two-pipe systems it is possible to achieve additional automatic control and effect greater economies in energy consumption by the provision of thermostatic radiator valves. Such valves reduce the flow of LTHW through individual radiators in response to casual gains by sunshine or electric lighting.

As a less obtrusive alternative to radiators, copper tubing fitted with aluminium fins to increase the heat transfer surface may be run in casings around the perimeter wall, either at skirting level or at cill height. The heat output of finned tube is almost entirely by natural convection. Forced convection heaters may also be installed sometimes, taking the form of small centrifugal fans driven by electric motors and blowing air over a coil of finned tube, fed with LTHW. Such units are assembled in sheet metal boxes and called 'fan coil units', or fan convectors. Their use is not uncommon in entrance halls or at the bottom of stair wells, because of the large heating capacity they can have.

A system popular for dwellings in the past but less favoured in recent years delivers warm air by means of a fan through ducts to supply grilles located in the various rooms. The air is warmed centrally by a gas-fired or an electric heater battery. Other systems of off-peak and direct electric heating are described in chapter 4.8.

4.2.8 Forms of cooling

A simple form of cooling is by means of an evaporative process: air is passed through a spray chamber handling a large amount of recirculated water and is cooled adiabatically, the heat required to evaporate the moisture coming from the airstream itself and lowering its temperature. The water evaporated is made good through a ball valve in the recirculation water tank. The change of state suffered by the airstream occurs at constant wet-bulb temperature and because the air becomes more humid in the process it cannot be cooled to below its initial wet-bulb. (Dry-bulb temperature is that indicated by an ordinary thermometer, shielded from radiation. A wet-bulb temperature is that indicated by a thermometer shielded from radiation but with a wetted cloth sleeve around its bulb; water evaporates from the sleeve at a rate depending on the relative humidity of the ambient air and a lower temperature than the dry-bulb is indicated.) Thus on a warm afternoon in the summer in London, with a typical outside air state of 28°C dry-bulb, 19·5°C wet-bulb, it might be possible to cool the air to 21°C dry-bulb and 19·5°C wet-bulb. At this condition the relative humidity is about 87% and the air is really too moist to be of use for comfort conditioning, although it might perhaps be appropriate for an industrial purpose. More commonly, the process of evaporative cooling described, is used in cooling towers where the object is to cool water. Air is induced by a fan over a large wetted surface across which water is passed in contra flow. A typical example is to cool the water from the condenser of a refrigeration plant which, for the London summer conditions mentioned, could be cooled from 32°C to 27°C and then returned to the condenser.

In the practical case of providing cooling in buildings, either for industrial or comfort purposes, it is necessary to use refrigeration plant if temperatures lower than those outside are to be maintained. The cooling is achieved by means of an array of several rows of finned tube, termed a cooler coil, located in an air handling plant. Air flows over the coil, is cooled and dehumidified, passes through a fan driven by an electric motor and is usually then ducted to the conditioned rooms.

In the smaller installations, the cooler coil comes as a package with its associated refrigeration plant and is located directly in the treated room, either as a free-standing unit, or fitted in an aperture in the wall under the window cill (a so-called 'room air-conditioning unit'). The heat removed from the room by air circulated over the cooler coil must be rejected to outside, through a condenser (section 4:2.9). With the room air conditioner the condenser is in the part of the unit that projects through the wall to outside and although this may also be true of the free-standing unit, if it backs onto a wall, it is more common to put the condenser on the roof, providing it is not too far away (maximum total distance about 17 m), and connect it to the unit in the room by a pair of refrigerant pipe-lines. Because such units are for comparatively small duties (under about 100 kW of refrigeration) cooling is achieved by a refrigerant that evaporates at a low temperature inside the cooler coil tubes. These coils are then termed 'direct-expansion' cooler coils and they are also found in small air handling plants having duties up to about 6 m^3/s. For larger installations, because of the restriction on the distance between the cooler coil and the refrigeration plant and because of the probable need for several, dispersed, air handling plants it is usual to chill water in a central refrigeration plant and pump it to the various cooler coils, instead of refrigerant. Such coils are then termed 'chilled water' cooler coils.

4.2.9 Refrigeration processes

4.2.9.1 Vapour compression process

Fig. 4.2.4 shows the relationship between saturation temperature and saturation pressure for a liquid and Fig. 4.2.5 illustrates a simplified version of the plant used for a vapour compression refrigeration cycle. The evaporator is either a direct-expansion air cooler coil or a water chiller, as discussed above. If the temperature of the evaporating refrigerant is sufficiently below that of the air to be cooled or the water to be chilled and if the corresponding saturation pressure has a practical value in relation to the mechanical strength of the materials used, a workable heat transfer process is possible. The heat removed at the evaporator causes the cold liquid refrigerant within to evaporate to a cold gas and this is then drawn along the suction line to a compressor (generally driven by an electric motor) that compresses it to the condensing pressure and discharges it into the hot gas line. Because of the power input to the gas at the compressor its temperature rises to a relatively high value at discharge. The hot, high pressure, gas flows along the hot gas line to the condenser.

At the condenser, the heat which was removed at the evaporator from the air or water, plus the energy imparted to the gas during the process of compression, must be rejected. This can be done if the temperature of the refrigerant gas in the condenser is significantly above that of the cooling medium used, such as air. Fig. 4.2.4 shows that it is possible to choose a saturation temperature that is above the temperature of the outside air and, in this way, the hot gas can at first be de-superheated (from states 3 to 3' in Fig. 4.2.6) in the condenser and then

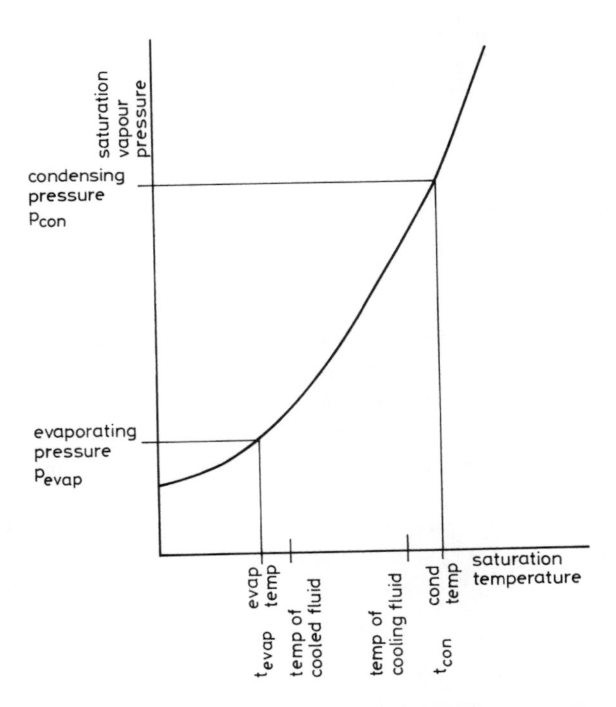

Fig. 4.2.4. *Relationship between saturation pressure and saturation temperature*

turned into a liquid by further cooling. The fluid leaving the condenser is a hot, high pressure liquid (state 4 in Fig. 4.2.6). Reference to Fig. 4.2.4 shows us that saturated liquid can only exist at a temperature t_{con} if its pressure is also p_{con}. The liquid refrigerant is therefore passed through a device termed a 'thermostatic expansion valve' (TEV) where it suffers a pressure drop from p_{con} to p_{evap}. Since a hot liquid cannot exist at t_{con} if its pressure is p_{evap} some of the liquid flashes to vapour and, because the energy of molecules in the vapour phase exceeds those in the liquid phase, energy is transferred from the liquid to the vapour in the process. This fall of energy level in the liquid is manifested as a reduction in liquid temperature. So the fluid coming out of the expansion is a cold, low pressure liquid, mixed with cold, low pressure bubbles of saturated vapour. The refrigerant has now completed the cycle and can be used again to remove further heat at the evaporator.

The process is a continuous one and the thermodynamics are shown in Fig. 4.2.6 as a simplified pressure-enthalpy diagram. (Enthalpy might be loosely defined

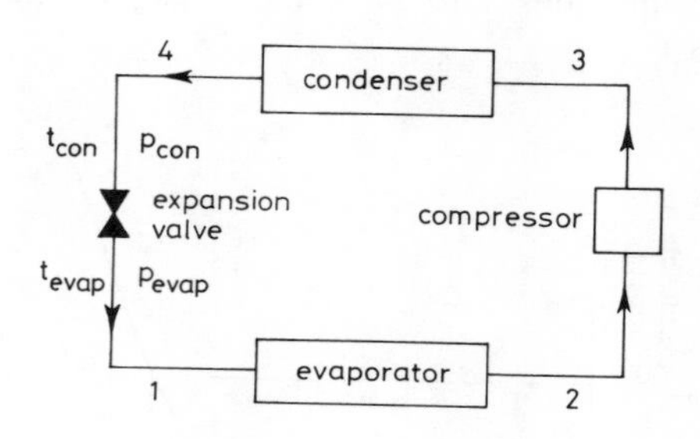

Fig. 4.2.5. *Diagram of a simple vapour compression refrigeration plant*

as the energy content of the refrigerant at a given state.) The process of evaporation from state 1 to state 2' is extended to include a small amount of superheating (about 8°C) from 2' to 2, to ensure that no liquid enters the compressor, where it would damage the machine. This is necessary because a characteristic of the performance of a refrigeration system at partial load is that less refrigerant is evaporated.

The effectiveness of the process is defined as a coefficient of performance (COP) instead of as an efficiency. The COP is expressed as the ratio of the heat absorbed at the evaporator (termed the 'refrigerating effect') to the energy input by the compressor. Practical values of COP are about four or five at summer design load in air conditioning systems.

Air is used to cool the condensers of the smaller sized installations up to about 200 kW of refrigeration, although beyond this is possible and not uncommon. For larger schemes, as in big office blocks or hotels, it is not convenient to have air-cooled condensers and the rest of the refrigeration plant close together and water is used for cooling. Even though it is possible that water from a river, the sea, or a lake with a constant throughput of water, could be used these opportunities are rare and often involve unforeseen complications. Taking water from the mains and discharging it to waste, some 20°C warmer, would be too extravagant and costly so it is common to make use of evaporative cooling by means of cooling towers, as described in section 4.2.8. The cooling towers can then be on the roof of the

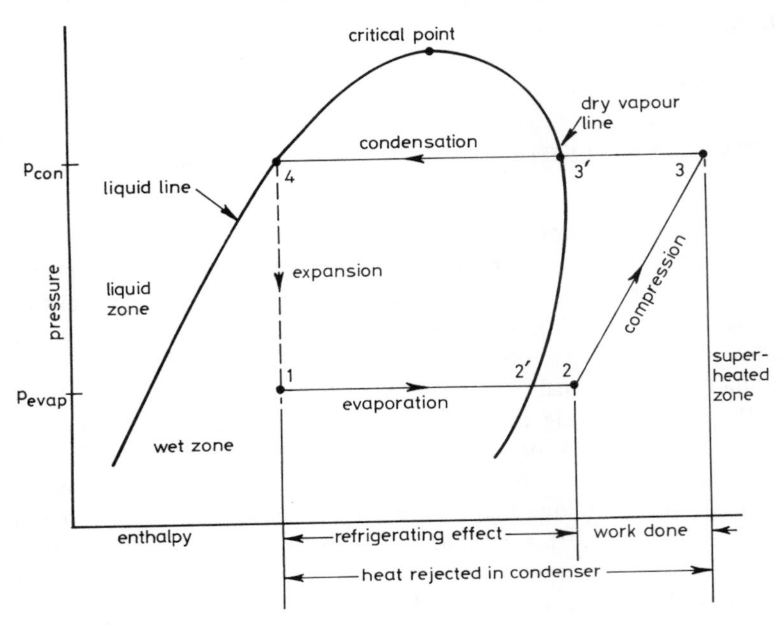

Fig. 4.2.6. *Pressure-enthalpy diagram for a vapour compression plant*

building, where there is plenty of cooling air available, and the water pumped to the condensers of the refrigeration plant in the basement.

4.2.9.2 Vapour absorption process

There are other processes of refrigeration, primarily that of vapour absorption. This uses a different type of refrigerant and differs from the vapour compression process in three notable aspects:

(a) Energy is supplied as heat in parts of the plant called the generator and the absorber, instead of as work at a compressor.
(b) The hygroscopic qualities of the chemicals employed in the process are used to induce the refrigerant from the evaporator and to discharge it into the condenser, instead of by means of suction and discharge valves, as with a compressor.
(c) The COP is of the order of 0·6 for an absorption machine, under design full load conditions.

Absorption systems do include electrically driven pumps to circulate the refrigerant and other fluids involved but there is no large input of electrical power, as with the vapour compression system. Because of their COP and their higher capital cost they have been much less used in the past than vapour compression plants.

4.2.10 Air distribution

There are two aspects of this: the distribution of air used for heating or cooling throughout a building by means of a duct system and the delivery and diffusion of the air in each treated room.

4.2.10.1 Ducted air distribution

To ensure that the correct quantities of air are delivered to the right places at the correct state, it is necessary to provide a system of ducts and an electrically powered fan. If the ducts are small in cross-sectional area, the quantity of air handled flows at relatively high velocity and, since the frictional resistance to this airflow is approximately proportional to the square of the velocity, the power of the motor driving the fan and the electrical running costs are higher. Conversely, using large ducts with a low velocity of airflow requires smaller motor powers and running costs. Building space has a value, particularly for commercial developments such as office blocks, and it follows that the designer is constrained to keep the ducts as small as possible. Doing this without due regard to the consequences frequently gives rise to noisy systems because of the excessive air turbulence generated in the duct system and increased noise production at the fan and motor.

A compromise must be reached and this is dictated by experience, involving the design of low, medium and high velocity systems with maximum velocities of the order of 10 m/s, 15 m/s and 20 m/s, respectively. The application, economics and the size of the building guide the designer in the choice of system, but a general good principle is to keep the velocity as low as possible because this tends to give quiet installations that are cheap to operate.

4.2.10.2 Diffusion in the treated space

For air change rates less than about 20 per hour (with ceiling heights of 2.7 m) it is possible to use conventional air distribution terminal devices, these having been specially designed for this purpose. As the air change rate becomes higher, it is increasingly difficult to do this and above about 25 air changes per hour it is necessary to adopt other techniques. Conventional devices are side wall grilles and ceiling diffusers. These make use of the Coanda principle. When a stream of air flows over a surface, such as a ceiling, a frictional pressure loss occurs at the boundary between the airstream and the surface. The air pressure in the room on the other side of the jet is then higher and presses it onto the surface. (Fig. 4.2.7.)

The jet leaving the grille intentionally entrains a large amount of air from the room. Because momentum is conserved its mean velocity falls, its temperature approaches that of the room air and the pressure drop at the interface with the ceiling decreases (being velocity dependent). Eventually the pressure difference across the jet is insufficient to keep it pressed to the surface which it then tends to leave, entering the occupied zone. The design intention is to ensure that when this occurs the air velocity is less than a comfortable limit of 0·25 m/s in a room temperature at about 22°C. The throw of the airstream to this limit is then $X + Y$ in Fig. 4.2.7.

Ceiling diffusers may be circular, square, rectangular or linear in form. In all cases the behaviour of the airstream issuing from the diffuser slot is the same as that described above for grilles. (Fig. 4.2.8). As an example, in the case of the circular diffuser the airstream leaves a circular slot in the ceiling and clings to it as it expands rapidly, entraining air and rapidly reducing in velocity. Because of the

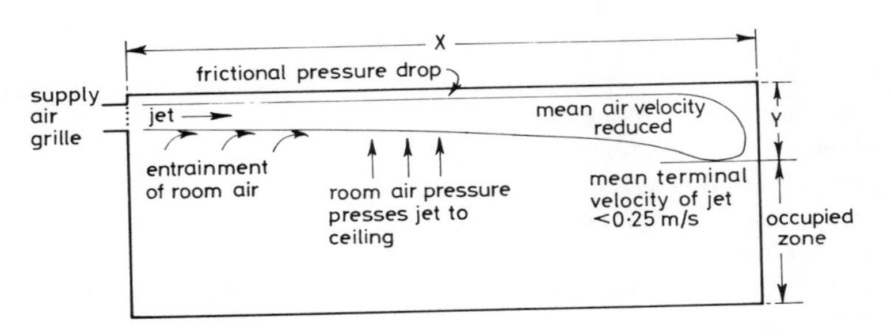

Fig. 4.2.7. *Airflow from a supply grille*

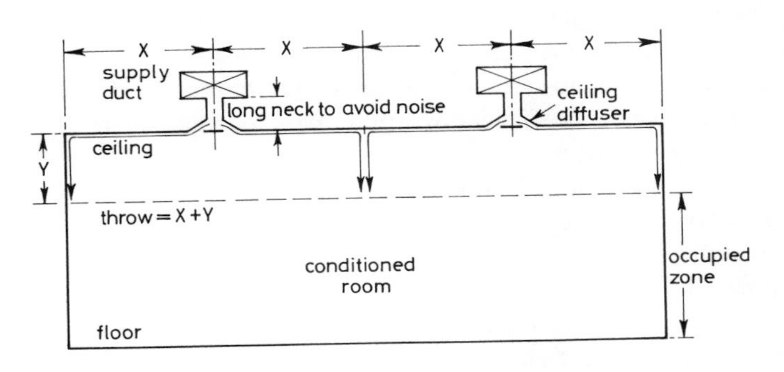

Fig. 4.2.8. *Air distribution from ceiling diffusers*

radial expansion, the velocity reduction is greater than that for side wall grilles or linear diffusers and it follows that, the throw being shorter, more air can be delivered to a given room by means of circular diffusers than by any of the other conventional air distribution terminals mentioned. Because of their simpler arrangement, side wall grilles are a cheaper form of air distribution in a room than diffusers.

The proper design of the supply air distribution system for a room is essential if comfortable conditions are to be maintained. On the other hand, the location of the extract grille is a good deal less critical because of the non-directional and uniform nature of airflow into a suction opening. One extract grille, of adequate size, is often sufficient for a ventilated room.

4.2.11 References

(1) CIBS Guide, Sections A4–9 'Air Distribution' and A9–3 'Estimation of Plant Capacity' 1979
(2) CIBS Building Energy Code Part 2a 1981

4.2.12 Glossary

A Cross-sectional area (m^2)
C Heat transfer constant for natural convection from a surface (W/m^2 °C)
L Thickness of a component
L_w Thickness of a wall (m)
Q Rate of heat flow (J/s or W)
T_1 Temperature of a surface (K)
T_2 Temperature of another surface (K)
U 'U' value, thermal transmittance coefficient (W/m^2 °C)
V Volume (m^3)
f_r Response factor of a building
h_c Convective heat transfer coefficient of a film of gas (W/m^2 °C)
h_r Radiative heat transfer coefficient of a film of gas (W/m^2 °C)
h_s Total heat transfer coefficient of a film of gas (W/m^2 °C)
h_{si} Total heat transfer coefficient of a film of gas (inside)(W/m^2 °C)
h_{so} Total heat transfer coefficient of a film of gas (outside)(W/m^2 °C)
k Thermal conductivity (W/m°C)
k_w Thermal conductivity of a wall (W/m°C)
n Number of changes per hour
p_{con} Condensing pressure (kPa or bar)
p_{evap} Evaporating pressure (kPa or bar)
q_c Rate of heat flow by conduction (W)
q_r Rate of radiant heat transfer (W)
q_v Rate of heat transfer by convection (W)
r_a Thermal resistance of an air gap (°C m^2/W)
r_{si} Thermal resistance of an inside surface film (°C m^2/W)
r_{so} Thermal resistance of an outside surface film (°C m^2/W)
t_1 Temperature of one section of a body (°C)
t_2 Temperature of another section of a body (°C)
t_a Ambient air temperature (°C)
t_{con} Condensing temperature (°C)
t_{evap} Evaporating temperature (°C)
t_o Outside temperature (°C)
t_r Room temperature (°C)
t_s Temperature of a surface (°C)
Σr Overall resistance to heat flow (°C m^2/W)

Chapter 4.3

Ventilation systems

W.P. Jones, M.Sc., C.Eng., F.Inst.E., F.C.I.B.S., M.A.S.H.R.A.E.
Air Conditioning Consultant, Haden Young Limited

4.3.1 Quantity of air required

The first step in the design of any system of ventilation is to establish the amount of air needed. This depends on the purpose for which the system is required: the provision of fresh air to an occupied space, the dilution of a contaminant to an acceptable level, the removal of waste heat, conveying a waste product associated with an industrial process to a place for disposal or recovery, and limiting the temperature rise in a room. Each of these merits further comment.

4.3.1.1 Provision of fresh air to an occupied space

People require only a very small amount of fresh air for breathing purposes, as little as 0·2 litres/s sufficing for one person. Two more important needs in practical terms are: keeping the concentration of carbon dioxide in the occupied space below an upper acceptable level and diluting the odours present to a socially tolerable limit. Carbon dioxide is naturally present in fresh air to the extent of about 0·03 to 0·04% but human beings can comfortably accept concentrations of 0·1% and, indeed, this value is sometimes regarded as the basis for a fresh air requirement. For example, in places of public entertainment, a public authority might stipulate a minimum supply of 7·8 litres/s for each of the people present and this corresponds to a concentration of 0·1% when a person is assumed to occupy the minimum statutory volume of 12 m^3. Of more importance is the provision of enough fresh air to keep the concentration of odours down and this is the basis generally adopted. Whether smoking is allowed in the ventilated space greatly affects the quality of air needed from outside and this is a factor in the recommendations of the CIBS. (Ref. 1). Thus 25 litres/s of fresh air is recommended for each person in a conference room where very heavy smoking is expected but only 8 litres/s is proposed for an office where there is to be little smoking. The risk of condensation in a room can be obviated by an adequate ventilation rate, as section

4.2.6 explained. The statutory minimum ventilation rate is not always enough to equate with best practice. For example, the minimum requirement often stipulated by a local authority for the ventilation of lavatories not having openable windows that could provide natural ventilation, is three air changes per hour or 6 litres/s for each WC pan or wash-hand basin, whichever is the greater. Experience suggests, on the other hand, that something like twelve air changes per hour ought to be provided.

4.3.1.2 Dilution of a contaminant

Industrial processes may produce fumes of gases of a toxic or objectionable nature and it is then necessary to reduce their concentration. The concept of Threshold Limit Values (TLV) is used as a criterion of success in such dilution techniques. The TLV is defined as the airborne concentration of a contaminant to which workers may be repeatedly exposed without adverse effects. Because people have varying degrees of response to potentially noxious or toxic concentrations there may always be a small percentage in a given environment who experience discomfort below the TLV.

4.3.1.3 Removal of waste heat

Industrial processes are often accompanied by the generation of large quantities of heat and this has to be taken away for the continued comfortable environment of the work people and the efficiency of their effort. Very commonly, particularly in buildings with large floor-to-ceiling heights, stack effect can remove the surplus heat by natural ventilation. The heat is then almost certain to go to waste. In many instances, where heat production is localised, hoods can be provided to channel the heat into an exhaust duct system. Mechanical ventilation then gives a controlled removal of the surplus heat, and an air-to-air heat exchanger can be incorporated to recover up to some 80% of the waste heat and use it for warming the incoming cold, fresh air that is necessary to make good the quantity extracted.

4.3.1.4 Industrial waste product exhaust

In some machining industries (eg woodworking) the process generates large quantities of waste material. The sole purpose of the ventilation system is then to collect the waste at the machine tool where it is produced and convey it to a place outside the building for disposal. Conveying the waste product (usually a solid material) involves a high velocity of airflow and the systems are consequently noisy and use a lot of electrical energy at the exhaust fan. The air removed from the building in this way has to be replaced by the introduction of filtered, warmed (in winter) air from outside, imposing an extra thermal energy requirement.

4.3.1.5 Limiting the temperature rise in a space

Commercial buildings can suffer heat gains from solar radiation through windows, from electric lighting and from people (Para 4.4.2.1). The temperature will rise within and this can be mitigated by ventilation, although a temperature less than that prevailing outside in summer can never be maintained inside by ordinary, mechanical ventilation. Whereas the fresh air quantities needed to control odour in a space are relatively small those required to limit the rise in temperature by mechanical ventilation can be much larger, about three to six air changes per hour being sufficient (except in lavatories) for the former, but something like ten to fifteen being wanted for the latter. The amount of air necessary to limit temperature rise can be calculated from the basic equation:

$$\text{Sensible heat gain } Q = \dot{m} \times c \times (t_r - t_s) \qquad (4.3.1)$$

wherein $\dot{m}$ is the mass flow rate of the air supplied in kg/s, c is its specific heat capacity in kJ/kg°C, t_r is the room temperature and t_s is the supply air temperature, both in °C. The sensible heat gain is then in kW. If we take values of 1·191 kg/m^3 for the density of air and 1·026 kJ/kg°C for its specific heat capacity we can show (Ref. 2) that, at 20°C, equation (4.3.1) can be re-expressed as:

$$\text{Sensible heat gain } Q = \dot{v} \times 1{\cdot}25 \times (t_r - t_s) \qquad (4.3.2)$$

where $\dot{v}$ is the volumetric airflow rate in m^3/s if the heat gain is in kW, or in litres/s if the gain is in W. Equation 4.3.2 is most useful because air handling units, ductwork and air distribution devices are all sized on a volumetric basis and not according to mass flow rate. The supply air temperature, t_s, will equal the outside air temperature, t_o, plus an allowance for the power input to the airstream by the fan (corresponding to a rise of 1°C for each kPa of fan total pressure (Ref. 2)). Because the room temperature, t_r, will exceed the supply air temperature there will be a heat loss to outside through the building fabric. If we try and take account of this we have:

$$\text{Sensible heat gain } Q = (t_r - t_o)\Sigma AU + \dot{v} \times 1{\cdot}25 \times (t_r - t_s) \qquad (4.3.3)$$

In fact, the balance temperature attained will be lower than the value of t_r, obtained from equation 4.3.3 in buildings of other than light-weight construction. This is because the material of a building stores some of the heat gain and acts as a damping agent. A simple generalisation cannot be made but, using a more involved technique (Ref. 3), a reasonable approximation is possible by calculation.

4.3.2 Type of system

The fundamental choice is between natural and mechanical systems of ventilation. The former use no energy in promoting airflow but lack flexibility in application and refinement. Mechanical systems generally use electrical energy to transport the air and their advantages are that their design can be tailored to suit the needs of the job and they give an assured rate of ventilation.

4.3.2.1 Natural ventilation

Two forces are used to produce airflow: wind effect and stack effect. Wind speed varies with respect to height because of frictional at the ground. The so-called 'meteorological wind speed' is the speed measured at a distance of ten metres above ground level, in open country, and data exist for various localities in different seasons of the year. Higher speeds are obviously to be expected in winter and lower ones in summer. The pressure exerted by wind on the upstream side of a building is positive and that on the downstream side negative. Although figures are published (Ref. 4) for such pressure difference in terms of building height and location, predicting and achieving a satisfactory, comfortable ventilation rate is generally unlikely to be successful.

Stack effect (Fig. 4.3.1) achieves air circulation because the weight of the column of air within a building is different from that outside. In summer the air

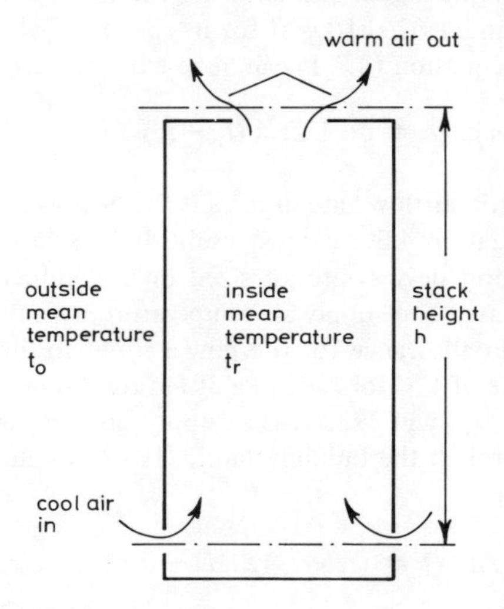

Fig. 4.3.1. *Ventilation by stack effect*

inside may be warmer than that outside owing to the sensible heat gains arising from sunshine, lights and people. Considering a column of air of 1 m^2 cross-sectional area and height h m ('stack height') the difference in mass between the two is proportional to $h(\rho_o - \rho_r)$ where ρ_o and ρ_r are the densities of the outside and room air respectively, and this will promote a force, because of gravitational acceleration, to drive the outside air through the inlet openings at low level and out of the openings at high level. The ventilation rate can be calculated (Ref. 4) with some confidence and such natural ventilation may well give very acceptable results in cases where the building height is great enough.

The higher a ventilator is situated above the point where cold air flows into a building, the greater will be the outflow of warm air from the building through the ventilator:

$$Q = 0{\cdot}12\, A\sqrt{h(t_r - t_o)} \tag{4.3.4}$$

where

Q = airflow in m^3/s
A = free area of inlets or outlets, whichever is the smaller, in m^2.
h = height between the centre-line of the inlets and outlets in m.
t_r = average indoor temperature over the stack height, °C.
t_o = average outdoor temperature over the stack height, °C.

The flow of air through a building by wind effect is described by

$$Q = EAV \tag{4.3.5}$$

where

Q = airflow in m^3/s
E = Effectiveness of the opening with a value of 0·5 to 0·6 for winds at right angles to the wall and 0·25 and 0·35 for winds oblique to it.
A = Free area of inlets or outlets, whichever is the smaller, in m^2.
V = wind velocity in m/s.

The greatest airflow, per unit area of inlet or outlet, is obtained from equations 4.3.4 and 4.3.5 when the areas are equal. If one exceeds the other a proportional increase in airflow is not obtained: thus if the outlet area is 50% more than the inlet area the improvement in airflow is only about 15%.

4.3.2.2 Mechanical ventilation

Systems of mechanical ventilation comprise three elements: an air handling unit, a ductwork system, and an air distribution system in the treated room. Such a system is then virtually unaffected by wind and stack effect and can give a calculable rate of airflow throughout the building, by virtue of electrical energy to drive its fans. The way in which the system is designed depends on the nature of the application. In principle, three forms of design are possible: supply, extract and balanced. In practice, however, it is really impossible to achieve an exactly balanced system; precise airflow rates cannot be obtained, even by the best commissioning procedures and there will invariably be a small surplus of supply over extract, or vice-versa. Usually, this is quite acceptable.

Extract systems handle used or contaminated air from occupied spaces or from an area in which some industrial process is occurring. The air is either discharged to waste or, if it is not contaminated, it may be mixed with some fresh air for use again, a desirable economy in the use of thermal energy being achieved. When air is extracted from a building and discharged to waste a slight negative pressure is created within the building and this tends to cause an inflow of air from outside. If the influx is through natural openings, such as doors, or through grilles in the walls the entering air will be both cold (in winter) and dirty. It follows that a mechanical supply system, able to filter and warm the incoming air, is often used.

Extract systems, or balanced systems that create a small negative pressure in the building, are adopted when it is desirable prevent a smell or contaminant from escaping outside.

4.3.3 Air handling plant

4.3.3.1 General

In the past an air handling plant consisted of an assembly of components joined by sheet metal or builders' work connexions but such arrangements are rarer to-day, except in the biggest installations, exceeding about 16 000 litres/s. Instead, the modern practice is to use packaged air handling units, as shown diagrammatically in Fig. 4.3.2. A typical unit comprises a mixing box for combining fresh and recirculated air, a filter for cleaning the mixed airstream, a heater battery to warm it as required, and a fan and motor section. The electric driving motor may sometimes be mounted outside the section and connected to the fan by belts and pulleys, its shaft projecting through the casing. Ductwork then distributes the air to the ventilated space. In some instances, where several rooms are treated and a measure of independent thermostatic control is wanted, there is no heater battery

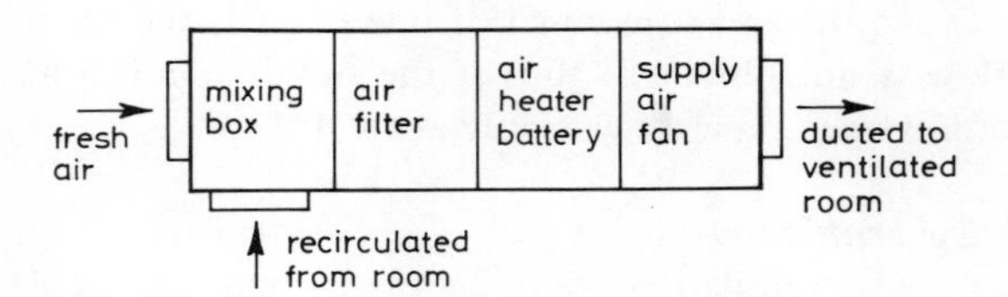

Fig. 4.3.2. *Diagram of a simplified air handling unit*

section, multiple heater batteries being fixed in independent ducts on the discharge side of the fan that delivers air to the various rooms. When such plants are used for air conditioning a cooler coil is also included in the package, as a separate section. It is generally best to put the cooler coil before the heater battery but if the unit handles 100% fresh air it is also necessary to have a pre-heater battery, before the cooler coil, to protect it from freezing in cold weather.

Although relative humidity is not to-day regarded as very important for comfort it is sometimes necessary to exercise control over it. A humidification section may then be included in the package.

A deeper consideration of the components of an air handling unit is now relevant.

4.3.3.2 Mixing chamber

The minimum amount of fresh air is often all that is desirable in winter, in order to conserve thermal energy but there are other times of the year when it is better to use more fresh air and less recirculated air. For example, doing this could permit a mixture of room air at 20°C with fresh air at a lower temperature in order to yield a mixed air temperature of, say, 12°C, appropriate as a supply air temperature to a space where heat gains were occurring. Mixing is achieved by the use of motorised louvres in the fresh and recirculated air openings of the mixing chamber, operating in opposition under thermostatic control. Incidentally, if good, turbulent mixing can take place there is then no need for a pre-heater battery after the mixing chamber, in most cases, the temperature of the mixed air not being below freezing point.

4.3.3.3 Filters

These may be broadly classified as dry, viscous and electrostatic, with further sub-classification as follows:

Fig. 4.3.3. *Dry filter*

(a) *Dry filters.* In their cheapest form these comprise panels of dry material, such as mineral fibre, assembled as a battery and fixed across the airstream, as illustrated in Fig. 4.3.3. Dust is collected progressively as the system runs, the air pressure drop across the filter increasing and the airflow rate decreasing until its useful life is finished and it must be replaced. Such filters operate with moderate efficiencies and are appropriate for a wide range of applications in commercial buildings (Ref. 4). To ease maintenance they are available in roll form and work automatically, the dirty filter fabric being collected on one motorised roller and replaced by clean fabric from another, similar, roller (Fig. 4.3.4). Higher efficiencies are obtained if

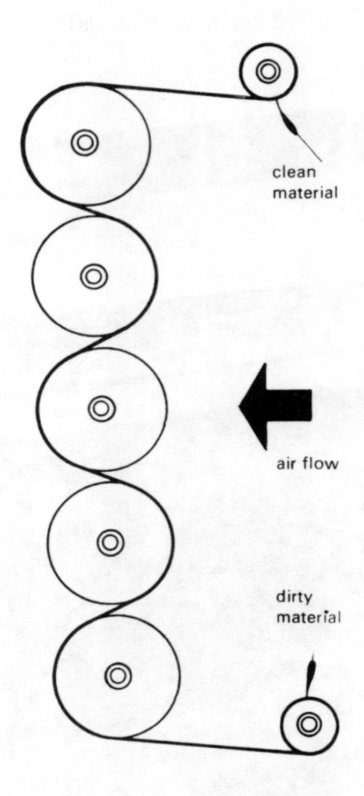

Fig. 4.3.4. *Principle of roll filter*

the fabric is arranged in bags to present a large surface area for the collection of dirt. It is possible to obtain filters of very high efficiency by using a suitable, paper material as a filtering medium, folded to offer an extremely large surface collection area and packed in cells for assembly as a filter battery across the airstream. Filters of this type are termed 'absolute filters' and are used in the most exacting applications (Ref. 5), such as the removal of bacteria and other contaminants from the air delivered to operating theatres.

(b) *Viscous filters.* The characteristic of these is that they have a large dust-holding capacity with a somewhat lower filtration efficiency than the dry fabric types. In cell form, viscous filters consist of a package of inert material, such as glass fibre, impregnated with an oil that has the desirable properties of non-toxicity, capillarity, viscosity, stability, etc. Dust is collected through the depth of the cell material. Some filters of this type may be cleaned periodically with a cold wash and automatic filtration is also possible, the latter comprising an assembly of metal plates with arrangements to keep them continually covered with a film of oil.

(c) *Electrostatic filters.* Appliances of this sort have efficiencies approaching those of the absolute filters but, although operating costs are lower (because of cheaper maintenance and a very small use of electricity), capital costs are rather high and a viable economic case for their use is not always easy to make. In principle, the airstream passes through an ionising unit between negative and positive electrodes across which from 7800 to 12 000 V is established. The molecules of air are ionised (about 80% positively and 20% negatively) and impart their charges to the dust particles present by collision. The charged dust particles then pass between plates having alternate charges of 6000 V and earth potential, where they are collected. Variants of this are in use but in all cases some form of after filter is provided, usually of the bag type, so that the filters fail safe. In one form of filter the dust particles are deliberately allowed to agglomerate and build up on the collection plates until the friction of the airstream between them blows them into a bag filter.

4.3.3.4 Heater Batteries

The heater battery is usually fed with low temperature hot water (LTHW) but medium temperature hot water, steam and electricity may be used. Direct-fired batteries are also sometimes adopted. A conventional heater battery comprises one or more rows of copper tubes with copper or aluminium fins. Water at 85°C enters the tubes, via a flow header, and leaves at 65°C, through a return header. Automatic control is achieved by using a two-port modulating valve to throttle the water flow or a three-port modulating valve to divert it past the battery. Occasionally, two-position control is adopted as an alternative to proportional control. On the smaller installations the automatic valve would be electrically operated but pneumatic actuation might be commoner on larger jobs. Electric heater batteries generally consist of conducting elements sheathed in protective, finned tubes for safety and to give a better heat transfer to the airstream blowing over the outer, extended surface. Automatic control can be in steps, using contactors, or may be modulating by means of silicon controlled rectifiers. All electrical heater batteries are fitted with high temperature cut-outs and their operation is interlocked with the fan starter so that the battery cannot be energised unless the fan is running. To guard against a stoppage of airflow (say by the inadvertant closure of a damper) it is desirable to include an airflow switch that de-energises the battery upon failure or airflow. In certain specialised and competitive applications (Ref. 5) (e.g. for shopping centres), air handling units may contain direct-fired heater batteries. Gas or oil may be burnt inside tubes which traverse the airstream, warming it in the process. The products of combustion are discharged to waste outside, through a small, local flue.

4.3.3.5 Humidifiers

These are sometimes fitted. They may achieve humidification by the evaporation of water in the airstream or by the injection of steam. In more detail the main types are:

(a) *Air washers.* Water is recirculated from a sump tank through an array of nozzles in the airstream that atomise the water. The air is simultaneously cooled and humidified by an adiabatic process with a humidifying efficiency dependent on the number and configuration of the banks of spray nozzles, ranging from 50% for a single bank to more than 97% for three banks. Washers of this sort are bulky and introduce maintenance problems. Furthermore, they must be very well cared for if the risk of bacterial growth is to be avoided. So-called 'capillary washers' in which a battery of fibre glass matting replaces the banks of spray nozzles and is wetted through its depth to provide a large surface area for humidification have also been used, but washers generally have fallen from favour in recent years and are seldom used to-day except for some industrial purposes.
(b) *Aerosol types.* Water is atomised by nozzles or other means and blown directly into the airstream. Most or all of the water is evaporated, the remainder being collected and drained to waste, rather than re-circulated. Sometimes water is sprayed onto rotating discs and fed through a toothed, peripheral ring to achieve atomisation.
(c) *Wetted surface types.* Water is directed onto a large surface of an inert material such as stainless steel or plastic to secure humidification. Unevaporated water is drained to waste.
(d) *Mains dry steam injection.* Steam is raised remotely by a boiler and is piped to the air handling unit for injection into the airstream. It is important that the steam should be dry and this is ensured by encasing the injection pipe in a jacket fed with dry steam at the same temperature as the injected steam. Any heat loss from the jacket causes condensation to occur therein (rather than in the injection pipe– and this can be returned to the boiler through a steam trap in the usual way, no free moisture going into the airstream).
(e) *Local steam generation and injection.* When central steam boilers are not available, steam may be raised locally, adjacent to the air handling unit. Immersion heaters or electrodes boil the water as required and dry steam is fed into the air-stream. Scale formation (because of the salts of hardness in the feed water) is minimised by periodic blowdown from the steam raiser and the electric elements or electrodes must be replaced when scaled up.

4.3.3.6 Fans and motors

Three types of fan are in common use for the circulation of air in buildings:

(a) *Propeller fans.* These have blades pressed into a curved shape and are generally used without any ducting for the local circulation of air. They cannot work against any significant resistance beyond, say, about 60 pascals (Pa). They are sometimes mounted at high level in walls or roofs to give exhaust ventilation, particularly in industrial applications. They are generally employed in simple cases to handle relatively small airflow rates. (Fig. 4.3.5). The motor invariably drives the fan directly.

(b) *Axial flow fans.* These are similar to propeller fans but have carefully designed blades with aerofoil sections and are far more efficient. Fig. 4.3.6 illustrates one

Fig. 4.3.5. *Propeller fan*

such fan with its driving motor externally mounted, the fan being driven through vee-belts and pulleys. It is more usual to drive the fan directly, the fan and motor having a common shaft. The clearance between the tips of the blades and the fan casing is very critical and must be a minimum if the highest mechanical efficiencies (of the order of 85%) are to be achieved. Operation against high external resistances is common, two stages being used when necessary. Axial flow fans tend to produce noise and to need silencing if they work against other than the lowest external resistances. Although the straight-through nature of the airflow implies convenience in plant layout this is often not so because to achieve the performance required it is necessary to ensure smooth airflow conditions at entry to the fan and exit from it. Consequently several diameters of straight, smooth tapering duct may be needed on each side of the fan, giving an inconviently long plant arrangement. An advantage of axial flow fans is that they have a non-overloading power characteristic.

(c) *Centrifugal fans.* A typical example is shown in Fig. 4.3.7. The impellers of such fans may have many forward curved blades, as in Fig. 4.3.8, or fewer backward-curved blades, as in Fig. 4.3.9. The forward curved fan is very seldom used with a direct drive: because of the flexibility which is possible, vee-belts and pulleys are the norm. There is an infinite variety of external resistances possible in ventilation ductwork systems and if pulleys are used a departure from the design intention or

Fig. 4.3.6. *Axial flow fan*

Fig. 4.3.7. *Centrifugal fan driven by close coupled motor*

Fig. 4.3.8. *Forward curved centrifugal fan*

the unforeseen can always be dealt with by a change in fan speed, supposing the motor power is large enough.

Centrifugal fans are used for industrial as well as commercial purposes and in these cases the design and construction of the impeller must be appropriate for the application. For example, if used to handle wood shavings and sawdust in an industrial exhaust system the impeller would be of the radial blade type, with only a few, rugged blades, of radial configuration, able to withstand the wear of handling the abrasive material.

Fig. 4.3.9. *Backward curved centrifugal fan*

4.3.3.7 Duct distribution systems

Ducts of galvanised sheet steel construction are used to convey air from the air handling plant to the rooms where it is needed and to extract the air from the rooms, after it has been used, for recirculation or discharge to waste. The ducts oppose the flow of air along them by offering frictional resistance and by generating air turbulence. In order for a system designer to propose a system that will do the job of ventilation intended he must be able to select the correct fan, size the ducts, estimate the resistance to airflow they will offer, decide on the correct speed to run the fan and choose a motor of the right power to drive it.

The selection of the proper type of fan depends on the application. Thus with commercial ventilation the fan generally selected is the forward curved centrifugal, because it is smaller, cheaper, and quieter, for the same volumetric airflow rate than a backward curved fan, and usually more convenient in plant layout than an axial flow fan. The size of the fan depends on the airflow rate – and this is known from other considerations, such as the air change rate needed in the building to provide the fresh air wanted or to limit the temperature rise in the face of sensible heat gains. The speed at which the fan selected must run and so the power of the motor required to drive it will depend on the resistance offered to airflow by the elements in the air handling plant and the size of the ducts.

In essence, duct sizing is simple, the cross-sectional area (and so the size) being determined from the equation:

$$Q = AV \qquad (4.3.6)$$

in which Q is the volumetric flow rate in m^3/s, A is the cross-sectional area of the duct in m^2, and V is the mean velocity of airflow in m/s. In practice it is a little more complicated and three methods are in use, to varying extents. The one of most wide use is termed the 'equal friction method'. This involves selecting a rate of pressure drop that is apt for the application and using this to size the whole of the duct system. In approximate terms the rate of pressure drop is often taken as proportional to the square of the air velocity but the truth is more involved and a duct-sizing chart is available (Ref. 6) for easy use.

Because building space is valuable and ducts take up more space if the velocity of airflow in them is low, there has been a tendency in recent years to adopt higher velocities and pressure drop rates them hitherto. As a generalisation one might classify systems as: 'low velocity' for duct velocities less than 10 m/s, 'medium velocity' for velocities between 10 and 15 m/s and 'high velocity' for airspeeds exceeding this. (see Section 4.2.10.1). It is a good principle to keep air velocities as low as possible and never to exceed 20 m/s, except in very rare instances and then only for short distances.

The energy exchanges occurring in a duct system when air flows along it are described by Bernoulli's theorem which, simply stated is:

$$TP = VP + SP \qquad (4.3.7)$$

in which TP is total pressure in Pa, VP is velocity pressure in Pa and SP is static pressure in Pa. Frictional resistance to airflow causes the airstream to lose energy and, since the velocity of the airflow is governed by equation 4.3.6, and no significant air leakage occurs, this corresponds to a drop in total pressure and a corresponding fall in static pressure. A change in velocity pressure will occur if the section of the duct alters and this is invariably accompanied by the creation of some air turbulence, involving a further loss in energy. The total energy loss in the system is equal to the fan total pressure (FTP) created by the fan and Fig. 4.3.10 shows diagrammatically the pressure changes and energy losses in a simplified duct system.

How the system behaves when a fan is connected to it is shown in Fig. 4.3.11 by the intersection of the pressure-volume characteristics for the fan and duct system. Changing the fan speed is seen in the figure to give a different point of intersection. Certain laws indicate how the fan will behave if its speed changes, after it is fitted in a given duct system. Briefly these state that the volume handled is proportional to

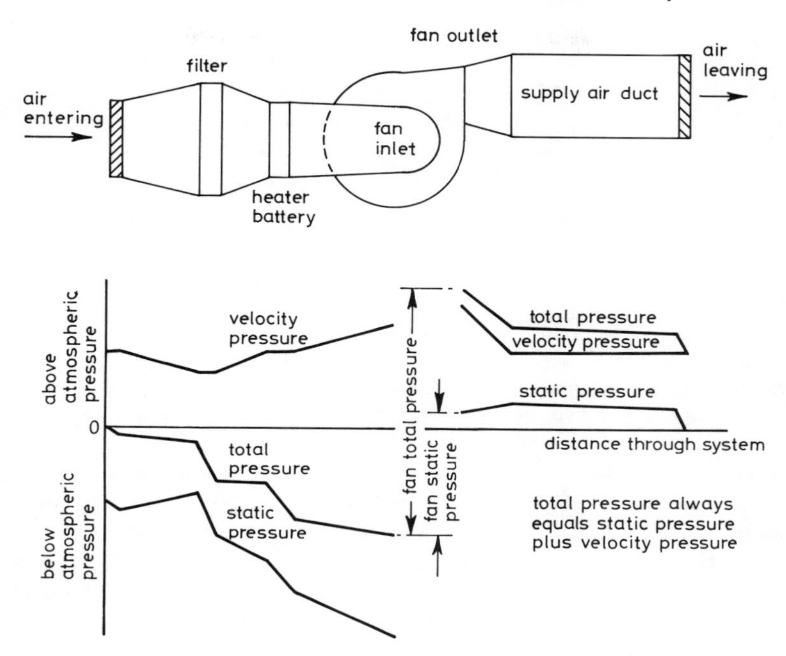

Fig. 4.3.10. *Total, static and velocity pressure variation in a simple ventilation system*

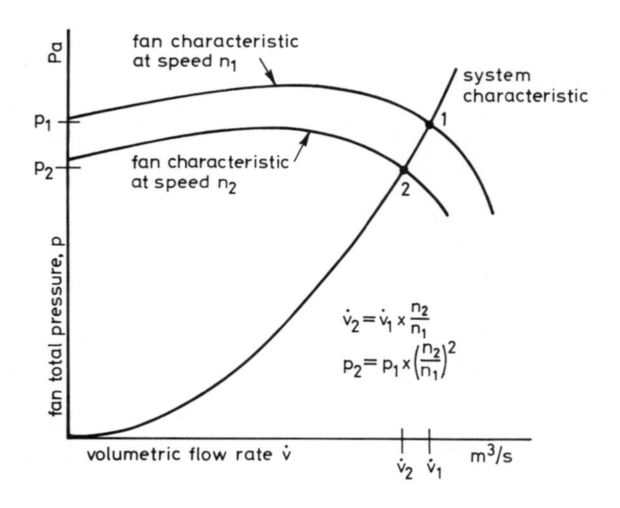

Fig. 4.3.11. *The intersection of fan and system characteristics*

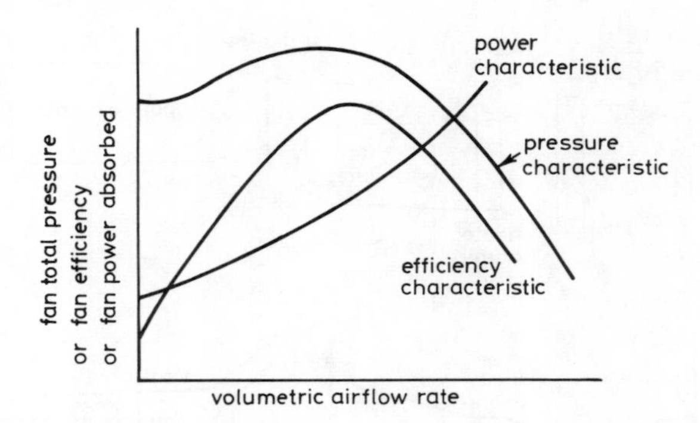

Fig. 4.3.12. *The relationships between fan total pressure, fan efficiency and absorbed fan power, and volumetric airflow rate, for a forward curved centrifugal fan*

the speed at which the fan runs, the fan total pressure is proportional to the square of the fan speed and the power absorbed at its shaft is proportional to the cube of the fan speed. The shape of the fan characteristics is determined by test in the maker's works and three separate curves are produced: pressure-volume (as discussed), power-volume, and efficiency-volume. Fig. 4.3.12 shows such curves for a typical forward curved centrifugal fan. We see that the power-volume curve rises as the volume increases and for this reason, to cover uncertainty in the precise nature of the duct resistance, and to provide enough torque to accelerate the fan impeller from rest on start-up, it is essential to provide a margin of some 35% over the net calculated fan power when selecting a motor to drive it.

4.3.4 References

(1) CIBS Guide Section A9–21 'Estimation of Plant Capacity', 1979
(2) JONES, W. P. 'Air Conditioning Engineering,' 3rd Edition, Edward Arnold (Publishers) Ltd.
(3) BRE Digest 162: 'Traffic Noise and Overheating in Offices.'
(4) CIBS Guide Section A4. 'Air Infiltration', 1976
(5) JONES, W. P. 'Air Conditioning Applications and Design.' Edward Arnold (Publishers) Ltd.
(6) CIBS Guide Section C4 'Flow of Liquids in Pipes and Ducts', 1977.

4.3.5 Glossary

A Area (m^2)
E Effectiveness factor for openings
Q Rate of sensible heat gain (W or kW)
Q Air flow (m^3/s)
SP Static air pressure (Pa)
TP Total air pressure (Pa)

U 'U value'. Thermal transmittance coefficient (W/m^2 °C)
V Wind velocity (m/s)
VP Velocity pressure of air (Pa)
c specific heat capacity of air (kJ/kg°C)
h height of a column of air (m)
$\dot{m}$ mass flow rate of air (kg/s)
n fan speed (rev/s or rev/min)
p fan total pressure (Pa)
t_o outside temperature (°C)
t_r room temperature (°C)
t_s supply air temperature (°C)
$\dot{v}$ volumetric flow rate of air (m^3/s)
ρ_o density of a column of outside air (kg/m^3)
ρ_r density of a column of room air (kg/m^3)

Chapter 4.4

Air conditioning systems

W.P. Jones, M.Sc., C.Eng., F.Inst.E., F.C.I.B.S., M.A.S.H.R.A.E.
Air Conditioning Consultant, Haden Young Limited

4.4.1 The need for air conditioning

It has already been seen (section 4.3.1.5) that, in the presence of heat gains, the temperature in a building cannot be maintained at a value lower than that of the air outside. Whilst the provision of mechanical ventilation may bring some relief, overheating will still occur, to an extent that depends on the magnitude of the heat gains and the ventilation rate. However, because the temperature maintained in a room converges to a limiting value equal to the outside temperature plus an allowance of a few degrees for the power input of the supply fan, increasing the number of air changes per hour by mechanical ventilation yields diminishing returns. In any case, for large air change rates, accommodating the distribution ductwork begins to pose a problem. The occupants of mechanically ventilated buildings must therefore always have the opportunity of opening windows in the warmest summer weather to augment the ventilation rate, and for psychological relief, in the presence of overheating.

Buildings that are erected in noisy, dirty, urban communities cannot easily offer relief to their inhabitants by allowing windows to be opened – otherwise dirt and noise will be admitted. Furthermore, high-rise buildings are subjected to greater wind velocities on their upper storeys, making the opening of windows harzardous because of the excessive, uncontrolled air movement produced in the rooms. It follows that if mechanical refrigeration is used to cool the air to a temperature less than that required in the room sensible heat gains can be offset and a comfortable condition is possible. In principle, the use of refrigeration in conjunction with a mechanical air supply is air conditioning. The extent to which air conditioning is needed depends on the conditions wanted in the room, the heat gains occurring therein and the use to which the room is to be put.

4.4.2 Heat gains

Heat gains which would cause the temperature to rise are called 'sensible heat gains' and must be offset by supplying air to the room at a temperature lower than that to be maintained in it. Heat gains arising from the liberation of moisture into the air are termed 'latent heat gains' and must be dealt with by delivering air to the room at a drier condition than that to be maintained.

4.4.2.1 Sensible heat gains
These fall into five categories: transmission (T) through the fabric of the building envelope by virtue of the air-to-air temperature difference; the heat liberated by people (P) because of their activities; the heat given off by electric lighting (L); the heat dissipated by any machines used (M); and the heat gain by solar radiation through the windows (S). The total sensible heat gain (Q_s) is then given by

$$Q_s = T + P + L + M + S \tag{4.4.1}$$

4.4.2.2 Latent heat gains
These arise from two causes: the moisture liberated by people and the infiltration of moister air, in summer, from outside. The former occurs because people give off moisture by insensible perspiration during their ordinary activities and by the exhalation of humid air from their lungs, and the latter by the natural processes of wind and stack effect, referred to earlier. In the case of industrial buildings certain processes may also give latent heat gains by the evaporation of water.

4.4.2.3 Transmission heat gains (See section 4.2.2.5)
In simple terms these are calculated in the same way as are heat losses except that the outside temperature is greater than the one inside. Equation 4.2.8 would be used. Transmission gain through glass is instantaneous because the glass has no thermal inertia but, for the case of walls and roofs, the calculation is complicated for three reasons: the outside air temperature varies with time, varying solar thermal radiation falls on the outer surface, and the mass of the structure and its specific heat introduce a delaying and diminishing influence. Evaluating the heat gain through walls and roofs becomes very complicated and it is fortunate that in most cases great accuracy is not necessary because such gains generally constitute less than five per cent of the total sensible heat gain from all sources. The exception is the case of the low-rise building with a large plan area, such as a hypermarket, where the roof gains may be very significant. Industrial buildings of modern construction also require more care over the calculation of gains through their envelopes because of the light-weight nature of the materials used.

Two methods are in use to account for the influences of outside temperature, solar radiation and thermal inertia: sol-air temperature and equivalent temperature differential. Sol-air temperature is a notional air temperature outside that gives the same rate of heat flow into (or out of) the external building surface as the real combination of temperature and radiation actually does. How much of this heat enters the room after flowing through the wall is then determined by applying a time delay and a decrement factor, the values of which depend on the density and thickness of the wall. Sol-air temperature (t_e) is tabulated (Ref. 1) for different times of the day, months of the year, latitudes and orientations, but it may be calculated from:

$$t_e = t_o + (\alpha I/h_{so}) \tag{4.4.2}$$

in which t_o is the outside air temperature, α is the absorption coefficient of the surface, I is the intensity of solar radiation (direct plus scattered) in W/m^2 normally incident on the surface and h_{so} is the outside surface heat flow coefficient in W/m^2 °C.

In the case of very light-weight building construction the time lag may be taken as zero and the decrement factor as unity. We then have a simplified equation for the heat gain Q through a wall or roof to a room (compare with Eqn. 4.2.8):

$$Q = AU(t_e - t_r) \tag{4.4.3}$$

For walls and roofs of more substantial construction the equation is

$$Q = AU(t_{em} - t_r) + AUf(t_\theta - t_{em}) \tag{4.4.4}$$

wherein t_{em} is the mean sol-air temperature over 24 hours, t_r is the room temperature, f is the decrement factor and t_θ is the sol-air temperature at time θ. The heat gain to the room, Q, is then at a later time, $\theta + \phi$, ϕ being the time lag of the wall or roof. Typical values of ϕ, for building structures of density less than 1200 kg/m^3 are: 2·7 hours for 100 mm thickness, 4·9 for 150 mm, 6·8 for 200 mm, 11·2 for 300 mm and 15·2 for 400 mm. Decrement factors depend on the position of the insulation and for corresponding thicknesses their values are shown in Table 4.4.1.

Equivalent temperature differences may be calculated using sol-air temperatures or other, more refined techniques. They are in common use in the United States but rather less popular in the United Kingdom. Tabulated values are published (Ref. 2) in relation to American practice in building construction. Equivalent temperature differences are much more convenient to use than are sol-air temperatures, since they merely involve the insertion of the appropriate value to replace ($t_r - t_o$) in equation 4.2.8.

Table 4.4.1 *Decrement factors*

No insulation:	0.87, 0.67, 0.48, 0.22, 0.11
Insulation inside:	0.67, 0.47, 0.33, 0.16, 0.08
Insulation outside:	0.51, 0.34, 0.22, 0.10, 0.04

Table 4.4.2 *Heat gains from humans*

Activity	Total Emission (W)	Heat emitted at various room temperatures. 20°C Sensible	20°C Latent	22°C Sensible	22°C Latent	24°C Sensible	24°C Latent	26°C Sensible	26°C Latent
Seated	115	90	25	80	35	75	40	65	50
Office work	140	100	40	90	50	80	60	70	70
Standing	150	105	45	95	55	82	68	72	78
Eating*	160	110	50	100	60	85	75	75	85
Dancing	265	140	125	125	140	105	160	90	175

* Includes an allowance for the heat given off by the food.

4.4.2.4 Heat gains from people
In the process of working, human beings liberate heat in sensible and latent form. The total amount of heat emitted depends on the rate of working and the proportion of this that is sensible is related to the temperature of the environment. People find it more difficult to lose sensible heat as the temperature goes up and the amount liberated by evaporation increases to compensate. Typical heat emissions from human beings are given in Table 4.4.2.

4.4.2.5 Heat gains from lights (see also section 4.9.5)
All electrical energy absorbed from the mains is ultimately dissipated as heat into the conditioned room. The rate of dissipation from lighting depends on the type of luminaire, whether or not it is ventilated, the type of lamp and the size and optical properties of the room illuminated. Nevertheless, it is possible to give approximate guidance, as indicated in Table 4.4.3.

The figures in Table 4.4.3 assume efficient fluorescent tubes are used. If tungsten lamps are adopted the heat liberated may be five times as much for the same illuminance.

If slots are cut in the top of the troffer and used air extracted from the conditioned space, through the ceiling void and thence back to the plant for discharge to waste or recirculation, as expedient, a significantly large proportion of the heat given off at the luminaire is removed. The ceiling void gets hotter but, even after allowing for the heat re-transmitted to the room through the ceiling (and to the room above) a conservative estimate is that 40% of the heat from the lights can be returned to the plant room for disposal. If the extract slots are provided at the long, lower edges of the luminaire then only about 30% is so removed. The advantage of doing this is that the heat gain to the room is reduced, less air need be delivered to it for conditioning, the ducts and plant size become smaller and the installation is cheaper. It is not necessary to make duct connexions to each extract ventilated luminaire – this is a waste of money. However a rudimentary extract duct system is needed above the suspended ceiling; this is fitted with dampered spigots for balancing and ensures that uniform extract distribution through the

Table 4.4.3 *Approximate Heat Gains from Electric Lights.*

Premises	Average illuminance lux	Heat gain W/m² floor area
Office – small	500	25
Office – large	500	21
Residential rooms	100	10
Schools	300	18
Factories	300–750	10–25

light fittings is achieved, it being arranged that no fitting is more than 18 m from any spigot.

4.4.2.6 Heat gains from machines

This can be easily assessed by referring to the name plate of each machine where details of voltage and full-load current may be seen. With industrial installations a problem that arises is estimating a reasonable diversity factor when more than one machine may be in use simultaneously, and this can generally only be resolved by establishing patterns on site. For commercial buildings, such as office blocks, it is customary to take between 5 and 10 W/m^2 of floor area as typical, to cover the use of electric typewriters, calculators, mini-computers and the like. The tendency in recent years has been for this allowance to increase.

4.4.2.7 Solar gains

These occur through walls, roofs and glazing but it is only the gain through windows that is usually of great significance (para 4.4.2.3). The intensity of solar radiation is largely a function of the altitude of the sun, being greatest when this is highest in the sky. Such radiant energy must be resolved in a direction at right angles to the glass for which the gain is to be calculated and allowances made for the reflective and absorptive qualities of the glass itself and any shading that is provided. (It is to be noted here that it is not possible for people to feel comfortable if they are in the direct rays of the sun coming through a window, for any length of time. It is not possible to provide an air conditioning system that can give comfort unless adequate shading from direct solar radiation is present.) When the radiant energy has entered the room it does not immediately constitute a load on the air conditioning system because the air is transparent to its passage and does not therefore warm up at once. When the solar radiation strikes the floor slab and other room surfaces it is absorbed by them. Their outer layers get heated, some of this energy travels deeper into the material and is temporarily stored while some of it is convected (Eqn. 4.2.5) from the warmer surfaces into the room air, causing the temperature to rise and so impose a load on the air conditioning system. This takes time to happen and there is thus a time lag between the instantaneous solar gain through the window and its impact on the room temperature. Further, since some of the energy is stored in the solid materials of the room, the amount released as a heat gain from them to the room is less than the original gain. The mass of the building (principally that of the floor slab) consequently has an effect on the solar heat gain, heavier buildings tending to reduce it. Furniture and furnishings also have an effect and, since they are less massive than the building structure, tend to lessen the benefit that a heavy building gives. Thus the presence of a carpet on the floor insulates the slab from solar radiation, gives a shorter time lag and a greater fraction of the instantaneous gain as a load on the air conditioning system.

4.4.3 Dealing with heat gains: system options

As discussed earlier and as typified by Eqn. 4.3.1 and 4.3.2, a building is kept at a desired comfortable condition of temperature and humidity by the supply mass-flow of air that is cooler than the temperature to be maintained and drier than the humidity required, in the presence of sensible and latent heat gains. Air is the medium used in most cases for achieving this but, in some instances, water is used as an auxiliary medium. There are thus many options of system choice available to the designer and the one he adopts should be related to the characteristics of building use and load change.

One method of classification commonly employed is:

Unitary systems
All-air systems
All-water systems
Air-water systems

The last two of these can really be grouped together as air-water systems.

The spur behind the development of air conditioning systems was the coincidence of a property market for office blocks in the hot, humid, summer climate of the eastern seaboard in the United States of America with the evolution of air conditioning in the period from 1930 to 1950 – although the origin of air conditioning is much earlier than this, of course. The consequence was that systems were developed to air condition offices during this time and merely modified as required for other applications.

4.4.4 Unitary systems

4.4.4.1 Self-contained, air-cooled, room air conditioners.
These are in very common use all over the world and have been popular since the thirties. A room unit of this sort comprises a direct-expansion air cooler coil, a supply air fan, a hermetic refrigeration compressor, an air-cooled condenser and a condenser fan. A simple, washable or disposable air filter is provided across the face of the air cooler coil and a drip tray is fitted beneath it. As the air passing over the cooler coil is dehumidified, condensate forms on the fins of the coil and must be drained away as it collects in the drip tray. Rather than providing an elaborate system of drainage pipework, it is common to feed the condensate onto a slinger ring around the blades of the propeller fan that cools the condenser. The condensate is thus distributed over the condenser where it evaporates and is discharged to waste. A less satisfactory alternative is to feed the condensate directly to waste through a pipe projecting to outside through the wall. The air cooler coil and supply fan are separated from the condensing section, which is arranged to be on the outside of the wall or roof of the room in which the air conditioner is fitted (Fig. 4.4.1). The condensing section must have ready access to a plentiful supply

of outside cooling air, otherwise the condenser will be unable to reject the heat removed from the conditioned room to outside and will continually fail on its high-pressure safety cut-out. The advantage of such units is that they can be easily installed, room-by-room, on an ad hoc basis. Their disadvantages are that air distribution is comparatively poor (being more vigorous and noticeable close to the unit), their control is two-position with a fairly wide differential (± 2°C, or more), they are often quite noisy and their life is fairly short, ranging from 3 to 10 years, depending on usage. Cooling capacities from 1·76 kW to 8·5 kW with electrical power consumptions from about 0·6 kW to 3 kW are available. A local connexion is often arranged to admit a small amount of fresh air from outside into the suction side of the supply fan. They do not work well in winter weather in the UK climate because condensing pressures fall too much.

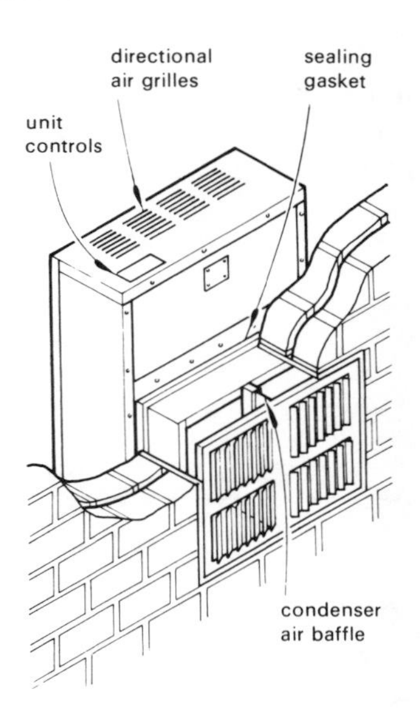

Fig. 4.4.1. *Unit air-conditioner installed in wall*

4.4.4.2 Split systems

These are air-cooled units arranged for convenience with part or all of the condensing set separated from the air cooler coil and located up to about 15 m from it. The unit in the room is consequently quieter than the self-contained air-cooled variety, but more expensive. There are limitations on the distance between the room unit and the remote air-cooled condenser or air-cooled condensing unit because of the pressure drops in the refrigerant lines connecting them and of the need to ensure the proper return of lubricating oil to the compressor. Such units are available with cooling capacities up to 60 kW of refrigeration when remote condensing sets are used, or up to 500 kW of refrigeration if the option with a remote air-cooled condenser is adopted. Absorbed electrical power is from about 0·6 kW up to 20 kW or up to 170 kW, respectively.

4.4.4.3 Water-cooled room air conditioners

Units of this type contain a supply air fan and direct-expansion cooler coils with a hermetic compressor and a water-cooled condenser fed with pumped water from a remote cooling tower. Because the temperature of the cooling water is less than that of the air used with the air-cooled version, in summer, compression ratios are less and so are power requirements. Water-cooled units are more expensive but quieter than self-contained air-cooled packages and are available for duties up to about 230 kW of refrigeration with absorbed electrical power up to approximately 60 kW.

4.4.4.4 Terminal heat pump/heat recovery units (see also section 4.5.2)

These are water-cooled room air conditioners fed with water at a temperature of about 27° to 24°C, summer and winter. The roles of the winter-cooled condenser

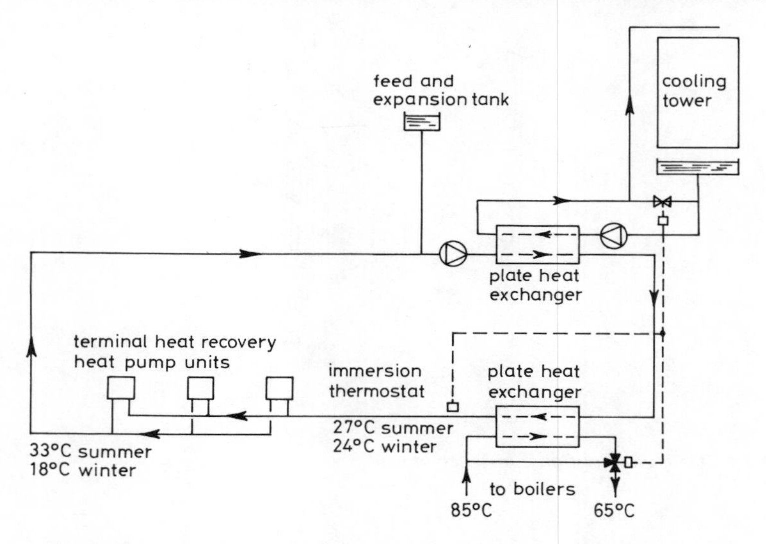

Fig. 4.4.2. *Typical piping diagram for heat recovery/heat pump units*

and air-cooled evaporator can be selectively reversed by switching a valve in the refrigerant circuit; the former then becomes a water chiller cooling the water circulated through it and the latter becomes an air-cooled condenser, warming the room air blown over it. The units can thus provide both heating and cooling. By means of the connecting water loop it is possible for units on a sunlit face suffering a heat gain to transfer the heat removed from the treated rooms to those on the opposite, shaded face with a heat loss, which can then be warmed. A surplus of heat in the water loop (in summer) is rejected at a cooling tower and a deficit of heat in the loop (in winter) is made good by heat from a boiler. It is essential to separate the water loop from the cooling tower and the boiler by means of heat exchangers to keep the room units clean. (Fig. 4.4.2). Capacities from 1·5 to 3·8 kW of refrigeration and from 2·2 to 5·3 kW of heat are possible. Absorbed electrical powers are about 0·6 to 1·6 kW and this is always part of the heating output in winter, being rejected at the air cooled condenser into the room.

4.4.5 All-air systems. (See also section 3.5.9)

4.4.5.1 Constant-volume re-heat

Essentially, these are simple systems. All the air is first cooled and dehumidified, usually by means of a direct-expansion cooler coil, to a temperature appropriate for dealing with the maximum sensible heat gains. As the heat gains reduce, the supply air temperature is increased under thermostatic control, part of the capacity of the cooler coil being cancelled to meet the reduced load. It is wasteful of energy to cancel cooling with re-heating and a better alternative, for small applications, is to run the cooling and heating in sequence. Thus when a reduction in sensible heat gains occurs the cooling capacity is reduced (normally in one or two steps) and when this is eventually followed by a heat loss from the room the heater warms the air supplied. There is then no cancellation of cooling with heating, although it is not uncommon to have a high limit humidity override that brings on one section of cooling when necessary. An advantage of constant-volume re-heat systems is that they are very useful for industrial applications where it is important to control both temperature and humidity to close limits: the output of the cooler coil is controlled to deal with the latent gains by supplying cool air at a fixed moisture content (dew-point) while variations in sensible heat gain are offset by re-heat, under thermostatic control. Humidification may be added for industrial purposes but its use is rare for comfort applications.

Constant volume re-heat, or sequenced heat, systems may have chilled water cooler coils but since they are mostly used for small, commercial applications direct-expansion is the norm. Fixed proportions of outside and recirculated air are usual, the reduced capital cost that adopting this entails being more important than the smaller running cost that variable amounts would give by allowing the refrigeration plant to be switched off in winter when the outside air was cold enough.

4.4.5.2 Roof-top units

Although almost any weatherproofed unit could be so described, roof-top units have come to be regarded as those developed for conditioning low-rise shopping centres. They comprise: mixing box, air filter, direct-expansion air cooler coil, air-cooled condensing set, direct-fired air heater battery (gas or oil) and supply air fan with motor, drive and switchgear. The unit is weatherproofed and pre-wired at the factory, electrical connexions and gas fitting is done on site and a condensate drain line led from the cooler coil to a gulley on the roof. The capacity ranges possible are: 5 to 75 kW of refrigeration with 17 to 120 kW of heating. From about 2 kW to perhaps 35 kW of electrical power is absorbed.

4.4.5.3 Variable air volume systems

As sensible heat gains diminish the variable air volume (VAV) system delivers a reduced amount of cold air to the room to match the smaller load, instead of warming a constant volume of air to a higher temperature, as other system do. Apart from the advantage of no longer wastefully cancelling cooling with re-heat, less electrical energy is used to distribute the air throughout the building. This is because the pressure drop along the ducts is in proportion to the square of the volume handled and, since fan power is a function of the product of airflow rate and pressure developed, it would appear to be related to the cube of the quantity of air handled. The issue is a little more complicated than this because the pressure is not allowed to fall as low as implied, the air distribution terminals needing a minimum pressure for their proper operation and the automatic control of fan capacity also having a bearing on the matter. Furthermore, fan efficiency is not constant over the full range of operating volumes. Nevertheless, VAV systems undoubtedly use less electrical energy for their fans than do constant-volume systems and are popular for this reason.

When cool air flows over a ceiling from a supply grille or slot its throw to the point where it enters the occupied zone (Fig. 4.2.5) is roughly proportional to the volume as well as the velocity with which it leaves the slot or grille. There is therefor a risk with VAV systems that, with a reduction in air quantity helped by the anti-buoyancy effect of the low temperature, the air may leave the ceiling too soon and enter the occupied zone. If this happens and local discomfort results it is called 'dumping'. In fact, dumping can be avoided if the air distribution terminals are properly selected but the risk that it might occur limits the turn-down possible. Two types of device are in common use. One arranges to keep the supply air velocity constant as the volume is reduced and this type can turn down to about 20% of its design, maximum volume. The other type diminishes the supply air velocity in step with the volume and can only perform satisfactorily down to about 40% of design airflow. Fig. 4.4.3 illustrates this.

The inherent defect of the VAV system is that it has no natural heating capacity. The naive answer is to provide warm air in the winter, instead of cold, reversing the action of the thermostats controlling the air distribution terminals in each room so that they deliver more air upon fall in temperature, instead of less. This is not satisfactory because it is almost certain that not all rooms treated by the VAV system will simultaneously suffer heat losses – some rooms will have heat gains because of sunshine through the windows, say, coupled with the heat given off by people and lights. An increased supply of hot air to one room could be satisfactory but disastrous for another. There are three solutions possible: double duct VAV, terminal re-heat and perimeter heating. The first of these is expensive in capital cost and introduces complications: as the heat gains diminish the supply of cold air is throttled to its minimum acceptable value (in terms of providing enough fresh air and avoiding dumping) and is kept constant thereafter, further reductions in heat gain and subsequent heat losses being dealt with by mixing hot and cold airstreams. (Section 4.4.5.4).

The second possibility is to provide a re-heater battery at each VAV distribution device. The operative principle is similar to that of the double duct version: upon

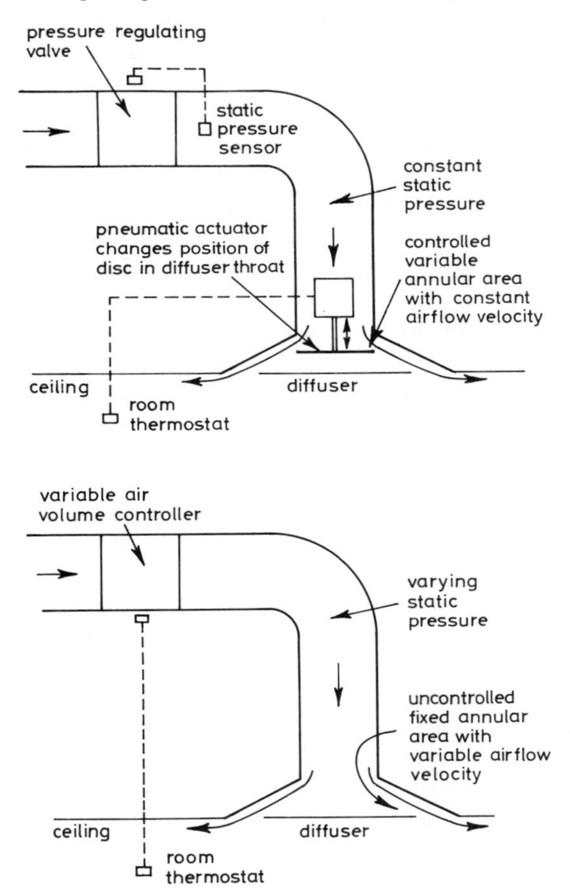

Fig. 4.4.3. *Variable and fixed geometry VAV terminals*

fall in temperature sensed by a room thermostat the airflow rate is reduced to its minimum after which it stays constant and further reductions in heat gain, followed by heat losses, are offset by warming the airstream by means of the re-heater battery. Terminal re-heat is usually provided by LTHW but it may be electric, if the loads are small. Waste heat from the condenser of the refrigeration plant has also been used, a plate heat exchanger being interposed between it and the cooling tower to make sure the heater batteries do not get fouled up. When condenser cooling water is used like this its flow temperature is likely to be of the order of 35°C to 40°C, so as to avoid problems of high condensing pressures, and the heater batteries may then have to be as much as four rows deep. The cheapest, most practical and most popular solution is to fit finned tube or radiators around the building perimeter. These are fed with LTHW at conventional temperatures (85°C flow, 65°C return) and deal with the fabric heat loss and the infiltration of cold air from outside. The flow temperature is compensated against outside air temperature from, say, 85°C in design winter conditions to perhaps 20°C when it is also 20°C outside. Although this is a little wasteful in thermal energy since no account is taken of the benefits of casual gains it does mean that the VAV system can be left to deal with heat gains only and so is simplified.

When a VAV system throttles the air quantity supplied to the building it also reduces the amount of fresh air delivered, unless something is done to prevent this. The ventilation rate of fresh air must be kept above a desirable, or even a statutory, minimum for obvious reasons, and the automatic control system must arrange for fresh air dampers to be opened and recirculated air dampers to be closed as the total volume handled decreases.

One other aspect of automatic control deserves attention: as individual VAV units throttle the air, pressure in the duct behind them builds up, making it more difficult for them to exercise proper thermostatic control, and increasing the noise produced. The solution is to sense the static pressure in the duct system and to reduce the capacity of the supply and extract fans as this increases. Fan capacity can be decreased by changing the inclination of variable position guide vanes at the fan inlet eye, if it is a centrifugal fan, or by altering the pitch angle of the blades if it is axial flow. The location of the pressure sensor is crucial if the full benefit of the energy saving characteristic of a VAV system is to be achieved. The worst possible position is at the fan discharge because this will then be controlled at a nominally constant pressure and, since the absorbed fan power depends on pressure, it will not fall very much as the fan turns down the total volume handled (Ref. 3). It is far better to follow current practice and to place the sensor from two-thirds to three-quarters of the way along the ducting from the fan discharge to the uttermost VAV terminal unit.

One further point: air distribution in the duct system supplying the VAV units is usually at medium velocity, in the range from 10 to 12·5 m/s, in order to minimise the fan total pressure and so reduce the fan power and the energy used. The extract fan also has guide vanes or variable pitch blades and is turned down in harmony with the supply fan. Its duct system is much less elaborate than that supplying air and is invariably sized on low velocity principles.

4.4.5.4 Double duct systems

Each air conditioned room is provided with an air distribution device termed a mixing box. A pair of ducts, one conveying cold and the other hot air, feeds the mixing boxes throughout the building and each box modulates the proportions of hot and cold air accepted by mixing them under the control of a room thermostat. Because two ducts are involved greater demands are made on building space for their accommodation and air distribution is at high velocity (15 to 20 m/s), as a rule. Double duct systems therefore tend to operate at high fan total pressures (1·75 to 2·25 kPa) and are consequently expensive to run. Their advantage is that they offer full cooling and full heating capacity at each terminal unit. Fig. 4.4.4 shows a schematic drawing of a double duct system and plant.

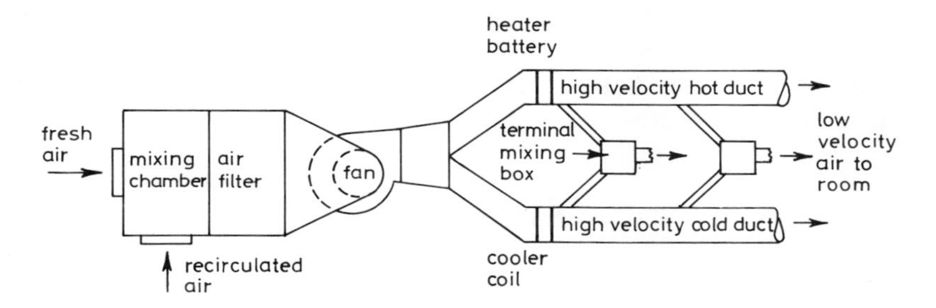

Fig. 4.4.4. *Diagram of a double duct system and plant*

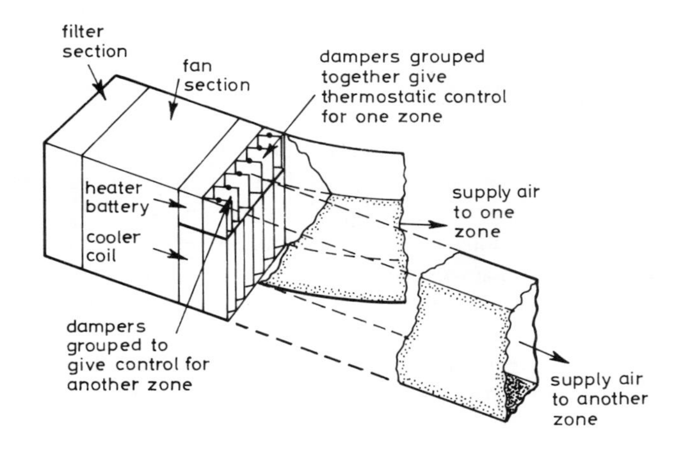

Fig. 4.4.5. *Diagram of a multi-zone unit*

4.4.5.5 Multi-zone units

An air-handling unit mixes recirculated and fresh air which is filtered and blown over a pair of coils. The coils are arranged one above the other, in the same plane. The uppermost is fed with LTHW and is termed the 'hot deck' while the lower may be a direct-expansion or chilled water coil and is termed the 'cold deck'.

Air from the fan is blown onto both coils but motorised dampers on their downstream side dictate the quantity that flows over each deck. Fig. 4.4.5 illustrates this and we see that by having the dampers across the hot deck 90° out of phase with those over the cold deck, rotation of their common damper spindles will cause them to open and close in opposition, thus achieving controlled mixing of hot and cold airstreams, downstream. Several ducts, handling roughly equal quantities of air, lead from the downstream side of the coils to the various treated rooms. Thermostatic control is achieved independently in each room by actuating the mixing dampers for each supply duct. In principle, this system is similar to the double duct, except that mixing occurs in the plant room rather than in the treated rooms. Because each conditioned space has its own supply duct the application of multi-zone units must be limited to cases where the air handling plant is comparatively close to the treated areas.

4.4.6 Air-water systems. (See also section 3.5.9)

Since water has a greater specific heat capacity than air and a very much greater density it has become the practice to deal with part of the heat gains by distributing chilled water to thermostatically controlled terminal units in the conditioned rooms and to augment this by the provision of treated air, less building space then being used than with an all-air system. Several systems of this type have evolved.

4.4.6.1 Perimeter-induction.

Originally conceived to suit the climate of the north-eastern part of the United States, with its severe winter sharply distinguished from its warm summer, a change-over version was at first devised. In this form secondary water and primary air are delivered to the induction units in each room, usually at the perimeter beneath the window cill. Fig. 4.4.6 shows a typical unit arrangement. In summer the water is chilled and its flow through the cooler coil in the unit is thermostatically controlled from a room or return air thermostat in the airstream induced over the coil. The primary air is filtered, cooled and dehumidified in a central plant and re-heated enough to offset the fabric heat losses. Thus, in summer design weather both the primary air and the secondary water deal with the sensible heat gains but as the outside temperature falls, with seasonal changes, the primary air is progressively heated (as was the LTHW fed to the perimeter heating system used with a VAV system) so that it just deals with the heat loss through the building envelope and the natural infiltration, according to Eqn. 4.2.9 and Eqn. 4.3.2, leaving the secondary water to cope with the sensible heat gains (P + L + S). In its winter mode of operation the primary air is humidified by adiabatic saturation in the air handling plant to a temperature of about 10°C. After allowing for a rise of 2°C or 3°C in temperature for fan power and duct heat gain it reaches the induction units at about 13°C and deals with the smaller sensible heat gain likely in winter. Meanwhile the secondary water is warmed to about 85°C in order to deal with the heat losses.

A changeover form of operation has not proved satisfactory in the variable climate of the United Kingdom. Our winters are generally not so cold that the large heating capacity of the secondary coil when fed with LTHW at 85°C is necessary and there are generally rather more heat gains in winter than the primary air alone can deal with. As a consequence a non-changeover version of the perimeter-induction system has been developed and this has proved most suitable for the United Kingdom climate. It is simple in operation: the system works in the summer mode throughout the year.

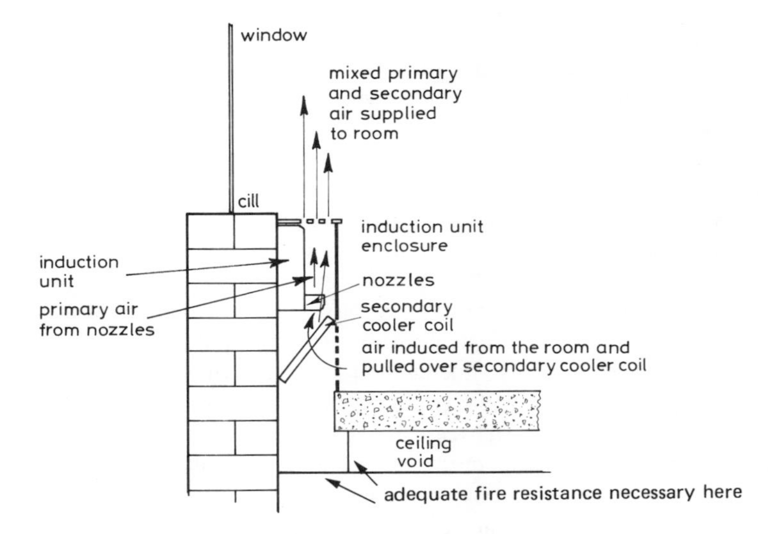

Fig. 4.4.6. *Section through a typical perimeter induction unit*

A more expensive form is the four-pipe perimeter-induction design. A pair of pipes conveys chilled, secondary water and another pair circulates LTHW. Each induction unit contains two secondary coils – one for heating and the other for cooling. Although automatic dampers (self-actuated by the static pressure in the primary air duct) have been used to vary the output of the two coils in sequence by throttling the induced airflow over them, some air leakage usually occurs and a pair of automatic valves, one in each of the cold and hot flow pipes, is a better form of control, no leakage of thermal energy then being possible. With this system the primary air is kept at a constant temperature of about 12°C or 13°C and full heating and cooling capacity is always available by means of the secondary coils. Because the two coils operate in sequence no cancellation of cooling and heating takes place and four pipe systems of this type are economical to run.

A four-pipe version that only uses one secondary coil is a possibility but hydraulic problems loom large and it is much better to use two coils. Even worse is the attempt to use only three pipes: a cold and hot pair plus a common return. This is a very bad system. The common return is at too high a temperature for the chillers and at too low a temperature for the boilers.

4.4.6.2 Fan coil units

The terminal unit positioned in each room comprises a small centrifugal fan, washable or disposable filter and chilled water cooler coil. Sometimes a re-heater is fitted and this may be either LTHW or electric. The unit is in the form of a metal cabinet and induces air through a grille in the front of the casing, blowing it out again through another grille in the top. In its commonest, single coil form, chilled water is piped to the units and its flow throttled or diverted around the coil by a motorised valve through the agency of a room or return air thermostat. If chilled water at a temperature significantly below the room dew-point is fed to the units then they provide latent as well as sensible cooling and a condensate drain line must be provided. If the units are piped in a secondary circuit that has its flow temperature controlled at a value that precludes anything except sensible cooling then a drain line is unnecessary. In their cheapest application winter heating is dealt with by operating the units on a changeover basis, LTHW being fed to them in cold weather. As remarked for the case of the induction system, this is seldom a satisfactory solution for the variable and relatively mild climate of the United Kingdom. Fresh air for ventilation purposes may, in the crudest designs, be simply supplied fortuitously through ill-fitting windows but it is more common in this country to fit an auxiliary, ducted ventilation system supplying filtered air. If the units are piped to do sensible cooling then dehumidification must be done by the ventilation system, in which case it includes a cooler coil fed with chilled water at an adequately low temperature for this purpose. It might be thought that heating could be provided by simply including a heater battery in the air handling plant but this is not a good plan because of difficulties during commissioning when it proves hard to balance the air delivered to each room so that it offsets the heat loss. Whereas a ten percent deficiency in the fresh air quantity supplied would escape notice a similar deficit in heating capacity would not. Two-pipe fan coil systems are very successful in tropical climates but the best form in Britain is with four pipes and two coils, when there is no problem with heating and control is excellent if water valves are used.

4.4.6.3 Chilled ceilings

If a secondary piping circuit is used to deliver chilled water at a temperature above the room dew-point to an array of pipes in a ceiling, a considerable amount of sensible cooling can be done by the ceiling, through radiation and natural convection. An auxiliary air supply to deal with the latent heat gains and give enough fresh air for ventilation purposes is essential, of course. Although originally conceived as steel pipes buried in the soffit of the concrete slab of an intermediate floor or a roof, the chilled ceiling in its modern form consists of loops of pipes attached to the upper surface of a suspended metal ceiling (usually aluminium).

As little as 200 mm is needed to accommodate the ceiling and pipework. Fig. 4.4.7 illustrates a typical arrangement and we see that sound-absorbing material can be laid between the pipes to give an acoustic effect. Ceilings to carry chilled water can have pipes at 200, 300 and 450 mm centres, giving flexibility in layout and sensible cooling capacities of the order of 100 W/m^2. Some of the pipes, near the perimenter, can be used to carry LTHW, at a suitably controlled temperature in order to offset heat losses. Automatic control is done in the usual way, water flow being throttled or diverted in sequence through the hot and chilled ceiling circuits under the command of a room thermostat, on a room or modular basis.

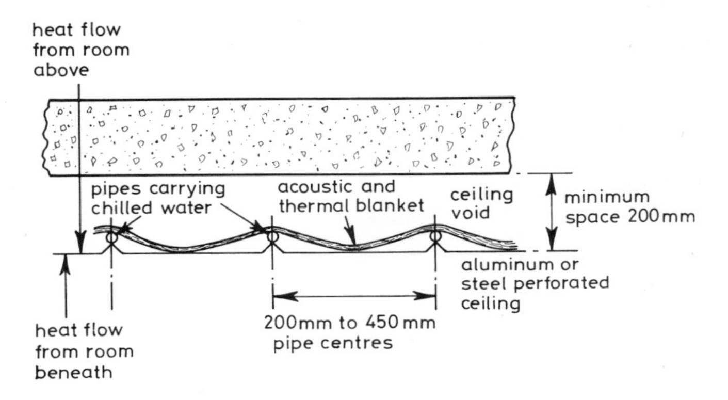

Fig. 4.4.7. *Metal pan chilled ceiling*

4.4.7 References

(1) CIBS Guide Section A2 'Weather and Solar Data' 1982
(2) ASHRAE Handbook 'Fundamentals'. Chapter 26. American Society of Heating Refrigeration and Air-Conditioning Engineers 1791 Tullie Circle NE Atlanta Ga USA 30329
(3) JONES, W. P. 'Air Conditioning Applications and Design'. Edward Arnold (Publishers) Ltd

4.4.8 Glossary

A Area (m^2)
I Intensity of solar radiation normal to a surface (W/m^2)
L Rate of heat emission by electric lighting (W)
M Rate of heat emission by machines (W)
P Rate of heat emission by people (W)
Q Rate of sensible heat gain (W)
Q_s Total rate of sensible heat gain (W)
S Rate of heat gain by solar radiation through windows (W)

T Rate of heat transmission through the fabric of a building by virtue of air-to-air temperature difference (W)
U 'U value'. Thermal transmittance coefficient (W/m^2 °C)
f A decrement factor
h_{so} Outside surface heat flow coefficient (W/m^2 °C)
t_e Sol-air temperature (°C)
t_θ Sol-air temperature at time θ (°C)
t_{em} Average sol-air temperature over 24 hours (°C)
t_o Outside air temperature (°C)
t_r Room air temperature (°C)
α Absorption coefficient of a surface
ϕ Time lag of a wall or roof (h)
θ Time (h)

Chapter 4.5

Heat recovery

James Leary, C.Eng., M.I.Mech.E., M.C.I.B.S.
Head, Environmental Engineering Section, The Electricity Council

4.5.1 Introduction

Equipment is available for the recovery of energy from almost any energy source to be found within a commercial building or factory. Very often the energy source is exhaust air from ventilation systems or industrial processes. Sensible heat or latent heat can be recovered and recycled. Energy can be recovered from flue gas exhausted from direct combustion in boilers and drying processes. Energy is available for recovery either from factory process or refrigeration systems in which the energy is normally discharged in cooling towers or air cooled condensers.

Once a waste heat source has been identified, it must be matched with a simultaneous heat demand of comparable size and not too distant. Regarding the type of heat recovery equipment to be used in any particular application the main factor is the temperature range of the heat demand relative to the heat source. Where the temperature of the heat source is greater than the temperature range of the heat demand, a direct heat exchanger can be used. Examples of such equipment are thermal wheels, heat pipes, recuperators, run-around coils, plate heat exchangers, shell and tube exchangers. In applications where the temperature of the heat source is lower than the temperature range of the heat demand a heat pump would be necessary to upgrade the energy to a sufficiently high temperature at which it can be usefully employed.

When examining the economic viability of heat recovery plant the two major factors to be taken into consideration are the average load on the plant and the number of hours of operation during the year. If plant is correctly sized it will tend to have a high load factor and will therefore tend to be cost-effective. Furthermore the viability of the installation will improve as the hours of operation increase. Many industrial process applications operate 16 and 24 hours per day. Hospitals are in continuous operation and swimming pools and leisure centres operate at least 12 hours per day. Premises such as these are usually found to be sources of cost-effective heat recovery installations and many other examples of the use of heat recovery equipment may be found in commercial and industrial premises.

4.5.2 Heat recovery from gases

4.5.2.1 Comparative performance

Before considering the choice of equipment for a specific application, it is important to ensure that the performance of each type of equipment is compared on a similar, objective basis. A common mistake is to express efficiency in terms of the ratio of temperatures, which is only correct for equal or balanced mass gas flows. The user is only interested in the amount of energy that can be recovered from that which was previously being wasted.

Let us define the temperature of the contaminated exhaust as t_c and the mass flow rate (or standard volume flow rate, since the constants cancel out in this calculation) as q_c, the recovered temperature t_r at a flow rate q_r and the ambient temperature t_a.

The energy in the exhaust is then proportional to

$$q_c(t_c - t_a) \tag{4.5.1}$$

The recovered energy is proportional to

$$q_r(t_r - t_a) \tag{4.5.2}$$

The heat recovery efficiency is therefore equal to:

$$\frac{q_r(t_r - t_a)}{q_c(t_c - t_a)} \tag{4.5.3}$$

Each type of heat exchanger has performance characteristics from which the heat recovered or the heat recovery efficiency can be calculated, as above, under given conditions.

Each of the above parameters can be measured in practice and the actual performance confirmed. Since the only possible heat losses from a heat exchanger are radiation losses from the frame (which should in any case be insulated) and this is minimal, the actual performance should conform with predicted performance within reasonable limits of the errors of measurement. The most common reason for an apparent discrepancy in performance is an incorrect flow rate which cannot be measured accurately due to ductwork configuration. If one flow rate is known, however, the performance can be derived from this and the four temperature measurements.

The heat gained by the supply air must be equal to that lost from the exhaust stream, since there is nowhere else for it to go. If the final exhaust temperature $= t_f$, it follows that:

$$q_c(t_c - t_f) = q_r(t_r - t_a) \tag{4.5.4}$$

or

$$\frac{q_c(t_c - t_f)}{q_r(t_r - t_a)} = 1 \tag{4.5.5}$$

i.e.: the ratio of the mass air flows can be calculated accurately from the measurements of temperature. The object of referring to this calculation is to emphasise that the performance can be measured and should conform with calculated predictions. If is does not, there must be a logical, and resolvable, explanation.

The only remaining variable to consider is the pressure drop, or the resistance introduced into the air stream by the heat recovery equipment and any comparison of different types of equipment should, therefore, be based on performance calculated from the same air flow rates, temperatures and pressure drop. However, performance is not the only criterion. Each type of equipment has specific advantages and disadvantages which need to be considered in the light of the specific application.

Table 4.5.1 covers the principal types of equipment for the majority of general commercial and industrial applications. The efficiencies given are on the basis already stated, for approximately similar pressure drops and what might be expected in a practical configuration in use. Each type of unit has its own specific advantages and disadvantages and these need to be considered for a given application, but it is logical to consider the more efficient equipment preferentially, as that is likely to produce the best capital return.

Table 4.5.1 *Air or gas heat exchangers: performance comparison*

	Heat Transfer Efficiency	Maximum Temperature
Heat Regenerators	75% Total Heat	Normal environmental conditions
	80% Sensible Heat	200°C – Aluminium 400°C – Stainless Steel
Heat Pipes	55–65% Sensible Heat	150°C – Aluminium 400°C – Copper
Heat Recuperators	55–65% Sensible Heat	70°C – Aluminium 170°C – Aluminium 400°C – Stainless Steel
Run Around Coils	50–60% Sensible Heat	Normal environmental conditions

Note: These are typical practical performances for similar pressure drops and operating conditions, and would apply to the majority of the most common applications.

The choice of equipment depends firstly on the temperature of the discharge and secondly, on the chemical and/or physical nature of any contaminants in the exhaust stream.

4.5.2.2 The sensible heat regenerator (The "thermal wheel".)

Regenerators are of all metal construction, with variations in materials and design to satisfy a wide range of operating conditions. Heat recovery performance, reliability and in particular, the capability to recover heat from contaminated discharges with insignificant cross-contamination of the supply air, have all been proved in practice in a wide range of industrial and other applications. Examples are:

contaminated space heating – workshops, laboratories, hospitals, swimming pools
recycling – all types of process drying plant, e.g. for paper print, board textiles, food products, rubber, plastics, resins
recovery for other use – kilns, furnaces, ovens, gas-fired boilers.

The standard range of units covers flow rates of 0·16–39·4 m^3/s and exhaust temperatures of up to about 950°C. The heat transfer media for the various operating temperatures are given in table 4.5.2.

The regenerator is installed with one half in the exhaust air duct and the other half in the fresh air intake duct, such that exhaust and intake air streams counterflow. (Fig. 4.5.1) The rotor rotates between the two air streams. Sensible heat in the exhaust system is absorbed by the heat exchange media and given up to the supply air stream, by a surface heat transfer effect. An equilibrium condition is established resulting in an effective flow of sensible heat from the warmer to the cooler air stream, providing preheated fresh air which can then be returned to the plant air intake or used to meet any other heating demand.

Where the exhaust is cooled air, energy flow is in the reverse direction and the supply air is pre-cooled – although this application is less common for sensible heat regenerators. The amount of heat recovered is determined by the temperature and mass flow rate of each airstream. The heat transfer efficiency is determined by rotor speed and the velocity of each airstream, which should be balanced for

Table 4.5.2 *Heat Transfer Media*

Maximum temperature °C	Media	Rotor
200	Aluminium	Aluminium
425	Stainless Steel	Stainless Steel
950	Stainless Steel	Stainless Steel

optimum performance. For a given flow rate, controlling rotor speed therefore controls the recovered air temperature, if this is required.

A purge unit is designed to prevent contamination of the supply air; this is a segment of ducting at the central division, into which each segment of the rotor is 'flushed' by supply air as it moves from the exhaust to the supply air stream. Entrained exhaust air or gases and any dust particles, are, in the standard unit, returned to the exhaust stream. (Fig. 4.5.2)

Fig. 4.5.1. *Sensible Heat Regenerator. ('Thermal Wheel')*
(Curwen and Newbery Limited)

4.5.2.3 The total heat regenerator

The unit is similar to the sensible heat regenerator described previously except that the heat exchange material is designed to absorb moisture from the warm air stream and transfer it to the cold stream in addition to the sensible heat. The heat exchange material is manufactured from non-metallic fibrous material and is permanently bacteriostatic, inert to any contamination normally found in ventilation air and cannot itself cause any contamination of intake air. It is assembled in sections within each segment of the rotor and can be removed for easy cleaning or servicing, if necessary. This should only be infrequently required, if at all. The nature of the material permits moisture absorption (giving latent heat transfer) without any physical change of state. This means that it is not necessary to avoid conditions causing condensation, provided icing conditions are avoided. The medium can be washed with water or a light detergent solution or may be cleaned with low pressure steam. The distribution of fibre in the material breaks up the air flow through it, improving heat transfer. Experience has shown that this cannot cause dust particles to be trapped within it, as the supply/exhaust air counterflow results in any accumulation of dust on or near the surfaces and this may be removed by periodic vacuum cleaning or washing.

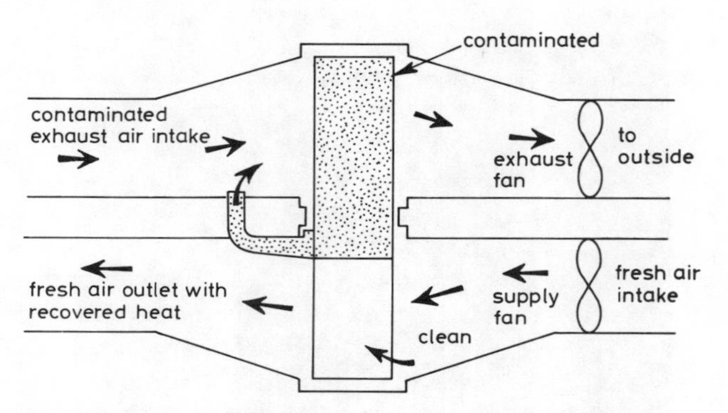

Fig. 4.5.2. *Purge unit in heat regenerator*

Fig. 4.5.3. *Heat Pipe Recovery Unit* (Curwen and Newbery Limited)

4.5.2.4 The heat pipe

The heat pipe recovery unit is designed to recover energy normally exhausted to atmosphere in air or gaseous discharges. The recovered energy is transferred to a counterflowing supply airstream. A unit is illustrated in Fig. 4.5.3. Working with dry airstreams, the heat pipe recovery unit is a sensible heat exchanger, but when handling humid exhaust airstreams a degree of latent heat recovery is achieved with the advantage of not transferring moisture. Generally speaking the transfer of moisture in the vapour phase is only required for air conditioning systems and in such cases the heat pipe recovery unit should not be used.

As both the supply and exhaust airstreams are separated by a division plate the two airstreams cannot intermix.

The heat pipe recovery unit ideally should be used where:

Air/gas streams are between − 10°C to + 300°C.
High static pressure differences exist between the two airstreams.
There is limited headroom.
Fan positions are fixed
No intermixing of air/gas streams can be permitted
There are low to medium levels of contaminants in the air/gas stream
Moisture is likely to condense out on the exhaust air/gas side
There is a considerable imbalance of masses or volumes between the two airstreams

4.5.2.5 Construction of heat pipes

(a) *Flat plate fin*

For low temperatures up to 200°C and certain industrial applications flat plate fin units may be used. The flat plate fins can be either of aluminium, pre-painted aluminium, copper or pre-tinned copper. The heat pipes would be of seamless copper tubes pre-tinned if required.

The heat pipes are designed on a staggered pattern 40 × 40 mm allowing for maximum fin efficiency, and are mechanically expanded and thoroughly fixed to the plate fins to ensure maximum heat transmission from the heat pipes to the fins. The framework for the flat plate fin units is manufactured from galvanised sheet steel. The framework can also be made from aluminium or stainless steel.

(b) *Spiral fin*

For higher temperature applications up to 315°C the secondary heating surface would be spirally wound onto the heat pipes. The heat pipes and secondary heating surface are usually of copper and can be electrotinned if required. The framework for spiral fin units is manufactured from black mild steel.

(c) *Division plate*

Both types of heat pipe recovery units are supplied with division plates which separate the two air/gas streams. The division plate is constructed of the same material as the framework. To accommodate imbalanced airstreams the division plate can be located between $\frac{1}{4}$ and $\frac{3}{4}$ of unit length from one end.

(d) *End covers*
The ends of the heat pipes are protected by airtight end covers constructed of the same material as the framework. The side panels of the frame are designed to allow free expansion of the heat pipes into the depth of the end covers.

(e) *Capillary wicks*
When fitted horizontally, or near to horizontal, all heat pipes will be fitted with capillary wicks. All vertical heat pipes are designed to operate as thermosyphons. In the latter case the evaporator must always be below the condenser.

(f) *Contaminated exhaust airstreams*
When the exhaust airstream contains low to medium quantities of dust/fibre the exhaust airside of the heat pipe recovery unit should be selected with a low number of fins, one fin per 2·5 mm or 3·2 mm. In these cases the supply airside can have a higher number of fins, one fin per 1·8 mm or 2·1 mm. For very dirty applications filters must be used and several heat pipe recovery units are preferable to one large unit. For example a single 8 row unit may be supplied as two 4 row units. Ductwork connections between the two units should be provided with access doors.

4.5.2.6 Operation of heat pipes
The heat pipe recovery unit consists of a large number of individual pipes. Each heat pipe is capable of high thermal conductance. The basic heat pipe consists of an external shell, two end plugs, a capillary wick and a small amount of working fluid. When one end of the heat pipe is heated, (the evaporator) the working fluid vaporises and moves to the cold end of the heat pipe, where it condenses, (the condenser). The condensate then returns back to the evaporator via the capillary wick

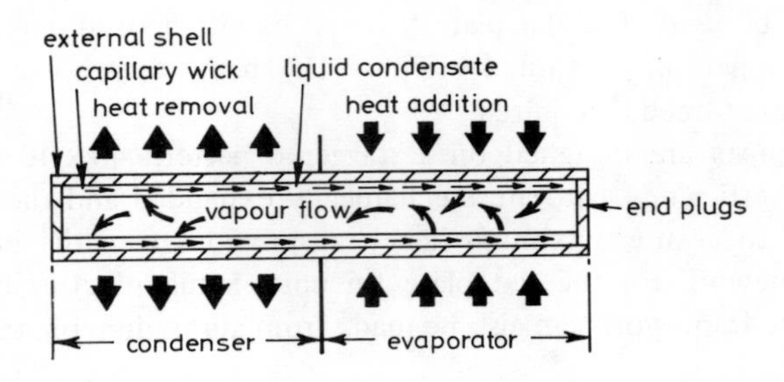

Fig. 4.5.4. *Cutaway view of a single basic heat pipe*

to complete the cycle. The amount of heat transported depends on the latent heat of the working fluid. Large amounts of heat can be transferred with small working fluid mass flow rates and small temperature differences. The operation is indicated in Fig. 4.5.4.

4.5.2.7 Application of heat pipes
The heat pipe recovery unit is well suited for applications where there is a limited

amount of space or low headroom. Units may be supplied with finned heights of 400, 600, 800, 1000 and 1200 mm. For the optimum selection the height should be 50% of the length.

Both the supply and exhaust air fan sets can be fitted in any position relative to the heat pipe recovery unit. Therefore if fan positions are fixed and cannot be moved the heat pipe is a good choice of heat exchanger.

4.5.2.8 Run around coils

The twin coil run around system is designed to recover heat from ventilation or hot air discharges and to preheat supply air, where supply and exhaust ducts are remote from each other – or where, for any other practical reasons, heat regenerators, heat pipes or recuperators cannot be used. The coils are linked together with a simple loop pipe circuit, which contains Ethylene Glycol solution pumped and controlled at the required volume. Sensible heat recovery efficiencies of up to 60% can be obtained with balanced air flows, and energy can be saved all the year round in air conditioning plant.

The schematic drawing, Fig. 4.5.5, indicates how a typical run-around system

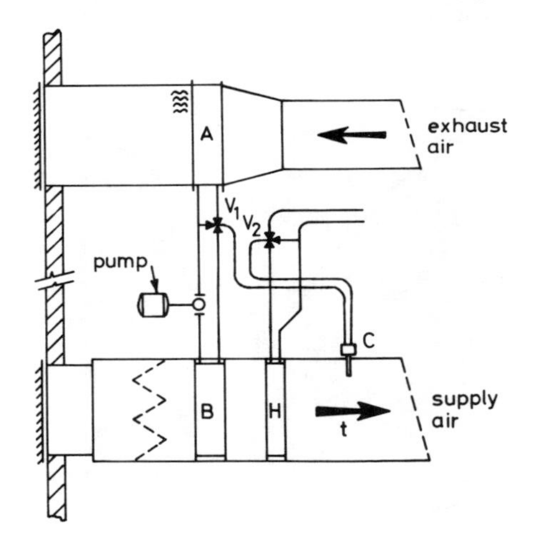

Fig. 4.5.5. *Diagram of run-around coil heat recovery installation*

recovers heat from exhaust air during the heating season. Depending upon the temperature in the discharge duct a solution of Ethylene Glycol is circulated at the required velocity by pumped circulation through the recovery coil *A*, fitted in the exhaust air ductwork, where heat is picked up by the circulating Glycol, which in turn is then circulated through the supply air pre-heat coil *B*. This is fitted in the fresh air intake duct which pre-heats the incoming air stream. The pipe circuit is closed circulation and requires a correctly sized circulating pump, a suitable air separator, expansion tank and, where temperature control is required, a three-way mixing valve can also be fitted.

4.5.2.9 Regulation of run-around coils

The twin coil run-around heat recovery system can be easily regulated. The amount of heat transferred is controlled by a pre-set thermostat to maintain a constant supply air temperature. In Fig. 4.5.5, the heat is absorbed during the winter heating cycle from the exhaust air stream by the heat exchanger A and is transferred to the incoming air stream via the closed pipe circuit and heat exchanger B. The thermostat C controls the heat transfer B via the motorised 3-way valve V_1, sequentially controlling additional heating from the heater battery H via the 3-way valve V_2 in order to maintain the air temperature t constant at the pre-set level. If the demand for heat falls V_2 cuts out before B is reduced.

4.5.2.10 Heat recuperators

Heat recuperators are available in various forms of construction and materials to meet a wide range of operating conditions and are complementary in application to heat regenerators, heat pipe units and run-around coil systems in air to air heat recovery.

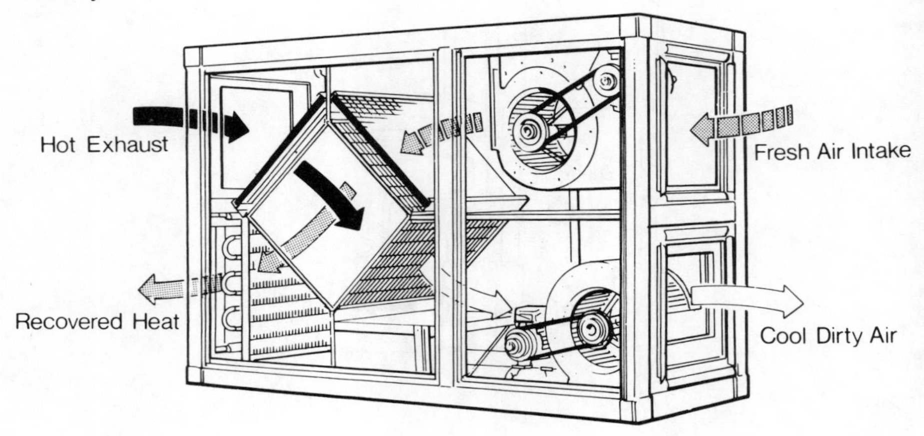

Fig. 4.5.6. *Heat recuperator installed in a ventilation system handling a contaminated extract*

The principal advantages of heat recuperators are:

(a) Positive separation of air streams e.g., for certain types of contaminated exhausts with very high humidity, toxic vapours, or other types of contamination the nature of which will allow recuperator cleaning.

(b) Physical configuration – there may be advantages in certain applications.

(c) Capital cost – this can be lower than alternative equipment in certain applications.

The choice depends on:

(a) Maximum probable exhaust air temperature
(b) The nature and levels of any vapours, dust or other exhaust contamination.

This will depend on ductwork configuration, any space limitations, and the type of recuperator. Typical applications are in heating and ventilating systems, high humidity discharges, and dealing with contaminated industrial discharges. (Fig. 4.5.6)

4.5.3 Heat recovery from flue gases

Heat exchangers are available for recovering heat from the exhaust gases from direct fired processes or boilers. The heat exchangers can be installed in series in the exhaust where sufficient pressure is available. Fig. 4.5.7 illustrates a heat exchanger suitable for installation in the exhaust of a forced draught boiler. The heat exchanger is designed on a firetube principal and consists of black or stainless steel tubes welded into tube end plates. The hot air or gases pass through the tubes

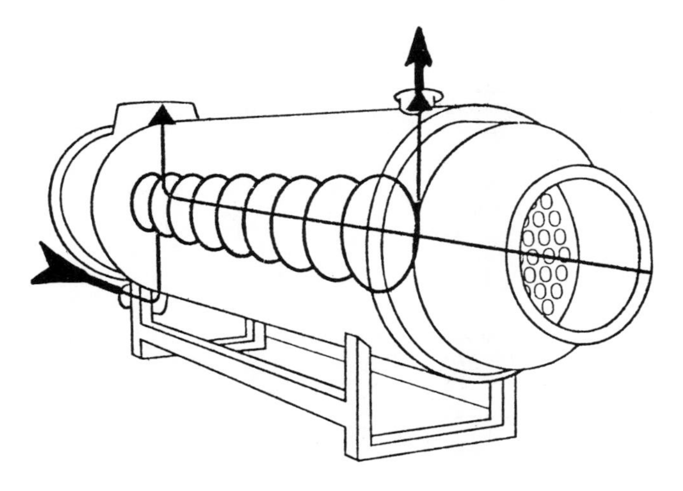

Fig. 4.5.7. *Heat Exchanger suitable for exhaust of forced draught boiler*

(Curwen and Newbery Limited)

which are fully immersed in water or heat transfer fluid. The external shell is insulated with glasswool and clad with aluminium and is constructed from either black mild steel or Cor-ten. As the recovered heat is contained in a thermal fluid or water it can be pumped, distributed and controlled very efficiently. Units are also available for steam raising. Fig. 4.5.8 indicates the heat exchanger mounted in the exhaust from an incinerator and supplying hot water for space heating. In this

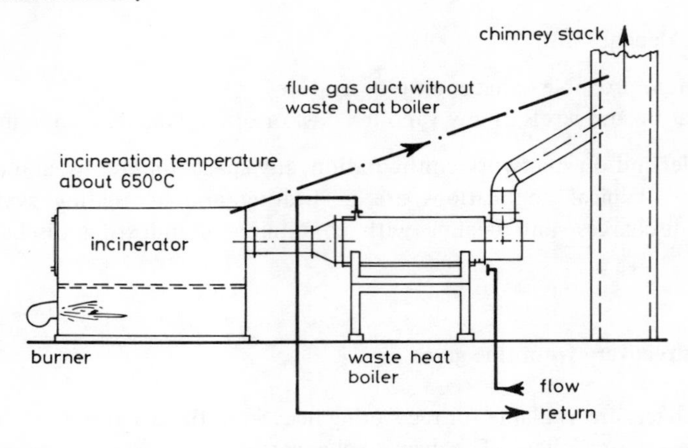

Fig. 4.5.8. *Heat Exchanger in Incinerator Exhaust* (Curwen and Newbury Limited)

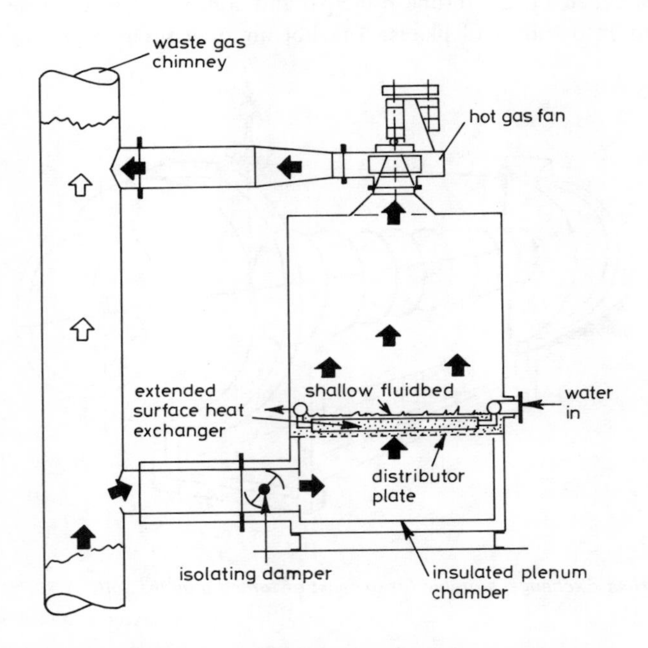

Fig. 4.5.9. *LPHW fluidised bed heat recovery unit installed in a chimney*

(Stone Platt (Crawley) Ltd)

example there is a continuous demand for the hot water, otherwise steam will be generated in the water coil.

A controlled flue gas heat recovery can be effected by installing a heat exchanger in parallel with the exhaust chimney. A packaged heat exchanger of this type may be used to extract useful energy from hot waste gases and transfer it to a secondary fluid. It is based on the principle of shallow fluidbed heat transfer, which is used to simulate a liquid on the waste gas side of the heat exchanger. (Fig. 4.5.9) The fluidised bed principle provides heat transfer rates which are 5–10 times that of a conventional system. The package supplied is complete with waste gas fan and all controls necessary to automatically provide specific outlet conditions for the secondary fluid. Waste heat exchangers are normally installed in parallel with an existing waste gas flue, allowing ease of installation, control of heat recovery to suit required heat loads, ready accessibility for maintenance and operation without affecting the heat source. The secondary fluid can be water (LPHW or HPHW), steam or thermal fluid and can be fed to an existing system or through a completely isolated system.

Heat exchangers are suitable for recovering heat from gases up to a temperature of 1000°C. A range of units can be supplied with outputs of 75 kW–1500 kW, applicable to heat recovery from the combustion products of natural gas, LPG gas oil and other combustible materials. Larger outputs can be achieved by the installation of multiple units.

4.5.4 Heat recovery from liquids

The most common source of heat recovery from liquids is from cooling systems where the energy is normally dissipated over an open cooling tower. The heat dissipated in liquids is usually low grade and therefore close approach temperatures are necessary in the heat exchangers that are provided for heat recovery. (The approach temperature is the difference between the outlet temperature of the fluid being cooled, and the inlet temperature of the fluid being heated.) In order to give a close approach temperature the primary and secondary fluid should have a direct counter flow characteristic and a large surface area. The two types of liquid heat exchanger available are plate heat exchangers and shell and tube exchangers. Plate heat exchangers incorporate a direct counter flow exchange as its basic feature whereas shell and tube exchangers normally operate by cross flow. Therefore a closer approach temperature can be obtained using plate heat exchangers and they tend to be more readily applied in heat recovery applications.

A plate heat exchanger consists of a frame in which independent metal plates supported by rails are clamped between a head and a follower. The plates are sealed at their outer edges and around the ports by gaskets. The system is arranged to give direct counter flow. Gaskets are arranged to give a double seal between the liquid streams and make intermixing impossible. The space between the seals is vented to the atmosphere so that if a leak occurs it is seen and there is an escape path for the pressurised fluid. The pressure limit is 15 to 22 bar and operating temperatures can be at 260°C.

The closely spaced plates have troughs which produce turbulence in the liquids flowing between the plates in thin streams of large area. Without the troughs the cooling liquid, particularly those of higher viscosities, would have laminar flow producing a slow moving insulating layer near the walls and decreasing efficiency. The various designs of plate will induce turbulent flow at Reynolds Numbers between 10 to 250, while in shell and tube heat exchangers velocities must be increased to obtain Reynolds' Numbers of 2300 in order to prevent laminar flow. (The Reynold's Number is an indication of the degree of turbulence).

As the gap through which the cooling water flows in plate heat exchanger units is 3 to 5 mm rather than the 15 to 25 mm in a shell and tube heat exchanger, filtration is important. Self cleaning strainers are incorporated in plate heat exchanger units to deal with filtration.

4.5.5 Heat pumps (See also chapter 4.6)

In applications where heat has to be upgraded to a higher temperature so that it can be usefully employed, a heat pump must be used. A heat pump is exactly the same as any refrigeration machine in that it extracts heat from gas or liquid at a low temperature level and by the vapour compression cycle rejects the heat in a condenser at a higher temperature level. The amount of heat rejected relative to the motive power of the compressor is generally in the range of 2:1 to 5:1 depending upon the operating temperatures and the temperature lift from the cool or evaporator side to the hot or condenser side of the machine.

The terminology that is usually employed when referring to the cold or evaporator side of a refrigeration machine or heat pump is the 'evaporating temperature' when the machine is operating primarily as a refrigeration machine to provide cooling, chilling or freezing, and the 'heat source' when the function of the machine is simply a heat pump to produce high grade energy from a waste heat source. Similarly when referring to the heat rejection side of the machine, it is known as the 'condensing temperature' when operating as a refrigeration machine and the 'condensing temperature' or 'heat demand temperature' when operating as a heat pump. As a fine distinction in terminology, recovering heat from the condenser of a refrigeration machine can be termed 'heat recovery', and when a heat pump is applied to extract heat from a waste heat source it can be termed 'heat reclaim'.

4.5.6 Refrigeration machines

4.5.6.1 General

Refrigeration has been established for many years for chilling and freezing in the food industry and for industrial process work; air conditioning also requires refrigeration. In all these applications chilling is the prime function and in every example heat can be recovered from the condenser rather than be rejected to the atmosphere through cooling towers and air cooled condensers.

4.5.6.2 Dehumidification and drying

Refrigeration equipment is now also being used for purposes of dehumidification and drying rather than the traditional methods which use large quantities of fresh air and raw heat. There are many industrial drying applications, and swimming pools are a good example of dehumidification.

The process of drying is exactly the same as dehumidification. The air within the space is circulated through a dehumidifying coil and the heat extracted is recycled from the condenser back into the air which is returned to the space either for the drying of materials or space heating. Very often supplementary heat is required to give space temperature control throughout the variations in external weather conditions.

There are two basic types of refrigeration plant used for chilling or dehumidification and for simplicity can be referred to as direct and indirect. 'Direct' is where the evaporator or condenser is applied directly into the medium being cooled or heated and in an 'indirect' system water is chilled at the evaporator, and water is used at the condenser in a water cooled condenser. There are a number of permutations in the plant arrangement but the most significant item of plant in connection with the design and control of heat recovery installations is the type of condenser. Heat recovery from a water cooled condenser is a simpler engineering problem than a direct condenser arrangement but is usually more expensive. The water cooled condenser would usually be employed in large installations or where heat is to be circulated to a number of heat exchangers or over large distances. In relatively small installations and where the heat demand is concentrated in one or two closely located heat exchangers a direct air cooled condenser would often be used.

For evaporating temperatures below 5°C the refrigerants usually employed are R11, R12, R22 and R502, and the associated saturated gas temperature at the condenser would be a maximum of 60°C. Where condenser temperatures of the order of 90°C are required, R113 and R114 would be used.

To indicate the plant arrangement and method of control, typical systems using water cooled condensers are described.

4.5.7 Heat recovery from water cooled condensers

4.5.7.1 General

In a refrigeration heat recovery system, where the refrigeration machine employs a water cooled condenser, the condenser and heating water circuits are integrated as illustrated in Fig. 4.5.10. The basic principle of control of the system is that the heat input from the heating plant and the heat rejection at the cooling tower are sequential from the one sensor, T_1, located in the heating water flow and the heat produced at the condenser of the refrigeration machine is supplied directly to the heating circuit. If this heat is insufficient to meet the heating requirements of the building, as sensed by a fall in the heating water flow temperature, then the supplementary heating valve V_1 is modulated open allowing heat to enter the heating circuit. If the condenser heat exceeds the heating requirements as sensed by a rise in the heating water flow temperature then the cooling tower bypass valve V_2 is modulated so that the surplus heat is rejected.

As a point of distinction, it should be noted that whereas with the conventional air conditioning design, the cooling tower is controlled to maintain a constant water temperature 'on' to the condenser, with the heat recovery design, the cooling tower is controlled to maintain a constant water temperature 'off' the condenser. Additionally it will be seen that the heat recovery design uses a closed circuit from the condenser so as to prevent contaminants entering the heating circuit. This can be achieved by a closed cooling tower or provision of double condensers.

The heat produced at the condenser is necessarily low grade; the water flow

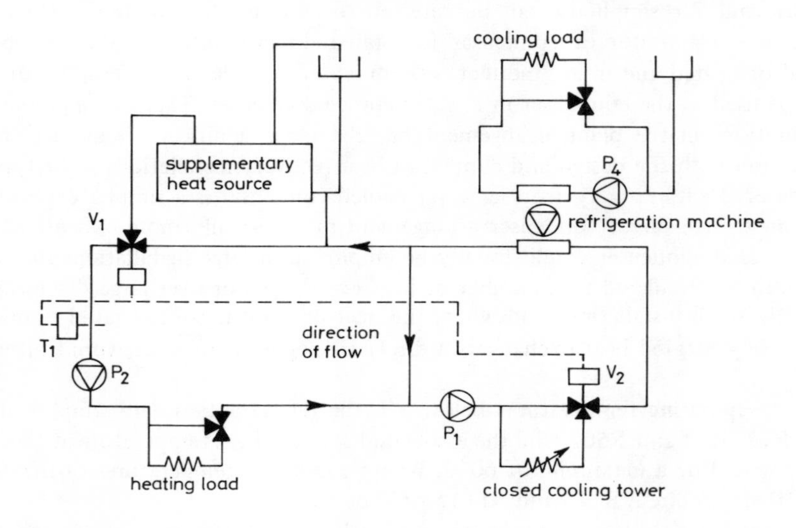

Fig. 4.5.10. *Basic Heat Recovery system with closed cooling tower*

temperature being governed by the maximum condensing pressure of the refrigeration machine. The heating equipment must therefore be sized for lower water temperatures. However, to minimise the size of the heating equipment, and therefore its costs, the aim of the heat recovery design is to produce at times of design heating load as high a heating water flow temperature as possible within the limitations imposed by the refrigeration machine. The maximum heating water flow temperature is achieved by employing small control differentials of the sensor T_1 and operating the condensing pressure near to the safety cut out pressure of the refrigeration machine. However it is vitally important that the control bands and dead zones are set sufficiently wide to ensure stable and correct operation of the heat recovery system. Generally, when a heat recovery system fails to operate at its optimum performance, it is the control design and the settings of the control differentials which are normally at fault.

The maximum water flow temperatures that can be achieved by the refrigeration plant are governed by the manufacturer's maximum working discharge pressures. With reciprocating machines the limits imposed on working pressures are determined by the condenser strength, the compressor being normally capable of operating at greater pressures and refrigerant temperatures. However, with screw machines, in addition to the condenser design, the maximum refrigerant temperature is limited due to the method of lubrication and motor cooling. In hermetic screw machines, the motor windings are cooled by a mixture of discharge refrigerant gas and lubricating oil. The motor winding temperatures are therefore dependent on the condensing temperature. With open screw machines, the motor cooling is achieved by the ambient air and therefore higher condensing temperatures can be used.

The condensing pressure is prevented from exceeding the manufacturer's limits by two safety pressure devices, the high pressure cut out and the pressure relief valve. The high pressure cut out switch shuts off the refrigeration machine should the condensing pressure exceed its set point. This control has to be manually reset before the machine can restart. If the pressure continues to rise above the high pressure cut out setting, then the pressure relief valve will open and allow refrigerant to discharge to atmosphere.

4.5.7.2 Condenser arrangements

The heat recovery system illustrated in Fig. 4.5.10 uses a refrigeration machine with a single bundle condenser and a closed cooling tower. Many manufacturers offer refrigeration machines with two condenser water circuits allowing separate water circuits for the cooling tower and the heating system. This enables an open cooling tower to be used without the risk of contaminating the heating circuit. Fig. 4.5.11 illustrates the types of condenser arrangements. A double bundle condenser comprises a single shell with two banks of tubes. The refrigerant gas which passes between the shell and the tubes can give up its latent heat to either water circuit. Some manufacturers adopt the twin condenser arrangement whereby two standard single bundle condensers are piped into the refrigeration circuit. These are connected either in series or in parallel. With the series arrangement the refrigerant gas is firstly piped to the heating condenser where it totally or partially condenses, giving up its latent heat to the heating circuit. The gas and liquid mixture then passes to the cooling tower condenser where the remainder of the gas condenses. In the parallel arrangement, the refrigerant can flow into either the heating or cooling tower condenser. To ensure stable gas flows, it is necessary to maintain equal pressures within the condensers. For this reason gas and liquid equalising pipes are fitted between the condensers.

The fundamental principle of the heat recovery system is that the addition of supplementary heat by the heating plant and the rejection of heat at the cooling tower are controlled in sequence by a single sensor T_1 located in the heating water flow as illustrated in Fig. 4.5.10. This control prevents the addition and rejection of heat occurring simultaneously. However, there will be fluctuations in the condenser water flow temperature due to the capacity control of the refrigeration machine and it is necessary that the control differentials are set sufficiently wide to prevent these fluctuations causing hunting between the two control functions. In all heat recovery installations delay timers are required on the capacity loading of the compressors so as to give sufficient time for the controls to respond before any successive increase in condensing pressure.

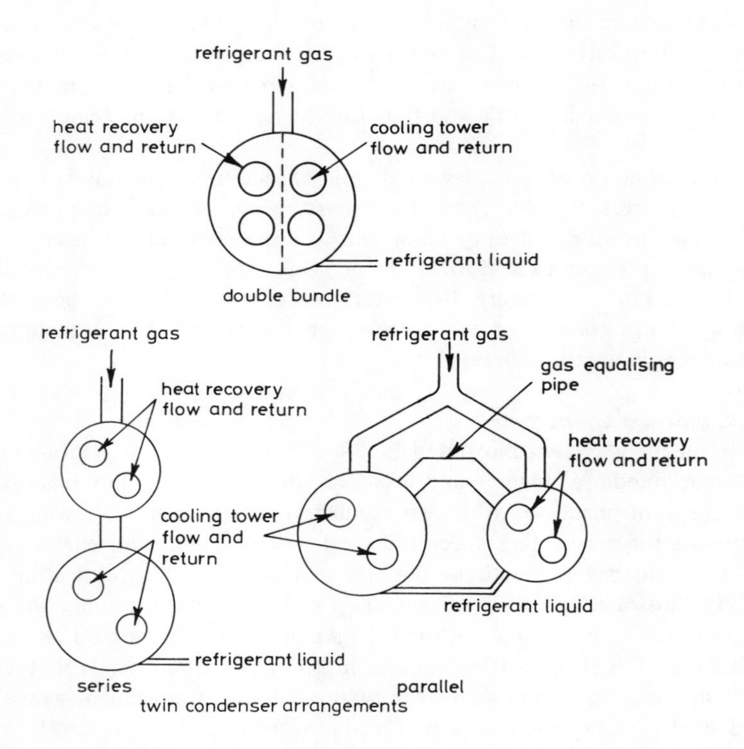

Fig. 4.5.11. *Configurations of heat recovery condensers*

4.5.7.3 Control bands

The control bands necessary for stable operation depend on a number of system parameters and would normally be set up as required at the commissioning stage of the system. However, the design engineer requires an estimate of the control differentials at the design stage of the plant, to determine the maximum heating water flow temperature and hence the size of the heating equipment.

The control bands for the supplementary heat injection and cooling tower rejection depend on the type of control used and the hydraulic system response. It is clear that wide control bands used with proportional control will ensure good stable operation but this is detrimental to the aim of the heat recovery system which is to provide at times of design heating load as high a heating water flow temperature as posssible. It is therefore necessary to select the controls to give control bands as narrow as possible.

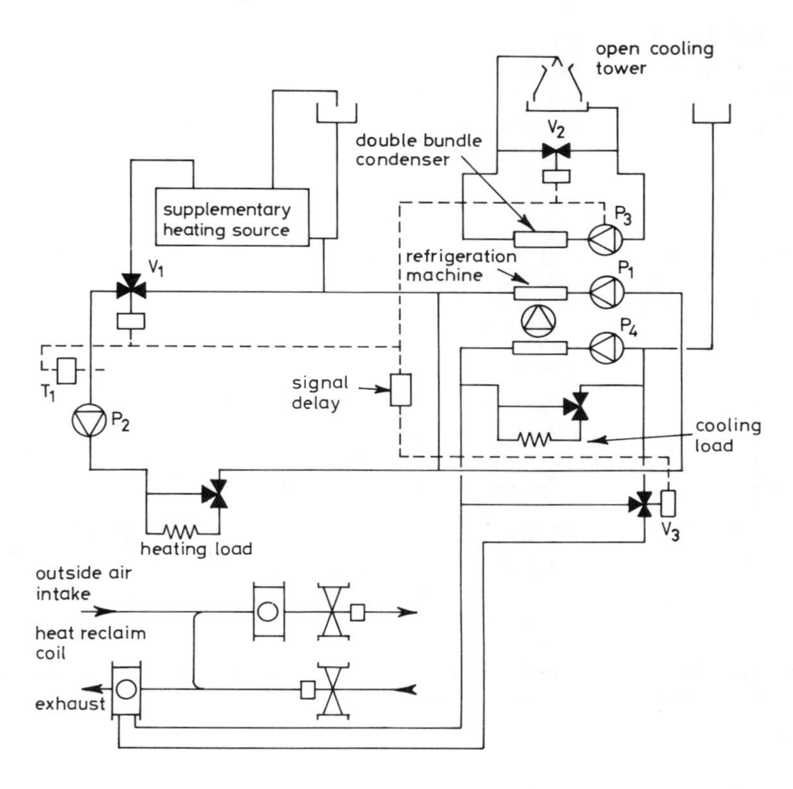

Fig. 4.5.12. *Heat recovery system with open cooling tower and incorporating exhaust air heat reclaim*

The control bands are separated by a dead zone which is calculated to prevent hunting between the two control functions of providing supplementary heat and heat rejection. The dead zone must encompass the fluctuations in heating water flow temperature due to the capacity control of the refrigeration machine. The temperature variations in the condenser water flow due to the cyclic changes in refrigeration capacity determine the required dead zone.

Fig. 4.5.12 is a schematic diagram of a heat recovery air conditioning installation where the refrigeration machine employes a double bundle condenser together with an open cooling tower. In addition to heat recovery from the cooling system a heat reclaim coil is installed in the ventilation air exhaust. The control differential for the main control sensor is indicated in Fig. 4.5.13. Note that at the minimum temperature of the heating flow at sensor T_1 the heating valve V_1 is fully open and on rise in temperature the following sequence takes place:

(i) Heating valve V_1 closes
(ii) Heat reclaim valve V_3 closes
(iii) The cooling tower pump P_3 comes into operation
(iv) The cooling tower valve V_2 opens

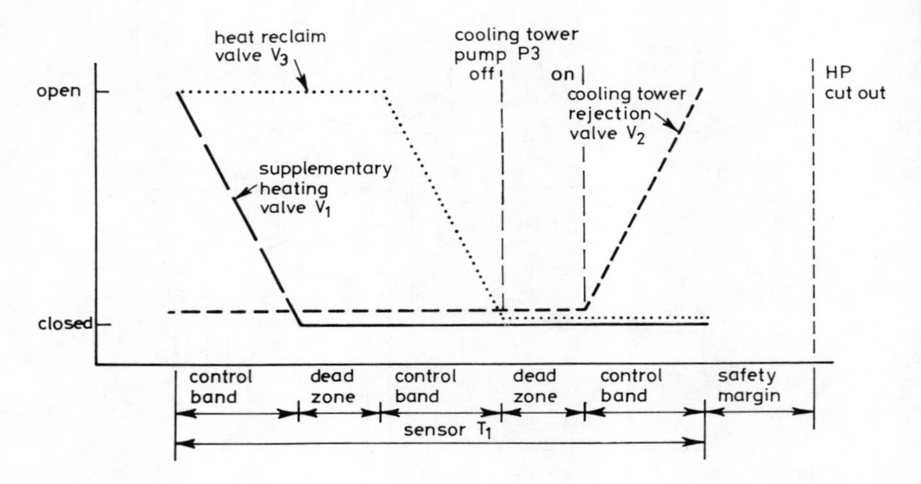

Fig. 4.5.13. *Control differentials of heating water flow sensor for a heat recovery system incorporating exhaust air heat reclaim*

4.5.7.4 Heat recovery with direct condensers

The term direct condensers in this context refers to refrigerant condensers where the cooling medium which dissipates the heat is applied directly to the refrigerant condensing coils. An air cooled condenser is an example of this type of equipment where ambient air is blown across the coils and the heat dissipated. In a heat recovery installation an air cooled condenser coil would be installed direct into the ductwork of an air heating system and the condenser heat usefully employed for space heating. The benefit in this arrangement is the lower capital cost as compared with a water cooled condenser and higher air operating temperatures because of the direct heat exchange between the refrigerant and the air itself.

In air conditioning installations the direct condenser heater battery in the conditioned air supply duct would operate in conjunction with an air cooled condenser which would be required for summer operation. Usually air cooled condensers are associated with relatively small fully self contained packaged air conditioning units and generally these are installed in single zone applications such as shops, supermarkets, lecture rooms or single offices. In such applications the cooling and heating do not operate simultaneously and therefore any heat recovered from the cooling process must be applied in another zone, preferably an area that is heated only. For example, in supermarkets and shops, recovered heat would be supplied to adjacent stockrooms. Generally in packaged air conditioning systems there are adjacent heated only areas where recovered heat can be supplied for space heating.

Condenser heat recovery cannot be obtained from a standard packaged air conditioning unit without some modifications to the refrigeration pipework and additional controls in the refrigeration circuit. Indeed the refrigeration system would require engineering to the particular application and this may well counter the low capital cost advantage of packaged equipment. A more positive example of heat recovery is in dehumidification and drying. In these cases the evaporator is positively controlled to reduce the moisture level and the condenser heat is recycled to maintain the dry bulb temperature within the space.

In all direct heat recovery installations delay timers are required on the capacity loading control of the refrigeration compressors. As with water cooled condensers the delay is necessary so as to give sufficient time for the controls to respond before any successive increase in condensing pressure.

4.5.8 Examples of heat recovery

4.5.8.1 Air conditioning in a stockroom (See also chapter 5.4)
Fig. 4.5.14 represents a simple air conditioning system where the heat is to be recovered to heat an adjacent stockroom. The compressor would be loaded and unloaded according to the cooling requirements of the conditioned space and heat applied from the heater when required. It is understood in this example that the cooling and heating to the conditioned space would be controlled in sequence from a room control. The significance of this in a heat recovery system is that when the cooling is operating the rejected heat can only be used in another system. Regarding the refrigerant condensers, head pressure controls are required to control the heating condenser and the air cooled condenser with priority to the heating condenser.

The control of the heating in the stockroom would be a sensor in the extract duct controlling face and bypass dampers or solenoid valves on the heating condenser and a supplementary heater in sequence. The dampers would be fully open to the coil before heat was applied to the supplementary heater. In addition any demand for heating would open the reheat condenser valve V_1 in the hot gas line from the compressor. As the stockroom temperature began to rise the sensor would reduce the air flow through the heating condenser by opening the bypass dampers.

The condensing head pressure would begin to rise and this would be sensed by the condensing pressure regulator valve V_2 which would open to the air cooled condenser. On further rise in head pressure the head pressure sensor would control the air cooled condenser fan. The receiver pressure regulator valve V_3 opens on fall in pressure to ensure that the head pressure does not fall below the safe low limit conditions.

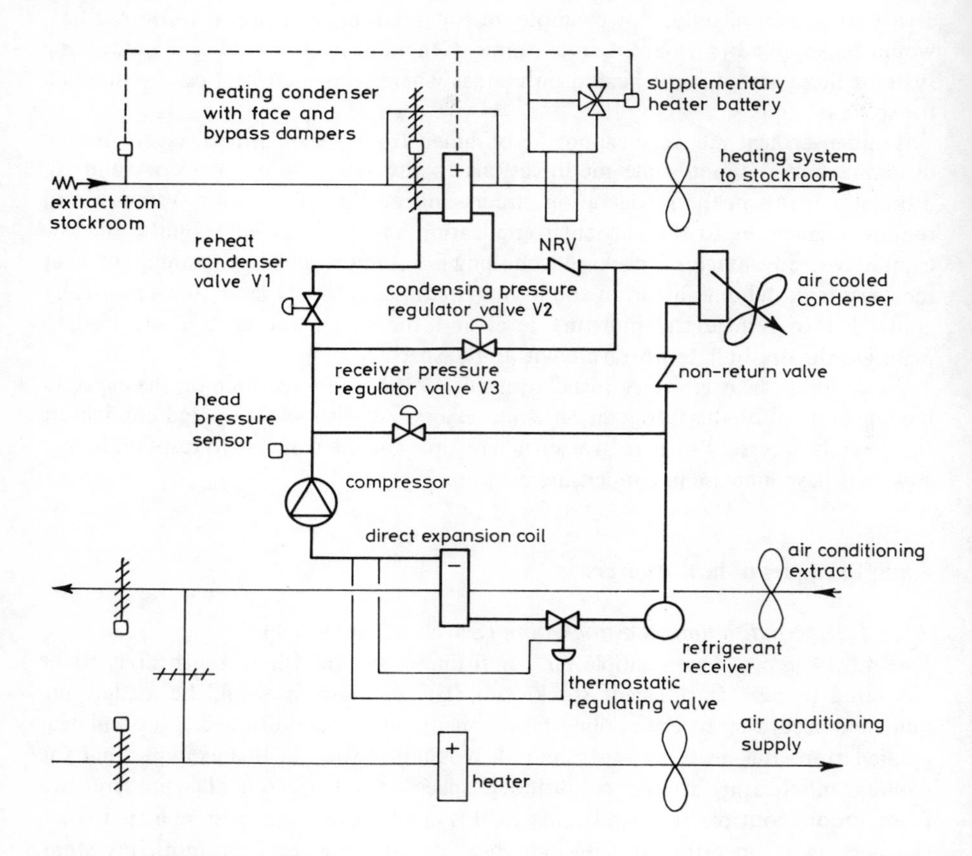

Fig. 4.5.14. *Air conditioning with direct heat recovery*

4.5.8.2 Drying application

A simple application of the dehumidifying and heating of a drying room is indicated in Fig. 4.5.15. The relative humidity controller situated in the extract duct would control the loading of the compressor, and the heat would be rejected to the heating condenser in the supply duct to the drying room. The room temperature would be controlled by a dry bulb sensor in the return air duct. On rise of the room temperature above the set point the damper in the exhaust, recirculation and fresh air duct would be modulated to admit more fresh air. It is understood that the drying room temperature is higher than the maximum ambient temperature experienced during the operation of the plant. To control the fresh air dampers, the signal from the dry bulb sensor would pass through a recycling timer which limits the speed of opening of the dampers.

Drying or dehumidifying equipment is usually provided in the form of packaged fully self contained units with a free blow into the space. A typical arrangement of the equipment is shown diagrammatically in Fig. 4.5.16. Air is drawn from the

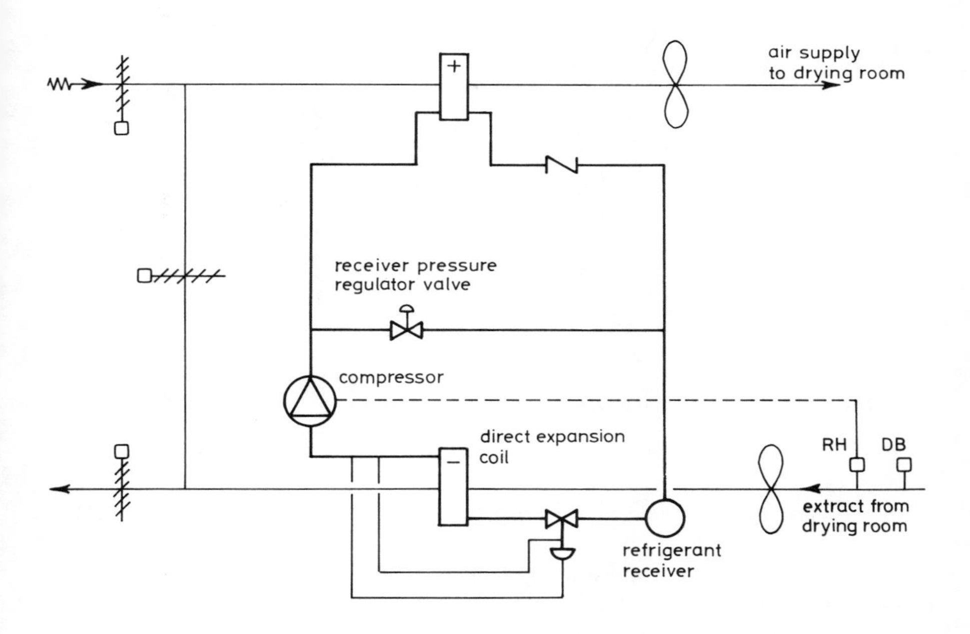

Fig. 4.5.15. *Drying room with direct expansion refrigeration plant*

room and a fixed portion of the air is passed over the dehumidifying coil and the remainder passes through a fixed bypass. The cold dehumidified air mixes with the bypass air and, via the condenser, where it is heated, is returned to the room. Where close control of relative humidity is required the compressor would be controlled by a humidistat; otherwise the machine can be allowed to operate continuously under the protection of the normal refrigeration high and low pressure safety controls.

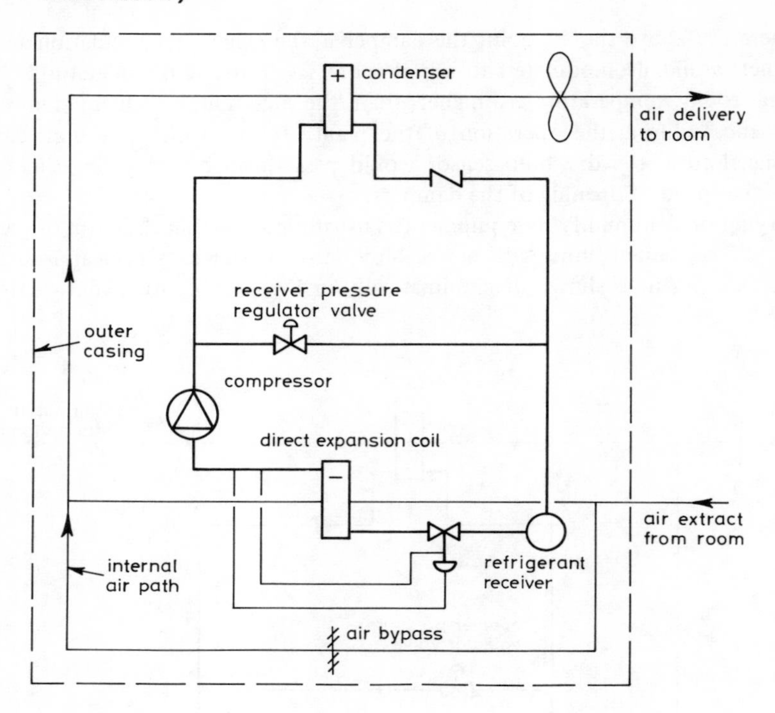

Fig. 4.5.16. *Fully self contained packaged dehumidifying unit*

4.5.8.3 Swimming pool hall dehumidification (See also chapter 5.15 and section 4.6.4.6)

In a swimming pool, moisture evaporates from the surface of the water and the air in the pool hall requires dehumidification. Traditionally this was done by introducing fresh air and heating which used a large amount of boiler energy. It is far more economical to dehumidify using refrigeration and heat the pool water and air from the recovered condenser heat. When using water cooled condensers the plant arrangement and control would be as described earlier for water cooled condensers. When using direct condensers the arrangement is as indicated in Fig. 4.5.17.

The dehumidification at the direct expansion cooling coil is controlled by the relative humidity sensor situated in the return air duct which progressively loads the compressor on rise in relative humidity. The dry bulb temperature within the pool hall is controlled by a dry bulb sensor which controls face and bypass dampers or solenoid valves on the main condenser air heater in the supply duct, and a supplementary heater battery in sequence.

There are two condensers mounted in series in the refrigerant condensing line; the air heater condenser and a water cooled condenser which heats the pool water.

The air heater has priority and when the condensing capacity is reduced by the resetting of the face and bypass dampers from the dry bulb sensor the condensing pressure rises and the condensing pressure regulator valve V_2 opens to admit hot gas direct to the pool water condenser. On further rise in condensing pressure the head pressure sensor opens the fresh air dampers. This has the effect of lowering the relative humidity which in turn will unload the compressor. To control the

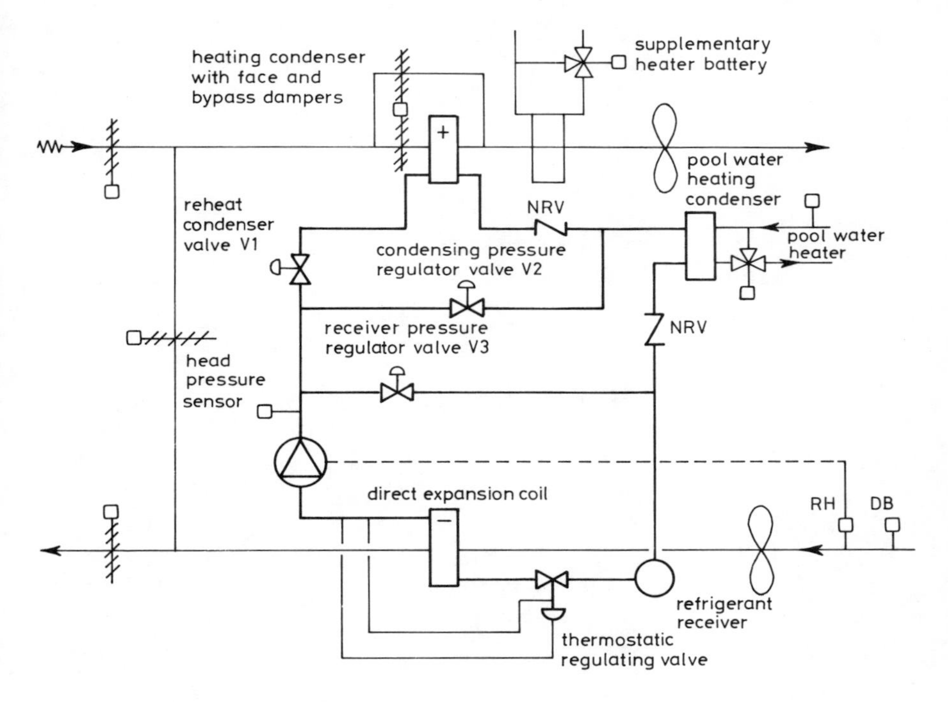

Fig. 4.5.17. *Swimming pool installation with direct expansion refrigeration plant*

dampers, the signal from the pressure switch to the dampers passes through a recycling timer which limits the speed of opening of the dampers. The speed should be set on site so as to give stable operation without excessive hunting of the damper setting. A typical setting might be to limit the fresh air adjustment to a change of 25% of the range over the time interval of 1 air change. If the supply air provided 4 air changes per hour then the control would admit a rate of one air change per hour over a time interval of 15 minutes.

Heat pump units on roof of a hypermarket (Lennox Industries)

Chapter 4.6

Heat pumps

E.G.A. Goodall, M.Sc., C.Eng., M.I.E.E., M.C.I.B.S., M.Inst.R.

4.6.1 Introduction

4.6.1.1 General

Since physics define heat as a molecular state of movement of matter which ceases at absolute zero, i.e. $-273°C$, then at all temperatures higher than this, heat is present. In order to produce cooling, energy must be removed at the point where we wish to have a lower temperature but this can only be achieved by the expenditure of high grade energy. A device which does this is a refrigerator which in effect removes heat at lower temperature and effectively 'pumps' it to a higher temperature, but since energy cannot be lost, energy removed at low temperature plus the high grade energy expended must be given off at a higher temperature. If cooling is the desired effect, the device will be a refrigerator, or a heat pump if heating is desired.

At one time there was no alternative other than to use a refrigeration machine to produce a cooling effect; consequently its capital cost had to be accepted from a commercial point of view. With the heat pump the situation was quite the opposite. Heating could be achieved by the burning of cheap fossil fuels, in low cost furnaces or hearths. The heat pump on the other hand was high in capital cost and used relatively expensive electrical energy. With the lower price ratio of fossil fuels to that of electricity which has occurred in recent years the situation has altered in favour of the heat pump, particularly with the introduction of reliable and inexpensive mass produced compressors specially designed for heat pump operation, and the availability of low cost off-peak electricity which can also be used for preheating the building. The heat pump in many instances can now produce heat at a cost comparable with, if not cheaper than, the use of fossil fuels. A world wide acknowledgement has now resulted in the acceptance of the heat pump as an alternative heating device. An important aspect of heat pump installations is the need for well controlled systems, particularly with respect to the use of supplementary heat, if the full potential of an installation is to be obtained.

4.6.1.2 Classification of heat pump types

It has become generally accepted that in defining the type of heat pump and its mode of operation, the heat source is identified first and the heating means second, i.e. in an air/water unit for example, air is the heat source and water is the means whereby the heat is distributed. Various low grade heat sources exist, air (external and exhaust), ground water, surface water, effluent water, and the ground itself.

A dual-fired heating system consists of an air/water heat pump and a fuel fired boiler operating in some predetermined manner. Where a heat pump without defrost capability is used it would normally be switched off when the outdoor temperature fell below + 3°C. Below this temperature the fuel fired boiler would supply the full heating requirement; such an arrangement is known as 'alternative operation'. In 'parallel operation' the heat pump supplies the full base load down to its lowest operating design temperature (− 10°C approximately) with the fuel fired boiler supplying the make up heat below the 'balance point temperature' (Fig. 4.6.5). Depending on the lowest operating point of the heat pump a third arrangement is known as the dual-fuel 'parallel-alternative'. Here the heat pump and boiler operate together until the lowest operating temperature of the heat pump is reached, below which temperature the boiler supplies the full heating load (section 4.6.4.2).

4.6.2 Working principles

The majority of present day refrigerators or heat pumps consist of a closed circuit comprising an evaporator (or outdoor coil), compressor, condenser (indoor coil) and an expansion device, in which a refrigerant circulates. Fig. 4.6.1 shows a typical circuit used in a commercial unit which includes a reversing valve to change the desired effect from cooling to heating a vice versa. The reversing valve is also used in the defrosting mode, Fig. 4.6.2.

Within the circuit the refrigerant (which has a low boiling point) enters the evaporator in liquid form at low pressure and temperature where it evaporates, extracting heat from the medium to be cooled. This vapour is then drawn into the compressor and directed to the condenser, where it gives up its heat and liquefies. The high pressure liquid is finally passed back to the evaporator, where after being metered by an expansion device it enters the evaporator and once again evaporates, thus completing the cycle.

As a thermodynamic cycle the heating efficiency is measured by the ratio of useful heat out to the energy input, which can be greater than 1. The ratio, called the Coefficient of Performance (COP) is given by

$$\frac{T_1}{T_1 - T_2},$$

and is known as the Carnot efficiency where T_1 and T_2 are the condensing and evaporating temperatures respectively in Absolute degrees (K). It can clearly be

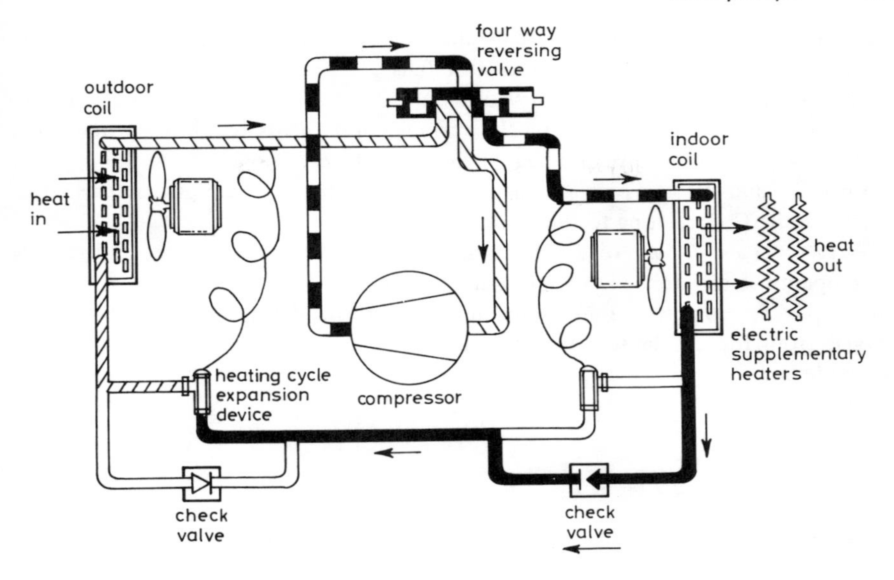

Fig. 4.6.1. *Heat pump: heating cycle*

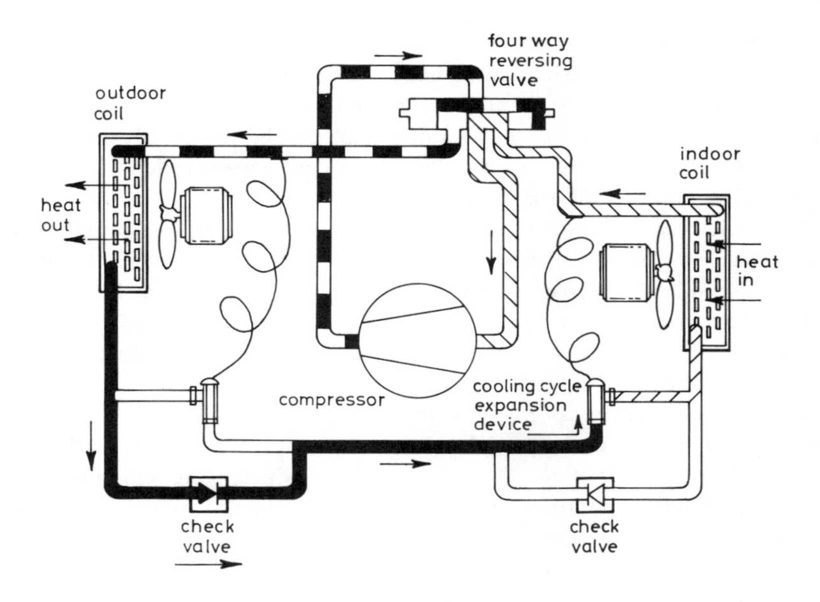

Fig. 4.6.2. *Heat pump: cooling cycle and defrosting* (Electricity Council)

seen that the COP falls as the difference increases; in other words, the output of the heat pump falls as the outdoor temperature falls.

In practice the actual COP achieved is only about 50% of the Carnot efficiency, due to losses and inefficiencies of the various components within the circuit, i.e. compressor, expansion valve and heat exchange surfaces.

Since T_1 and T_2 can only be measured within the heat pump it is sensible to determine the COP relating to the system.

If $\Delta T_2 = T_S - T_2$ where T_S is the temperature of the heat source and ΔT_2 is the temperature difference in or across the evaporator
and $\Delta T_1 = T_1 - T_F$ where T_F is the temperature of the air or water being discharged from the condenser, and ΔT_1 is the temperature difference in or across the condenser
then the COP is given by:

$$\frac{T_F}{T_F - T_S + \Delta T_1 + \Delta T_2} \eta$$

where T_F and T_S are system parameters, ΔT_1 and ΔT_2 are heat pump parameters and η is the system efficiency.

4.6.2.1 Differences between refrigerators and heat pumps

When heating is the desired effect a high condensing temperature is required, but in the heating cycle a number of operational features occur which are not present with standard refrigerating equipment such as air conditioning units.

(a) With the wide range of fluctuating source temperatures occurring during a heating season the expansion device has to cater for a varying load on the evaporator, and at the same time it must ensure that no liquid refrigerant is drawn into the compressor as this can result in serious damage. The degree of superheating of the gas is allowed for, but if this is excessive the compressor, which relies upon the suction gas for cooling, will become overheated and fail.

(b) In cold weather condensing pressures can fall, leading to erratic behaviour of the expansion device which in turn can lead to liquid floodback to the compressor, reduced heating capacity and extensive icing of the evaporator coil.

(c) In heat pump operation as opposed to air conditioning only 50% of the refrigerant is utilised and hence the remainder has to be stored either in the condenser, which reduces its efficiency, or in an accumulator.

(d) Whether the compressor is working at high head pressure and low suction pressure, or high head pressure and high suction pressure, stress conditions arise. The early development of air conditioning units which were modified as heat pumps with the incorporation of a reversing valve did not take these operating conditions into account, and as a result wide scale failures occurred. Since that time however development work on heat pump compressors has reduced the effect of the stress conditions. Compressors developed specifically for heat pump operation have better bearings and valving, motor cooling has been improved and high temperature oils have been developed. Motor protection using internal overloads prevents the compressor becoming overheated. Reliability of heat pump compressors has improved to such a degree that one leading heat pump manufacturer offers a five year guarantee on his unit.

A final difference which the heat pump has to cope with arises during defrosting if reversal of the refrigerant flow is used to remove ice from the outside coil. Liquid refrigerant held in the condenser can be pulled back into the compressor whilst a pressure rise in the outdoor coil causes vapour collapse and a suction pressure applied to the compressor can pull oil out of the crankcase.

Consequently, with high stress conditions arising during normal operation together with the long hours of use, the heat pump must now be regarded as a sophisticated heating machine and not as an air conditioner operating in reverse.

4.6.2.2 Additional components in heat pumps

Two components unique to the heat pump are the reversing valve and defrost control system.

(a) *Reversing valve*

This device changes the direction of refrigerant vapour flow on the suction and discharge side of the compressor so that the evaporator becomes the condenser, and the condenser the evaporator. The reversing valve itself is operated via a solenoid pilot valve which in turn is controlled by the room thermostat when a change from heating to cooling is required or by a defrost thermostat when defrosting is required of the outside coil.

During cooling the solenoid coil is energized and the pilot valve connects one end of the main reversing valve to the compressor suction line. Pressure in that end of the valve is reduced to suction pressure. Pressure on the opposite end of the main valve piston is connected to the compressor discharge line.

The pressure differential across the piston causes it to move to the position shown in Fig. 4.6.3. Refrigerant is routed through the valve in the direction indicated.

The solenoid coil on the pilot valve is de-energized when the system room thermostat is placed in the heating position. The pilot valve allows suction pressure to be applied to the opposite end of the main valve piston causing it to move to the position shown in Fig. 4.6.4. The position of the piston determines the direction of refrigerant flow in the heat pump refrigeration system. Fig. 4.6.4 indicates the direction of flow in the heating mode of operation.

(b) *Defrost control systems*

One of the most important and at the same time most difficult problems with the air source heat pump is to defrost the outside coil at the right time. During defrosting the heat pump will remove heat from the building and the average COP will be reduced. Reverse cycle defrosting must be carried out as quickly as possible and as soon as the evaporator is free of ice the heat pump must be switched back to its heating cycle. In most air/air heat pumps using this method the outdoor fan is switched off during defrosting and electric supplementary heaters are switched

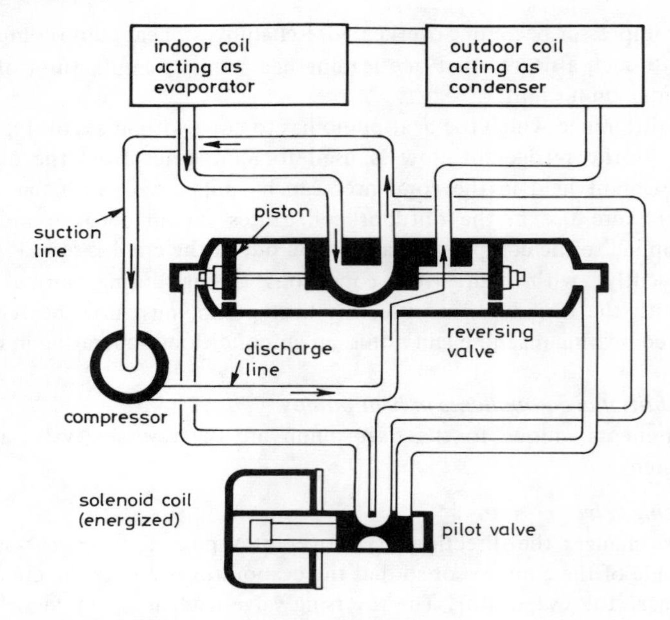

Fig. 4.6.3. *Reversing valve: cooling cycle and defrosting*

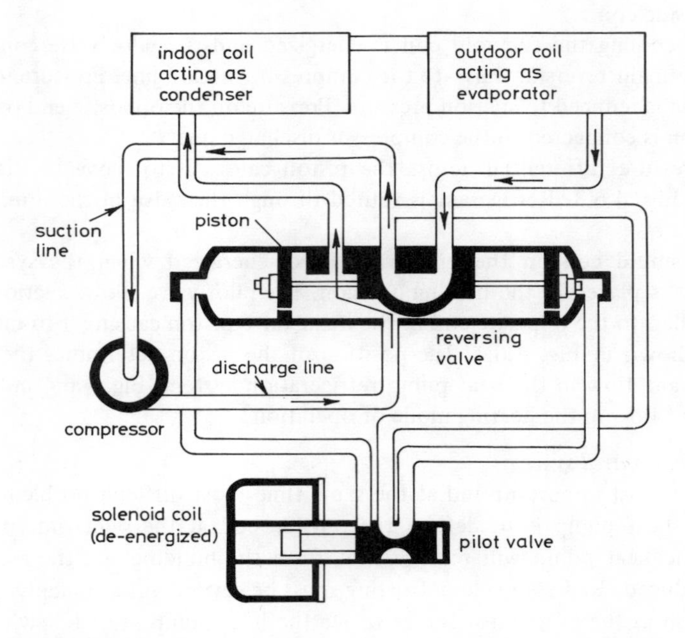

Fig. 4.6.4. *Reversing valve: heating cycle*

on to temper the cold air being discharged into the building. With air/water units however the thermal capacity of the heating system is such that no appreciable effect will be noted during the period of defrost operation. Defrost times of less than 4 minutes are common with the time/temperature system, which is one of the most widely used systems out of the four methods available, namely:

Time/temperature
Temperature differential
Air pressure differential
Evaporation pressure

(c) *Time/temperature*
Defrost is initiated at fixed time intervals anytime the outdoor coil is cold enough to allow ice to form. The controller will also switch off the outdoor fan during defrost whilst its timer will only run when the compressor is operating, thus eliminating spurious 'defrosts' which can occur on a fixed defrost time arrangement.

The temperature sensor generally initiates defrost at $-2°C$ and terminates at $+13°C$ (this temperature being sensed on the suction side of the compressor). The timer, which can be adjusted to initiate at 30, 45 and 90 minutes of compressor running time, allows for defrost time variation to be modified for different climatic zones. If the termination temperature is not reached (i.e. on cold days, or windy conditions) a fail safe time of 10 minutes terminates the defrost cycle. The speed of operation of the reverse cycle defrost system, operated by whatever control system the manufacturer has employed, enables the heat pump to revert quickly to its full 'ice free' efficiency.

Hot gas by-pass systems are alternative to the reverse cycle method but considerably longer defrost cycles occur, and whilst the energy used for defrosting with both methods must be the same, with the hot gas defrost method it is possible that the effect of the fall off of heat into the heating system could be felt.

A further feature particularly with air/air heat pumps is the use of additional electric supplementary heaters. As the output falls with temperature additional supplementary heat is required to meet the building heat load, which increases as the outdoor temperature falls. Electric supplementary heaters are low in capital cost and are easily controlled. (Para 4.6.4.1(a)).

4.6.3 Heat sources

Since the practical COP and hence the economics of the heat pumps are largely determined by the temperature of the heat source, whilst the type of heating system is determined by the temperature of the heating means, one seeks therefore to use heat pumps with high temperature sources so as to give as low a pumping temperature as possible, and a low temperature type of heating system, i.e. warm air, under-floor or pumped warm water systems using appropriately sized radiators.

As the heat demand rises with falling external temperatures and since many heat sources such as soil, air, ground and surface water follow external temperature fluctuations in winter to some degree, the requirements for total economic heat pump selection and operation are somewhat incompatible and certain compromises or specific designs have been developed to achieve economic viability. Generally, it is uneconomic to select a heat pump whose output meets the full heat demand of the building at the lowest external temperature.

4.6.3.1 Air

Normal atmosphere is the ideal heat source in that it can supply almost an unlimited amount of heat, although unfortunately at varying temperatures. For optimum dimensioning of an air/air heat pump it is important to know the frequency distribution of temperatures. In London the temperature only falls below 0°C for about 280 hours in an average year and consequently it would not be economic to select a heat pump to provide full heating for this small percentage of the heating demand.

If the heat pump is selected to provide full heating when the outdoor temperature is approximately 2–4°C, then the heat pump will provide approximately 80% of the energy required for heating at a COP well in excess of 2. The point at which the output of a given heat pump meets the building heat demand is known as the "balance point". The short fall of heating capacity below the balance point must be provided by some additional supplementary heat, but with air/air heat pumps, which still continue to operate well below 0°C, this supplementary heat does not have to be selected to provide the full heating load as would be the case in dual fuel air/water heating only heat pumps and oil fired boiler systems.

In any reverse cycle air/air heat pump, defrosting of the outside coil between 0 and 4°C will be necessary. As already described this is clearly achieved by reversing the flow of refrigerant to the outdoor coil, during which time the heat pump will now act as a cooling device, and cold air discharged into the building. To temper this cold air, electric heater batteries are brought into operation which consequently lead to loss of total system efficiency. However, measurements have shown that less than 4% of the total energy input is used for defrosting.

4.6.3.2 Soil

Soil would at first appear to be a very suitable heat source in view of its availability, consistency and storage capacity. Unlike the daily fluctuations which arise with air temperatures, soil temperatures at 10 m depth for example are those of the average annual air temperature, or even 1 or 2 degrees higher. Early heat pump applications using ground as a heat source considered pipes and plates buried in the soil, but only recently, particularly in Sweden, has there been any large scale application of the earth source heat pump.

In using the soil as the heat source, it is important to note its physical properties, particularly moisture content and mobility, which has a great influence on the soil conductivity. A practical problem which invariably arises with the use of pipes is the formation of ice which at first improves the soil contact but on thawing the displaced soil does not return to its original position. Thus a void is created and heat transfer in the next heating season becomes impaired.

Calculations show that the length of pipe required to remove 1·2 kW of heat will vary between 150 m in dry soil to 50 m in wet soil. Such coils are normally buried in 1–1½ m depth, set at a distance of 1 m. With such a system it can be taken that the average heat output will be 28 W/m of pipe. The diameter of the pipe (12–50 mm) has little effect on the heat exchange characteristics of the system.

Present day heat pumps use brine as the primary heat exchange medium since direct evaporation of refrigerant into the ground coil can lead to oil lubrication problems and should a failure in the pipe occur, resulting in loss of refrigerant, this can be very costly. A rule of thumb guideline is that the surface area required for the ground coil should be approximately 2½ times the area of the house to be heated.

4.6.3.3 Water

Because of its heat capacity and good heat transfer properties, water is the ideal heat source. However, its availability limits its wide scale usefulness. For any kind of water extraction, authorisation from the local water company should normally be obtained.

(a) *Ground water*

The temperature of ground water is approximately that of the annual average temperature or may be a degree or two higher, but in order to ensure that at least 2–3 m^3 per hour of water is available to serve as a heat source for a single family house, a well or test boring will be necessary. As a guide for calculating water quantity, area of house in $m^2 \times 10$ gives required quantity of water in litres per hour, × 10 for a full day's heat requirements.

A further important point is that of discharge; here a separate well may be required if the liquid drainage system cannot be used. An additional problem with water is that of corrosion due to dissolved chemicals which can produce unacceptable maintenance costs, although a plate heat exchanger in the 'cold' circuit would minimise this problem. Recent work in Denmark has led to the development of a single well being used. The well, lined with a porous tube, is some 50 m deep (below the water table) and water to the heat pump is taken from the bottom and discharged back into the top of the well. (Ref. 1)

(b) *Surface water*

Little information is available on the temperature fluctuation of surface water. Small rivers not used industrially show a temperature variation which follows an average monthly air temperature, whilst in winter if the flow rate falls freezing can be expected. If such a feature occurs then a heat pump using river water as a heat source will require additional heating plant which, as with many dual-fuel systems, must have an output equal to the full heating load requirements. Nevertheless rivers can be used to supply a very high percentage of the heat requirement of a building.

Due to algae growth and dissolved chemicals, evaporators of the shell and tube type are less acceptable. An additional plate type heat exchanger which can be dismantled and cleaned has been shown to be more appropriate. Such systems using sewage water or industrial effluents are now being actively developed (Ref. 2)

4.6.4 Types of heat pumps

4.6.4.1 External air/air heat pumps

(a) *General*

Air/air heat pumps are generally reverse-cycle and can provide warm air heating or cooling. Using the outside air as the heat source, they can provide on average 2·6 kW of heat for every one kW of input to the compressor and outdoor fan. The relative efficiencies of various machines can best be judged by comparing the fall off of the COP with temperature below 2–4°C, whilst effective value for money is compared by taking the cost per kW of heat output at + 7°C outdoor (with American machines this is the American Refrigeration Institute standard performance testing temperature.)

In the package design of air/air units (i.e. where the outdoor and indoor sections are together in one unit) an additional feature is often incorporated on the larger units – namely, an 'economizer'. This device uses and controls the use of fresh air to cool the building before the heat pump switches to mechanical cooling. In all package type heat pumps the electric supplementary heaters are incorporated with their controls into the unit.

A split heat pump is one in which the indoor section or air handler is within the building and is connected to the outdoor section which includes the compressor, by refrigerant pipes. These lines, up to specific lengths, are available fully charged with refrigerant, and simple sealed end connections are fitted which enable connection to the indoor and outdoor units (also fully charged) to be made without having to evacuate and charge the system. Where long lines are necessary it is essential to refer to the manufacturer's technical details regarding horizontal and vertical length limitations, diameters of the respective gas and liquid lines, the effect of length of line on cooling/heating capacity, whether or not oil traps have to be used, additional use of accumulator, and, above all, the charge of refrigerant by weight for the additional length of pipes.

As with packaged units the air handling equipment is designed to accommodate the additional supplementary electric heaters, and various air handlers are designed for vertical or horizontal mounting – with or without ductwork connection.

Whilst air/air heat pumps are normally designed for mounting outside the building, they can be used for example in a plant room where waste heat from refrigeration compressors is being dumped. This waste heat is taken up by the heat pump, thereby increasing its effective COP and reducing the frequency of defrost. Care needs to be taken however in ensuring that the propeller fan fitted to the heat pump is capable of discharging the air from the heat pump, through a separate duct to the outside of the building. Capacities of units, both packaged and split, are available with outputs in excess of 100 kW.

(b) *General principles for sizing an air/air heat pump used for cooling/heating or heating only*
In determining the size of heat pump which has to provide cooling as well as heating, the first consideration is the cooling requirement, which in many instances will be greater than or at least equal to the heating load. This is because:

(i) if the cooling capacity is too small there is no remedy other than to install a larger heat pump;
(ii) if the cooling capacity is too large humidity control will be poor and the heat pump will operate frequently on mild days.

Nevertheless some compromise between cooling and heating should be attempted since it is important to ensure the heat pump provides as much of the heating requirements as possible.

In the heating only situation, sizing the heat pump to meet the peak heating load at $-1°C$ would be clearly uneconomical due to the relative infrequency of this temperature. Selecting a heat pump whose output meets the building heat loss when the outdoor temperature is between $2°C$ and $4°C$ (Balance Point) (Fig. 4.6.5), will result in the heat pump providing at least 80% of the energy requirements. Since the output of the heat pump continues to fall below the balance point, additional heat in the form of electric supplementary heaters is incorporated into the system, so that at $-1°C$ the total output of the heat pump and supplementary heaters is equal to the heat demand (fabric and ventilation) or 1·5 times the fabric heat loss, whichever is the greater, in order to ensure the system has adequate pre-heat capacity.

With such a capacity adequate pre-heating of most building types can be achieved within a pre-heat period not exceeding 6 hours. During this period fresh air to the building should be shut off allowing full recirculation to take place (Ref. 3) (CIBS Guide, Table A9.9: Allowances for intermittent heating). Where a long pre-heat period is necessary or where the Electricity Authority offers a day/night Maximum Demand tariff there can be a strong economic case to operate the heat pump and its supplementary heat throughout the night and for daytime operation to isolate the supplementary heaters altogether. In such a case, building fabric temperature will be maintained during the night and the building up to temperature at the start of occupation. Early morning electrical maximum demand will be minimized and the heat pump will not be struggling to get the building up to temperature, which could be the case with short pre-heat periods and the subsequent use of supplementary heat at full day rate cost. Use of the day/night Maximum Demand tariff enables the heat pump effectively to supply energy for preheating at approximately a quarter of day rate costs and even the supplementary heat costs no more than approximately half.

Since such a mode of operation does not create an early morning maximum demand the operational costs on the building are not penalized by the operation of the heat pump, which would be the case when a heat pump was operated on short pre-heat periods, with subsequent early morning maximum demand. A recent analysis by the Electricity Council has shown that using an optimum start controller, up to 60% of the building's energy requirement for heating can be supplied during a pre-heat period when MD charges are not incurred and the cost per kWh is at its cheapest.

It is important when a heat pump is operated on a maximum demand tariff to recognize the economic significance between kWh costs and MD charges.

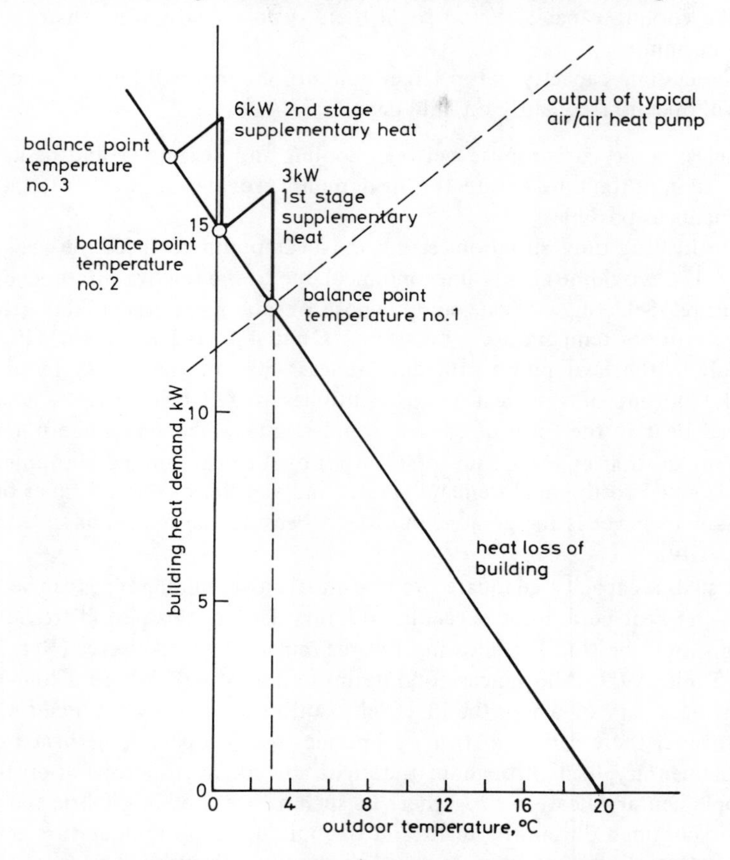

Fig. 4.6.5. *Determination of balance point of heat pump and building heat demand*

(c) *Control of heat pump output*

The most common and simplest form of output temperature controller is the 2 stage cooling, 2 stage heating, room thermostat. This control provides the multi-role function of room temperature control in both heating and cooling modes, changeover from heating to cooling and operation of the electric supplementary heating. Excessive use of supplementary heaters is overridden by the use of outdoor thermostats since only when the outdoor temperature falls below the balance point of the system are they allowed to come into operation. Since stage 2 of the room thermostat will call for supplementary heat it is normal for outdoor thermostats to be used to stage the respective levels of supplementary heat available by being set at progressively lower temperatures (Fig. 4.6.5). During defrosting the control system will by-pass the outdoor thermostats and allow some of the supplementary heat to be used to temper the air into the building. Should there be a compressor malfunction an emergency manual switch on the room thermostat allows the supplementary heaters to be brought into operation under control of the room thermostat.

4.6.4.2 Air/water heat pumps

(a) *General*

Using external air as the heat source the air/water heat pump can provide water at 55°C for heating systems. Air/water heat pumps using R12 refrigerant are now available which produce water up to 70°C, thus enabling a replacement of fuel fired boilers with radiators sized for high flow temperatures to be made. Air/water heat pumps can be either of packaged or split design and incorporate some means of defrosting the outdoor coil when this becomes necessary.

The internal refrigerant/water heat exchanger is normally a co-axial helix, which, though compact, has a high (water) pressure drop and often requires an additional pump to be included in the heat pump circuit. Safety devices in the heat pump control circuit will often include a high pressure cut out (manual), flow switch, and temperature limiter.

Some larger air/water heat pumps are also designed for reverse cycle operation, i.e. to provide heating in winter and cooling in summer using either hot water or chilled water with fan coil systems. A summer/winter switch-over control is necessary to prevent the room thermostat hunting between heating and cooling at the beginning and end of the heating season. During defrosting on reverse cycle systems the thermal capacity of the heating system is so high and the defrost period so short that no additional supplementary heat is required, as is normal with air/air units. Capacities of air/water heat pumps are now available up to 300 kW and can operate down to outside temperatures of − 15°C before switching off.

(b) *Domestic application of air/water heat pumps*

In Europe including the UK many domestic installations using oil fired boilers and radiators are to be found. The cost of running these installations has in recent years risen sharply and an alternative or supplementary solution has been sought. The solution which has been forwarded is for the electric air/water heat pump to supply between 60–80% of the energy at present provided by the oil fired boiler, and for the boiler to operate as a supplementary means of heating. This dual-fuel system has the added feature of alternative or parallel operation, which refers to the mode of operation and not to the integration of the heat pump into the heating distribution system.

'Alternative' operation is where a heating-only heat pump supplies heat to the house down to its lowest operating temperature, normally about 3°C outdoor temperature and just below the balance point, at which temperature it is switched off. Below this temperature the boiler operates to supply the full heating requirement on cold days. Such a system enables a heating-only heat pump to be used, i.e. one with no reverse cycle defrosting feature; however, balance points of 5°C and above are required and with the climate in the UK the heat pump is unlikely to supply much more than 50% of the energy requirement. The economic value of such a system would, therefore, be in some doubt.

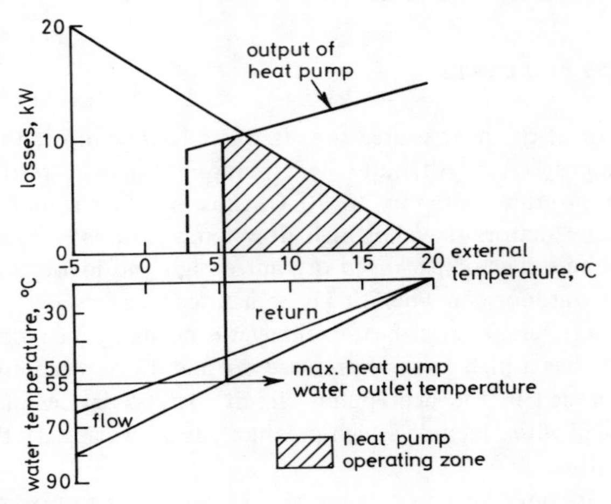

Heating elements undersized
(Heat pump operation for above zero external temperatures)

Fig. 4.6.6. *Dual-fuel alternative system* (CIAT France)

Fig. 4.6.6 shows the operating characteristics of such an arrangement, where the radiators are effectively undersized for satisfactory operation for a dual-fuel parallel system. A heating only heat pump with a cut off point at + 3°C outdoor temperature could still supply heat into the system since on mild days a flow temperature of less than 50°C is sufficient to provide the reduced heat load. If the radiators can effectively be regarded as oversized (i.e. when using water at 80°C) then using water at 55°C flow, a heat pump with defrosting capability can provide heat down to its lowest operating temperature, with the fuel fired boiler supplying the make up heat below the system's balance point temperature. Fig. 4.6.7 shows a dual-fuel parallel-alternative system in which, because of slight undersizing of the radiators, at −2°C the heat pump is switched off due to the high return water temperature and the boiler alone then supplies the full heating load down to −5°C.

If the heating system had been designed for an outdoor temperature of – 2°C then the heat pump would have supplied the base heating load and the fuel fired boiler the deficiency. Such an arrangement would be identified as dual-fuel parallel. (Ref. 4). Where an air/water heat pump is being integrated into a fuel fired heating system it is important to ensure that the output of the heat pump can meet the building heat demand down to an outdoor temperature of between 3–5°C when the heat pump will provide between 80–60% of the heating energy.

In any radiator system it is not necessary to provide high water flow temperatures

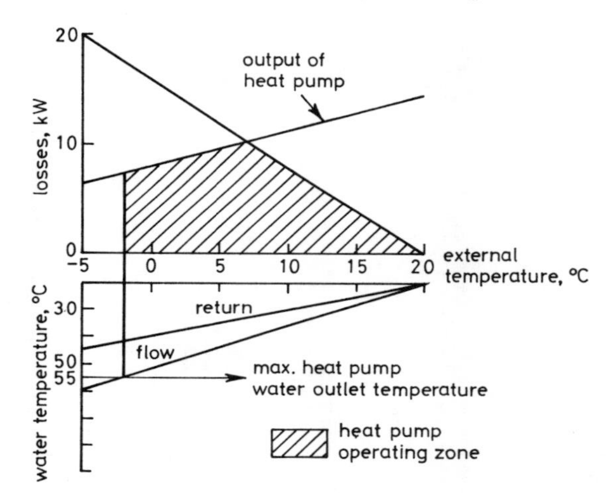

Fig. 4.6.7. *Dual-fuel parallel-alternative system* (CIAT France)

on mild days – Fig. 4.6.7 shows that on mild days a lower flow temperature would provide the lower heat demand. Providing the return temperature in the system is less than 50°C (produced by the heat pump and boiler) then the heat pump will continue to operate until a return temperature greater than 50°C is demanded by the system, at which point the heat pump switches off. This switch off temperature may well be higher than the lowest operating temperature of the heat pump. A simple dual-fuel system can be controlled with a 2 stage room thermostat, stage 1 controlling the heat pump, whilst stage 2 will bring the boiler into operation when the output of the heat pump is insufficient to meet the increased heat demand below the balance point temperature. However, to prevent the boiler being brought into operation on mild days an outdoor thermostat set just below the balance point temperature is incorporated into the boiler control circuit.

(c) *Integration of heat pump into existing oil fired boiler system*

Generally one does not know the existing rate of water flow in a system, but since it is important for a minimum rate of flow of water to pass through the condenser of the heat pump, a second pump is fitted. Since the pressure drop through the heat pump's condenser is high, this second pump will also eliminate any pressure drop problems. The use of a three-way mixing valve operated by the second stage of the room thermostat allows higher flow temperatures to be produced by the boiler. (Fig. 4.6.8). This scheme, typical of one manufacturer, can be

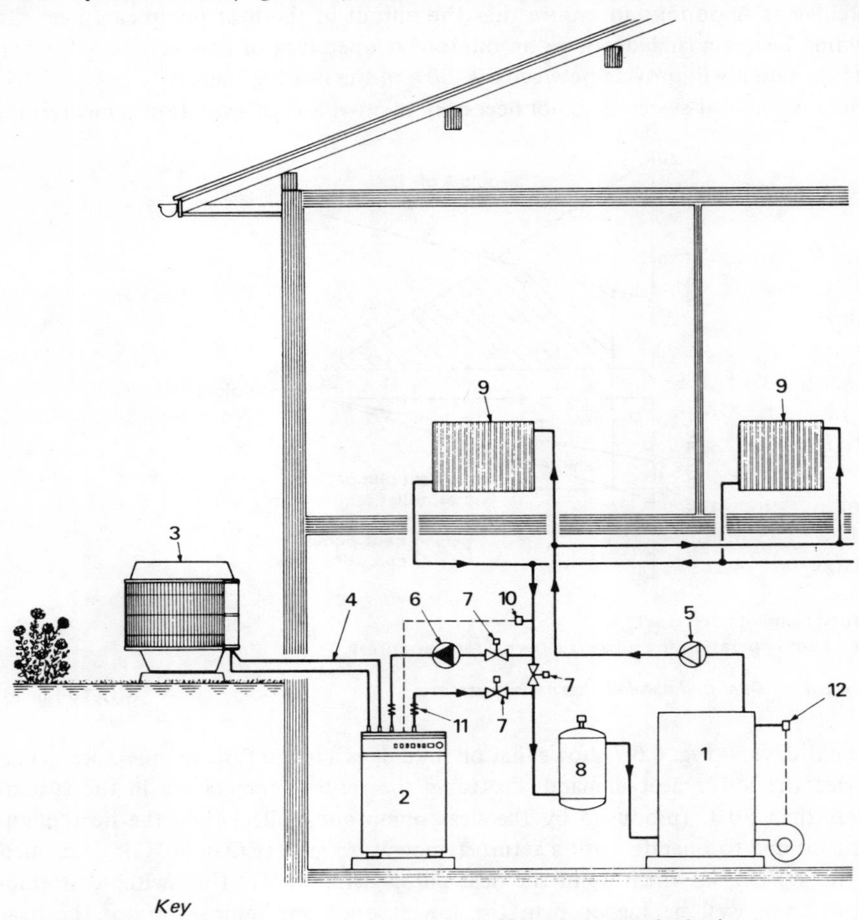

Key

1. Boiler
2. Heat pump (internal section)
3. Fan/evaporator(external section)
4. Precharged refrigerant lines
5. Heating circuit pump
6. Heat pump circuit pump
7. Manual or motorised valves
8. Heat storage vessel
9. Heating elements
10. Heat pump control thermostat
11. Flexible couplings
12. Boiler aquastat

Fig. 4.6.8. *Integration of heat pump and boiler* (CIAT France)

modified still further by the addition of an inside-outside proportional controller controlling a 3 or 4 way valve, but again the boiler must only operate below the balance point of the heat pump. (Ref. 5)

The development of the application of domestic air/water heat pumps into existing oil fired boiler systems has only just begun in the UK and it is probable that many schemes different to the above will be developed in the next few years.

(d) *Combined oil fired boiler and heat pump*
Units are available which combine an oil fired boiler and heat pump in a single casing. Such dual-fuel heat pumps are yet to be applied in the UK, though they do offer the opportunity of a compact installation with interlinking pipework and controls being integrated into one unit, the outdoor section of the heat pump being connected to the indoor section by refrigerant pipes. Capacities up to 30 kW boiler, 15 kW heat pump are available.

4.6.4.3 Extract air/air heat recovery heat pumps
Unlike thermal wheels or other non-regenerative heat recovery devices whose efficiency relies upon there being large temperature differences between the incoming and outgoing extract air, the air/air heat recovery heat pump has a higher efficiency when the temperature difference is small. Furthermore, with the input of high grade energy used to drive the compressor, the air subsequently delivered into the building will be at a higher temperature than the extract air.

Additional electric heater batteries can be incorporated to provide additional heat if the supply air temperature is unacceptable when the outdoor temperature is low. The normal range of operation of such units is with the maximum temperature of extract air at 30°C. Whilst designed for heat recovery applications, these units can be 'reverse cycled' to provide cooling in summer. Capacities from 10–60 kW are available covering extract air flow rates from 1800 to 13 000 m^3/h. Smaller units designed for domestic applications are also available.

4.6.4.4 Extract air/water heat recovery heat pump
As with the air/air heat recovery heat pump, the air/water unit recovers heat from exhaust air which it upgrades but transfers it into a water circuit at a maximum temperature of 55°C. Unlike the air/air unit which demands that exhaust and supply duct work is brought together at the unit, the air/water heat pump gives a greater degree of flexibility with the use of the recovered heat being transferred into a water circuit.

The maximum exhaust air temperature which the heat pump can accept is 32°C. Capacities up to 60 kW of heat output are available, with again a reverse cycle capability of providing chilled water for summer cooling.

4.6.4.5 Water/water heat pumps
Basically designed originally as chilled water sets, these units are now optimised for heating and with alternative refrigerants can provide hot water up to 70°C depending on the temperature of the 'cold' water source. Given any water source the water/water heat pump offers considerable scope for recovering waste heat from effluents or waste water in industrial applications, particularly since capacities up to 5000 kW are available.

Recent applications using such machines with sewage or geothermal energy sources enable large district heating schemes to be planned. Smaller units are compact since both heat exchangers are of the co-axial design, whilst the larger units use shell and tube heat exchangers which can be cleansed if they become fouled. If fouling is severe, an additional plate heat exchanger needs to be incorporated on the cold side of the system. If the temperature of the cold source falls below 8°C an intermediary glycol heat exchange circuit has to be fitted.

Such water/water heat pumps are also used for ground coil systems which are popular in Sweden and Denmark, but less so in the UK due to the large area of ground required and higher capital costs.

4.6.4.6 Dehumidification heat pumps (see also section 4.5.8.3)
The removal of moisture in a building or process by direct heating results in high energy costs and high ventilation rates. However, the recent availability of dehumification type heat pumps has now enabled both energy costs and ventilation rates to be substantially reduced. Swimming pools with high humidity levels which result in discomfort to the occupants and damage to the building fabric are an example of an area where dehumidification by a refrigerant process has been extremely successful.

Packaged units which are available, designed specifically for swimming pools, consist of two refrigerant circuits, circuit no. 1 being an air/air heat pump which removes moisture from the pool hall air by cooling it and then reheating the air to approximate pool hall temperature. It is important to appreciate that this type of heat pump does not provide heating and will only operate when the humidity level is higher than required. Circuit no. 2 in this type of heat pump consists of an air/water heat pump and only operates when humidity levels cannot be maintained by the air/air circuit. Excess heat from circuit no. 2 is delivered into a water circuit which can be used for pool water heating.

Since the heat pump is designed to cover the ventilation load only additional heat will still be required to maintain the fabric heat loss and pool water temperature – this will generally be provided by the existing fuel fired system. Heater batteries, electric or hot water coils, can be incorporated into these packaged heat pumps, thus enabling them to operate as an all air system. Sizes are available covering supply air volumes from 4000 m^3/h to 16 580 m^3/h. Larger units are available which also include thermal wheels which are used to reheat the small percentage of incoming fresh air from the outgoing exhaust air.

4.6.5 Energy calculations

Simple computer programs which use the 'bin' system of temperatures are generally available from the major heat pump suppliers. The 'bin' system consists of calculating the input and output of a heat pump for various temperature bands (normally 2·5°C) throughout the heating season. Such a method also takes into account the number of hours a given temperature occurs and the subsequent variation in the building heat demand together with the hours of occupation.

Whilst it is essential to determine the energy input to the heat pump, with the energy consumed by the supplementary heating being shown separately, it is equally important to relate the kWh consumption to the actual electricity tariff being used (taking into account any night/day difference) and to quantify the actual MD charges incurred by the heat pump only on a monthly, quarterly, or annual basis.

An alternative method has been developed by the Electricity Council. (Ref. 6)

4.6.6 Summary

This brief survey on electrical heat pumps at present available has also included some guidelines on their sizing-selection and control since whatever the performance claims may be for the machine, unless attention is given to these parameters the heat pump will not produce the energy savings of which it is capable.

Heat pumps of the types described are now being applied world wide, but already units with new features which will improve their performance still further are becoming available. Compressors with speed control, new methods of reducing starting currents, mixed refrigerants enabling the heat pump to operate more efficiently over a greater outdoor temperature range, and controls with micro-processors directly concerned in monitoring service faults, are all features which will be designed into the next generation of heat pumps.

4.6.7 References

4.6.7.1 References in text

(1) FORDSMAN, M. 'Experience with domestic heat pumps' IIR Essen Conference, September 1981
(2) JACOBSEN, C. and BRATT, A. 'Sewage water treated and untreated, a heat source for heat pumps' IIR Essen Conference, September 1981
(3) CIBS Guide, Book A9
(4) GOODALL, E. G. A. 'Careful heat pump sizing ensures successful space heating' Electrical Review Vol: 210 No 1, 8th January 1982
(5) 'Centratherm and the heat pump' Application Manual A23, PP Controls Ltd., Hounslow Middlesex TW3 2AD
(6) 'Heat Pump Systems: Design, Control and Energy Consumption'. Environmental Engineering Section, The Electricity Council

4.6.7.2 Bibliography

Von CUBE, H. L. and STEIMLE, F. 'Heat Pump Technology' Butterworth, London, 1981
HEAP, R. D. 'The Heat Pump' E. & F. Spon, London, 1979

Chapter 4.7

Sound and vibration

Derek J Croome, B.Sc., M.Sc., Ph.D., C.Eng., F.I.O.A., F.C.I.B.S., M.Inst.P., M.Inst.E., M.A.S.H.R.A.E.
Reader, School of Architecture and Building Engineering, University of Bath, Part-time partner, Buro Happold.

4.7.1 The role of sound control

Building services plant contributes significantly to the sound level in a building. It is the responsibility of the building services technologist to select services equipment and ensure that its design and layout in a building are arranged so that the sound criteria are satisfied. But sound is only one energy form comprising the environmental context of a building and it has to be considered along with other climatic factors around the building, such as sunlight and solar radiation.

The background sound level has to be assessed by the building environmental services engineer, because surrounding traffic and aircraft noise can enter the services inlets and travel down pipes and ducts. In other words, an integrated approach to sound control is needed, so that the architect receives the best advice, enabling him to select building fabrics and layouts that take into account this aspect. There are strong parallels with thermal and lighting design because a major share of the responsibility for achieving the level and quality of thermal comfort and lighting for a particular task lies with the building services engineer and this extends to the control of noise and sound quality in buildings.

The quality of sound in a space depends on its size, shape and the surface finishes. Speech and music have a different range of requirements (Refs. 1, 3). Although this sphere is often referred to as architectural acoustics, clients, engineers and architects should design the sound quality together.

4.7.2 Basic principles

4.7.2.1 Sound and noise

Sound is a form of mechanical radiation which can travel through fluids or solids: a wave velocity c is given by:

$$c = \sqrt{\frac{E}{\rho}} = \sqrt{\frac{\gamma p}{\rho}} \tag{4.7.1}$$

where E is Young's modulus of elasticity for a solid, p is the pressure, ρ is the density and γ is the adiabatic pressure coefficient. Because of the transmission of sound energy relies on particle vibrations within the material or the fluid, a vacuum does not conduct sound. At room temperature the speed of sound through the air is about 340 m/s.

Noise is sound unwanted by the recipient. Judgments about noise depend upon physical attributes of the waveform such as the frequency f and the wavelength λ of the sound related to the speed of sound by:

$$c = \lambda f \tag{4.7.2}$$

but also they are dependent upon subjective responses to sound which vary from one person to another. Audio frequencies range from 20 to 20 000 Hz. Ultrasonics and infrasonics refer to frequencies above and below this range respectively. In building design the term *vibration* refers to sound which is less than about 50 Hz. This radiation is usually conducted through the structure and is called *structure-borne* sound in contrast to the sound propagated through the air as *airborne* sound.

4.7.2.2 Measurement of sound power and sound pressure

The pressure variations produced by a soundwave travelling through the air are very small (i.e. as low as 2×10^{-5} Pa or N/m^2; note Pascals (Pa) are identical to N/m^2) compared to the average atmospheric pressure which is in the order of 10^5 Pa. Because of this large difference of magnitude and the fact that the hearing system perceives loudness differences logarithmically, a sound logarithmic scale ratio is used to express levels of sound power and sound pressure.

The sound power level L_w is defined in decibels (dB) as:

$$L_w = 10 \lg (W/W_0) \tag{4.7.3}$$

and the sound pressure level L_p by

$$L_p = 20 \lg (p/p_0) \tag{4.7.4}$$

where the reference sound power is $W_0 = 10^{-12}$ Watts and the reference sound pressure is $p_0 = 2 \times 10^{-5}\ N/m^2$. These reference values reflect the average threshold auditory response to sound. Some typical sound pressure and sound power levels are shown in Fig. 4.7.1.

Sound pressure level L_p is related to sound power level L_w by:

$$L_p = L_w + 10\,\lg\,(Q/4\pi r^2 + 4/R) \tag{4.7.5}$$

where Q is a directivity factor which varies from $Q = 1$ for an omnidirectional source and $Q = 8$ for a highly directional one; (Q also depends on the source position. $Q = 1$ for a free field source; $Q = 2$ on a flat plane; $Q = 4$ at the junction of two perpendicular planes; $Q = 8$ at the junction of three perpendicular planes);

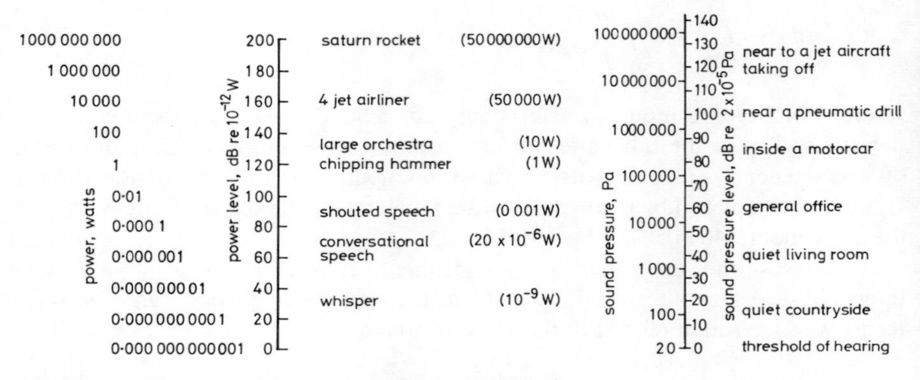

Fig. 4.7.1. *Typical sound power/pressure levels (Ref. 4)*

r is the distance between the listener and the sound source; R is the room constant and ($R = S\alpha/1 - \alpha$) for surface area S having sound absorption coefficient α. When r is small the direct field term ($Q/4\pi r^2$) is large but when r is large the reverberant field term ($4/R$) predominates and sound absorption can assist in controlling the sound level. The free field radius r occurs when the direct and reverberant fields are equal:

$$Q/4\pi r^2 = 4/R \tag{4.7.6}$$

and therefore

$$r = 0{\cdot}14\sqrt{RQ} \tag{4.7.7}$$

If a sound absorbent surface is at a distance greater than $0{\cdot}14\sqrt{RQ}$ from the sound source then absorbent treatment applied to that surface will reduce the energy in the reverberant field. A comparison of various forms of sound absorber is given in 'Noise, Buildings and People' (Ref. 1).

A description of the sound field around a sound source is shown in Fig. 4.7.2. Fig. 4.7.3 illustrates the effect of a live or reverberant space ($\bar{\alpha} \triangleq 0{\cdot}1$) and a dead or anechoic space ($\bar{\alpha} > 0{\cdot}5$). In the former case the reverberant field predominates, as a cathedral, but in the latter situation, such as a recording studio, the direct field is dominant.

The sound quality of a space is loosely defined by the reverberation time T (in seconds) where

$$T = 0{\cdot}16\,V/S\bar{\alpha} \tag{4.7.8}$$

for a volume $V\,\text{m}^3$; total surface area $S\,\text{m}^2$ and mean sound absorption coefficient $\bar{\alpha}$. For speech T varies from about 0·4 (conference room) to 1 second (large auditorium) and for music from about 0·8 as in an opera house to 2·5 seconds as in a concert hall depending on the size and the shape of the space (Refs. 1, 3 and 4). Typical variations of reverberation time with volume for auditoria are shown in Fig. 4.7.4.

Acoustic measurements (Ref. 4) are based on the sound pressure level often

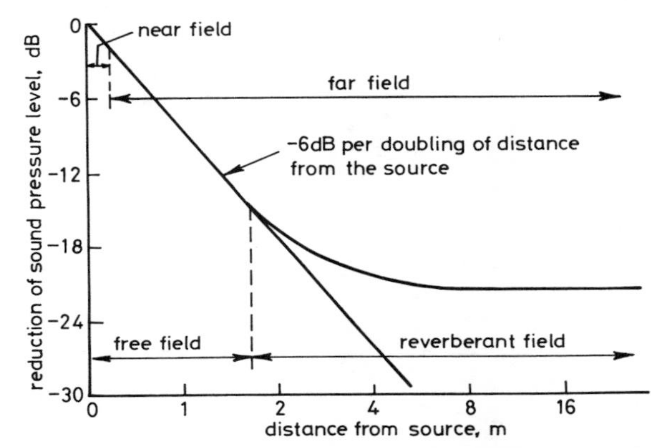

Fig. 4.7.2. *Description of the sound field around a sound source in a reverberant room*

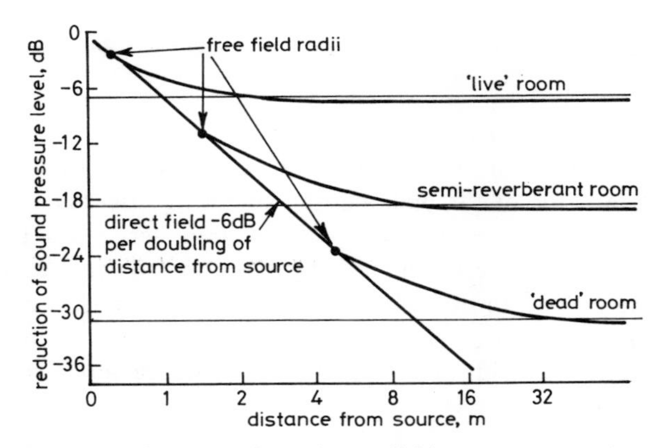

Fig. 4.7.3. *Combination of direct and reverberant fields*

referred to as the sound level because it is the sound pressure which excites the eardrum and triggers the human response to the sound. Particular patterns of sound pressure can be identified with sound from machinery, aircraft, road traffic, people or other sources. The ear does not have a constant linear response over the audio frequencies as dB levels assume and weighting networks take this into account so that the A weighting network, for example, gives levels in dBA which allow for the lack of sensitivity of the ear at low frequencies but identifies with the greater sensitivity of the ear at higher frequencies (about 2000 to 3000 Hz), (Ref. 1). The A weighting is commonly used because it also is a useful indication of peoples' overall reaction to noise nuisance.

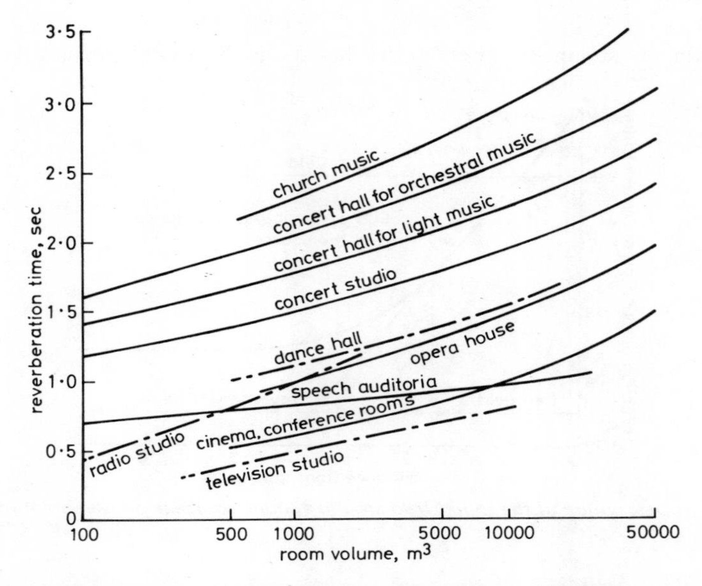

Fig. 4.7.4. *Typical variation of reverberation time with volume of auditoria*

4.7.2.3 Principles of sound and vibration control

In building design sound control is an important factor which needs to be considered when deciding the fabric of the building, the layout of spaces and the location of noisy equipment. There will be an overlap with certain thermal and lighting requirements particularly with regard to building construction and window design.

Sound and vibration control rely on four factors – *mass, damping capacity, stiffness* and *control of source.* The basic equation for sound control is analogous to that for an electrical resistance-induction-capacitance series circuit. Thus the equation of motion is:

$$m\ddot{x} + r\dot{x} + kx = F \sin \omega t \tag{4.7.9}$$

where mass m, damping capacity r and stiffness k control the motion described by deflection x, velocity $\dot{x}$ and acceleration $\ddot{x}$ caused by the periodic vibration force $F \sin \omega t$.

(a) Above the resonance frequency (i.e. when the mass and the stiffness factors are equal) a structure is mass controlled. In practice the mass law for a single leaf construction having surface density m (kg/m^2) gives the sound reduction as:

$$R = 10 + 14{\cdot}5 \lg m \qquad (4.7.10)$$

Hence if $m = 100$ kg/m^2 then the sound reduction due to this mass is 39 dB. If the mass is increased to 200 kg/m^2 then this reduction is increased to 43·4 dB.

For a double leaf construction with a cavity width of d (metres) this becomes:

$$R = 20 \lg (md) + 34 \qquad (4.7.11)$$

Hence if each leaf is 100 kg/m^2 and there is a 50 mm cavity the reduction is 54 dB.

(b) For a building element to have a high sound reduction over a wide frequency range it should have a high mass and a low stiffness. It can be shown that damping capacity

$$r = \frac{\delta}{\pi} \sqrt{(km)} \qquad (4.7.12)$$

where δ is the logarithmic decrement or the logarithmic ratio of successive displacements in a sound wave. Damping helps to reduce stiffness, resonance and coincidence effects (Ref. 1).

(c) Stiffness k is related to the shear modulus G, cross-sectional area A and thickness h thus:

$$k = GA/h \qquad (4.7.13)$$

Stiffness is important at low frequencies below resonance.

(d) The sound or vibration source characteristics are described by the function $F \sin \omega t$. Building designers do not design the equipment but can give high priority to careful selection by including acoustics as a consideration. Sound level changes with speed of operation so that running speeds should be chosen to give maximum efficiency and least noise. Maintenance is also important to ensure that design conditions are always achieved.

In practice great attention must be given to sound leaks and flanking transmission. Discontinuous construction assists in achieving high sound insulation.

4.7.3 Vibration isolation practice

Equipment with moving parts gives rise to structureborne sound, i.e. sound conducted through walls, floors or ceilings. Vibration isolators are usually installed. Their effectiveness is defined by transmissibility T, where:

$$T = 1/1 - (f/f_r)^2 \qquad (4.7.14)$$

for forcing frequency f and resonant (or natural) frequency, f_r, *vibration isolation efficiency* is:

$$\eta = (1 - T)100 \qquad (4.7.15)$$

Fig. 4.7.5 shows the variation of T with (f/f_r) and how an optimum amount of damping can increase the effectiveness of isolators.

In selecting suitable forms of isolation many factors are involved besides isolation performance. Cost, environmental conditions, ageing, corrosion, access, maintenance, fire risk, durability, serviceability are some of the aspects to which attention needs to be given. The degree of resilience necessary is, however, a principal factor. For instance if a 100 mm deflection is necessary a rubber isolator would need to be 1 m thick if the rubber is not to be excessively strained; this

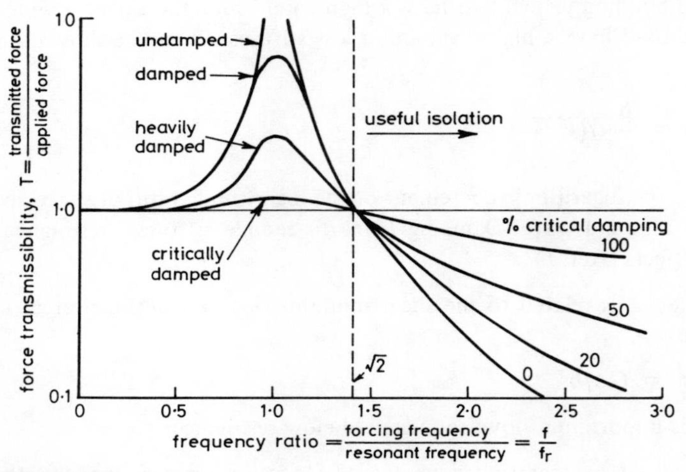

Fig. 4.7.5. ***Transmissibility function***

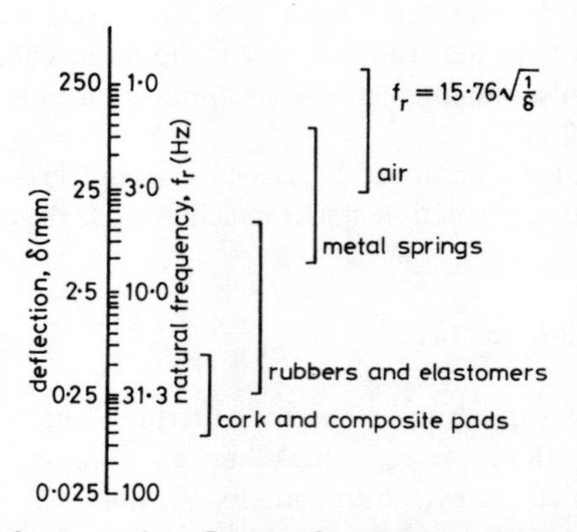

Fig. 4.7.6. ***Isolator performance data. Ranges of application of different types of isolator***

would be too costly and would take up too much space, so that a metal spring is a more realistic choice. Ranges of deflection and natural frequency obtained by various types of isolators are shown in Fig. 4.7.6 and Table 4.7.1; notice there is some overlap between the ranges, and some manufacturers are able to provide

Table 4.7.1 *Isolator performance data: approximate range of isolator performance based on a survey of British manufacturers*

Isolator Type	Approximate range of deflection (mm) Minimum	Maximum	Approximate range of natural frequency (Hz) Minimum	Maximum
Metal springs (load capacity up to 18 000 kg)	10	114	2	100
Polymers (load capacity up to 9000 kg)	0.25	23	3	31
Slab (cork, rubber, neoprene)	2	24	11	44

isolators with a performance outside a given range. In general, metal-coil or leaf-springs and air isolators are used for high deflection, and hence low, natural frequency applications, whereas cork and composite pads are utilised where low deflections are required. Rubbers, covering a range of natural rubber, silicone, butyl and nitrile elastomers, are suitable for intermediate ranges of application.

The following practical points are for general guidance in designing vibration isolation systems.

(a) Aim to keep the frequency ratio $(\omega/\omega_r) \geqslant 3$. For simple systems (ω) can be estimated from the speed of rotation N (rev/s) of the machinery, remembering that $\omega = 2\pi f = 2\pi N$; $\omega_r = 2\pi f_r$ harmonics can be neglected. Systems comprising two units (e.g. fan and motor) should estimate ω from the lowest speed unit.

(b) Use a minimum of three support points; in practice at least four supports are used. For optimum efficiency each isolator should carry an equal load.

(c) The dynamic performance data for isolators should be used in design calculations, because the dynamic stiffness can achieve values from 20 to 200% more than the static stiffness values. This means that the resonant frequency is higher in operation since $f_r = 1/2\pi\sqrt{k/m}$

(d) Isolators suffer static deflection due to the mass of the equipment. In critical areas the static deflection of the mounting should be about twenty times that of the supporting structure under the dead load of the equipment, whereas for non-critical areas this factor may be reduced to three.

(e) Inertia blocks can be used to reduce the displacement amplitude, to minimise the effect of unequal weight distribution and to stabilise resiliently mounted plant having unbalancing forces. The use of inertia blocks to lower the centre of gravity is of great value when the mounted natural frequency is below 3 Hz; ideally the centre of gravity should lie in a plane lower than that of the isolation mountings. The weight of the block should be at least equal to the weight of the equipment, and should be two to five times the weight if reciprocating machines are being used. Do not support machines and their ancillary drive equipment on separate bases; it is probably better to use an inertia block about twice the weight of the total assembly. In practice, inertia blocks have a minimum thickness of 150 mm.

(f) It has been found that high-pressure fans can exert high back pressures which exert a high turning moment on the fan base. This may be reduced by increasing the base frame length or by using an inertia block in conjunction with stiffer mountings.

(g) Use flexible connections on the inlet and the discharge side of fans and pumps.

(h) Some isolators are non-linear and this results in high natural frequencies.

(j) Isolate pipework and ductwork from the building structure as well as from heating and airconditioning plant. Beware of any possibilities of isolation bridging.

(k) Check with the manufacturer of the isolating equipment that the environmental conditions of the installation will not harm the isolators in any way. Certain temperature and moisture levels, oil or chemical-laden atmospheres can be detrimental to isolators. Also check the fire-precaution requirements.

(l) Ensure that there is sufficient access to the isolators for maintenance inspections.

(m) Consider the use of floating floors (Ref. 1).

4.7.4 Background noise levels in buildings

4.7.4.1 Sources of noise

Noise sources and their control are interrelated. It is the manufacturer's responsibility to produce quiet equipment. The building environmental engineer and the architect need to work together on the noise implications of their building design. Noise within buildings may originate from the mechanical engineering services (e.g. heating, ventilation and airconditioning systems, fluid supply and drainage systems), the electrical services (e.g. lighting); the circulation services (e.g. lifts); the communication services (e.g. telephones); process machines (e.g. forging machines, typewriters); people (e.g. impact noise from footsteps, slamming doors, movement of chairs, cross-talk between one space and another); and external sources (e.g. traffic, aircraft, machinery).

The acoustical environment in the occupied space is the resultant of the noise arriving at the space from the engineering services, from adjacent areas by direct or indirect transmission and cross-talk, from the external environment and from noise generation within the space. The building services technologist has a clear responsibility to consider noise problems.

The services plant-room may be within or outside the building housing the people. Noise emitted in the plant-room will be:

(a) conducted to the occupied space by the fluid distributing the energy or by flanking transmission in the distribution network;
(b) transmitted through the plant-room structure to adjacent areas inside and/or ouside the building.

Further, if the fluid velocities are too high, noise generation may occur in the distribution system and/or at the terminal units.

4.7.4.2 Noise criteria
Noise criteria are related to time by using L_{10}, L_{50} or L_{90} sound levels which refer to the levels exceeded for 10%, 50% or 90% of the time for the period (e.g. the 18 hour period from 06·00 until midnight) considered. L_{90} effectively describes the background level whereas L_{10} denotes the activity level and will include some of the 'peaks' responsible for noise disturbance. The 'peaks' will define the noise character of the source whether it is traffic, ventilation noise or speech.

68 dBA on the L_{10} (18 hour) index has been recommended as the upper external limit to which residential development should be subjected. This corresponds to about 58–63 dBA indoors with windows open. The L_{10} indoors level should not exceed 35 dBA in bedrooms at night. The number of complaints increases rapidly when the L_{10} sound level in a general office reaches 60 dBA; the Wilson Committee (Ref. 5) set an upper limit of $L_{10} = 55$ dBA in spaces where speech communication takes place but for concentrated work in private offices, classrooms and lecture rooms, an upper limit of 45 dBA is desirable.

The noise criteria listed in Tables 4.7.2 and 4.7.3 are expressed in terms of the noise pollution level (see footnote to Table 4.7.2) as well as dBA.

There has been concern about the multiplicity of emission measures used in the United Kingdom for planning and regulatory purposes. There has been a move to replace these measures by a single index of environmental noise called the 'Equivalent Continuous Sound Level' (L_{eq}) (Ref. 6)

For traffic noise, assuming a normal distribution of levels:

$$L_{eq} = (L_{10} + L_{90})/2 + (L_{10} - L_{90})^2/57 \qquad (4.7.16)$$

Aircraft noise in the UK is rated using the Noise and Number Index (NNI) (Ref. 1) and this may be related to L_{eq} by:;

$$L_{eq}\,(12\text{ hour}) = 0{\cdot}88\,\text{NNI} + 26{\cdot}5 \qquad (4.7.17)$$

There is a corresponding L_{eq} value for the Corrected Noise Level (Reference 1) used for assessing noise from industrial premises.

It can be deduced that:

$$L_{eq} = L_{NP}\text{dBA} - L_{50} - (L_{10} + L_{90})/2 \qquad (4.7.18)$$

Table 4.7.4 shows the sound insulation I required for a building in a given external noise climate with a specified internal noise level; the numbers in brackets are the mass requirements in kg/m^2. Buildings such as houses, hotels and factories employing night-shift workers require analysis of L_{10} daytime (6 am until midnight) and

Table 4.7.2 *General internal noise criteria (Ref. 2)*

	Minimum steady dBA	Optimum steady dBA	Maximum desirable adverse noise L_{NP} dBA[a] Bedroom	Maximum desirable adverse noise L_{NP} dBA[a] Living Room
Houses				
Rural	25	30	40	50
Surburban	25	35	45	55
Urban	25	40	50	60
Offices				
General	35	45	55	
Private	30	$N^{(b)}$	55	
Hospitals				
Wards	35	45	55	
Schools				
Lecture Rooms	25	30 or $N^{(b)}$	50[c]	
Colleges				
Universities				
Mixed-activity rooms	35	45	55	
Factories				
General areas where communication is important			65	

(a) Noise Pollution Level is defined as

$$L_{NP}\text{dBA} = L_{50} + (L_{10} - L_{90}) + (L_{10} - L_{90})^2/60 \qquad (4.7.19)$$

where L_{10}, L_{50} and L_{90} are all expressed in dBA
(b) $N = 70$ – attenuation of partition
(c) Depends on speech interference and size

Table 4.7.3 *External noise criteria in housing areas (Ref. 2)*

	Urban	Suburban
No advantage below these levels	50 L_{NP} dBA	45 L_{NP} dBA
Generally acceptable levels	70	65

Table 4.7.4 *Sound Insulation of Structure*

External noise level L_{10} dBA	Internal noise level L_{10} dBA		
	L_{10} = 35 dBA	45 dBA	55 dBA
60	I = 25 dB (10 kg/m^2)	15 dB (low)	5 dB (low)
70	35 (50)	25 (10)	15 (low)
80	45 (200)	35 (50)	25 (10)

L_{10} night (midnight until 6 am) conditions; the latter may be the determining factor in some situations.

4.7.5 Basic method of noise control

4.7.5.1 General

There is a threefold problem: to protect the building from external noise sources; to ensure that the building designed is not a noise nuisance to people in buildings and spaces nearby; and to control the amount of noise generated within the building.

Increasingly, the building environmental engineer and the architect are being requested to advise on all aspects of the problem. The degree of external protection and internal control required depends on the use of the building. For example, broadcasting studios and concert halls will require a stringent acoustical criterion. In a factory, however, the permitted noise levels will be much higher although in practice often much higher than audiologists would recommend. In designing the indoor noise climate, care is also needed to ensure that people in adjacent spaces outside the building are not aggrieved. The pattern of diagnosis and treatment for these situations is the same, that is, to:

(a) ascertain the acoustical characteristics of the source, propagation pathway and receiver;
(b) provide a mismatch between the source and the receiver, which will be designed from the data obtained in (a) and the acoustical criterion specified for the project.

4.7.5.2 Principles of noise control

Noise control involves employing one or more of the following principles:

(a) *Designing a source to achieve a set acoustical tolerance.* Building environmental engineers have little to say in this matter, which lies in the province of the equipment manufacturers, but they can exercise discretion in selecting fans, compressors and machinery, besides designing efficient aerodynamic and hydrodynamic energy distribution systems.
(b) *Providing a large separation between the source and the receiver* and thus making the most of natural attenuation. This involves planning of building sites and also the layout of spaces within the building.

(c) *Enforcing natural attenuation along the source-receiver pathway* by employing one or a combination of the following:

(i) a high-mass structure to reflect the energy before it reaches the receiver
(ii) an absorption attenuator to dissipate the energy via friction over a broadband frequency range
(iii) interference attenuators to reduce the sound level at specific frequencies by phase cancellation.
(iv) resonance attenuators, which may be tuned to provide attenuation over various frequency bandwidths by varying the mass, stiffness and damping characteristics of the attenuator cells
(v) materials or isolators with high isolation efficiency characteristics (i.e. low transmissibility) to minimise the propagation of structure borne sound.

(d) *Altering the acoustical conditions in the receiving space by:*

(i) using absorbent materials applied to various surfaces to reduce the reverberant energy level
(ii) using soft floor-finishes to minimise impact noise
(iii) introducing background noise where there are several functions requiring different sound levels taking place in the same space
(iv) isolating the room structure from that of adjacent spaces.

(e) *Restricted work schedules, also the use of ear-defenders.* In industrial situations the employment of ear defenders will be necessary by workers in acoustical environments equal to or exceeding noise levels of 80–85 dBA.
(f) *Legislation.* This is usually out of the province of the environmental engineer.

Sound control requires a lot of commonsense as well as technical expertise.

4.7.6 Acoustical design briefs and specifications for buildings

The brief and specification for a building design must include a comprehensive summary of the acoustical criteria. In order to make sure that the criteria have been selected wisely and can be achieved in practice, an integrated design team working from the design inception to building commissioning is essential. This is obvious when one considers that the required internal noise climate will depend upon the site; the choice of building structure will dictate the relationships between the inside and outside noise climate, and hence the architect and the building environmental engineer, together with the structural engineer, must evolve a joint decision on this matter. The main factors are:

(a) The orientation of the building will affect the noise exposure of occupied spaces.
(b) The internal planning of a building must also take into account the noise critical areas and place them as far away as possible, or shield them, from external and internal noise sources.

(c) Various degrees of privacy within the building will necessitate selecting internal wall partitions, ceilings and floors with this acoustical requirement borne in mind.
(d) Design of services systems has to meet noise level requirements; the choice of surface finishes will affect the sound distribution throughout the space;
(e) In the special case of a concert hall, a theatre or an opera house, the shape of the space must be taken into account when designing the sound distribution.

Thus, planning, layout, materials, surface finishes, shape, choice and design of systems are keywords in acoustic design. The problem is not made easier by other factors, such as:

(a) Cost constraints.
(b) The quality of building materials and workmanship of the construction.
(c) The interaction of acoustical requirements with other needs. For instance, the choice of building structure also depends upon the thermal insulation, the solar protection, the daylighting, the natural ventilation requirements, the fire safety, circulation, and the structual requirements; the choice of surface finishes also depends upon aesthetics, cleaning costs and durability; and the choice of the space shape depends upon the social environment and also governs the quality of the air movement distribution, besides acoustic considerations.
(d) The change of external noise climate with time. This usually increases from year to year, besides following diurnal patterns.

These problems cannot be overcome without good communication between the client, the architect, the building environmental engineer, the structural engineer and, at a later stage, the builder.

4.7.7 Selection of building structure

The relative importance of the factors discussed in Section 4.7.5 will be different for each building design, depending on the location of the building, its use, and the money available to build and operate it.

Sound insulation is defined as:

$$I = R - 10 \lg (S/A) \tag{4.7.20}$$

for a structure having sound reduction index R area S and absorption in the receiving space A; this formula shows that the sound-reduction index alone does not give the effective sound insulation, because the sound absorption of the space behind the structure plays a part in the sound-energy transmission process. Other limitations to the theoretical estimation of sound insulation are flanking transmission and the quality of construction.

Cracks permit sound to leak through the structure, but at the same time they allow infiltration of fresh air and contribute towards or fulfil, the ventilation rate of an occupied space. If the external noise climate dictates that sealed windows should be used, mechanical ventilation is necessary to provide the air needed to dilute and remove the odours released into the space. Up to about three air changes per hour of ventilation assists significantly in reducing overheating in summer.

Reflective films applied to glazing are more effective than heat-absorbent glasses in minimising the effect of solar radiation on indoor temperatures but they reduce the daylight factor. Likewise, mid-pane Venetian blinds are preferable to internal blinds, but the minimum overheating will occur with external sunbreakers although there is a high cost involved in cleaning and maintaining these devices. Reflecting solar energy away from building surfaces is wasteful, but at present there is no economical way of using all the internal building fabric as a solar collector and a thermal store while providing sufficient ventilation and daylight with a minimum of noise transfer, although work in Sweden using hollow block ventilated floors suggests economic solutions will become feasible soon; the use of chemical storage will further enhance these possibilities.

The design steps for selecting type and amount of glazing compatible with the environmental aspects of building design are as follows:

(a) select indoor L_{10} sound level
(b) select window with required external-internal sound insulation
(c) select peak indoor environmental temperature and daily range
(d) select daylight factor
(e) select solar control compatible with conditions in (c) and (d)
(f) check ventilation rate and see if mechanical ventilation is necessary.

4.7.8 Acoustic design problems of internal spaces

Each building present its own unique problems which can only be discovered as the design is formulated. But there are many problems which keep recurring, and it is these problems which are summarised here in the identification matrix shown in Table 4.7.5 although it should be emphasised that they are the minimum number shown that will occur in practice.

Background noise criteria for various types of building are given by the American NC curves and the Preferred NC curves, and the European NR standard curves. The NC and NR curves are similar. The PNC curves have values about 1 dB lower than the NC curves in the 125, 250, 500 and 1000 Hz octave bands; in the 63 Hz, and in the octave bands above 1000 Hz, they are about 4 or 5 dB lower than the NC curves. (Refs. 1, 3 and 4).

4.7.9 Acoustical design procedure

For the design and planning of a new building the environmental engineer needs to work in close collaboration with the client, the architect and the structural engineer.

Table 4.7.5 *Identification Matrix for Common Problems*

Acoustical problem	All	Dwellings	Hotels	Offices, large	Offices, private	Schools	Universities	Hospitals	Courtrooms	Theatres	Concert halls	Recording studios	Television studios	Factories
Sources of noise														
External	★	★	★	★	★	★	★	★	★	★	★	★	★	★
Plant room	★	★	★	★	★	★	★	★	★	★	★	★	★	★
Adjacent spaces	★	★	★	★	★	★	★	★	★	★	★	★	★	★
Machines				★									★	
Typewriter				★	★									
Telephones				★	★									
Duplicating machines				★										
Computers				★										
Footsteps		★	★	★	★	★	★	★	★	★	★	★	★	
Door slamming		★	★	★	★	★	★	★	★					
Heating/ventilation/ air conditioning		★	★	★	★	★	★	★	★	★	★	★	★	
Toilets		★	★	★	★	★	★	★	★	★	★	★	★	
People talking		★	★	★	★	★	★	★	★					
Others	list appropriately													
Other problems														
Privacy		★	★	★	★	★	★	★	★					
Deafness														★
Speech communication				★	★	★	★	★	★	★	★	★	★	★
Speech reinforcement						★	★		★	★				★
Echoes				★	★	★	★	★	★	★	★	★	★	★
Delay time										★	★			
Reverberation				★	★	★	★	★	★	★	★	★	★	★
Sound quality										★	★	★	★	

4.7.9.1 Planning stage

(a) Assess external noise climate

(i) measure 10% and 90% sound levels (L_{10}, L_{90}) and the frequency spectrum of particular sources
(ii) ascertain future developments which may affect the nature of level of the noise climate.

(b) Decide on the design criteria required within the building and plan the layout of the internal spaces, attempting to separate the quieter areas from the noisier ones.
(c) Decide on the sound reduction index for the external structure, and the orientation of the building, in conjunction with the client, the architect and other members of the building design team.
(d) Decide on the shape of any auditoria, or ceilings in the case of landscaped offices, in conjunction with the architect.
(e) Decide on the sound reduction index required for the internal walls, partitions, doors, ceilings and floors (also finishes required) with the architect; consult with the structural engineer concerning the effect of the mass of the building elements on the structure.
(f) Decide on the amount of absorption material required, especially in critical areas such as auditoria, recording studios or landscaped offices, in conjunction with the architect.
(g) Assess the acoustical performance of all equipment to be used in the building (to cover all mechanical and electrical services besides office equipment) in terms of octave-band (or narrow-band) spectra installation or operating device.

4.7.9.2 Assessment of noise control equipment required

(a) Estimate dynamic loss required on inlet and discharge side of the system to achieve the design acoustical conditions in the building. (Use method systematically laid out in Book B of the IHVE Guide, 1970).
(b) Detail final proposals for plant-room structure and any floating floor constructions that may be required.
(c) Check to see if either break-out noise from the system to a quiet area, or the converse, will occur.

4.7.9.3 Selection of noise control equipment

Having attempted to obtain the spectrum of attenuation required, select equipment in conjunction with a manufacturer, remembering that interference and reflection-type sound filters can be easily incorporated as part of the airconditioning network design, to give the degree of airborne and structureborne sound control required.

4.7.10 References in text

(1) CROOME, D. J., 'Noise, Buildings and People,' Pergamon Press (1977)
(2) WALLER, R. A., 7th Int. Congress on Acoustics, Budapest, Paper 245, 10 (1971)
(3) CROOME, D. J., (Editor), 'Noise and the Design of Buildings and Services,' Construction Press (1982)
(4) GINN, K. B., 'Architectural Acoustics,' Bruel and Kjaer (November 1978)
(5) 'Noise' HMSO 1963
(6) 'A Guide to Measurement and Prediction of the Equivalent Continuous Sound Level'. The Noise Advisory Council. HMSO, 1978.

4.7.11 Glossary

A	Cross-sectional Area (m^2)
A	Absorption in the receiving space
E	Young's Modulus of Elasticity
G	Shear Modulus
L_{eq}	Equivalent continuous sound level (dBA)
L_{NP}	Noise pollution level (dB)
L_p	Sound pressure level (dB, dBA)
L_w	Sound power level (dB)
L_{10}	Sound level exceeded for 10% of the time considered
L_{50}	Sound level exceeded for 50% of the time considered
L_{90}	Sound level exceeded for 90% of the time considered
NNI	Noise and Number Index
Q	Directivity factor
R	Room constant
R	Sound reduction index (dB)
S	Surface area (m^2)
T	Reverberation time (s)
T	Transmissibility
V	Volume (m^3)
W	Power (W)
W_0	Reference sound power (W)
c	Velocity of sound (m/s)
d	cavity width (m)
dB	decibels
dBA	decibels (A scale)
f	frequency (Hz)
f_r	resonant frequency (Hz)
h	thickness (m)
k	stiffness
m	mass requirement (kg/m^2)
p	pressure (N/m^2)
r	distance between listener and sound source (m)
r	damping capacity
s	logarithmic decrement in a sound wave
x	deflection (m)
$\dot{x}$	velocity (m/s)
$\ddot{x}$	acceleration (m/s^2)
α	sound absorption coefficient
$\bar{\alpha}$	mean sound absorption coefficient
η	efficiency
λ	wavelength (m)
ρ	density (kg/m^3)

γ	adiabatic pressure coefficient
ω	($2\pi f$) radial velocity (radians/s)
ω_r	($2\pi f_r$) resonant (natural) radial velocity (radians/s)
δ	deflection (mm)

Slim storage radiator (TI Creda)

Chapter 4.8

Electric heating

G. Haslett, Heating Specialist, The Electricity Council
R.J. Lane, Development Manager, TI Creda Limited

4.8.1 Introduction

Electric space heating can be broadly classified into direct and storage heating. Storage systems are operated on cheap off-peak supplies and can be designed to make full use of the thermal storage properties of a building and its contents. Direct appliances, which use electricity at the standard rate, have the advantages of flexibility of performance, convenience and immediate response. The two systems can be used independently or may be complementary to one another to meet particular heating requirements. Electric heating is clean, silent, requires little maintenance and is capable of automatic operation. Its installation is economical in builders' work, as no flue construction or modification is needed, and in planning, as no provision for fuel storage or stoking is necessary and no planning consents are required. The requirements of the Clean Air Act are fully satisfied and electric heating systems are eligible for grants under clean air and home modernisation legislation.

The Electricity Boards in the United Kingdom have actively encouraged the use of electricity at off-peak times. This has been achieved in various ways – by special agreements with industrial consumers entitling them to lower demand tariffs for loads supplied outside the winter day time peak periods; by general tariffs which encourage the continuous use of supply throughout the year once the capacity and fixed charges attributable to the supply had been recovered; and by a wide range of uses of electricity amongst different types of consumer to achieve maximum diversity. By the late 1950s off-peak tariffs were available which offered cheaper supplies via a separately metered circuit controlled by a time switch. These cheaper tariffs were generally restricted to supplies to storage type equipment and the growth of electric space heating has therefore been tied to some extent to the development of off-peak tariffs. Initially off-peak tariffs afforded supplies between 8 and 12 hours overnight and for a 3 hour afternoon boost. The success of off-peak development resulted in a temporary emergence of a system peak in the afternoon hours in 1969. The emphasis on off-peak development therefore changed and in 1969 Electricity Boards introduced two-rate tariffs (e.g. the White Meter tariff) which charged a low rate at night for all supplies – not just for storage appliances. The two-rate tariff has been the main off-peak tariff since 1969 and the current development of this is the Economy 7 tariff which was introduced in October 1978. With this tariff all the Electricity Boards in England and Wales charge the same overnight rate for seven hours of overnight electricity. The reduction in hours of charge overnight and the elimination of daytime boosts has meant that the performance of the equipment has been improved by using high capacity storage media and the use of insulation materials suitable for high temperatures. In the early stages it was also necessary to develop storage heating system design procedures. This needed a considerable amount of field trial work in order to determine the interaction of the heater performance, building structure and the effect of miscellaneous heat gains, and this work underpins the design procedures used today.

In practice both storage and direct acting appliances are often used in combination to form a heating system. This is particularly true of the home where storage heaters are used to provide the base heat load, contributing about 90% in consumption terms over the heating season, supplemented by direct acting heaters primarily to provide short term heating in the lounge, bedroom or bathroom.

4.8.2 Storage heating

4.8.2.1 General

Storage heating appliances are fairly simple in construction, being formed of a storage medium heated by elements and surrounded by thermal insulation and a casing. Table 4.8.1 shows some common storage media and insulation materials, all of which have been used over the period of the development of the equipment. Commercial pressures both to maintain a high specified performance whilst making storage heaters slimmer and more attractive has meant that the dominant materials used in current equipment are Feolite (a sintered iron oxide storage medium) and Microtherm, a high temperature insulant, 15 mm of which is equivalent to about 50 mm of a high density mineral wool. A central heating system known as Electricaire comprises a centrally sited storage unit from which warm air is ducted to the building.

Water deserves special mention because despite its relatively poor storage capacity it has many advantages that are associated with its simplicity. It can be used for both storage and heat distribution, and because water storage vessels can be designed with a low heat loss, the heat can be removed virtually as required, giving a high degree of controllability.

Table 4.8.1 *Storage and Insulation Materials Used in Off-Peak Appliances*

Insulation materials

Material	Density (kg/m^3)	Conductivity (W/mK) Hot Face Temp = 300°C	Hot Face Temp = 700°C
Calcium Silicate	240	0.063	0.085
Mineral Wool	240	0.057	0.103
Microtherm (opacified silica aerogel)	240	0.022	0.028
Rockwool	200	0.061	0.101

Storage materials

Material	Temperatures for Storage Calculation (°C)	Storage Capacity (kWh/m^3)
Water	95–49	53
Fire Clay	750–150	364
Olivine	750–150	495
Feolite	750–150	614
Alloy Cast-Iron	750–150	675

Table 4.8.2 *Controllability of Various Types of Storage Equipment*

Type	Controllable Output %
Storage Heaters	
Fan storage	40–50
Fan assisted heaters	20–30
With damper	0–20
Without damper	0
Electricaire	80
Floorwarming	0
Electric Boiler	95

In addition to storage heating appliances heat can be stored within the fabric of the dwelling. The most common place for this is the floor where plastic insulated resistance cables are embedded in the floor below the floor screed. The storage appliances or systems may be broadly categorised in accordance with the percentage of heat output that can be directly controlled by the consumer (Table 4.8.2). The most common equipment used in the home is the damper controlled storage heater in which the customer has control over about 20% of the output. British Standard 3456 (Specification for Safety of Household Appliances) sets standards for the electrical safety of storage heaters (Part 2:26) and Electricaire (Part 2:22). As far as performance is concerned the Electricity Council has drawn up performance specifications for high capacity storage heaters and for Electricaire units. Providing the heater complies with these the only information needed to decide the size of a heater for a particular duty is the overnight charge acceptance, i.e. the charge (in kWh) that the heater takes in a 7 hour period.

4.8.2.2 Freestanding storage heaters

There are four main types of freestanding storage heater, the substantial difference being the method of achieving output control:

Fig. 4.8.1. *Interior of storage radiator* (TI Creda)

(a) the basic storage heater designed without any output control.

(b) the damper control model which has an arrangement whereby the room air can be passed through the core so achieving a boost in output either automatically or manually as the customer requires (Fig. 4.8.2).

(c) the fan assisted storage heater is not significantly different in construction from (a) or (b) but it incorporates a small fan to boost the output. The main output is still achieved through the case.

(d) the fan storage heater has more insulation surrounding the core and achieves a much greater measure of output control (Fig. 4.8.2).

Types (a), (b) and (c) are commonly marketed in three capacities of 12 kWh, 18 kWh and 24 kWh charge acceptance over 7 hours. Fan storage heaters generally range between 21 kWh and 42 kWh charge acceptance.

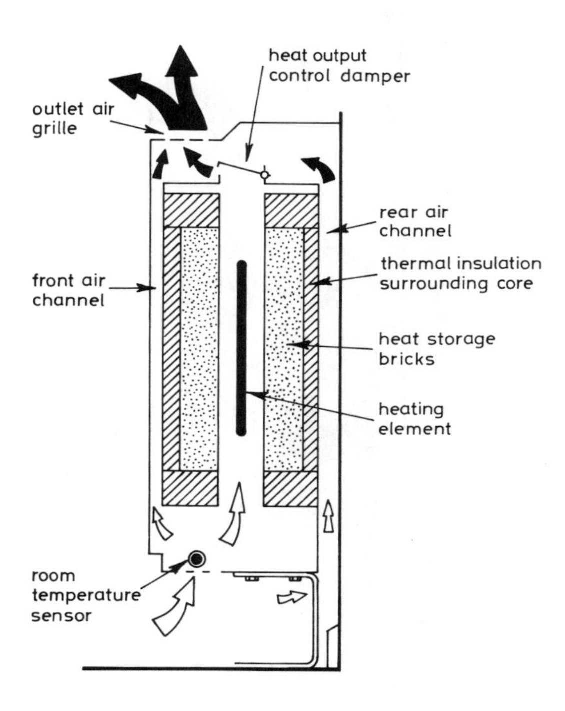

Fig. 4.8.2. *Section through damper control storage heater*

4.8.2.3 Electricaire

Electricaire is a ducted warm air heating system. At the heart of the system is the Electricaire unit (Fig. 4.8.3) which has an extremely well insulated storage core such that only about 20% of the total energy taken is emitted through the case. The majority of the heat output is achieved by a fan drawing return (room) air via a filter through the hot core mixing this with return air to achieve acceptable temperatures and distributing the warm air via warm air registers. Damper and fan speed arrangements are incorporated for commissioning. It is essential to minimise duct runs and the most appropriate system often combines a central siting of the Electricaire unit with short stub ducts to three or four outlets. This type of system is fairly common in the home and in recent years has started to grow in popularity in commercial premises such as stores or warehouses. The Electricaire units range mainly between 42 kWh to 105 kWh charge acceptance, although larger units are sometimes built for commercial premises.

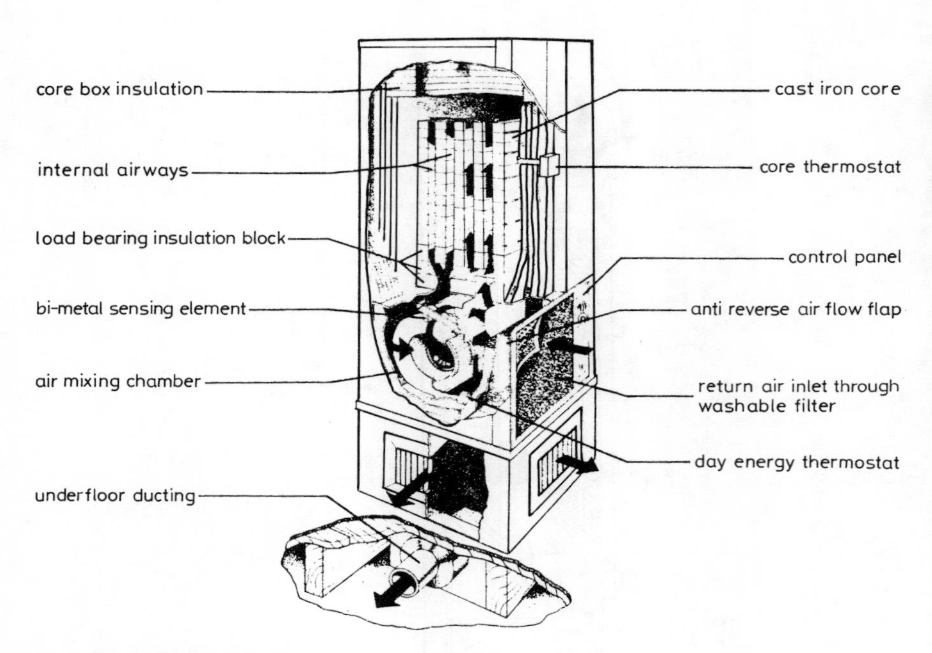

Fig. 4.8.3. *Electricaire unit*

4.8.2.4 Water storage

Although the system incorporating water storage has often been used in commercial premises it has not been commonly used in the home because of difficulties in finding space for the storage vessel. The advent of much better thermally insulated houses together with a market emerging as a replacement to oil fired boilers has renewed interest in this type of system. The system is simple (Fig. 4.8.4) and is based on a well insulated storage vessel which is heated overnight by low side-entry immersion heaters. The hot water mixed with return water is pumped around the radiator system in the normal way. Upper elements are provided for direct use should the stored energy run out. The system is a traditional open vented type connected to a cold feed and expansion vessel in the roof space.

Domestic hot water arrangements are carried out by a separate system thus eliminating some of the heat losses experienced in the traditional system.

In domestic premises the system shown in Fig. 4.8.4 is used. In commercial premises requiring in excess of about 30 kW element loading the immersion heaters

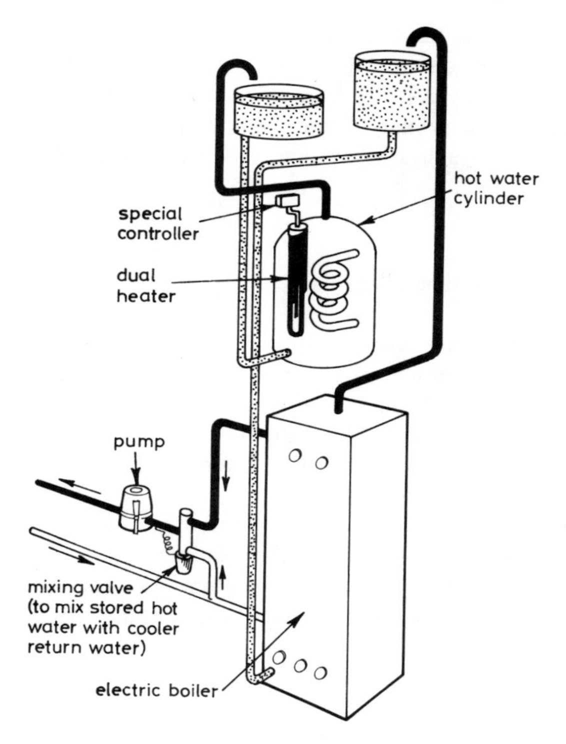

Fig. 4.8.4. *Water storage heater replacing oil fired boiler*

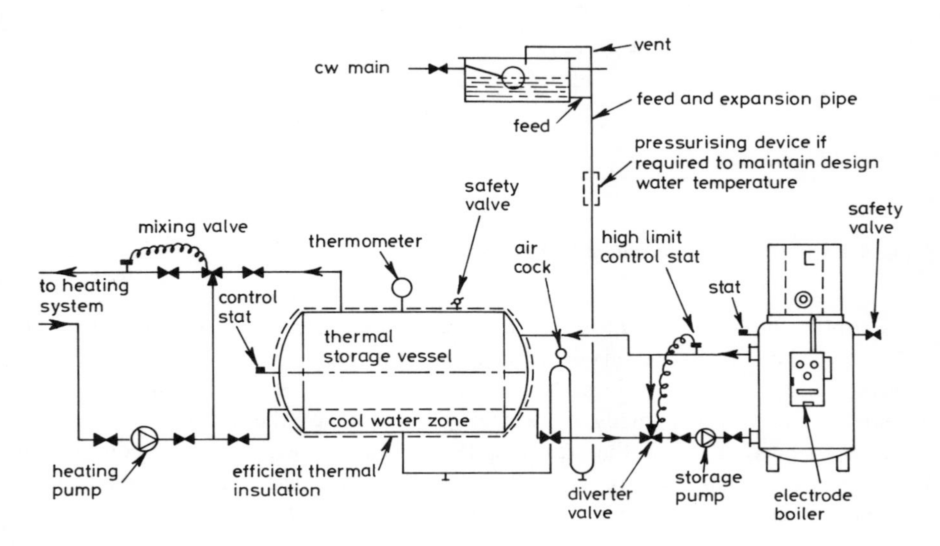

Fig. 4.8.5. *Commercial water storage heating*

are replaced by a separate flow heater. In commercial and industrial premises where electrical loadings in excess of 250 kW are required electrode boilers are used. In this case a 3 phase supply is generally needed. Where a flow heater or an electrode boiler is incorporated, a primary heating circuit is introduced to pump the heat into the storage vessel. The heating system is fed from the storage vessel as shown in Fig. 4.8.5.

4.8.3 Storage heating system design

The detailed design of systems incorporating various forms of electric storage heating is described in a number of Electricity Council publications which are listed in the references. It is worthwhile, however, touching upon the crucial differences in the sizing philosophy between the main types of storage systems and the traditional systems. Floor warming has rather different design considerations to other storage systems and is dealt with separately.

The shape of a typical heat demand curve for a traditional intermittently operated direct system is shown in Fig. 4.8.6. This indicates a preheating demand in excess of the steady state calculated heat loss. The heat demand is shown to reduce as the fabric of the building becomes heated. If a continuous heating regime

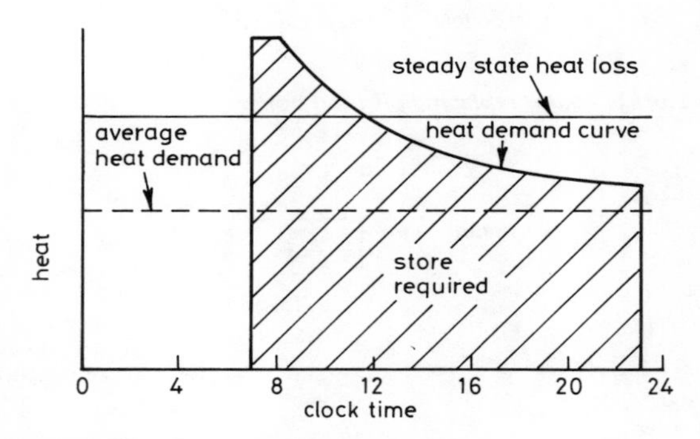

Fig. 4.8.6. *Heating curve, intermittent operation*

is adopted the heat demand is shown to vary only a little (Fig. 4.8.7) throughout the day, there being no major requirement for preheating. Comparison of the average heat demand of Figs. 4.8.6 and 4.8.7 shows the continuously operated system to require marginally more energy but both of the average demands are shown to be well below the steady state heat loss. The percentage reduction in energy requirement by turning the system off overnight is well established and is dependent upon the thermal weight of the building and the response of the heating system.

The lower energy average heat demand (compared with the design heat loss) is attributed to the effect of miscellaneous gains (solar, body and other appliance usage) and overestimation in the design heat loss. At one time traditional heating engineers were sceptical of this explanation but the proof is now well documented by many organisations.

With the traditional direct heating system it is the maximum instantaneous demand that is the basis of sizing the equipment and this is commonly based upon the design steady state heat loss with a margin for intermittent operation. The approach is rather similar for both boiler system or direct electric heaters.

Whilst the mechanical design of pipework or ducting is similar when associated with storage heating systems there is an additional crucial requirement of sizing the store required. Assuming there is going to be no injection of energy to the store during the day time the overnight charge acceptance (CA) needs to be sufficient to provide the energy required during the period that the heater is disconnected (the shaded areas in Figs. 4.8.6 & 4.8.7) together with any overnight heating. The latter

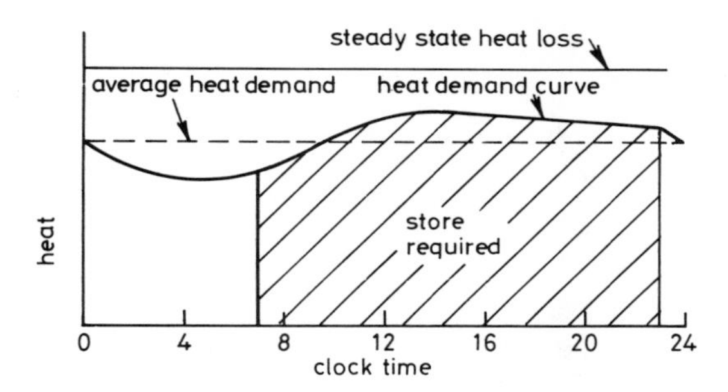

Fig. 4.8.7. *Heating curve, continuous operation*

is a characteristic of storage heater and floor warming systems because of their continuous output nature. Electricaire, central water storage or fan storage heaters have a very large measure of output control and any overnight heating takes place largely during the preheating period of the system. The charge acceptance is therefore given by:

$$CA = 24HZ/1000 \qquad (4.8.1)$$

where

CA = overnight charge acceptance, kWh

H = steady state design heat loss, W

Z = a factor established from long experience which reflects the proportion of the theoretical steady state requirement to be met by the heating system.

It is important that the calculation of the heat loss should be in accordance with the Chartered Institution of Building Services Guide Section A9 'Estimation of

Table 4.8.3 *Typical Z-Factors for Storage Heating Appliance Sizing*

Domestic	
Type of System	Typical Z-Factor
Electricaire or Water Storage	0·65–0·70
Floorwarming	0·70
Storage Heaters in:	
2 rooms	0·75
3 rooms	0·72
4 rooms	0·67
5 rooms	0·64
6 or more rooms	0·59

Storage heating in offices		
	Typical Z-Factor	
	Proportion of external wall glazed	
Mean 24 hour heat gains (W/m^2 floor area)	20%	50%
3·5	0·83	0·73
7·0	0·77	0·70
11·5	0·68	0·58
16·0	0·52	0.43

Plant Capacity', and does not include any additional safety allowances. Typical values of Z from Electricity Council field trials for various applications are given in Table 4.8.3. As far as storage heaters are concerned these are rated by overnight charge acceptance. In the case of controllable output of storage heating it is essential to estimate the active store required.

This varies depending upon the estimate of energy used for preheating in the morning and the modest amount of case loss from the unit. The minimum active store required:

$$S = \frac{24\,HZ - (bZ)}{1000} \qquad (4.8.2)$$

where

S = active store kWh

b = number of overnight hours

The term Z approximates to the preheating requirement, and whilst Z at night may be slightly reduced to say between about 0·40 to 0·50 the term is still worth between $2{\cdot}8H$ and $3{\cdot}5H$ in reducing the active store. Whilst it may be common practice to start heating with hot water radiator systems from about 5·00 a.m. (i.e. 2 hours before the end of the off-peak hours) thus allowing a recharge of the heater, this may not be the case with warm air systems which are often used in a very intermittent fashion. In the case of the Electricaire system the overnight heating will more likely resolve to the case emission and the active store required will therefore be:

$$S = \frac{24HZ}{1000} - CE \tag{4.8.3}$$

where the case emission of the unit is given by

$$CE = 4(0{\cdot}0135S + 0{\cdot}68) \tag{4.8.4}$$

where

S = active store, kWh

CE = case emission, kWh

The straightforward application where no injection is made to the store during the day has so far been considered. However, the Electricity Boards' Economy 7 tariff allows the electricity supply to be connected during the day time although at the higher day rate. The restriction is largely an economic one therefore and it is not wise from this viewpoint to design for systems that require more than 10% day energy on a seasonal basis. In the case of storage heaters the day time top-up should be introduced through other equipment (e.g. a panel heater) and not injected into the storage heater. In the case of Electricaire and water storage systems day time injections can be introduced efficiently and the store can be reduced accordingly by applying a further factor, Y, to the term $24HZ$. Thus equation 4.8.2 becomes:

$$S = \frac{24HZY - (bZ)}{1000} \tag{4.8.5}$$

where Y = a factor for assessing the proportion to be met by the storage heating on a design day for a particular design seasonal day percentage.

Values of Y are given in Table 4.8.4. This shows for example that if 80% of the heating requirement of the design day ($-1\,^\circ$C external) is met by the storage system then 20% needs to be supplied by direct or day heating on that day and 4% over the season. This factor is a function of the distribution of days at various mean temperatures throughout the heating season.

The storage elements need to be sufficient to charge the heater overnight allowing for any night usage:

$$E_n = \frac{CA}{b} \tag{4.8.6}$$

where

En = storage elements, kW

CA = charge acceptance, kWh

b = hours of overnight charge

The day elements, should these be incorporated into the Electricaire unit or water storage unit, should be sized as a minimum to meet the heat loss. In the case of an Electricaire unit it is common practice to operate a convenient proportion (depending upon the element arrangement) of the night storage elements during the day.

Table 4.8.4 *Values of Y (seasonal day percentage factor)*

Percentage day energy over a season	Proportion to be met by storage on design day Y-value
0	1·00
1	0·90
2	0·85
3	0·82
4	0·80
5	0·76
6	0·74
7	0·72
8	0·70
9	0·68
10	0·67

4.8.4 Direct heating

Direct heating is provided either by individual appliances or incorporated as part of the building fabric, as with ceiling heating. The latter is dealt with separately in section 4.8.7. There is a wide range of individual appliances to suit each applications. The following provides brief descriptions of the types available and their applications:

4.8.4.1 Panel heaters

Panel heaters are distinguished by the type of output. Radiant panels usually comprise an encapsulated element in a plastic laminate or similar inert and thermally stable material encased in a metal finish. The panels operate at a surface temperature of about 80°C. Although called radiant panels some of the heat loss is by convection. A similar type of appliance is the oil filled radiator, which is designed to look like a hot water radiator. In this case, however, a light grade oil is heated by an immersion heater sited at the base of the heater. The output characteristics are similar to a radiant panel heater. Most other types of panel heaters have purposely designed convection channels and depending upon the convective component are called radiant convectors or convectors. Panel heaters are all generally capable of very close control by their own integral thermostat. Sometimes individual panel heaters are installed in a home to provide whole house heating, being the main means of heating in each room except the bathroom. More commonly they are used to provide short period heating.

4.8.4.2 Fan convectors

Fan convectors are small forced convection appliances designed to provide quick response heating. A special type called a 'down flow' heater has been developed primarily for use, wall mounted in the bathroom or kitchen.

4.8.4.3 Skirting heaters

Skirting or tubular heaters are designed to be sited at low level in order to give an even temperature distribution throughout the room. The tubular heater comprises a mild steel or aluminium tube having an open spiral element wound on a mica fomer running internally throughout the length. The heat from the element radiates directly to the tube surface and then is transmitted by re-radiation and convection to the room. In the skirting heater the element is suspended inside a slotted casing over its entire length.

4.8.4.4 Radiant fires

High temperature radiant fires are designed to provide localised heating and more often than not a focal point for the room. Many are designed to incorporate a visual effect reminiscent of the solid fuel open fire. Infra-red types have been developed for the bathroom and kitchen.

4.8.5 Floor warming

4.8.5.1 General

Electric floor warming uses plastic coated resistance cable embedded in the concrete screed (see Figure 4.8.8). Insulation to the equivalent of 50 mm of load bearing flooring grade polystyrene should be incorporated below the floor base above the damp proof course. Because the maximum surface temperature of the floor is limited for comfort reasons to about 28°C, in the past systems operated with a day time boost. However systems can be designed that provide the bulk of the heating requirement on a 7 hour night charge. To minimise the temperature drop between morning and evening the premises needs a high standard of thermal insulation and 70–100 mm of screed thickness.

With electric floor warming three aspects are of particular concern to designers. The first of these is the limitation imposed by the maximum surface temperature as it is generally considered undesirable to design for mean maximum daily temperatures of more than 25°C. The second concerns the downward heat loss component, whilst the third relates to the fall-off in room temperature which can occur over the discharge period. While the fall-off in temperature is a complicated function of the type of floor, the screed thickness and the hours of charge and discharge, perhaps too much attention is paid to the calculation of a fall-off in temperature and not enough to established guidelines that will bring good results. Essentially floor warming can rarely be designed successfully using an overnight charge only unless there is some form of topping up. In offices it may not be essential to provide heating equipment to provide the top-up as the lighting and normal heat gain may be entirely sufficient. In industrial premises the modest fall-off in temperature may well be acceptable. In domestic premises the topping-up will usually take the form of a direct acting fire in the living room.

Floor warming installations need good building thermal insulation standards to

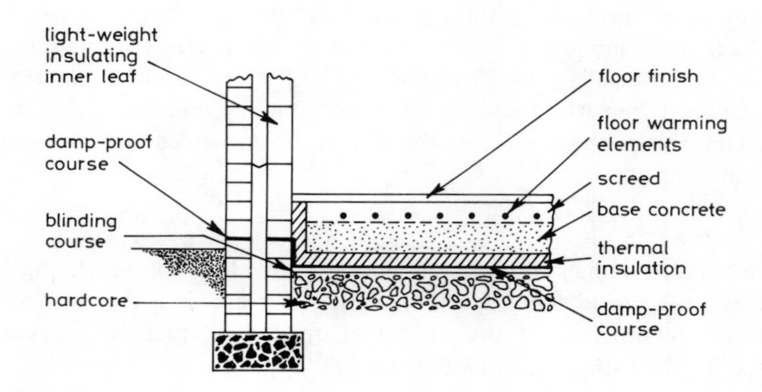

Fig. 4.8.8. Floorwarming installation

operate effectively, as the temperature differences are generally limited to between 4° and 9°C, equivalent to 44 W/m^2°C and 99 W/m^2°C output. A domestic building to current Building Regulations standards would possess a heat loss of 40–60 W/m^2°C, i.e. within the range to permit successful floor warming designs.

The mean floor surface temperature taken for design purposes should not exceed 25°C otherwise the occupants of the room may start to experience discomfort through hot or tired feet. This temperature has been chosen in the realisation, of course, that it exceeds that level for the first few hours after the end of the charging period. Whilst the constant of emission is more correctly related to the arithmetic average of the air temperature and the weighted mean surface temperature it is sufficiently accurate to relate it to air temperature alone, using 11 W/m^2°C difference between floor surface and air.

4.8.5.2 Design

The design of the system is in some ways similar to that of the other storage systems. The upward emission from the floor is given by:

$$E = \frac{HZ}{A} \times K_1 \qquad (4.8.7)$$

E = mean upward emission required, W/m^2

A = Area of particular floor under consideration, m^2

K_1 = Applies only to floors gaining heat from a heated floor above (Table 4.8.5)

Z = Factor in accordance with Table 4.8.3

The factor K_1 will therefore generally only apply to multistorey dwellings or offices. Values of K_1 have been estimated and given in Table 4.8.5. The value of E that can be incorporated without unreasonable room temperature swing is limited, depending upon the type of floor and thickness of screed and the discharge period recommended. In Table 4.8.6 maximum values of E to be adopted are given. If the value calculated from the equation exceeds the value given in the table for a 7 hour charge it will be necessary to consider improved building insulation, topping-up from another heating source, or an injection of energy during the day of from 1–3 hours, or combination of all these. It will be noted from Table 4.8.6 that the position of the insulation is important. If this is placed below the base concrete (floor type 2) the storage of the floor is enhanced, particularly if carpet is added. From a performance viewpoint this is the best type of approach as for a particular heat emission it limits room temperature swing.

The element power needs to be sufficient to charge during the night hours the daily upward emission required ($24E$), together with the daily perimeter edge loss or downward losses in accordance with equation 4.8.8 on p. 391.

Table 4.8.5 *Values for K_1 for floor warming*

Intermediate floors gaining from heated floor above assuming floor above has 50 mm insulation	
Finish of floor above	K_1
No carpet	0·92
Carpet tiles	0·85
Woollen carpet with felt underlay	0·78
All other floors $K_1 = 1$	

Table 4.8.6 *Maximum upward emission using 7-hour night charge in domestic premises*

Floor description			Maximum upward emission (W/m²)
floor type 1 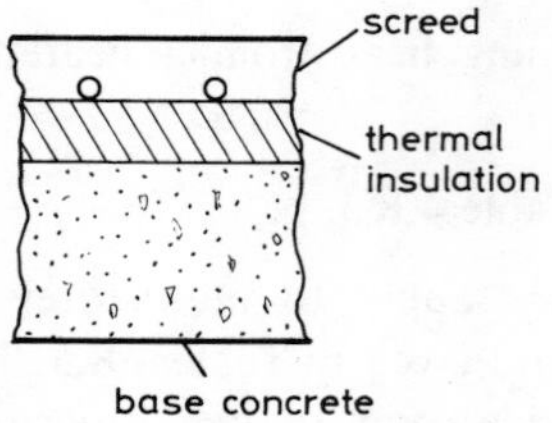 (screed, thermal insulation, base concrete)	With carpet	50 mm screed	20
		100 mm screed	31
	Without carpet	50 mm screed	17
		100 mm screed	28
floor type 2 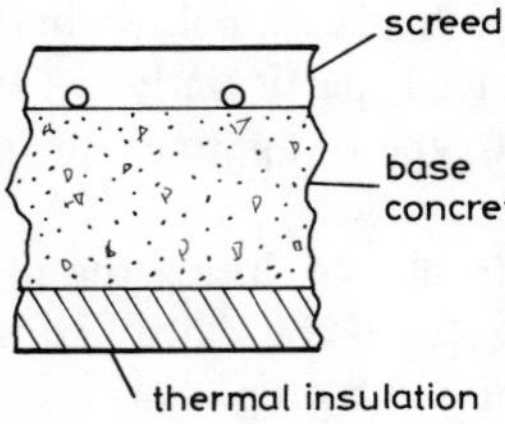 (screed, base concrete, thermal insulation)	With carpet	50 mm screed	42
		100 mm screed	68
	Without carpet	50 mm screed	31
		100 mm screed	55
floor type 3 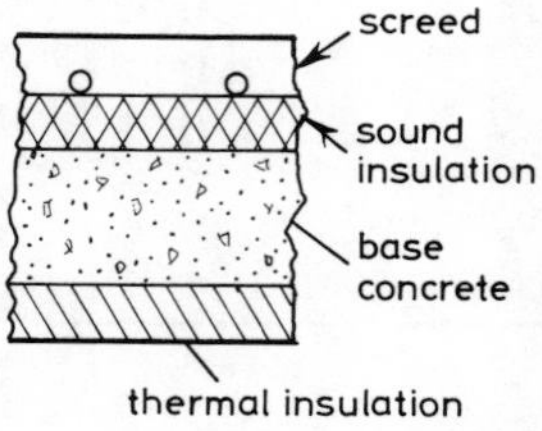 (screed, sound insulation, base concrete, thermal insulation)	With carpet	50 mm screed	30
		100 mm screed	48
	Without carpet	50 mm screed	23
		100 mm screed	39

$$L = \frac{24\,Ep + 24\,EK_2}{b} \tag{4.8.8}$$

where

L = Installed load, W

E_p = perimeter edge loss of suspended floor only, taken as 5 W per metre of external perimeter.

K_2 = factor for downward loss shown in Table 4.8.7

b = hours of overnight charge availability

Table 4.8.7 *Values of K_2 for floors with 50 mm insulation*

	Value of K_2		
	Floor Finish		
Floor	No Carpet	Carpet tiles	Woollen carpet & felt underlay
Intermediate or top floor:			
(i) No temperature drop to void below	1·09	1·17	1·27
(ii) 10°C drop to void below	1·20	1·29	1·38
(iii) 20°C drop to void below	1·31	1·40	1·50
Ground floor:			
(i) Domestic or small offices	1·19	1·25	1·30
(ii) Large offices (24 m x 18 m)	1·16	1·20	1·25

4.8.6 Heat pumps (See also chapter 4.6)

The inherent thermodynamic characteristics of the heat pump allow it to extract low grade "free" heat from an available source and convert it into useful heat. This feature has attracted scientists and entrepreneurs for almost a century. Until recently the convenience and cheapness of using traditional fuels for boilers presented major development along the heat pump lines except in countries where air conditioning is often used in commercial premises of all types. The type of unit used is reverse cycle, that is it cools in summer and heats in winter, the low grade heat source most used being the outside air. The ratio given by dividing the energy output by the total energy input to the machine (used by compressor and fans) is described as the coefficient of performance (COP). With external air source machines this declines in design winter conditions generally to about 2 to 2·5 rising to about 3·5 at 12–15°C external temperature. Over a heating season a typical average value of about 2·5 might be expected. The air/air heat pump has been well developed through American experience and the market is expected to continue.

In the housing sector there is no significant requirement for air conditioning and most heating systems installed have hot water radiators. If the market is to generally develop in the UK therefore it is likely to be with a simple air/water heat pump. There are a number of obvious design problems that are primarily concerned with the limit, for efficiency reasons, of about 55°C in the output temperature of air/-water heat pumps. Most existing radiator systems have been designed on a flow temperature of about 80°C. Invariably extra thermal insulation of the dwelling is required so that flow temperature to the radiators can be reduced. Nonetheless trials are being carried out to establish design criteria and to ascertain how best to apply the heat pump in the domestic sector. It is likely that the inclusion of a hot water storage tank (230–550 litres) with an off peak immersion heater will have significant advantages beçause it enables the heat pump to be sized to meet less than the design heat loss and it can be used to top-up the heat pump in severe weather when the COP is at its lowest. A typical installation configuration is shown in Figure 4.8.9.

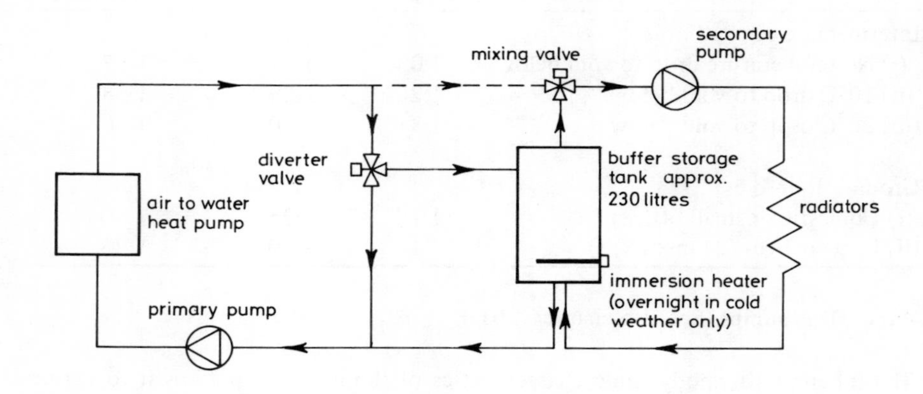

Fig. 4.8.9. *Typical configuration of heat pump and hot water storage tank*

In the industrial sector the main application is in association with heat recovery from process heating. A typical example is where chilling systems are required for surface drying of food products. Finally swimming pools deserve a special mention since they are a particularly rewarding area for reducing energy consumption. In the past considerable wastage of energy has occurred because of the high ventilation rates required to remove the smells and moisture. Dehumidification is most easily carried out using a cooling coil to condense the moisture on its cold surface. The condensed water can be collected and returned to the pool, being virtually distilled. The cooling is carried out by heat pumps, the energy reclaimed being available for use elsewhere. (See also section 4.5.8.3)

4.8.7 Ceiling heating

4.8.7.1 General

Ceiling heating is a direct acting heating system with a mainly radiant output. It comprises a heating element installed immediately above and in contact with the ceiling finish. Ceiling heating has the advantage of taking up no useful floor or wall space and is virtually maintenance free.

The system requires a layer of insulation at least 150 mm thick immediately above the elements to prevent upward heat loss although where the heating is situated in an intermediate floor this may be reduced to 80 mm. The heating elements generally take the form of either a flexible membrane or a wire set in preformed panels. Output from these is normally designed not to exceed 200 W/m^2.

Ceiling heating operates at around 40–50°C and relies upon reflections and re-emission of absorbed heat by all other room surfaces to produce a comfortable internal environment. This produces an even temperature distribution with minimal temperature stratification. A high standard of fabric insulation is recommended with ceiling heating, with special attention being paid to the floor.

Ceiling heating has a relatively high thermal inertia in that it does not rapidly increase air temperature in a room that has cooled although the effect of the radiant output may be felt fairly quickly. This is because the initial absorption of the radiant output by the building mass and the need to heat the ceiling mass give rise to a delay in warming the air itself. This means that the system is more suitable for continuous operation or with temperature setback rather than for operating intermittently. Close temperature control of each room or area is required and the system is therefore readily adapted to zonal control.

4.8.7.2 Design

The design heat loss of each room is calculated in accordance with the CIBS Guide Section A9 but assuming a heating plane temperature of 40°C for roof losses. For a continuously operated system, the element ratings for each room should be sized at the room design heat loss plus 10%; for a system which incorporates temperature set-back (i.e. overnight reduction), the element ratings should be the design heat loss plus 25% to ensure a reasonable rapid recovery of design temperatures. When considering the available ceiling area, allowance should be made for the presence of joists, beams, etc and also for any ceiling fittings such as lighting pendants, ventilators and the like. At least 100 mm is allowed along the ceiling length to provide access to connecting boxes and wire terminations.

The elements should then be chosen at the lowest watts density available to cover the maximum designated ceiling area. A possible exception might be made in the immediate vicinity of a high heat loss area such as a picture window, where elements of higher loading may be used. Normally a maximum loading of 150 W/m^2 would be used in domestic situations although, if necessary and if the ceiling material permits, loadings of 175 W/m^2 or 200 W/m^2 may be used on the external perimenter. In an area where two or more elements are controlled by the same thermostat, all elements should have the same watts density in order to avoid parts of the ceiling overheating.

4.8.8 Control

In general an efficient control system should aim to provide the comfort conditions required at the minimum running costs for a particular type of system. In the case of the domestic consumer, the user is responsible for paying the running costs and providing full information is given on the operation of the system and its controls are easily understood, a large degree of freedom can be given over the operation of the controls. In commercial or industrial premises there may be no such desire on the employee's part to limit running costs. The controls in this case must be generally automatic although a limited amount of control can be given to the individual or each office.

4.8.8.1 Controls on appliances

Most electric heating appliances incorporate their own energy controls in addition to the safety or over-temperature controls required in case abuse occurs. In the case of direct acting heaters of the convective type the control generally takes the form of a thermostat that is sited in the path of air induced from the room. Two types are in common use, the simple bimetal and the more sophisticated thermistor which is incorporated in a balancing electronic control that has the effect of proportioning the energy input as the set temperature is reached. This limits overshoot in room temperature and gives a much closer control than the bimetal type. Radiant heaters dominantly rely on manual switching elements although one controller is available which gives a measure of control over 1 or 2 radiant elements by incorporating a type of fast-acting energy regulator. The difficulty with controlling a radiant heater is one of safety. Occupants associate a bar which is not glowing with the heater being off; a control which can eliminate the glow at some stage represents a hazard.

There are now some storage radiators with automatic input controls, rationing the overnight charge by sensing changes in the overnight room air temperature. Separately-sited room thermostats have proved successful in saving running cost and this has recently led to heaters with built-in thermostats, either of the electronic sort with the sensing thermistor mounted away from the heater or special thermo-mechanical thermostats of close accuracy and cyclic differential, entirely enclosed within the heater casing.

The output of a storage heater is boosted by a damper arrangement. This provides a convective path through the core of the heater. The damper is operated automatically and in the case of one manufacturer is room temperature controlled via a thermostat sited in the induced air stream. In the case of fan storage heaters there is a bimetal type input control whilst control of output through the fan is usually via a wall air thermostat.

4.8.8.2 System controls (See also chapter 3.5)
(a) *Mixed storage and direct systems*
In the home where the system is made up of a combination of storage heaters and direct heaters the appliance energy controls are generally sufficient. Further sophistication can be added by using programmers to time the operation of the individual direct heating appliances. There is advantage in doing this in rooms where the heating is required for fairly short periods but which are required to be warm on entering. As far as the storage heaters are concerned these are timed to charge at off-peak hours using the Electricity Board's tariff time switch. In addition to the storage heater appliance controls automatic control can be achieved either through local addition of a close differential room thermostat or centrally by a controller sensitive to external temperature.

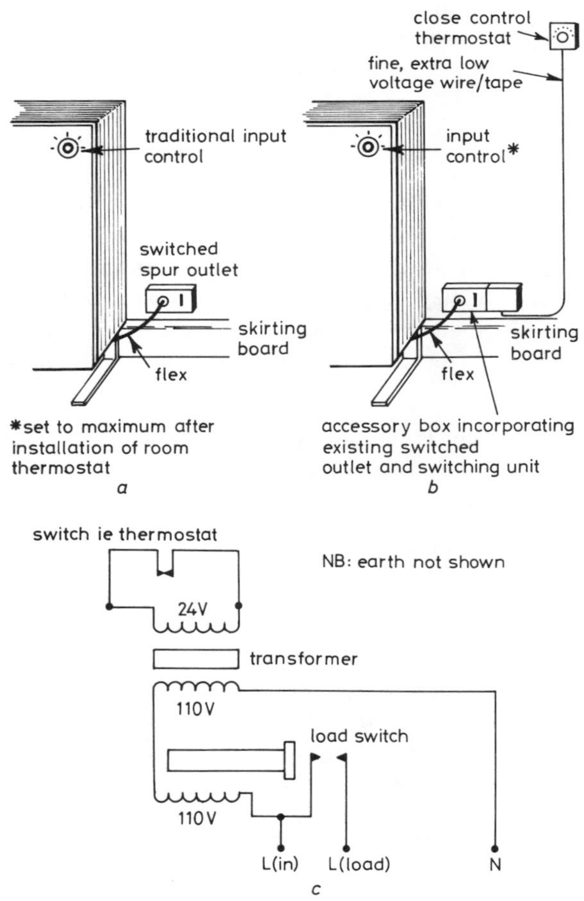

(a) original arrangement
(b) altered arrangement
(c) extra low voltage switching unit

Fig. 4.8.10. *Room thermostat controller for storage heaters*

Room thermostat control is achieved by a close differential thermostat which operates an extra-low voltage switching unit. The assembly is contained within a 2-gang accessory box which is designed to accept the power outlet that supplies the storage heater via a flexible cable. Connection between the switching unit and the room thermostat is made with an unobtrusive extra-low voltage wire. (Fig. 4.8.10).

External temperature or weather sensors can be used to control the input to storage heating of all types but is most applicable in the case of storage heaters in commercial premises (e.g. where a form of central automatic control is required). This type of control comprises an external sensor (usually a thermistor) and an internally sited control unit, which in the models now marketed usually takes the form of a printed circuit which is designed to compare continuously the temperature from the sensor with that of a predetermined charge/temperature charcteristic. This characteristic setting for the internal unit would normally be to ensure that 100% charge is taken at an external of $-1°C$ reducing to no charge at about 15°C external temperature.

(b) *Electricaire*

In the case of an Electricaire system the controls are very simple. The Electricaire unit input control is generally sufficient although in commercial premises particularly there is a benefit from using an external controller. The output control is achieved through a single central thermostat controlling the fan although in extensive installations it may be worth considering motorised dampers controlled by a thermostat in the room where close control is required. The unit incorporates mixing arrangements and controls to ensure a stable output air temperature.

(c) *Floorwarming*

The input of floor warming is best controlled by an external controller, although in small installations in a room a thermostat is sufficient.

(d) *The electric boiler* (off peak water storage)

With the off-peak water storage system there is a need to fulfil four main control functions. These are:

(i) to control the normal operating temperature of the stored water and to limit it if exceeded by malfunction.
(ii) to control the heat output to the radiator system.
(iii) to ensure the heat output to the radiator system.
(iv) and where the unit has additional elements for day usage to ensure that the arrangements maximise the use of stored heat.

The traditional room thermostat controlling the pump, and a simple thermostatic mixing valve, fulfil the functions described in (ii) and (iii). Items (i) and (iv) can be fulfilled by using traditional rod thermostats in the control circuit shown in Fig. 4.8.11. This circuit arrangement has however been developed to a point where the control arrangement using platinum resistance probes has been incorporated in a single box.

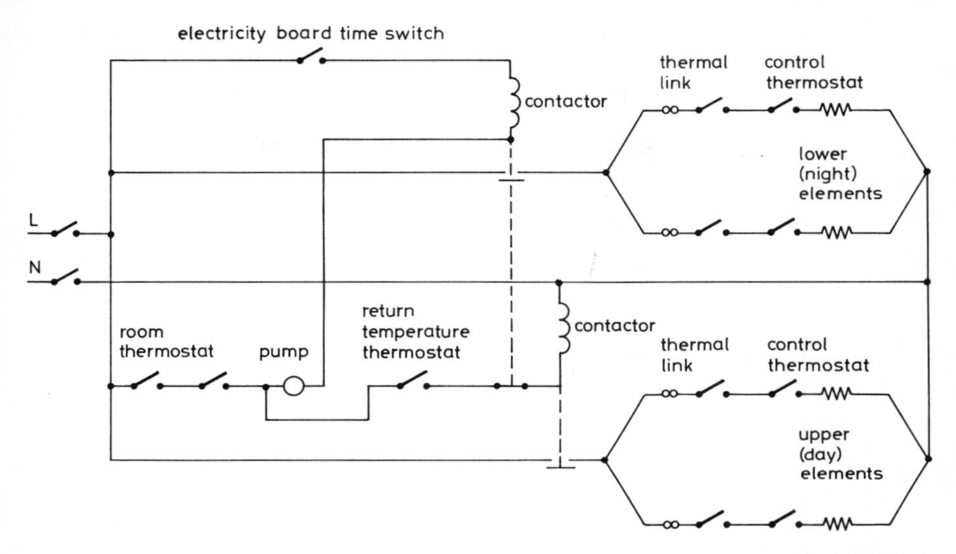

Fig. 4.8.11. *Control circuit for water storage heating (Immersion heaters with individual thermostats)*

4.8.9 Electricity consumption

There has been considerable difficulty in matching theoretical calculations of electricity consumption of space heating systems with practical results. Other than the efficiency of the system the main reasons for this are the variation in ventilation rates and the effect that miscellaneous gains have on reducing energy consumption. In well insulated homes the effect of the latter can be so marked that they provide half or more of the gross space heating requirement. A simple and accepted way of expressing the electricity consumption during the annual heating period is in terms of equivalent hours run at the calculated heat loss. Field research shows that consumption falls within an extremely wide band between 1000 and 2500 hours at the design heat loss with variation being largely explained by the degree of ventilation and the increasingly proportionate effect of miscellaneous gains as the heat loss reduces. The trend towards thermal insulation in housing makes it essential to adopt a more detailed approach.

Seasonal space heating consumption is given by:

$$Q_s = \frac{HE_h KI}{1000 e_s} \tag{4.8.9}$$

where

Q_s = seasonal space heating consumption, kWh

H = design heat loss calculated in accordance with CIBS Guide Section A9, W

E_h = Equivalent hours run at the heat loss required after taking into account the effect of miscellaneous gains, and based on set seasonal internal and external temperature conditions.

I = Intermittency factor dependent broadly on the number of hours that the heating is used.

K = Seasonal weather variation factor

e_s = System efficiency

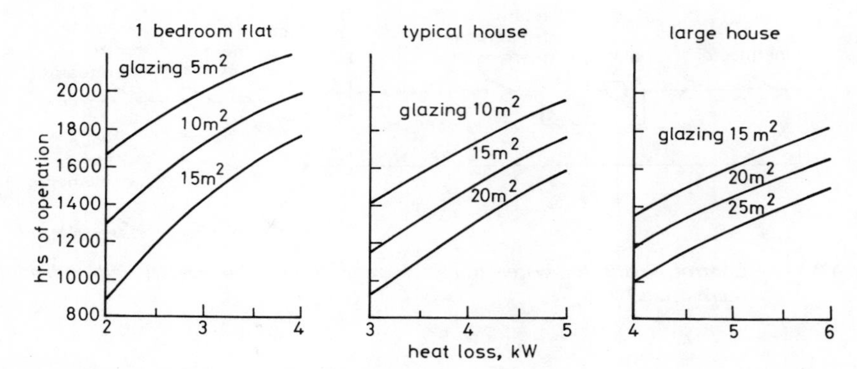

Fig. 4.8.12. *Annual hours of operation*

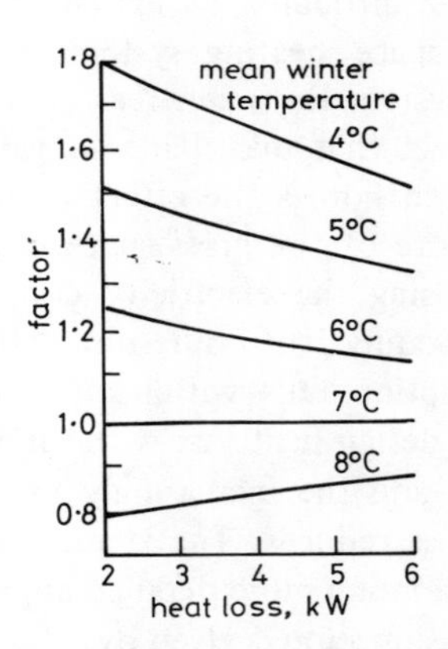

Fig. 4.8.13. *Factors for variation in mean seasonal temperature*

Values for these are given in Figs. 4.8.12 and 4.8.13, and Table 4.8.8. Since evidence of space heating consumption in commercial premises is fairly limited it is not possible to treat them with the same precision. Although as a general rule the seasonal electric space heating consumption lies between 1800 and 2200 hours at the design heat loss, each installation should be treated individually.

Table 4.8.8 *Seasonal efficiency factors and intermittency factors for calculation of space heating consumption*

System	Seasonal efficiency factor (e_s)	Intermittency factor for daily hours of operation (I)	
		16 hours	12 hours
Electricaire	0·85–0·90*	0·95	0·89
Panel convectors	1·00	0·85	0·78
Storage heaters plus panels	0·95–1·00	0·95	0·89
Floor warming	0·75–0·80**	1·00	1·00

* includes allowance for ducting heat losses
** includes allowance for downward floor heat losses

4.8.10 References

4.8.10.1 Legislation (See also Appendix 6.1)

Building Regulations, 1976
Building (Second Amendment) Regulations 1981
Clean Air Act 1956

4.8.10.2 British Standards (See also Appendix 6.2)

BS 3456 covers safety standards for domestic electrical appliances, including electric heaters.

4.8.10.3 Bibliography

CIBS Guide: Books A and B (The Chartered Institution of Building Services)
Heat Pumps For Domestic Installations: Guide to Good Practice (Heating and Ventilating Contractors Association)
Technical Information Sheets (The Electricity Council):
DOM 3 Standard Heat Losses From Dwellings
DOM 6 Storage Heater Sizing
DOM 8 Simplified Design of Mixed Storage Heater/Direct Systems
DOM 10 Off-Peak Water Storage Space Heating
DOM 11 Improved Control For Storage Heaters
Electricaire Design Manual (The Electricity Council) (EC 4074)
Direct Electric Heating Design Manual (The Electricity Council) (EC 3312)
The Complete Guide for Installers (the Economy 7 Boiler) (The Electricity Council) (EC 4500)
Reports of field trials (Environmental Engineering Section, The Electricity Council):
ECR/R 1317 The Control of Storage Heaters in Well Insulated Dwellings at Hartwell
ECR/R 1318 The Control of Storage Heaters in Well Insulated Dwellings at Chelmsford
ECR/M 1379 The Performance of Room Thermostat Control for Storage Heaters in Well Insulated Dwellings
ECR/R 1409 Mixed Storage and Direct Electric Heating Systems in Well Insulated Dwellings at Baguley
ECR/R 580 White Meter Electricaire Field Trials

ECR/R 1356 Direct Electric Space Heating in Well Insulated Houses at Washington
ECR/R 1325 Electric Ceiling Heating, Goldsworth Park
ECR/R 1444 Ceiling Heating in Well Insulated Two Bedroom Flats at Plumstead, London
ECR/R 1289 The Effect of Thermal Insulation on the Energy Consumption of Electricaire Systems
ECR/R 1369 The Effect of Thermal Insulation on the Energy Consumption of Direct Electric Heating Systems.

4.8.10.4 Glossary

A Floor area (m^2)
b Number of overnight hours of charge (hrs)
CA Charge acceptance (kWh)
CE Case emission (kWh)
E Floorwarming mean upward emission (W/m^2)
E_h Equivalent hours run at design heat loss (hrs)
E_n Rating of overnight elements (kW)
E_p Floor perimeter edge loss (W)
e_s System efficiency
H Steady state design heat loss (W)
I Intermittency factor
K Seasonal weather variation factor
K_1 Floorwarming ceiling gain factor
K_2 Floorwarming downward loss factor
L Floorwarming installed load (W)
Q_s Seasonal space heating consumption (kWh)
S Active store (kWh)
Y Factor for the proportion of heating to be supplied by storage on a design day
Z Factor for the proportion of the theoretical heating requirement to be supplied by the heat system

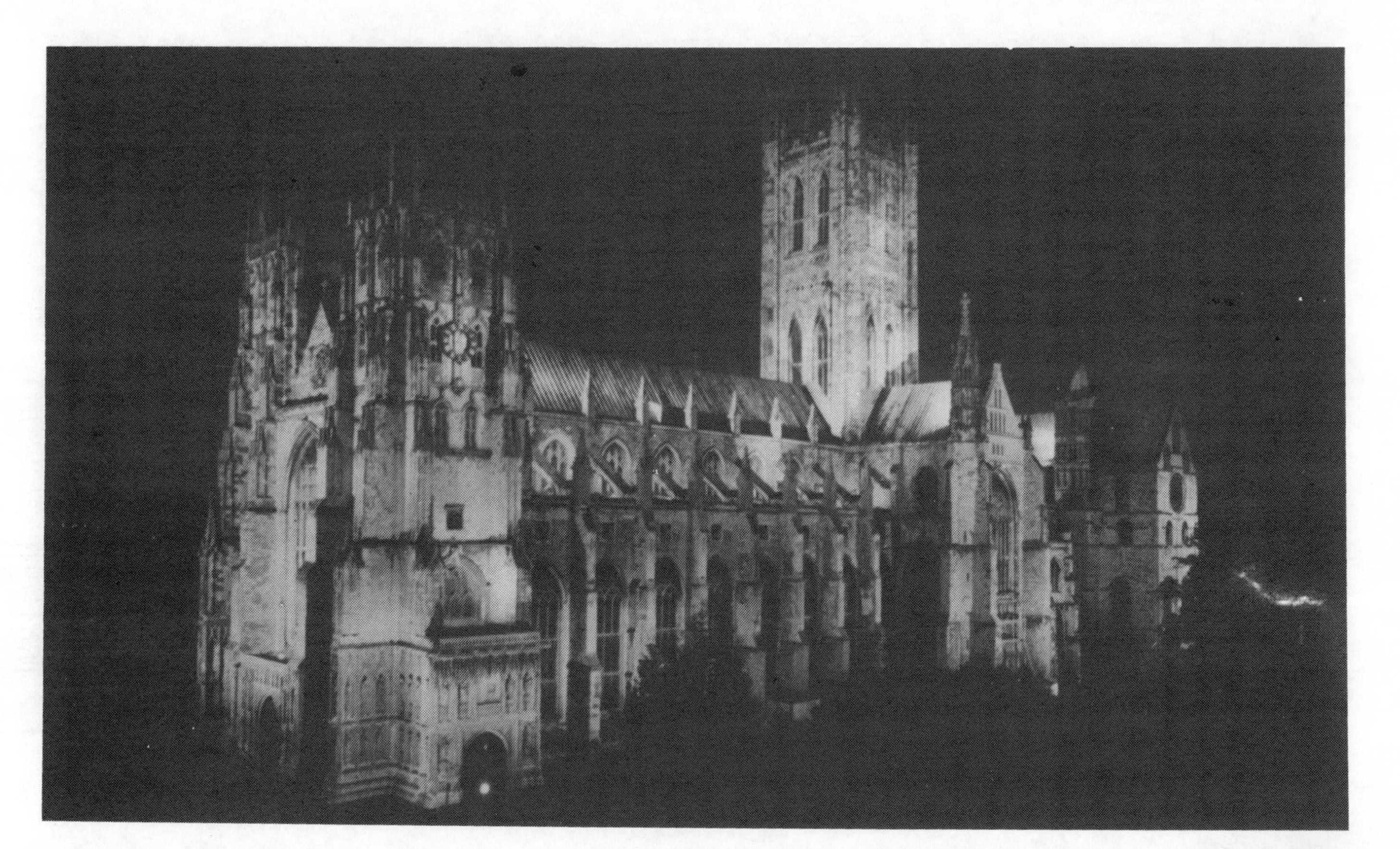

Canterbury Cathedral (Philips Lighting)

Chapter 4.9

Lighting

Ir R. T. A. Hendriks
Manager, Engineering Group Indoor Lighting, Philips International

4.9.1 Principles of light and vision

4.9.1.1 Physical aspects

In the course of the seventeenth century two theories were put forward concerning the physical nature of light. One propounded the conception that light is a wave phenomenon, whereas the second considered light to have a corpuscular (that is, atomic) structure. In the modern conception of light these apparently conflicting opinions are reconciled. In some characteristics the atomic nature becomes evident, whereas others can only be explained by the wave conception. As with any other wave phenomenon, light is characterised by the speed of propagation of the waves, the wavelength and the frequency.

$$c = \nu \times \lambda \qquad (4.9.1)$$

where

c = speed of wave propagation (m/s)

ν = frequency (Hz)

λ = wavelength (m)

Light waves need no medium for propagation and the speed of light in vacuum, or in air, is about 300 000 km/s. In other media the speed is a function of the wavelength.

The electromagnetic spectrum from $\lambda = 10^{-14}$ m up to 10^{+4} m is subdivided into cosmic-rays, gamma-rays, X-rays, ultraviolet, visible light, infra-red, radar and radio waves (Fig. 4.9.1).

In general, only radiation of wavelengths between 380 and 780 nm (1 nm = 10^{-9} m) is capable of creating the impression of light.

The wavelength of 380 nm represents a very dark violet colour whilst 780 nm appears as very deep red. Between these extremes we find the whole range of pure colours familiar to us as the colours of the rainbow (Fig. 4.9.2).

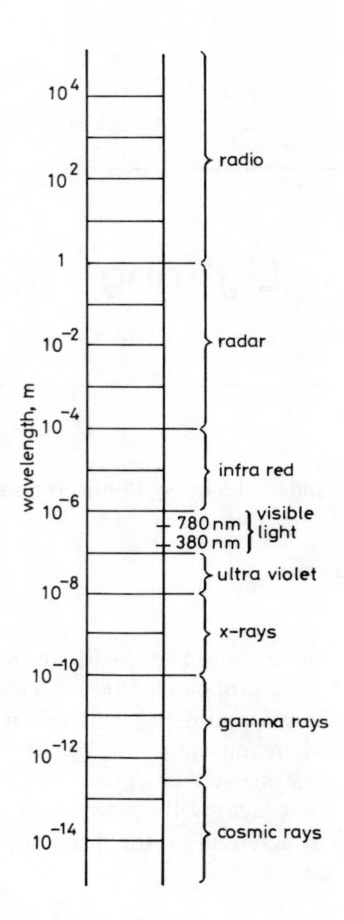

Fig. 4.9.1. *Spectrum of electromagnetic waves*

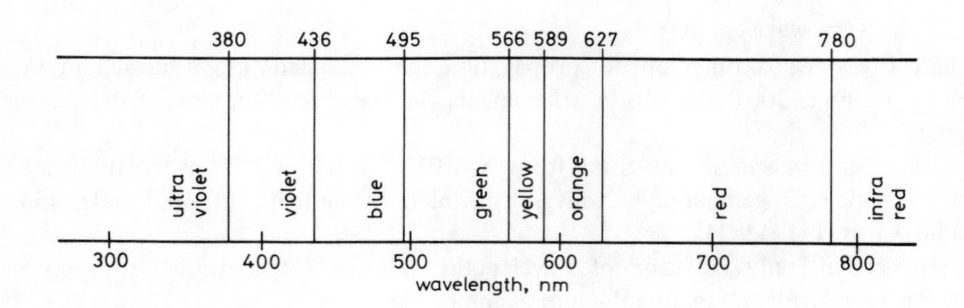

Fig. 4.9.2. *Spectrum of light*

4.9.1.2 Physiological aspects

(a) *Visual perception*

The eye is the most important connection between the human and his surrounding, but the perception of the form, colour and structure of the surroundings depends not only on the ability of the eye to see but also on the quality of the lighting.

The organ of sight has three parts:

(i) the eyes,
(ii) the nerves, which connect the eyes with
(iii) the centre for vision in the brain.

Light is emitted directly from a light source but mainly it reaches the eyes after reflection from an object. Radiant energy, as it reaches the eye, is absorbed in the retina, which covers the inside of the eye. In this way a current of electric pulses arises which goes via the nerves to the brain.

Vision deteriorates with age in many ways, e.g. the depth of field decreases; the lens developes a pigment similar to that of the skin; the absorption of some blue and green reduces the total transmission and makes discrimination in these colours more difficult; and there is more scattering of light within the eye, so the susceptibility to glare increases. Older people, however, often compensate in experience and skill for what they lack in acuity or speed of response.

(b) *The retina*

The retina may function as a black and white, or as a colour film, and is characterized by a variable light sensitivity. The eye sensitivity of a person is different for various wavelengths; it is at a maximum for light with a wavelength of 555 nm (Figs. 4.9.3, 4.9.4).

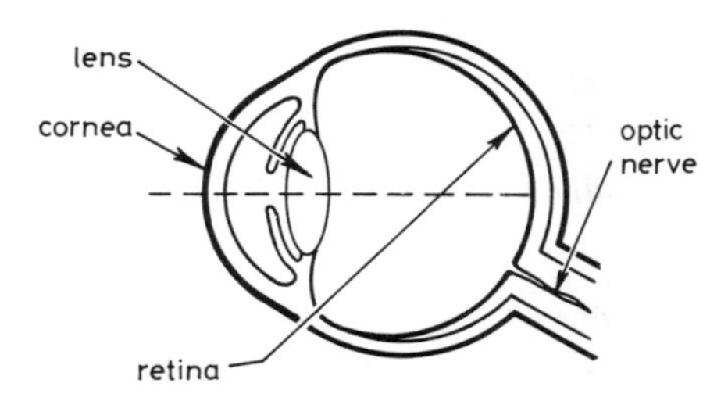

Fig. 4.9.3. *Cross-section of the human eye*

(c) *Glare*

Glare, either direct or reflected, is experienced if light sources are too bright compared with the general brightness within the field of view.

Glare can take two forms:

(i) Disability glare, affecting the ability to see clearly.
(ii) Discomfort glare, generally experienced as a feeling of discomfort after having been in an area where there is a minor amount of glare for some length of time.

(d) *Visual performance*

The term 'visual performance' is used to indicate quantitatively how a person 'performs' in terms of speed and accuracy or probability of detection when detecting, identifying and responding to details in his visual field. Visual performance depends both on intrinsic task properties (size, shape, position, colour and reflectance of detail and background) and on the perception as influenced by the lighting. Above the point below which no visual performance is possible, increase in luminance produces an improvement in visual performance which is initially rapid, but eventually flattens off at a level which further increase in luminance will not improve. Visual performance is however influenced by factors such as glare, non-uniformity of illuminance, visual distraction and confusion with a patterned background.

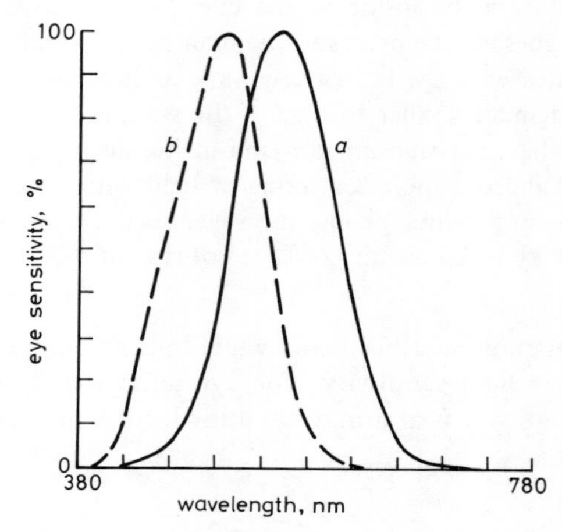

curve a: vision by day (photopic)
curve b: vision by night (scotopic)

Fig. 4.9.4. *Relative spectral efficiency curves*

The size of the object viewed is a major factor, and performance can often be improved by enlarging detail, bringing the object nearer to the viewer or using optical aids. Another major factor is contrast, and where possible tasks should be designed to optimise this. Visual performance of tasks of small size and/or low contrast can be improved by providing high levels of luminance, but performance of tasks of large size and high contrast rapidly attains an optimum at moderate values of luminance. In lighting the task to provide the required luminance levels, care must be taken over the direction and diffusion of the light to avoid reducing the contrasts by veiling reflections, or by reducing the inherent contrasts required for the perception of solid objects by excessive diffusion of the light. Some shadow is often helpful in the perception of solid objects but confusing shadows will make this more difficult.

4.9.1.3 Units and interrelations

Four basic concepts can be distinguished in the passage of light between the light source and the eyes of an observer. (Fig. 4.9.5).

(a) *Luminous flux*

The light power emitted by a source, or received by a surface, is known as the luminous flux. The quantity is derived from radiant flux (power) by evaluating the radiation in accordance with the spectral sensitivity of the 'standard' eye.

Symbol: ϕ. Unit: lumen (lm).

The lumen is defined in such a way that light emitted with a wavelength of 555 nm and a power of 1 watt corresponds to 680 lumens.

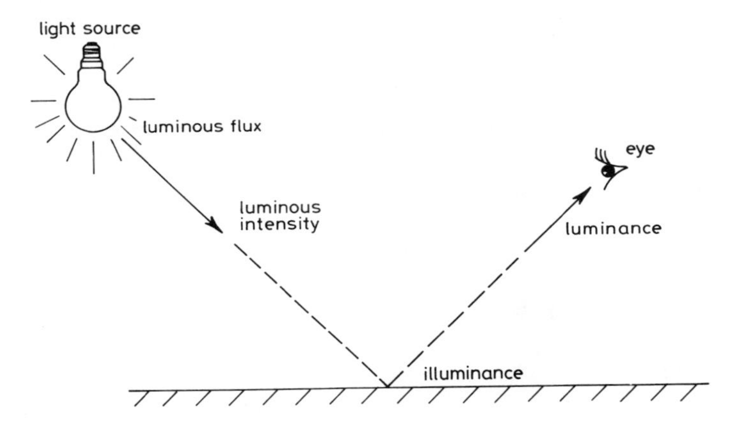

Fig. 4.9.5. *Basic Lighting Concepts*

(b) *Luminous intensity (of a source in a given direction)*

Luminous intensity defines the intensity of light emission of a source or illuminated surface in a given direction. It is the luminous flux emitted in a very narrow cone containing the given direction, divided by the solid angle of the cone.

Symbol: I. Unit: candela (cd).

(c) *Illuminance*

Illuminance is defined as the luminous flux per unit of area of the surface illuminated.

Symbol: E. Unit: lux (lx).

Thus one lux is the illuminance of an area of 1 m^2 produced by a luminous flux of 1 lm, or $E = \phi/S$ where ϕ is the luminous flux and S the surface area.

(d) *Luminance*

Luminance is the physical measure of the stimulus which produces the sensation of luminosity (brightness), in terms of the luminous intensity in a given direction (usually towards the observer) per unit area of a self-luminous or transmitting or

reflecting surface. It is the luminous intensity of the light emitted or reflected in a given direction from a surface, divided by the area S of the surface projected in the same direction.
Symbol: L. Unit: candela per square metre (cd/m^2).
Thus $L = I/S$, where I is expressed in cd and S in m^2.

If a light source radiates in all directions within a solid angle ω, with a luminous intensity denoted by I, the luminous flux ϕ in this solid angle will be $\phi = \omega I$. In a sphere with the light source as centre and with radius r, the spherical surface S corresponding to ω will receive luminous flux ϕ.

The illuminance of this surface is ascertained by

$$E = \frac{\phi}{S} = \frac{\omega I}{\omega r^2} = \frac{I}{r^2} \qquad (4.9.2)$$

This is known as the Inverse Square Law.

The Inverse Square Law applies only at a point in a plane when the plane of which the illuminance is to be determined is perpendicular to a line connecting the light source and that point, i.e. with normal incidence of the light at that point in the plane.

4.9.2 Lighting fundamentals

4.9.2.1 Lighting levels

The first question to be asked when planning a lighting installation is 'What lighting levels are needed?'. But even before this question can be answered it is necessary to clarify what is meant by the term 'lighting level'.

The brightness of the surface illuminated, or its luminance, is directly proportional to the product of the illuminance and the surface reflectance, the latter being the ratio of the reflected luminous flux to the incident luminous flux. These two quantities, illuminance and luminance, are thus closely interrelated, the connecting link being the reflectance of the surface illuminated. In the case of diffusely reflecting surfaces, the interrelation is

$$L = \frac{\rho E}{\pi} \qquad (4.9.3)$$

where L is the luminance in cd/m^2, ρ the reflectance and E the illuminance in lux. It is because of this close interrelationship that the two quantities illuminance and luminance are referred to collectively as lighting levels. The required lighting level will depend on the type of interior being considered. In 'working interiors', i.e. rooms or areas in which visual tasks have to be carried out, the required lighting levels will usually depend on the difficulty of the task and the level of performance desired, although a worker's satisfaction with his visual environment must also be considered. In circulation areas and places intended for social contact and relaxation, the visual performance criterion is not so important and emphasis is then placed on the criterion of visual satisfaction.

As a result of investigations into the subjective assessment of illuminance levels, it is recognised that the degree of visual satisfaction produced by lighting is an important additional criterion in all types of environment.

4.9.2.2 Preferred illuminances for working areas

Investigations based on the criterion of visual satisfaction have been carried out with the object of establishing a preferred range of illuminance levels for working interiors having average values of room-surface reflectance. The results of the investigations are shown in Fig. 4.9.6, the curves in the figure indicating that percentage of a group of observers which considers a particular illuminance as being satisfactory. The mean curve has its maximum at approximately 2000 lux, the range between 1000 and 2000 lux appearing to be the optimum for working interiors.

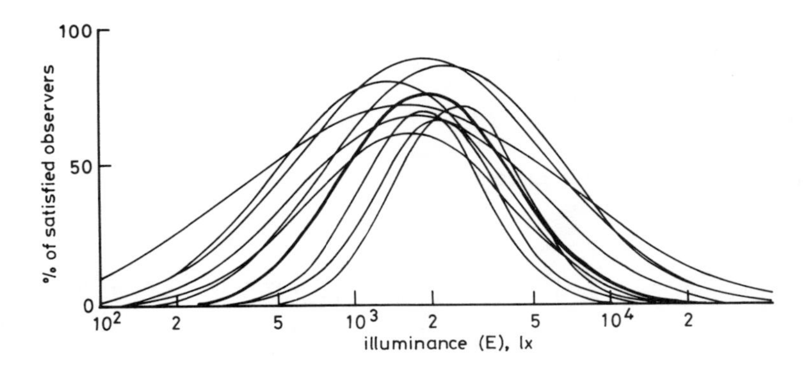

Fig. 4.9.6. *Preferred illuminance levels*
Subjective assessments of the illuminance levels in working interiors obtained by plotting the percentage of satisfied observers, against the level of illuminance.

4.9.2.3 Minimum illuminances for working interiors

Perception of the features of the human face is judged as being 'just acceptable' (i.e. these features can be satisfactorily recognized without any special effort) at a luminance of 10–20 cd/m^2 providing there is a controlled background luminance. This means that a vertical illuminance of 100 lux, and an even higher horizontal illuminance, is required.

A horizontal illuminance of 200 lux is regarded as the minimum acceptable for rooms in which people stay for long periods, and for all working interiors.

4.9.2.4 Minimum illuminance for circulation areas

To be able just to discern the features on a human face a luminance of approximately 1 cd/m^2 is necessary, calling for a horizontal illuminance of approximately 20 lux. For this reason 20 lux is regarded as the minimum illuminance for circulation (non-working) areas.

Table 4.9.1 *Recommended Scale of luminance for Interiors*

cd/m²	Description
10000	Permissible luminance for luminaires (1000–10000)
5000	
2000	
1000	
500	
200	Preferred task luminance (100–500)
100	Preferred wall and ceiling luminance (50–200)
50	
20	Satisfactorily discernible — Features of human face (2–20)
10	
5	
2	Just discernible
1	(Recommended road luminance)

4.9.2.5 Range of preferred luminances (Table 4.9.1)

The limits to the range of luminance over which the eye can respond without there being any serious loss of sensitivity to brightness discrimination, or any feeling of discomfort, have been found by research. The luminance values of the various objects in an observer's field of view – e.g. task area, luminaires, walls, ceiling, sky (seen through a window) – must, therefore be arranged to fall with this range. When recommending luminance values for each of the objects or areas in an observer's field of view it is customary to quote the following:

(a) Minimum values when referring to the luminance of human features: 1 cd/m^2 for the features to be just recognisable, or 10–20 cd/m^2 for an acceptable level of recognition.

(b) Optimum values when referring to the luminance of walls, ceiling, task area, and human features: 50 cd/m^2–150 cd/m^2 for walls, 100 cd/m^2–400 cd/m^2 for the task area, and about 250 cd/m^2 for human features.

(c) Maximum values when referring to the luminance of the sky and of luminaires: 2000 cd/m^2 marks the beginning of glare from the sky, and 1000 cd/m^2–10000 cd/m^2 (depending on illuminance level and type of luminaire) for interiors.

4.9.2.6 Glare

Direct glare (para 4.9.1.2(c)) can be caused by a bright light source appearing in the normal field of view of an observer. Glare which induces a feeling of discomfort is termed discomfort glare; the degree of discomfort can only be assessed subjectively. In interior lighting practice, discomfort glare is more likely to present problems than is disability glare and measures taken to control the former will normally take care of the latter also. Four systems of glare evaluation are currently in use. Three of these are tailored to meet national – British, American and Australian – requirements. The fourth system, known as the Luminance Curve Method, which is perhaps more concise than any of the other three, has gained wide support within Europe as well as within the International Lighting Commission (CIE).

4.9.2.7 Veiling reflection and reflected glare

Light from a bright source reflected by a glossy or semi-matt surface into the eyes of an observer can produce feelings ranging from mild distraction to considerable discomfort. Where this reflection occurs in a task it is referred to as a 'veiling reflection'; where it occurs outside the task, the more general term 'reflected glare' is used. Veiling reflections, apart from deflecting the eye from its task, reduce task contrast and result in a loss of detail.

The decrease in visibility of a sample of printed text in the presence of veiling reflection is dependent on the reflection characteristics of the task details, on the luminance and the size of the light source causing the veiling reflection, and on the average luminance of the task area. Veiling reflections and reflected glare can be minimized by:

(a) Designing the lighting system by locating the working areas in such a way that no part of the task is at or near the mirror angle with respect to the eye and any bright light source.
(b) Increasing the amount of light falling sideways on to the visual task at approximately right angles to the direction of view.
(c) Using luminaires having a large surface area and low luminance.
(d) Using working surfaces, paper, writing materials, and office machines which have matt surfaces in order to reduce the effects of reflection.

For evaluating numerically the influence that a given lighting installation will have on the task contrast, and hence on the task visibility, a system based on the use of the concept of the Contrast Rendering Factor (CRF) has been developed.

4.9.2.8 Colour

The lighting engineer is not fully equipped to deal with the many and varied problems that can arise during the course of designing an indoor lighting installation unless he has at least a basic understanding of colour and the role played by colour in interiors.

Colour begins at the light source. The phenomenon of the colour of objects appearing to change when they are viewed under the light from different sources is familiar to everyone. It is the difference in the spectral distribution of the different types of source that, in part, is responsible for this apparent change in object colour.

These colour rendering properties of a light source cannot be assessed from its colour appearance. Two colours may have the same colour appearance and yet have entirely different colour rendering properties. Equally, two sources may exhibit a marked difference in colour appearance and yet, under certain circumstances, be capable of giving equally acceptable colour rendering. The preferred colour appearance of both sources and objects is often important in connection with the lighting level in an interior. The atmosphere created in an interior is greatly influenced both by the colour of the light used and the brightness impression created by that light.

Colour temperature is a term used to describe the colour appearance of a light source by comparing it with the colour of a 'black body' radiator. A body that reflects none of the incident radiation is called a 'black body' or a full radiator. The temperature of an incandescent black body is usually given in degrees centigrade on the Kelvin scale, which begins at absolute zero, so the melting point of ice is 273 K and the boiling point of water is 373 K. The temperature of the black body at which a colour match is obtained is said to be the colour temperature of the source. The colour of a black body would be red at a temperature of 800 K to 900 K, yellowish-white at 3000 K, white at about 5000 K and a pale blueish white colour between 8000 K and 10000 K.

White light sources may be loosely divided into three groups according to their colour appearance (correlated colour temperature). (Table 4.9.2). For lighting to be of good quality, the colour temperature of the light from the relevant light sources should be related to the illuminance level. From experience, it has been found preferable that, as the illuminance level increases, the colour temperature of the light sources should also increase. The general impressions associated with different illuminance levels and different colours of fluorescent lighting are given in Table 4.9.3.

Colour rendering is defined as the appearance of objects under a given light

Table 4.9.2 *Colour Appearance of Lamps*

Colour Appearance Group	Colour Appearance	Correlated Colour Temperature (K)
1	warm	< 3300
2	intermediate	3300–5300
3	cool	> 5300

Table 4.9.3 *Colour Appearance and Illuminance*

Illuminance (lux)	Colour appearance of light: Warm	Intermediate	Cool
⩽ 500	pleasant	neutral	cool
500–1000	↕	↕	↕
1000–2000	stimulating	pleasant	neutral
2000–3000	↕	↕	↕
⩾ 3000	unnatural	stimulating	pleasant

source compared with their appearance under a reference illuminant. For objective indication of the colour rendering properties of a light source the general colour rendering index R_a has been introduced. It has a value of 100 if the test source gives exactly the same effect as the reference illuminant. This figure becomes progressively less as the colour rendering properties of the test lamp deviate increasingly from those of the reference source. For practical applications, four colour rendering groups have been introduced, as indicated in Table 4.9.4.

Table 4.9.4 *Lamp Colour Rendering Groups*

Colour rendering group	Colour rendering index range	Colour appearance	Examples for use: preferred	acceptable
1	$R_a \geqslant 80$	warm) intermediate)	Homes, hotels, restaurants shops, offices, hospitals	
		intermediate) cool)	printing, paint and textile industry, fine industrial work	
2	$60 \leqslant R_a < 80$	warm) intermediate) cool)	industrial buildings	offices, schools
3	$40 \leqslant R_a < 60$			interiors where colour rendering is of comparatively minor importance
4	$R_a < 40$			

4.9.3 The generation of radiation

4.9.3.1 Light sources

In order to explain the generation of light, a short discussion must be included on the structure of matter. An atom must be considered to consist of a positively charged nucleus surrounded by a cloud of electrons, making up a total negative charge equal to the positive charge of the nucleus. The simplest atom is hydrogen with one electron; the next element in the series is helium, with two electrons. Mercury has 80 electrons, each of them having an orbit with defined characteristics.

The electrons moving around, each in its own orbit, possess different amounts of energy, this being greater as the electron is moved to an orbit further from the nucleus. Each orbit, therefore, corresponds to a certain energy level. Not all numerical values of distance are possible, however; all the possible orbits conform to very definite laws, known as the quantum rules.

In the normal atom only the lowest possible energy levels are occupied by electrons, the atom being said to be in the ground state. If one of these electrons is transferred into a state of higher energy, when the atom is bombarded by particles or struck by radiation of sufficient energy, then the atom is said to be in the excited state. According to Bohr, the electronic transition from one orbit to another is responsible for the absorption and emission of electromagnetic radiation. In absorption, an electron is transferred from its original orbit to another orbit with higher energy, whereas the emission of radiation originates from the return of an electron from a high level to one of less energy. Because the excited state of an atom is not a stable situation, the atom will return to the ground state, emitting electromagnetic radiation. The frequency of the emitted radiation is related to the amount of energy released in the electron jump.

At room temperature the electrons occupy the lowest possible energy levels. Therefore, to produce light, means have to be found to bring atoms into the excited state. The less the amount of energy needed to excite atoms in order to produce a quantity of visible light, the more efficient the process will be. This is expressed as the 'efficacy' of the light source, i.e. the quantity of light in lumens produced per unit of power. (Unit: lumens/watt).

(a) *Incandescence*

In an incandescent lamp, visible radiation is produced by virtue of a metal filament which is heated to incandescence when an electric current flows through it. The light thus radiated covers the whole of the visible range in the form of a continuous spectrum. To withstand the high temperature at incandescence (2400°C) the filament is made of high melting point tungsten, and evaporation of the filament is reduced by filling the bulb with an inert gas. (Fig. 4.9.7).

(b) *Gas discharge*

When the voltage between the electrodes of a tube, filled with a suitable gas, is sufficiently high, an electrical discharge will take place. Collisions will occur between the thermionic electrons of the discharge and the atoms of the gas, and will generate 'excited' atoms. After a short period, the electrons of the excited atoms will return from a high level of excitation to one of less energy, which will initiate the emission of electromagnetic radiation. The gas discharge will produce a spectrum with

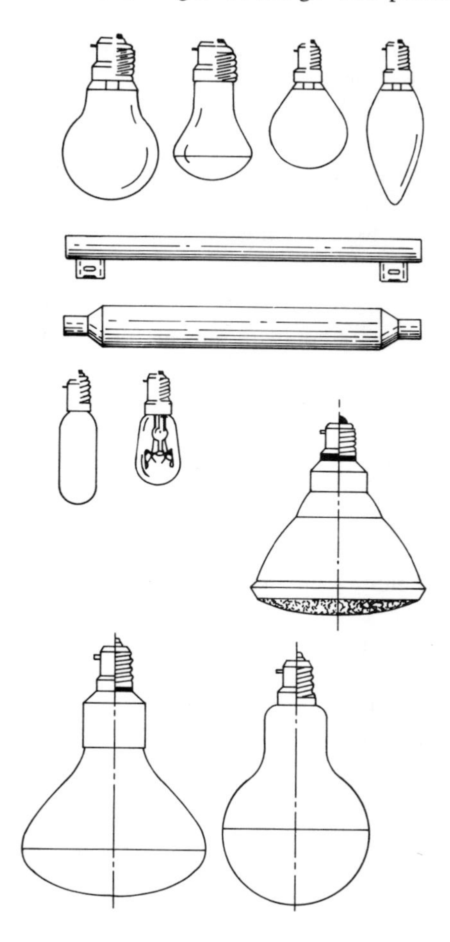

Fig. 4.9.7. *Typical shapes of incandescent lamps*

emission within the visible region or the invisible ultraviolet region; the spectrum will depend on the type of gas and the gas pressure within the tube.

(c) *Fluorescent*

If the discharge tube is filled with a low pressure mercury vapour, the electromagnetic radiation will be mainly in the invisible ultraviolet range. This ultraviolet radiation is converted into visible radiation by lining the inside of the glass tube with a fluorescent coating. The composition of this coating will determine the spectral energy distribution of the light emitted by the lamp.

4.9.3.2 Lamp types

(a) *Incandescent lamps*

Incandescent lamps form the oldest family and remain the mainstay of home lighting, basically because they are cheap and easy to work with. The glass bulb of the lamp is available in many forms, as well as types of glass, finishes and shapes, depending upon particular needs. The efficacy (section 4.9.3.1) is 10–15 lm/W, and related to its continuous spectrum the colour rendering index R_a (section 4.9.2.8) is 100. The colour appearance is warm (2600 K) and the life approximately 1000 hours, or 2000 hours for "long-life" lamps.

(b) *Halogen lamps*

The high temperature of the filament in a normal incandescent lamp causes tungsten particles to evaporate and condense on the bulb wall, resulting in blackening. Halogen lamps have a halogen (e.g. iodine, fluorine, bromine) added to the normal gas filling, and work on the principle of a halogen regenerative cycle to prevent blackening.

The tubular envelope of the halogen lamp is made of special quartz glass which is resistant to the high temperatures needed for the halogen cycle to function. The lamps are much smaller than normal incandescent lamps.

The main advantage of these lamps, namely, their reasonably high efficacy (up to 30 lm/W), excellent colour rendering ($R_a = 100$), small size and high luminance, are well illustrated by the extensive use made of these lamps in motor car lights, projectors, spotlights and reflector lamps – in short, all those applications in which an optical system demands a concentrated light source with good colour rendering. The lamp life depends on the specific type and varies between 300 and 2000 hrs. The colour temperature is approximately 3000 K.

(c) *SL and PL lamps*

The SL lamp is a miniature low-pressure mercury fluorescent lamp, complete with its own control gear, contained inside a glass bulb and fitted with a conventional incandescent lamp cap. It can be employed as a direct replacement for an incandescent lamp having the same base, but uses only 25% of the energy consumption of an incandescent lamp with comparable light output. The SL has a warm-white colour appearance and gives a good colour rendering ($R_a = 82$). The efficacy is 50 lm/W and its life is 5000 hours.

The PL lamp is a compact single ended low-pressure mercury fluorescent lamp consisting of two narrow tubes welded together. The starter is built into the cap. It has good colour properties ($R_a = 82$), and a low energy consumption (efficacy 58–79 lm/W).

(d) *Fluorescent tubes (MCFE or TL)*

The fluorescent lamp consists of a tubular bulb having an electrode sealed into each end, and containing mercury vapour at low pressure. The inner surface of the tube is coated with fluorescent powders. When a current is passed through the gas mixture, predominantly ultraviolet radiation is produced. The fluorescent powders transform this radiation into visible light. The long life (over 7500 hrs), high efficacy (40–95 lm/W), and good colour rendering ($R_a = 66–98$) of these lamps makes them eminently suitable for numerous applications in both indoor and outdoor lighting. Fluorescent tubes are available in colour temperatures from 2800 K up to 6500 K, and in three diameters – 16 mm, 26 mm and 38 mm. (Fig. 4.9.8).

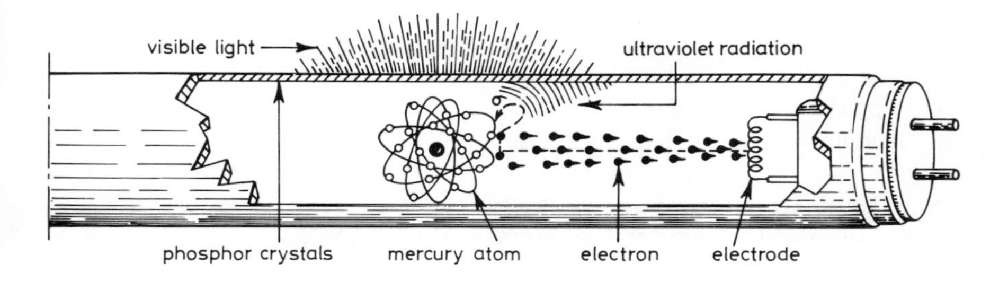

Fig. 4.9.8. *TL fluorescent lamp*

(e) *High pressure discharge lamps*

The light from a high pressure discharge lamp is produced by passing a current through a gas under high pressure contained in a small discharge tube. This discharge tube is enclosed in an outer bulb or tube, one of the functions of which is to protect the discharge tube from external influences. A general description often used for this type of lamp is High Intensity Discharge (HID), because of the small discharge tube with its high luminous intensity.

(i) *High pressure mercury lamps (MBF/U or HPL–N)*

The discharge tube, which is filled with mercury at a high pressure (0·2–1 MPa), has a main electrode sealed into each end. Adjacent to one of these electrodes is an auxiliary starting electrode. The glass outer bulb is coated with a fluorescent powder, to convert the small amount of ultraviolet which is also generated, into light. The efficacy is 40 lm/W for the lower wattages and 60 lm/W for the higher wattages. The colour rendering index $R_a = 45–56$, and the colour temperature 4000 K. The average life is more than 10000 hours.

(ii) *Metal halide lamps (MBI or HPI)*

These lamps are very similar in construction to the high pressure mercury lamp, the major difference being that the metal halide discharge tube contains one or more metal halides in addition to mercury. A typical combination of halides used is that comprising the iodides of sodium, indium and thallium. These halides give an increase in intensity in three spectral bands, viz. blue, green and yellow-red. Colour rendering and efficacy is improved in comparison with that of the MBF/U lamp.

The efficacy is 75 up to 95 lm/W. The colour rendering index $R_a = 70$ and the colour temperature 4000 K. The average life is approximately 7500 hours. Metal halide lamps are available in two versions: diffuse ovoid (MBI) and clear tubular (MBI/T).

(iii) *High-pressure sodium lamps (SON)*

The discharge tube in a high-pressure sodium lamp contains an excess of sodium to give saturated vapour conditions when the lamp is running at a pressure of between 13 and 26 kPa, and to allow for internal surface absorption. The discharge tube, which is made of sintered aluminium oxide to withstand the intense chemical activity of the sodium vapour at the operating temperature of 700°C, is housed in an evacuated protective hard glass envelope.

High-pressure sodium lamps radiate energy across much of the visible spectrum, and in comparison with the low-pressure sodium lamp, give acceptable colour rendering. The efficacy is 65 lm/W for the lower wattages and 130 lm/W for the 1000 W lamp. Colour temperature is approximately 2100 K, and average life is 6000 hrs for the 70 W lamp and 15 000 hrs for the 1000 W lamp.

High pressure sodium lamps are available in two versions: diffuse ovoid (SON) and clear tubular (SON/T). SON lamps are primarily used in outdoor lighting applications, and also in indoor lighting in industrial buildings.

(iv) *Blended-light lamps (MBFT or ML)*

The blended-light lamp consists of a gasfilled bulb coated on its inside with a phosphor and containing a mercury-discharge tube connected in series with a tungsten filament. The filament acts as a ballast for the discharge, so stabilizing the lamp current, no other ballast being needed. The efficacy is 11–28 lm/W, with a life of 6000 hours. The colour rendering index $R_a = 60$ and the colour temperature approximately 3500 K.

(f) *Low pressure sodium lamps (SOX)*

The glass discharge tube contains sodium which vaporizes at 98°C and a mixture of inert gases at a pressure of approximately 300 mPa to obtain a low ignition voltage. The discharge tube is contained in an evacuated, tubular glass envelope coated on its inner surface with indium oxide. This coating acts as an infra-red reflector and so maintains the wall of the discharge tube at the correct operating temperature (270°C). The low pressure sodium lamp is characterized by its nearly monochromatic radiation, high luminous efficacy of 130–175 lm/W, and long life (12 000 hrs). It therefore finds application where colour rendering is of minor concern but where contrast recognition is important e.g. highway lighting.

4.9.3.3 Ballasts

All discharge lamps, including fluorescent lamps, need a series impedance to limit the lamp current. If such a device were not used, there would be nothing to prevent this current from increasing to the point at which destruction of the lamp would take place. Such an impedance is called a ballast and forms part of the control gear necessary for the operation of these lamps. An effective form of ballast is the reactor, or choke, placed in series with the lamp. Inherently, the power factor of such a circuit is low, about 0·5 lagging. This can be increased to 0·85 or greater by connecting a capacitor across the a.c. supply. An overall power factor approaching unity can be achieved by combining the uncorrected 0·5 lagging circuit with a circuit that gives 0·5 lead, and which can be obtained by connecting a suitable capacitor in series with the choke ballast. To reduce watt losses, electronic ballasts (HF) for fluorescent lamps have been developed. (Fig. 4.9.9)

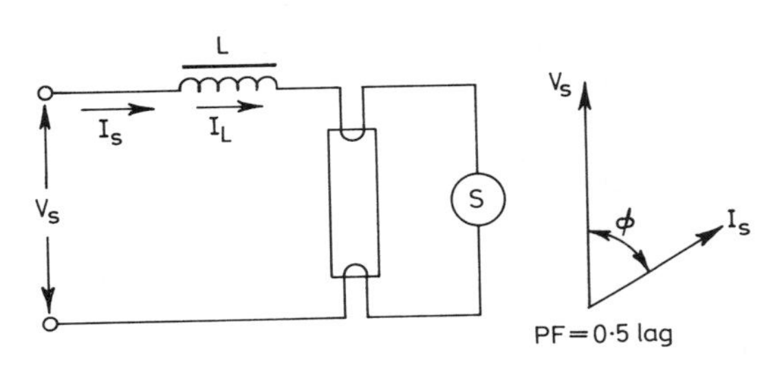

Fig. 4.9.9. *Switch start TL lamp circuit with simple choke ballast*

4.9.3.4 Starters and ignitors

Most arc-discharge lamps need a voltage higher than that of the mains supply to initiate the discharge. In general, where this is the case, the lamp concerned must be operated in conjunction with some sort of starting device.

This device may constitute a separate item of control gear or it may form an integral part of the ballast or an integral part of the lamp, depending on the lamp type concerned. Fluorescent lamps of the preheat switch-start type are started by heating the lamp electrodes before application of the high starting voltage. This preheating, which takes a few seconds, is usually accomplished by a starter switch, and the transient voltage caused by the opening of the switch causes the lamp to ignite. Starting time can be reduced by using an electronic starter.

4.9.4 Luminaires

4.9.4.1 General lighting types

The basic requirements for a luminaire are that it must provide support and electrical connection to the lamp or lamps within it, and that it must control and distribute the light from the lamp.

The luminaire most frequently used in commercial lighting applications houses one or more tubular fluorescent lamps. This is also the preferred type for use in many industrial applications where the mounting height is less than about five to six metres. Mounting heights above six metres call for the use of high-bay luminaires housing the more powerful high intensity discharge lamps, and fitted with mirror reflectors. Small directional lighting luminaires, which are used mainly to provide accent lighting, fall into two groups: spotlights and downlights. Lamps used in these luminaires vary from normal incandescent lamps, pressed-glass, blown-bulb and bowl reflector lamps, halogen, SL and PL lamps. Screening attachments can be used in combination with different lamp types to provide the desired degree of beam cut-off. Attachments are also available that permit the chosen spotlight to be mounted in a flexible manner on walls, ceilings, pedestals, rails or power track. A downlight is, in effect, a special type of spotlight that can be suspended from or built into the ceiling such that all the light is distributed downward.

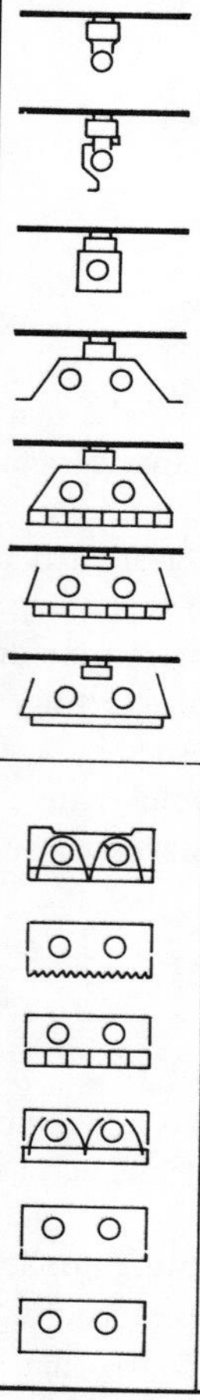

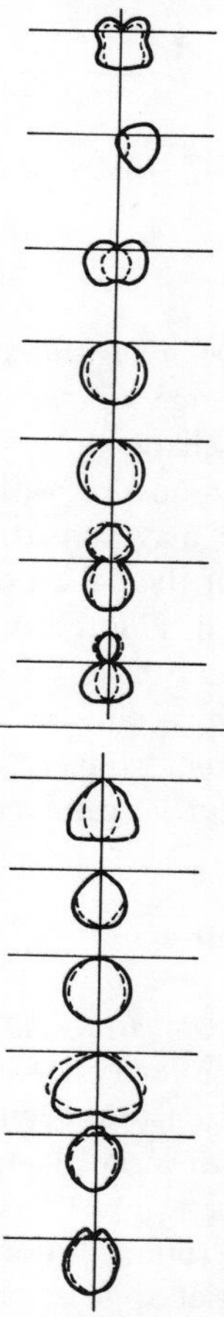

luminaire cross-section	description	light control element(s)	typical luminous intensity distribution
	batten luminaire and attachments	none	
		single-sided reflector	
		wrap-around diffuser	
		trough reflector	
		trough reflector plus square-mesh louvre	
		side panels plus square-mesh louvre	
		side panels plus transverse louvre	
	closed-top box luminaires and attachments	mirror reflectors with mirror shielding	
		prismatic diffusing panel	
		square-mesh louvre	
		side mirror reflector with louvre shielding	
		diffusing panel	
		wrap-around diffusing panel	

Fig. 4.9.10. *Cross sections of luminaires for fluorescent lamps*
(Luminous intensity distribution is shown perpendicularly to the lamp axis by the solid line and parallel to the lamp axis by the dotted line.)

The range of luminaires for MCFE lamps is extensive. (Fig. 4.9.10). In its simplest form, the luminaire consists of a batten fitting in which is housed the control gear for the fully exposed lamp. At the other end of the range is the multi-lamp ventilated luminaire complete with reflectors (mirror or otherwise) and metal louvre or prismatic cover. What distinguishes one type of luminaire from another is the type of light control used (and hence the luminous intensity and luminance distribution), the number of lamps employed, or the method of mounting.

The primary purpose of light control is to direct the light in the required directions whilst reducing it in directions in which it might cause discomfort glare or be wasted. In some cases the reflector itself is designed to provide a certain degree of lamp shielding, but where more effective shielding is required, some form of louvre is added.

A louvre, in shielding the lamp from direct view, also serves to reduce the luminance of the luminaire in directions where it could otherwise cause glare. The louvres, square-mesh, diamond-mesh or lamellae, may be made from thin strips of white opalescent plastic or metal. In some cases, however, the strip is given a V-shape cross-section and a mirror finish to help reduce still further the luminaire's brightness. A prismatic (or refractor) panel serves to give the light some slight directional character, whilst reducing the luminance of the luminaire in directions where glare could cause discomfort. These panels are generally available in a variety of patterns to offer a choice of lighting effect. The luminance of a luminaire fitted with an opalescent diffusing panel is virtually uniform in all directions. Such a luminaire does not, therefore, afford the directional control of the light needed for efficient high illuminance installations.

Luminaires may be recessed into the ceiling, mounted on the surface or suspended from some part of the ceiling structure, or suspended from special trunking erected specifically for the purpose.

4.9.4.2 Luminaires for use in special areas

Two further important types of luminaire are those suitable for use in moisture and dust-laden atmosphere, and those designed for use in hazardous areas.

Luminaires for fluorescent lamps intended for use in moisture or dust-laden atmosphere are of two types. In one type the lamps are fully exposed to the surrounding atmosphere, but the connection between lamp cap and lampholder is sealed by means of a rubber gasket. In the other, the lamps are protected by a plastic cover which is sealed to the housing. The exact nature of the sealing in each case determines the degree of resistance of the luminaires to the ingress of water and dust. Shower rooms and laundries are typical areas which require gasketted luminaires.

Pressure-resisting encapsulation luminaires are designed to withstand the pressure caused by an internal explosion, so preventing the ignition of any potentially explosive atmosphere surrounding the luminaire. This means that the luminaire must be of robust construction. Luminaires of this type bear the internationally agreed symbol Ex_d.

Increased safety luminaires make use of a 'restricted-breathing' cover which virtually eliminates the possibility of explosive gases entering the housing. If, despite this precaution, explosive substances should enter the housing, special safety devices in the circuitry and the switching equipment ensure that no explosion can occur. Luminaires of this type bear the internationally agreed symbol Ex_e. In the UK, the certification body for this type of equipment is the British Approvals Service for Electrical Equipment in Flammable Atmospheres (BASEEFA)

4.9.4.3 Technical luminaire data

Much of the information on which lighting calculations are based is supplied by the equipment manufacturer in the form of photometric or technical data sheets. A technical data sheet should contain the light output ratio, the optical light output ratio, the luminous intensity diagram, the luminaire luminance diagram and a utilization factor table.

4.9.5 Integration of lighting and air-handling equipment (See also sec. 4.4.2.5)

4.9.5.1 General

In a modern building electric lighting supplements daylight or replaces it entirely, and forced ventilation or air conditioning take over from natural ventilation. Such technical facilities as these can be designed to work together efficiently, but only if they are considered from the outset as forming one coherent, or integrated system.

Air conditioning and lighting are combined in such a way that the return air is exhausted through the luminaires, so making use of a single unit for both lighting and air handling. This reduces the heat load created by the lighting, the heat radiation from lamps and luminaires, and the temperature of the air surrounding the lamp, so increasing their luminous flux, and hence their efficacy. Three different types of integrated system are at present in use:

4.9.5.2 Plenum-exhaust air handling system

In this system (Fig. 4.9.11), conditioned air is supplied to the living zone via air supply units built into the ceiling and connected to an air supply duct. The plenum, which is at a lower pressure than the room, acts as a duct for the return air which is extracted from the living zone via slots in the air-handling luminaires.

Because the return air absorbs an appreciable amount of heat produced by the lighting, the plenum will become warm. Part of the heat absorbed by the plenum will be transferred downwards to the room through the false ceiling and upwards to the floor above.

The amount of heat absorbed and transferred in this way will depend on the efficiency of the plenum's heat insulation and on the volume of return air.

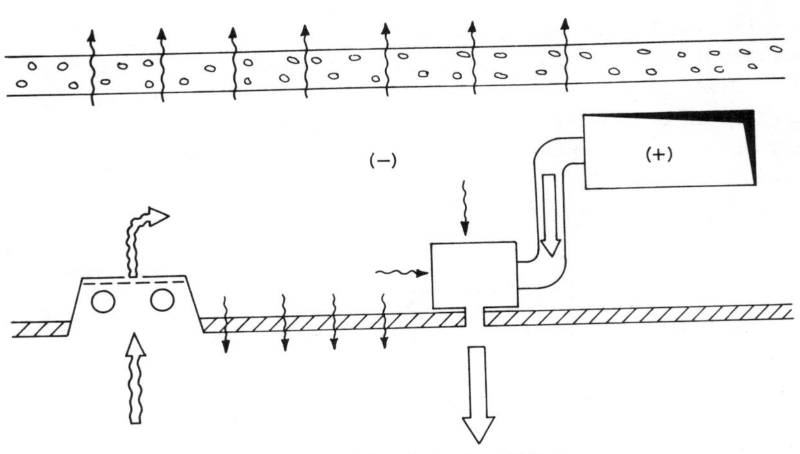

Fig. 4.9.11. *Plenum-exhaust air handling luminaire installation*
(+) over-pressure duct
(—) under-pressure plenum

4.9.5.3 Plenum-supply air handling system

In this system (Fig. 4.9.12), the over-pressure plenum acts as a duct to supply conditioned air to the living zone via injection strips in the ceiling. The return air is exhausted from the living zone through slots in the air-handling luminaires, which are connected to the return air duct. Heat exchange will take place between the return air and the air in the plenum unless luminaire and ducting are well insulated. This system should be chosen for use in areas which have a low ceiling height, as in such areas it is difficult to supply air-using induction units without causing turbulence.

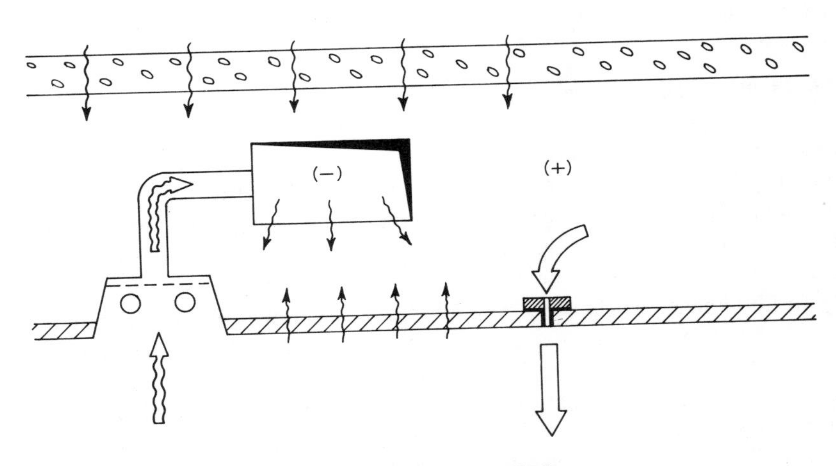

Fig. 4.9.12. *Plenum-supply air handling luminaire installation*
(+) over-pressure plenum (—) under-pressure duct installation

4.9.5.4 Two-ducted air handling system

In this system (Fig. 4.9.13), conditioned air is supplied to the living zone via air supply diffusers which are connected to an air supply duct. The return air is extracted through slots in the air-handling luminaires which are connected to a return air duct

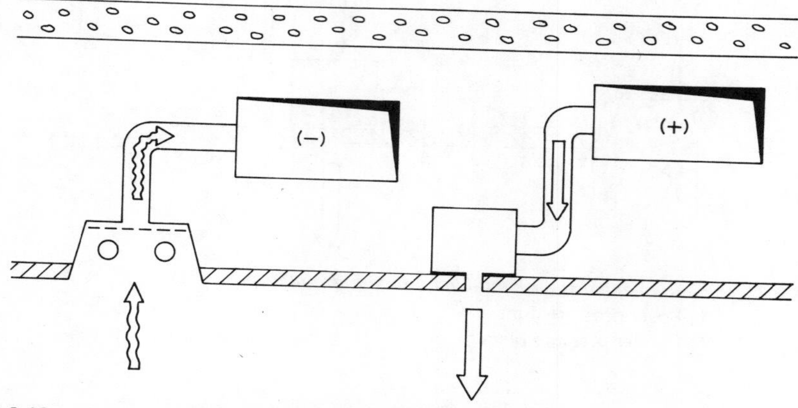

Fig. 4.9.13. *Two duct air handling luminaire installation*
(+) over-pressure duct (—) under-pressure duct

4.9.5.5 Characteristics of air-handling luminaires

In addition to the usual lighting characteristics the data concerning luminaires for use in integrated ceiling systems provides information on the resulting heat removal, the increase in luminous flux, the air pressure drop, and level of noise produced. The quantity of heat exhausted via the luminaires and the increase in luminous flux of the lamp depends on the type of luminaire used and the volume of air exhausted. Thus, each type of luminaire has its own air-handling characteristics.

4.9.6 Lighting maintenance

4.9.6.1 Need for good maintenance

A lighting installation will continue to operate efficiently only when it is well maintained. Poor maintenance can accelerate lamp ageing and failure, whilst the accumulation of dirt on lamps, luminaires and room surfaces will bring about an unacceptable reduction in the amount of useful light available. This can lead not only to illuminance levels which are substantially below those required, but also to the installation assuming a neglected appearance. Initial illuminance values can be maintained by cleaning or replacing lamps at suitable intervals. (Fig. 4.9.14). The design of the lighting installation should make allowance for possible depreciation in light output by initially providing an illuminance which is higher than that required. The amount of such allowance will depend on the maintenance schedule agreed between the designer and the user.

4.9.6.2 Dirt on lamps and luminaires

The rate of depreciation caused by dirt deposited on light-controlling surfaces is effected by the angle of inclination, finish and temperature of the surface, by the degree of ventilation or dust tightness of the luminaire, and by the degree to which the atmosphere surrounding the luminaire is polluted. Luminaires with open bases and closed tops collect dirt at a higher rate than do those that are ventilated. In ventilated luminaires, convection currents carry dust and dirt out through holes or slots in the canopy or reflector and away from the reflecting surfaces.

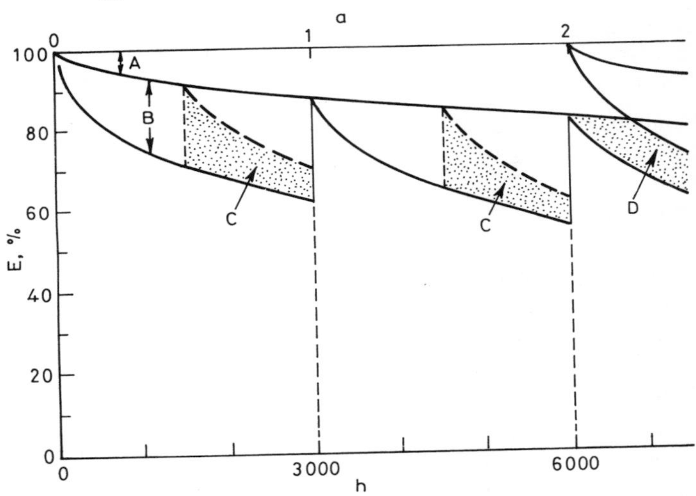

Fig. 4.9.14. *Benefits of good lighting maintenance*

Effect of depreciation, cleaning and lamp renewal on illuminance E from a scheme using fluorescent lamps where

a = years at an assumed 3000 hours per year
h = hours of use.
A = loss due to lamp deterioration.
B = loss due to luminaire soiling.
C = gain if cleaned every six months.
D = gain if relamped.

4.9.6.3 Lamp lumen depreciation

The lumen output of all lamps decreases with use, but the rate of decrease varies widely between lamp types. Lighting calculations must, therefore, take into account the specific depreciation in luminous output of the particular lamps involved.

4.9.6.4 Maintenance factor

When determining the number of lamps necessary to provide the required illuminance for a particular lighting installation, it is usual to apply a maintenance factor to the calculations. This factor is defined as the ratio of the average illuminance on the working plane after a certain period of use to the average illuminance obtained under the same conditions for a new installation. It takes into account, therefore, the overall depreciation caused by the various factors already described.

If no information is available on the depreciation of lamps, luminaires and room surfaces or cleaning schedule, the following total maintenance factors can be used:

clean area: 0·8
average area: 0·7
dirty area: 0·6

If, in the manufacturer's data, the lamp flux is given in Lighting Design Lumens (measured at 2000 hours), these maintenance figures should be multiplied by 1·1.

4.9.7 Lighting design

4.9.7.1 Lighting criteria

The level and quality of the lighting provided by a given installation can be identified by means of the following parameters:

Lighting level
Luminance distribution in the field of view
Glare
Colour appearance and colour rendering

It is of fundamental importance that there should be sufficient light in an interior to allow work or other activities to be carried out efficiently, safely and in comfort. The amount of light, i.e. the lighting level, may be specified by the illuminance on the imaginary horizontal working plane or on a specific task. Research has shown that levels in the order of 1000 lux would seem realistic for working interiors in which the tasks are not of a prolonged or visually very exacting nature and that the minimum, based on the visual comfort criterion, lies at about 200 lux.

In practice, a compromise has often to be made between desirable illuminance and that which is related to the economic conditions prevailing. In consequence, it may be necessary to accept a lower standard of lighting than that which would be desired from visual performance or visual satisfaction. A scale of recommended illuminance levels published by the CIE given in Table 4.9.5.

The planned distribution of luminance in an interior should be regarded as being complementary to a design based on illuminance. It should be limited in application to the task and its immediate surrounds (luminance ratios), the ceiling, walls and floor (luminance ranges), and the luminaires (luminance limits).

The luminance of the area immediately surrounding a task should be lower than the luminance of the task itself, but not less than about one-third of this value. In offices the visual tasks mostly involve the use of matt-white paper seen against a matt or semi-matt desk top. For tasks of this nature, the luminance ratio referred to above may be obtained by ensuring that the surface reflectance (section 4.9.2.1) of the desk lies between 0·25 and 0·5. The luminance of the background should be again less than the luminance of the task and the area immediately surrounding a task, but not less than about one-tenth of the task luminance.

Where the luminaires are of the fully recessed type the ceiling will be lighted purely by reflection from the floor and the difference between the actual and the recommended luminance for the ceiling may be considerable. The reflectance of

Table 4.9.5 *Recommended Illuminances for Interiors*

Range	Recommended illuminance (lx)	Type of activity
A		
general lighting	20	
for areas used	30	public areas with dark surroundings
infrequently	50	
or having	75	simple orientation for short temporary visits only
simple visual	100	
demands	150	rooms not used continuously for working purposes e.g. storage areas, entrance halls
	200	
B	300	tasks with limited visual requirements e.g. rough machining, lecture theatres
general	500	
lighting for	750	tasks with normal visual requirements e.g. medium machining, offices
working	1 000	
interiors	1 500	tasks with special visual requirements e.g. hand engraving, clothing factory inspection
	2 000	
C	3 000	very prolonged and exacting visual tasks e.g. minute electronic and watch assembly
additional	5 000	
lighting for	7 500	exceptionally exacting visual tasks e.g. micro electronic assembly
visually exacting	10 000	
tasks	15 000	very special tasks e.g. surgical operations
	20 000	

the ceiling should, therefore, be as high as possible and certainly not less than 0·7. The recommended range of wall reflectance is between 0·5 and 0·8 for installations in the order of 500 lux and between 0·4 and 0·6 where the illuminance is around 1000 lux.

Glare control begins at the luminaire itself by ensuring that excessively high luminances are avoided. The luminance of the luminaires used has to be limited in such a way that the glare produced by the installation as a whole is within an acceptable quality class according to the CIE Luminance Curve method of glare evaluation.

The measures taken to control direct glare will not necessarily take care of reflected glare also. The occurrence of reflected glare in general, and veiling reflections in particular, is dependent not only on the luminance of the luminaires and their arrangement, but also on the lay-out of the luminaires relative to the working areas and on the illuminance level prevailing. Ideally, no part of a task or its surround should be at or near to the mirror angle with respect to the eye and any bright source of light. Loss of task contrast will be at a minimum if the light falls on the task from the same direction as the direction of view or from the side. Glossy or high-reflectance surfaces should also be avoided. The colour qualities of a lamp are characterized by its colour appearance and its colour rendering, i.e. its ability to influence the colour appearance of the objects it illuminates. The colour qualities of the selected lamp should be in accordance with the requirements of the lighting installation, and the illuminance level.

4.9.7.2 Design criteria

Drawings, showing the suggested plan and cross-section of each room, including the proposed constructional details of the ceilings and walls, are required for consideration by the lighting engineer. If there is to be a ventilation or air-conditioning system, the routing of ducting and the lay-out of luminaires should be considered jointly with the design engineer. In order to make the necessary detailed calculations concerning the type and quantity of lighting equipment necessary, information on the surface reflectance of walls, ceilings, and floors is required. Similarly, calculations concerning the luminance ratios in the interior call for details of the interior decor and furnishing.

4.9.7.3 Lighting systems

The requirements of the lighting installation are dependent upon the type of work to be carried out in the space in question; also, the function of the room, its occupancy, and the visual tasks to be carried out will determine the choice of lighting system to be used. The most common lighting systems are those providing general lighting, localized lighting, or local lighting plus general lighting.

(a) *General lighting*

A general lighting system provides the required horizontal illuminance over the total area with a certain degree of uniformity. The average illuminance should be equal to the required illuminance for the specific visual task. General lighting is obtained by a regular arrangement of luminaires over the whole ceiling area or by a number of equally-spaced continuous rows of luminaires.

(b) *Localized lighting*
A localized lighting system provides a non-uniform horizontal illuminance in the room. The illuminance on the main task areas should be sufficiently high to meet the task requirements, whereas in other locations such as circulation areas, the illuminance is normally limited to approximately 50% of the illuminance for the visual task, but should not be less than 300 lux. Localized lighting is obtained by concentrating luminaires in certain areas or by switching selected luminaires in a general lighting arrangement. Because working places may not be permanent, provision should be made for repositioning the luminaires.

(c) *Local lighting plus general lighting*
Local lighting is produced by placing luminaires close to the visual task so as to illuminate only a small area. Depending upon the desired ratio between the illuminance of the task area and that of its surroundings, local lighting should be supplemented by general lighting (Fig. 4.9.15).

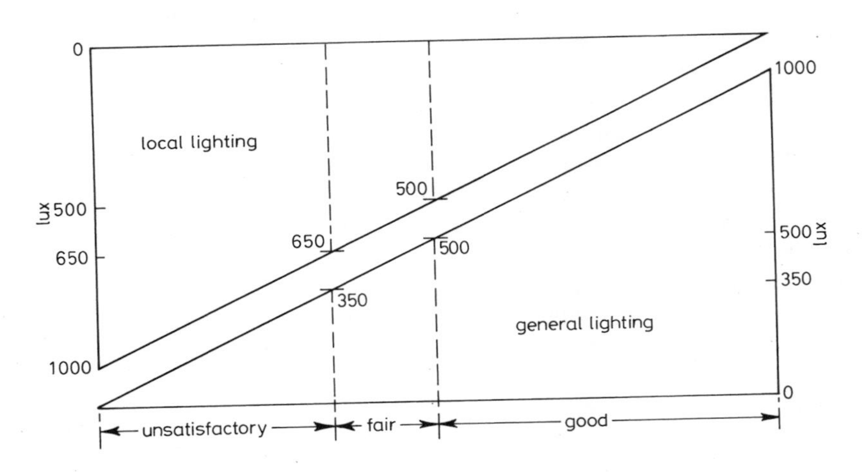

Fig. 4.9.15. ***Balance between general lighting and local lighting***

Local lighting is recommended when:
(i) The work involves very critical visual tasks, requiring illuminance of 1000 lux or more.
(ii) Viewing of forms or textures requires the lighting to come from a particular direction.
(iii) The general lighting, due to obstructions, does not penetrate certain areas.

(iv) Higher illuminances are necessary for the benefit of older workers or workers with reduced visual performance.
(v) The area is only partly occupied for long periods.

4.9.7.4 Lighting codes

In a number of countries national organisations, e.g. Chartered Institution of Building services (CIBS) in U.K., the American Illuminating Engineering Society (IES) and the Netherlands Lighting Society (NSVV) in Holland have developed their own individual recommendations. The main points of difference between national recommendations are in the ways in which illuminance levels, luminance ratios, glare evaluation and colour rendering are dealt with for various types of interior and activity. It can be expected that the future development of these recommendations will be influenced to some extent by the Guide on Interior Lighting prepared by the CIE. Information relating to illuminance levels for use in interiors appears as:

(i) codes issued by standards organisations and illuminating engineering societies and giving recommended levels based on the criteria of efficiency and comfort;
(ii) specifications or legislation defining minimum levels as dictated by the needs of safety and welfare. These levels are in general lower than those recommended above.

In codes issued by standards organisations, either 'service' values or 'minimum' values of illuminance are recommended, depending on the country in which the code originated.

'Service illuminance' is the mean illuminance throughout the maintenance cycle of the lighting system and averaged over the relevant area, which may be the whole area of the interior, or the area of the visual task and its immediate surround. This means that the initial illuminance must be higher than the recommended value to allow for the fact that the illuminance will inevitably drop below this value by the end of the cleaning and relamping period.

'Minimum illuminance' values represent minimum values on the task at any time. This means that the initial illuminance on the task must be considerably higher – the exact amount will depend on the degree of light depreciation due to lamp ageing and the accumulation of dust and dirt.

In some codes, the illuminance values are specified in terms of the 'standard service illuminance'. This is the service illuminance recommended for standard conditions. A flow chart is included in the code which shows how the standard service illuminance for particular activities should be increased or can be decreased to compensate to some extent for unusual features in the task or observer (e.g. age) There are also differences in the way in which light loss (maintenance) factors and lamp lumen values are applied in lighting design. The UK uses 'Lighting Design Lumens' (average lumen output after 2000 hours) for lighting calculations, instead of the 100-hours values generally used elsewhere.

Within Europe, the levels recommended in the schedules of the various national bodies for similar types of application are roughly comparable. Illuminance levels

Table 4.9.6 *Recommended Illuminances for selected Activity Areas*

Area or Activity	Service illuminance (lx)
Bakeries:	
General working areas	300
Decorating, inspection	500
Breweries:	300
Canning and Preserving Factories:	500
Chemical Works:	
Interior plant areas	200
Grinding, mixing	300
Calendering, injection	500
Control rooms	500
Laboratories	750
Colour matching	1000
Chocolate Factories:	
General working areas	300
Decorating, inspection	500
Dairies:	
Bottling milk	300
Electrical Industries:	
Coil winding	500
Assembly work: Fine	1500
Very fine	2000
Adjustment, inspection	1000
Foundries:	
Rough moulding, pouring	300
Fine moulding, core making, inspection	500
Glass Works:	
Mixing rooms	200
Forming, blowing	300
Decorating	500
Etching	750
Leather Factories:	
Pressing, glazing	750
Cutting, sewing	1000
Grading, matching	1500

Table 4.9.6 *(Cont.)*

Area or Activity	Service illuminance (lx)
Machine Shops:	
Rough bench and machine work, welding	300
Medium bench and machine work	500
Fine bench and machine work	750
Very fine work	1000
Very fine precision work	2000
Paper Mills:	
Paper and board making	300
Potteries:	
Firing	200
Moulding, pressing	300
Enamelling, decorating	750
Printing Works:	
Printing machines, book binding	500
Hand composing	750
Retouching, etching	1000
Textile Mills:	
Carding, spreading	300
Reeling, spinning	500
Weaving plain cloth	750
Weaving fine worsteds	1000
Inspection	1500
Warehouses:	
Storage rooms	150
Packing and dispatch	300
Woodworking Shops:	
Rough sawing and cutting	200
Rough bench work	300
Medium bench work	500
Finishing, final inspection	750
Offices and Schools	
Offices:	
Conference rooms	300
General offices:	
Normal	500
Deep-plan	750
Drawing boards	1000

Table 4.9.6 *(Cont.)*

Area or Activity (lx)	Service illuminance (lx)
Schools:	
Classrooms, lecture theatres	300
Laboratories, libraries, reading rooms, art rooms	500
Shops, Stores and Exhibition Areas	
Shops:	
Conventional shops	300
Self-service shops	500
Supermarkets	750
Show Rooms:	500
Museums and Art Galleries:	
General:	
Light-sensitive exhibits	150
Exhibits insensitive to light	300
Public Buildings	
Cinemas:	
Auditoria	50
Foyers	150
Theatres and Concert Halls:	
Auditoria	100
Foyers	200
Churches:	
Nave	100
Choir	150
Homes and Hotels	
Homes:	
Bedrooms:	
General	50
Bed-head	200
Bathrooms:	
General	100
Shaving, make-up	500
Living-rooms:	
General	100
Reading, sewing	500

Table 4.9.6 *(Cont.)*

Area or Activity	Service illuminance (lx)
Stairs	100
Kitchens:	
General	300
Working areas	500
Workroom	300
Nursery	150
Hotels:	
Entrance halls	300
Dining rooms	200
Kitchens	500
Bedrooms, bathrooms:	
General	100
Local	300
Miscellaneous	
Indoors:	
Circulation areas, corridors and stairs in industry	150
Outdoors:	
Entrances, exits	30
Industrial covered ways, gantries	50
Docks, quays	100
Service station forecourts	200

as recommended within Europe for a selection of areas and activities are given in Table 4.9.6.

4.9.7.5 Illuminance calculations

Lighting calculations fall into two main groups: those performed by the equipment manufacturer in converting hardware measurement data into a form suitable for presentation to the lighting engineer, and those performed by the lighting engineer himself during the actual lighting design phase. Little need be said here concerning the first group of calculations, other than that today increasing use is being made of computers. The sort of design data supplied in this way can be seen by examining a luminaire data sheet. (Section 4.9.4.3)

For the lighting engineer, use of the speed, accuracy and convenience of the computer has considerably aided design work. Programs for calculating illuminances (horizontal, vertical, and on an inclined plane) are readily available, with output presented numerically or graphically as required. In practice, however, for most routine design work it will prove quite sufficient to make use of simple, manual design techniques, which necessarily involve the determination of illuminance and luminance. The lighting level of work rooms will be defined in terms of the average illuminance on the working plane, this being an imaginary plane considered to be at the height of the work above the floor (normally 0·75 m to 0·85 m) and covering the entire floor area. This average illuminance has to be created by a regular pattern of ceiling-mounted luminaires. In order to determine either the necessary number of lamps and luminaires for a specified lighting level, or the average illuminance obtained from a particular lighting design, the Lumen Method of calculation is employed. The lumen method is based on the formula

$$E = \frac{SPHI \times UF \times \phi_f \times MF}{A} \qquad (4.9.4)$$

in which:

E = illuminance on the surface (lx)

$SPHI$ = total luminous flux of all lamps installed (lm)

UF = utilization factor for the surface

ϕ_f = correction factor for light output

MF = maintenance factor

A = floor area (m^2)

The utilization factor, UF, is found as follows:

(i) Calculate the room index, K, according to the formula

$$K = \frac{a \times b}{h_m(a + b)}$$

where a and b are the lengths of the sides of the room (in metres) and h_m is the mounting height, in metres i.e. the distance between the plane of the luminaires and the working plane.

(ii) Ascertain the reflectances of the ceiling, walls and working plane from the following scale:

white and very light colours 0·7
light colours 0·5
medium colours 0·3
dark colours 0·1

For the working plane 0·1 should normally be selected and 0·3 only in exceptional cases.

(iii) Using these values for room index and reflectance factors, select the utilization factor from the utilization factor table for the type of luminaire and lamp under consideration.

The correction factor for the light output is found by determining the air flow rate, V, (m^3/s) exhausted through the luminaire, and then selecting ϕ_f from the thermal diagram for air-handling luminaires. The lumen depreciation, due to lamp ageing and dirt accumulation, is represented by a maintenance factor, MF (section 4.9.6.4), the value chosen depending on local conditions.

In general, the number of rows of luminaires and the number of luminaires per row cannot be chosen arbitrarily; there can be a difference, especially in interiors with a low room index, between the calculated number of luminaires and the number that is finally selected. Because of this the illuminance has to be calculated for the number of luminaires finally selected.

The following is a practical example of these calculations:

A lighting installation providing an average illuminance of 750 lux on the working plane is required for a chemistry laboratory.

The dimensions of the room are: length $a = 30$ m, width $b = 7{\cdot}5$ m, height $h = 3{\cdot}15$ m and height of the working plane $= 0{\cdot}75$ m. The reflectances of ceiling, walls and working plane are 0·70, 0·50 and 0·10 respectively.

Type of luminaire selected: recessed mounted luminaire with low brightness mirror optic for two TLD 58 W lamps.

Calculation:

(i) Room Index K

$$K = \frac{a \times b}{h_m(a+b)} = \frac{30 \times 7{\cdot}5}{(3{\cdot}15 - 0{\cdot}75)(30 + 7{\cdot}5)} = 2{\cdot}5$$

(ii) Utilization factor UF is ascertained from the luminaire data provided by the manufacturer. For a room index $K = 2{\cdot}5$ and reflectances of 0·70, 0·50 and 0·10 the UF for the luminaire is found to be 0·57.

(iii) From Eqn. 4.9.4, the total luminous flux to be installed is

$$SPHI = \frac{E \times a \times b}{UF \times \phi_f \times MF} = \frac{750 \times 30 \times 7{\cdot}5}{0{\cdot}57 \times \phi_f \times MF} = \frac{296 \times 10^3}{\phi_f \times MF}$$

(iv) Luminaire without air exhaust

Correction factor $\phi_f = 1{\cdot}0$
Maintenance factor $MF = 0{\cdot}80$

$$SPHI = \frac{296 \times 10^3}{0{\cdot}8} = 370 \times 10^3 \text{ lm}$$

Luminaire with air exhaust

Airflow rate per luminaire
$V = 0{\cdot}03$ m^3/s
Correction factor $\phi_f = 1{\cdot}03$
Maintenance factor $MF = 0{\cdot}85$

$$SPHI = \frac{296 \times 10^3}{1{\cdot}03 \times 0{\cdot}85} = 338 \times 10^3 \text{ lm}$$

The number of fluorescent lamps of type TLD 58 W (5400 lumens) required will thus be:

$$\frac{370 \times 10^3}{5{\cdot}4 \times 10^3} = 69 \text{ lamps} \qquad \frac{338 \times 10^3}{5{\cdot}4 \times 10^3} = 63 \text{ lamps}$$

(v) For which the number of luminaires of selected type, each incorporating 2 × TLD 58 W lamps, will be:

$$\frac{69}{2} = 35 \text{ luminaires} \qquad \frac{63}{2} = 32 \text{ luminaires}$$

(vi) The luminaires will be arranged in three rows parallel to the length axis of the laboratory. In the case of luminaires without air exhaust 12 luminaires per row will be required and in the case of luminaires with air exhaust 11 luminaires will be required per row.

(vii) Illuminance on the workplane will be:

$$E = \frac{36 \times 2 \times 5400 \times 0{\cdot}57 \times 1 \times 0{\cdot}8}{30 \times 7{\cdot}5} = 788 \text{ lux} \qquad E = \frac{33 \times 2 \times 5400 \times 0{\cdot}57 \times 1{\cdot}03 \times 0{\cdot}85}{30 \times 7{\cdot}5} = 790 \text{ lux}$$

4.9.7.6 Daylight and artificial lighting

Daylighting and size and type of windows should not be considered in isolation. It is necessary to study the interactions of daylighting aspects with other design criteria such as energy consumption, artificial lighting, heat loss, heat gains, and sound transmission. In the interest of energy conservation, daylighting should be seriously considered as a means of satisfying the visual requirements prevailing. However, when doing so, direct sunlight should be excluded. Direct sunlight disturbs the physical and visual environment to such an extent that measures must be taken to prevent it reaching the working areas.

Daylight reaching the working area in the building can be expressed by a 'daylight factor', which is the ratio of the daylight illuminance at a point on a given plane inside the building due to the light received directly or indirectly from a sky of assumed or known luminance distribution, to the illuminance on a horizontal plane under an unobstructed hemisphere of this sky. Direct sunlight is excluded from both values of illuminance. The daylight factor comprises three components: the sky component, the externally reflected component and the internally reflected component.

Calculation of daylight factor is based upon the assumption that the sky is completely overcast and that its luminance is defined by the CIE definition of a standard overcast sky. Fig. 4.9.16 shows daylight factor as a function of distance from the window in a specific building.

Lighting installations are designed to function during periods when there is no daylight available, but to avoid waste of energy, steps should be taken to restrict the use of artificial lighting at times when daylight would be capable of providing the required working illuminance.

Artificial lighting in an interior in relation to the available daylight can be controlled by manual on/off switching, automatic on/off switching, automatic step control, and automatic dimming.

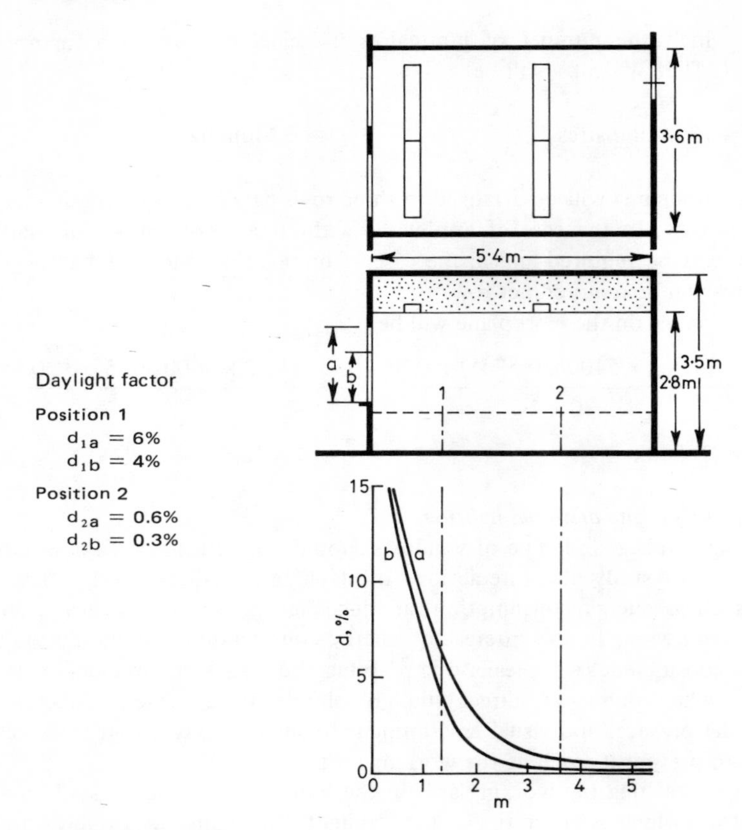

Fig. 4.9.16. *Daylight factor in a small room*

4.9.8 Lighting in industry and commerce

4.9.8.1 General

The type of work carried out in industry and commerce covers a wide range of visual tasks, the subjects of which may range from extremely small to very large, may be dark or light, and may involve flat or contoured surfaces. For the purposes of visual perception, such tasks are graded according to their degree of fineness. The less critical the task, the lower are the demands on the level and quality of the lighting. Conversely, the finer the work, the higher must be the illuminance level and freedom from glare.

Where the general lighting fails to meet the special requirements of a particular task, it must be supplemented by some form of local lighting, and such a general plus local lighting system should be carefully planned if an irregular, and possibly unpleasant, luminance pattern is to be avoided. The local lighting should, of course, allow a task to be performed in comfort for all suitable positions of the work.

For the visual task, both national and international recommendations are available which cover the minimum illuminance on the work surface, the illuminance uniformity, the brightness limits of the light source and surrounding surfaces, and the colour rendering. But lighting involves more than merely ensuring that the visual task is lighted in accordance with the minimum norms. Lighting in fact has a threefold function to perform: it should light the visual task so that this can be performed comfortably and well, light the total space in such a way as to create a stimulating atmosphere in which to work, and reinforce and accentuate the decor.

4.9.8.2 Drawing offices

As drawing involves the accurate discrimination of fine detail, the illuminance in drawing offices should be at least 750 lux. Veiling reflections can occur on the surfaces of drawing boards which may be badly positioned with respect to the luminaires; the easiest way of minimizing such reflections is to position the boards accordingly. The problem of providing suitable lighting is much simplified if it can be arranged that all occupants of the office face one way, and the office layout is limited to fixed rows of work positions. Rows of fluorescent luminaires can then be mounted parallel to the direction of view on both sides of the drawing boards. With this arrangement the absence of any luminaire directly above a given work position serves to keep glare and veiling reflection to a minimum, whilst the lighting coming from both sides of a worker effectively eliminates hard shadows.

4.9.8.3 Lighting for VDU work stations

In general, the visual requirements for general office lighting are equally valid for video display unit (VDU) work stations. However, there are certain additional features of VDU work which have to be taken into account when planning the lighting if visual performance and comfort are not to be impaired.

In the first place, the screen of the VDU constitutes an important additional part of the task area and light sources such as luminaires and windows which reflect in the screen can produce a considerable deterioration in the legibility of the characters. Such reflection should therefore be avoided by employing a 'Mirror-Image Suppressor" (MIS). The MIS-device eliminates all specular reflections, even that of the user. A display screen fitted with the MIS-device can be sited anywhere in the room without giving rise to unwanted reflections. If a MIS-device is not available, the screen should be placed in such a position that the surfaces in the room having a high luminance (windows, luminaires etc) are not seen mirrored in it. In the latter case the problem can be reduced by using low-brightness luminaires. The optimum illuminance will lie somewhere between 400 lux for light (high reflectance) screens and 700 lux for dark (low reflectance) screens, both provided with low-brightness luminaires.

4.9.8.4 Emergency lighting (See also Sec. 2.2.2.4)
Emergency lighting is lighting which is designed to come into operation if the normal lighting fails. Emergency lighting is referred to in BS 5266 and can be divided into the following categories:

(a) Escape lighting, defined as lighting sufficient to enable a building to be evacuated quickly and safely during an emergency.
(b) Standby lighting, providing sufficient lighting to allow activities of vital importance to be continued during an emergency, and lighting sufficient to ensure the safety of persons engaged in work of a potentially hazardous nature (e.g. operating a circular saw) during an emergency.

Technically there are two types of emergency lighting:

(a) Permanent emergency lighting supplied from a separate, self-supporting, power system. The power supply is completely independent of the mains supply, except for charging, and consists of reliable, mains-rechargeable batteries. In the event of a power failure, the batteries are automatically switched in.
(b) Non-permanent emergency lighting with automatic switching. This type of lighting works from a central emergency generator or battery supply which automatically switches in during a mains failure. A disadvantage of this system is that it relies on the internal wiring of the building for distribution of the emergency power and can thus easily become disrupted in the event of fire or structural damage.

4.9.9 Floodlighting of buildings and areas

4.9.9.1 Working areas
Many large spaces, for example marshalling yards, carparks, building sites and storage compounds, are illuminated using high-mast floodlighting. High-mast lighting is preferred mainly on account of its economy in the use of lighting masts – a factor which also contributes greatly to freedom of movement in the area illuminated. The most economical height of the masts is generally between 20 and 30 metres. At greater heights the cost of the masts rises considerably, whereas at lower heights the number of masts, lamps and luminaires becomes disproportionately large. If, however, relatively tall constructions are already present within the area to be lighted, lower mounting heights should be used in order to avoid heavy shadows.

The lighting level should at least be specified in the horizontal plane. Sometimes the vertical illuminance should also be checked, as, for example, where reading tasks are involved or where goods must be inspected or moved. The lighting levels and uniformities needed depend on the difficulty of the visual task. The draft CIE Publication 'Guide on Area Lighting', gives an indication of the level and uniformity requirements for different categories of areas. The required degree of glare limitation is, of course, dependent upon the category of the area concerned. Sometimes, the floodlights should be fitted with special louvres.

The most frequently used lamps are the SON/T high-pressure sodium and MBI/T metal halide types, although where colour discrimination is not necessary, the SOX low-pressure sodium lamp also can offer a good solution.

4.9.9.2 Buildings and monuments
The floodlighting of a building exterior is intended to attract attention to the building concerned and to create a favourable impression with passers-by. In the case of business premises such as offices and stores, floodlighting is often a subtle and dignified, yet highly effective, form of advertising.

During the hours of daylight, a building is lit by direct sunlight, by diffused light radiated from the sky, or by both. The result is that the architectural features of the building are emphasized by a continuously changing interplay of light and shadow. The design of a good floodlighting installation calls for a close study of these lighting effects, for this is often the best way of deciding which features are the most attractive. Thus, the technique of floodlighting a building is not based solely on the principles of lighting engineering; appreciation of the aesthetic values of the architecture is just as important.

For the positioning and the choice of floodlights one has to consider the direction of view, the viewing distance, the surroundings and background, and possible obstacles. There will generally be several directions from which a building can be viewed, but often a particular one can be decided upon as the main direction of view. The viewing distance will determine the amount of detail visible on the facade. If the surroundings and background of the building are dark, a relatively small amount of light will be needed to make the building lighter than the background. If there are other buildings in the close vicinity, their lighted windows will give an impression of brightness, and more light will then be needed for the floodlighting if it is to have any impact. In this case a solution can be found in the creation of a colour contrast instead of a brightness contrast.

Trees and fences around a building can form a decorative part of an installation. An attractive way of dealing with these is to place the sources of light behind them. Firstly, the light sources are not seen by the viewer and secondly, the trees and fences are silhouetted against the light background of the facade. As a lighted building will be reflected in the surface of water, which serves as a 'black mirror', one can take advantage of any expanse of water in the foreground, such as a lake, moat, river or canal.

Lamps employed in floodlighting range from the special incandescent type of 25 watts, which may be used to provide fill-in light (perhaps under an arch), to the metal-halide MBI/T lamps of 2000 watts needed to light the top of a tall building.

4.9.10 References

4.9.10.1 British Standards (See also Appendix 6.2)
Amongst the more important British Standards concerned with lighting are the

following, some of which are identical with IEC Standards:

BS 839 Flameproof electric lighting fittings
BS 1853 Tubular fluorescent lamps for general lighting service
BS 3767 Low pressure sodium lamps
BS 4533 Luminaires
BS 4727 Glossary of terms
BS 5225 Photometric data for luminaires
BS 5266 Emergency lighting
BS 5489 Code of practice for road lighting
BS 5971 Tungsten filament lamps
BS 6170 Tungsten filament lamps (with lives of 2000 hours)
BS CP 1007 Maintained lighting for cinemas

4.9.10.2 Bibliography

BELLCHAMBERS, H. E. and GODBY, A. C. 'Illumination, Colour Rendering and Visual Clarity' (Lighting Research and Technology vol. 4. pp 104–106. Published by CIBS).

BOER, J. B. de and FISHER, D. 'Interior Lighting' (Philips Technical Library)

BOYCE, P. R. 'The Contrast Rendering Factor and Office Lighting' (Electricity Council Research Centre ECRC R1133)

BOYCE, P. R. 'The Influence of Illumination Level on Prolonged Work Performance' (Lighting Research and Technology vol 2, p 74. Published by CIBS)

CIBS (formerly IES) Code for Interior Lighting.

Commission Internationale de l'Eclairage (CIE) Guide on Interior Lighting, Publication CIE 29.

CIE Calculations for Interior Lighting – Applied Method. Publication CIE 40.

(CIE Publications are available in Britain from Jules Thorn Lighting Laboratories, Great Cambridge Road, Enfield EN1 1UL)

HENDRIKS, R. T. A. 'Integration of Daylight and Artificial Lighting'. (Proceedings of CIE Symposium on Daylight, Berlin 1980)

4.9.11 Glossary

A floor area (m^2)
CRF Contrast Rendering Factor
E illuminance (lux, lx)
I luminous intensity (candela, cd)
K room index
L luminance (cd/m^2)
MF maintenance factor
R_a colour rendering index
S surface area (m^2)
$SPHI$ total luminous flux (lumens, lm)
UF utilisation factor
V air flow rate (m^3/s)
a length of room (m)
b width of room (m)

c speed of wave propagation (m/s)
h_m mounting height of luminaire above the horizontal working plane (m)
r radius of a sphere (m)
ϕ luminous flux (lumens, lm)
ϕ_f correction factor for light output
λ wavelength (m)
ν frequency (Hz)
ρ reflectance
ω solid angle (steradians)

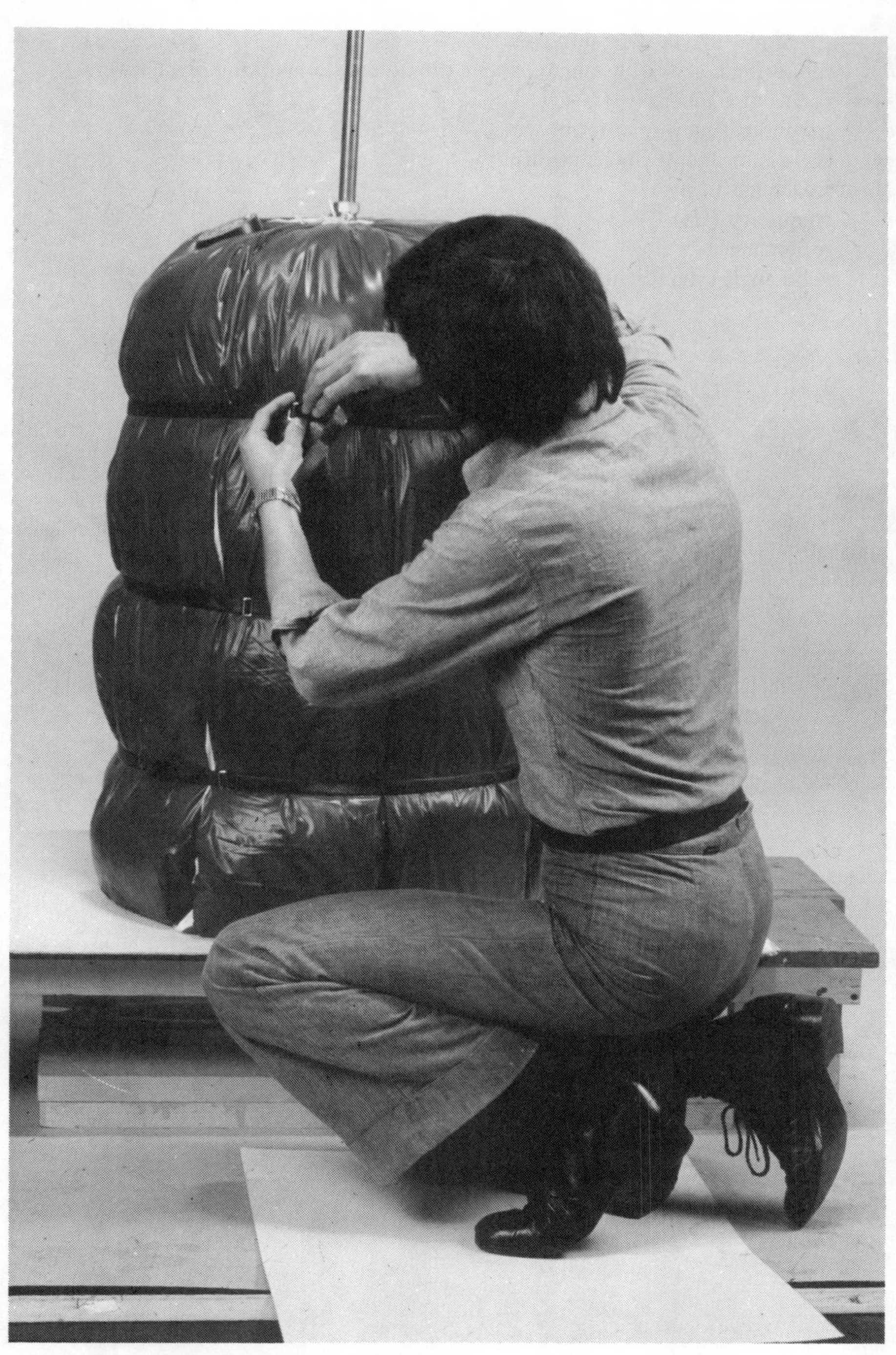

Fixing lagging jacket to hot water cylinder

Chapter 4.10

Water heating

G. Haslett
Heating Specialist, The Electricity Council

4.10.1 Introduction

4.10.1.1 Systems

Where a fossil fuel boiler is installed for space-heating, it has been traditional practice to provide the water heating service from the same boiler using a central storage system. This type of system developed largely during a period when it was common to install solid fuel boilers. These require a substantial basic heat load to offset their lack of controllability and to prevent boiling. Both gas and oil fired boilers use the same type of combined central system although in the larger commercial buildings the water heating may be provided by a separate boiler. Such systems are often supplemented by electric heaters, generally either of the immersion type or point of use heaters. However, it may often be more economical to concentrate on a wholly electric installation.

4.10.1.2 Corrosion and scale formation

Water systems are subjected to two forms of chemical attack, particularly when the water is heated, from

(a) corrosion arising from electrolytic action or aggressive substances in the water. Corrosion may be lessened by using an all copper or all galvanised iron system.
(b) hardness, either 'temporary', which causes precipitation and scaling at temperatures above 60°C, and which can be removed by appropriate treatment, and 'permanent', which does not cause scaling but which is less readily removed.

To minimise the effects of corrosion and scale, electrical elements for heating water are safeguarded with a protective finish, preferably titanium.

4.10.2 System efficiency

Figure 4.10.1 shows schematically the central storage system heated by a boiler, to illustrate the areas where heat losses occur and which can reduce the overall system efficiency to as little as 15%. In principle, installations in domestic and commercial buildings are very similar excepting that commercial buildings commonly have a pumped secondary circuit, since long lengths of piping are generally involved. The areas of heat loss are:

(a) Combustion and case losses at the boiler. (In this respect whilst the boiler efficiency may be 75% or more at full load, this will rarely be the situation. In summer for example the boiler will often be on loads representing 10–20% of the maximum and at this level a boiler efficiency above 30% would be unusual).
(b) Primary flow and return pipe losses between the boiler and cylinder.
(c) Cylinder heat losses.
(d) Secondary pipework losses. (In any system, care must be exercised to avoid unnecessary waste of energy occurring due to circulation of hot water or in long 'dead legs' to hot water taps.)

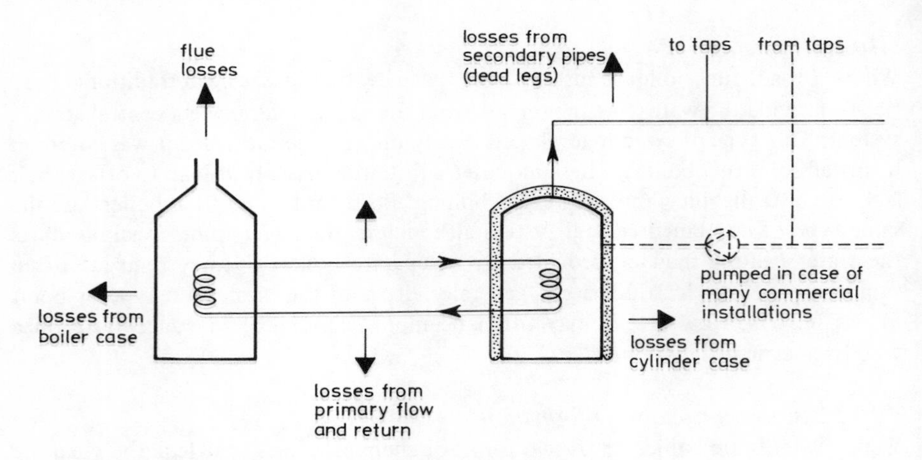

Fig. 4.10.1. *Losses in a central storage hot water system*

A system having all these losses can have an overall system efficiency as low as 15%.

Electric central storage systems have only the losses indicated in (c) and (d). In most domestic premises the secondary pipework is relatively short and cylinder losses can be reduced by good insulation, particularly if factory insulated cylinders or purpose built encased water heaters are used and for this reason it is possible to obtain system efficiencies of around 75%. Table 4.10.1 compares the efficiencies

Table 4.10.1 *Comparison of System Efficiencies*

Fuel/System	Overall System Efficiency
Domestic Systems	
Electric	
Instantaneous local heater	95–100
Small storage (up to 20 litres) local heater	85–95
Central Storage (120–210 litres)	68–75
Gas	
Instantaneous single point	50–55
Instantaneous multi point	40–50
Central storage fired by	
(a) circulator	40–45
(b) lightweight central boiler	30–40
(c) heavyweight central boiler	20–30
Oil	
Central boiler	20–30
Solid Fuel	
Independent Boiler	20–25
Central Boiler	15–25
Commercial/Industrial Systems	
Electric Instantaneous local heater	95–100
Off-peak electric storage local to use	70–80
Central storage using fossil fuels	
small premises with short distribution piping	20–40
large premises with extensive distribution piping	10–20

of various types of systems. As far as commercial buildings are concerned, the central storage system is shown to be particularly low in efficiency. Furthermore, measurements in offices maintained by the Electricity Council have shown that the quantity of hot water used in commercial premises is only a fraction of that often assumed for design purposes. At the measured water usages the economics of a central system are seriously questioned and generally the most appropriate choice for commercial premises will be local electric water heaters.

4.10.3 Domestic installations

4.10.3.1 General

Well over 90% of homes in Great Britain have a hot water storage cylinder. More than 11 million households own an immersion heater and about half of these use it as the main source of heating hot water. The most common system comprises a copper cylinder of type size BS7 (120 litres capacity) usually heated by a single top entry immersion heater 580 mm or 690 mm in length commonly operating on the normal domestic tariff. Such a system may be controlled at say 60°C by a thermostat and either left switched on or switched by hand to meet individual needs. However, it only requires a modest modification to make this arrangement suitable for Economy 7 tariff, (see Section 2.1.8.4) so that most of the energy can be taken at the overnight rate, currently less than half the normal domestic rate.

4.10.3.2 'Economy 7' modifications

Since the unit cost of Economy 7 night rate is less than 40% of the Economy 7 day rate, the principal aim of any modification is to maximise the use of night energy whilst providing a high quality of service. The split between day and night consumption is dependent for a particular cylinder size on the amount of water used and the immersion heater arrangement and its control. Where immersion heaters are used as a sole means of heating hot water, Electricity Council research indicates a range of usage between 800 and 4500 kWh per annum. This would indicate a weekly usage ranging between 450 and 1125 litres. Although considerable variation does occur between households of the same size the research work of many organisations suggests that a consumption of 225 litres/person/week is a reasonable guide. Table 4.10.2 indicates the immersion heater consumption expected for households of between 2 and 5 persons. The energy consumption is based on the type BS 7 cylinder (120 litres) specified in BS 699, and it will be noted that larger cylinders have a slightly higher annual energy emission loss due to the greater surface area.

Table 4.10.2 *Typical hot water usage based on a BS 7 cylinder*

Type of Use	Approx Litres/Week	Typical Household Size	Typical Annual Electricity Consumption
Very Small	450	2	1800 kWh
Small	675	3	2350 kWh
Average Family	900	4	3050 kWh
Large	1125	5	3750 kWh

4.10.3.3 Economy 7 controller

The simplest modification involves the addition of an Economy 7 controller to operate the existing 580 mm or 690 mm top entry immersion heater. This controller has been developed specifically for this application. A schematic of the internal wiring of this controller is shown as figure 4.10.2. It incorporates a fixed cam-timing arrangement, an automatic changeover switch and a run-back timer. The cam-timer ensures that the immersion heater is normally switched on (under thermostat control) for a set period (usually 4–5 hours) during the cheaper night time hours. The overall aim is to provide a good store of hot water at the end of the night rate hours. However, if the stored water does run out during the day a boost can be obtained by turning the run-back timer.

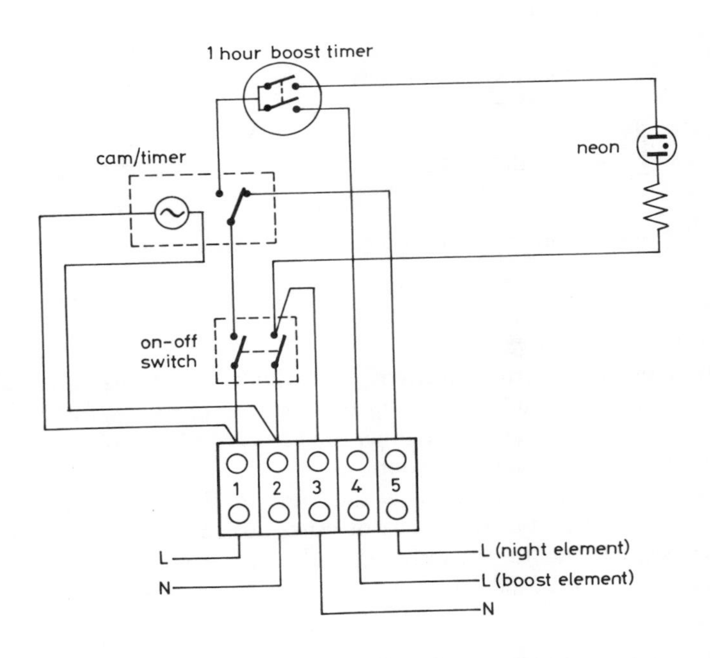

Fig. 4.10.2. *Schematic internal wiring diagram of Economy 7 water heating controller*

The disadvantages of this modification centre on the use of the existing immersion heater to provide both the overnight store and the day boost. Firstly the existing top entry 690 mm immersion heater is probably of the straight type (i.e., without a turned up loop). The straight type, even if fitted with a 460 mm thermostat, will generally only heat about 70 litres of water in a standard BS7 cylinder.

(See figure 4.10.3). Furthermore, the use of the same element to provide the day time boost could lead to 70 litres being heated at the more expensive day time rate which would in turn reduce the ability of the system to take the cheaper night rate energy the following night. None the less, the modification is simple and with reasonable management the energy split (see table 4.10.3) should provide worthwhile cost savings compared with the standard domestic tariff.

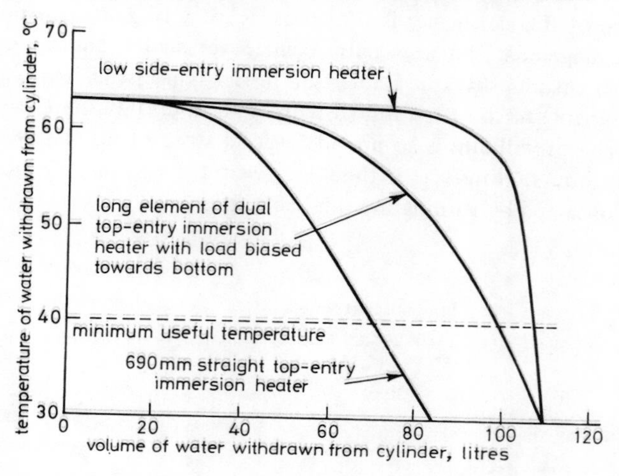

Fig. 4.10.3. *Profile of draw-off temperature for a type BS7 water cylinder*

4.10.3.4 Two element arrangements

To exploit Economy 7 tariff effectively the cylinder should be fitted with two elements; one to charge the cylinder up overnight to provide a full tank of hot water ready for the next day, and another to heat 35–45 litres of hot water at day rates should the stored hot water run out.

Three such arrangements are possible and these are shown in figure 4.10.4. The arrangement (a) is preferable since the hot water does not suffer the temperature gradients associated with the standard top entry immersion heater. Furthermore, the position of the low side entry element gives an increased storage capacity.

Table 4.10.3 *Annual consumptions with an Economy 7 water heating controller*

	Modification with Economy 7 Controller, existing top entry heater and cylinder (BS 7)		
Type of use	Night units (kWh)	Day units (kWh)	Total units (kWh)
Very small	900	900	1800
Small	1050	1300	2350
Average family	1300	1750	3050
Large	1500	2250	3750

Comparison of the profile of draw off temperature against volume of water drawn off from a standard BS7 (120 litre) cylinder clearly illustrates this point (See fig. 4.10.3). The arrangement (a) should therefore be adopted for new cylinder installations as it represents best practice. Existing installations, however, generally have only a top entry boss, and to avoid the fixing of extra bosses, arrangement (c) the dual immersion heater can be adopted. Providing the right type of heater is used, the arrangement can overcome the previously discussed disadvantages of vertical elements. The long element of the dual needs to be about 690 mm to fit in a standard BS7 cylinder but if this is achieved by turning back a 915 mm element a considerable increase in water storage can be obtained (figure 4.10.3) (about 100 litres compared with 70 litres of the standard top entry). The thermostat should be of the 455 mm long rod type. It is worthwhile noting that the same element with an 280 mm thermostat produces only about 55 litres of hot water.

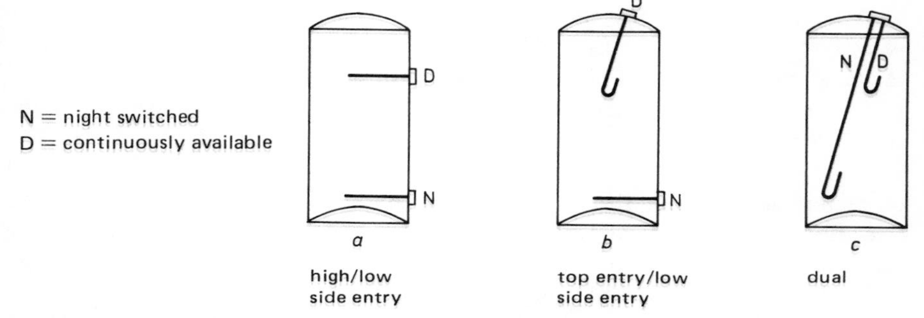

Fig. 4.10.4. *Two element immersion heater arrangements*

The short element of the dual must give adequate storage for a reasonable bath. For this reason the short element should be 405 mm (bent back from a standard 535 mm) and have a 280 mm thermostat. A one hour boost of a 3 kW element of this type will give about 40 litres of water above 43°C and at an average temperature of 55°C.

Again, the length of thermostat is important since the same element with a

Table 4.10.4 *Annual consumptions with an Economy 7 water heating controller and two element immersion heater arrangement*

	Modification to two element arrangement with Economy 7 controller and existing BS 7 cylinder		
Type of use	Night units (kWh)	Day units (kWh)	Total units (kWh)
Very small	1550	250	1800
Small	1850	500	2350
Average family	2200	850	3050
Large	2500	1250	3750

180 mm thermostat would reduce the effective storage to about two thirds this level. This specification for the short element should also apply to the top entry element of arrangement (c).

The Economy 7 controller mentioned earlier is suitable for any of these arrangements since it incorporates a changeover micro-switch so that there is no need for an additional electrical circuit to supply the extra immersion heater. The internal wiring of the controller ensures that supply is given to the long or short low side entry element during a set night period and that on completion of that period the electrical supply is switched to short or top side entry element. The latter only operates when the customer turns the run-back timer. The day/night consumptions of dual or two element arrangements are given in table 4.10.4. The cost of the dual element and Economy 7 controller is generally recovered in about two years.

4.10.3.5 Cylinder insulation

Cylinder insulating jackets should comply with BS 5615. This requires that the daily standing loss of a standard BS7 type cylinder should not exceed 3 kWh at a temperature difference of 50°C (i.e., water to test room ambient). Correction factors are given for jackets designed for other cylinders. This provision of the British Standard is currently being reconsidered and a standing loss not exceeding 2·5 kWh per day has been suggested. The insulating jacket will only meet this type of performance if well fitted and for this reason pre-insulated cylinders should generally be recommended for new installations. Table 4.10.5 compares the daily standing heat loss of a BS7 cylinder insulated with polyurethane foam with that with a typical jacket. Due to some intermittency of use and lower water temperatures during heating up periods, the standing loss test exaggerates the loss in the practical situation by about 30–50%.

4.10.3.6 New installations

In the case of new installations it is very worthwhile increasing the cylinder size to maximise the use of the cheap night rate energy, particularly in households likely to require substantial amounts of hot water. British Standard 699 includes a type size 9E cylinder specifically for off-peak usage. The cylinder has a capacity

Table 4.10.5 *Daily standing loss from a BS 7 cylinder for various types of insulation*

Type of insulation	Standing heat loss over 24 hours. (kWh)
Factory sprayed insulation:	
Nominal 12·5 mm thick	3·9
Nominal 25 mm thick	2·9
Nominal 50 mm thick	2·4
80 mm cylinder jacket (well fitted)	2·6

of 210 litres (46 gallons) with the dimensions indicated in figure 4.10.5. The two element arrangement shown should ensure the day/night energy splits indicated in table 4.10.6.

In some new applications, albeit in new or modernised dwellings, the cold water cistern may not be available or practicable in which case purpose built cistern water heaters (figure 4.10.6) or packaged plumbing units (figure 4.10.7) provide a ready answer. In this instance, the physical size of these units may limit the amount of hot water storage capacity. Encased cistern type units sufficiently attractive to stand in the bathroom are manufactured up to a 135 litre hot water capacity whilst the packaged units can be provided with or without an outer case depending upon the nature of siting. A futher variation where space is at a premium is the UDB (under draining board) water heater designed largely for application in flats and other small dwellings. Whilst these may have a maximum capacity of about 115 litres, provided with a two element arrangement they are still suitable for application on Economy 7.

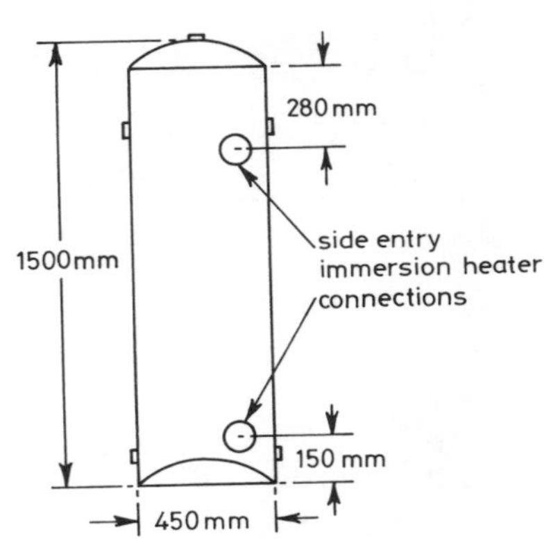

Fig. 4.10.5. *Type BS9E hot water cylinder*

Table 4.10.6 *Annual consumptions with a BS9E water cylinder*

	Replacement BS9E cylinder with Economy 7 controller and two side-entry immersion heaters		
Type of use	Night units (kWh)	Day units (kWh)	Total units (kWh)
Very small	2070	10	2080
Small	2560	100	2660
Average family	3200	250	3450
Large	3710	450	4160

N.B. These figures assume insulation by BS 5615 jacket. A factory insulated cylinder with 50 mm sprayed insulation reduces consumption by about 200 kWh/annum.

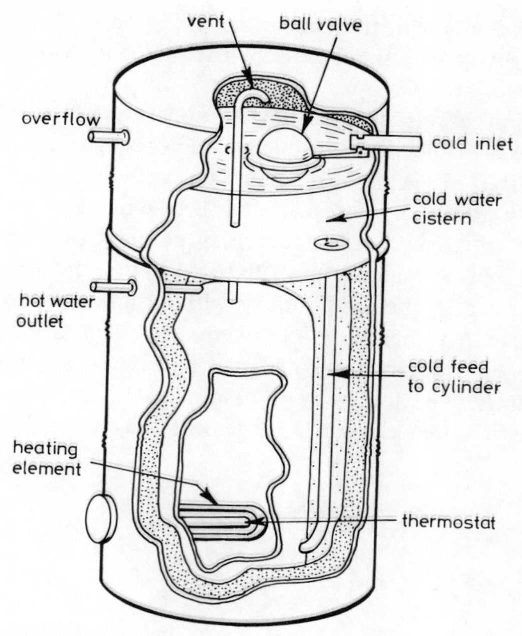

Fig. 4.10.6. *Cistern water heater*

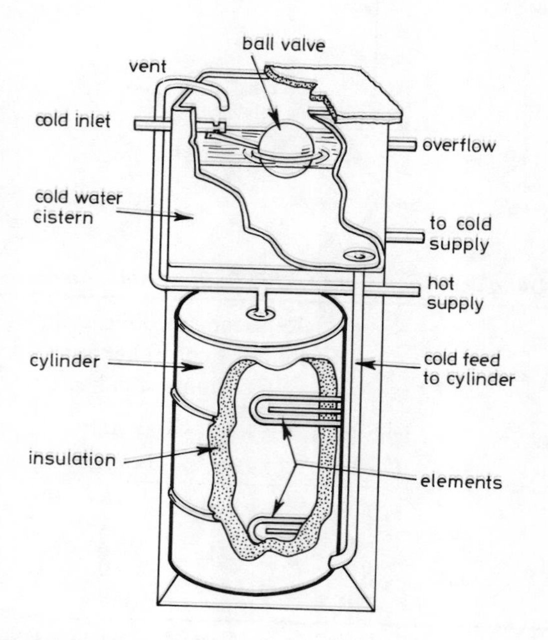

Fig. 4.10.7. *Packaged plumbing unit*

4.10.3.7 Point of use heaters

Electric water heating is seen at its most flexible with direct point of use heaters. Provided the storage capacity is limited to below 22.5 litres, a water heater can be connected directly into the cold water mains near to the point of application (e.g., kitchen sink, bathroom basin or bath). Virtual elimination of secondary pipe losses means the heaters approach 100% efficiency and where spray attachments are used make them economical in their use of hot water. Whilst the electric instantaneous shower is probably the most popular example, there is a wide choice of manufactured appliances that fall into five categories:

(a) Instantaneous heaters – Normal loading about 3 kW giving 6 litres per minute at 40°C, designed for hand washing.
(b) Over sink heaters – Normal loading about 3 kW, 7–14 litres capacity designed for hand washing or light kitchen use.
(c) Under sink heaters – Similar to (b) but provide an alternative where wall space is limited.
(d) Wall mounted kettles – Normally 3 kW with capacity of 4·5 litres. The amount of water may be varied as desired. May be permanently plumbed or simply connected by a flexible hose to a nearby tap.
(e) Instantaneous shower – Models range from 6 kW to 10 kW rating with temperature control.

4.10.4 Commercial premises

4.10.4.1 General

Where central boiler plant is installed for space heating it has been common practice to heat hot water for the office toilets using the same central system. Measurements carried out by the Electricity Council in twelve office blocks with various types of system, however, seriously question the economics of this practice for two main reasons:

(a) the central boiler system is between 2 and 3 times more expensive to install than a local electric system and is more difficult and costly to maintain.
(b) the hot water requirements of this service were found to be only a fraction of those often specified for design purposes.

The latter finding is particularly important since the level of energy requirement is a crucial factor affecting the choice of the system. At low levels of water usage the central boiler system declines in efficiency due to the fairly constant nature of system heat losses (via the cylinder and primary and secondary piping) and boilers are known to decline severely in efficiency at low loads. The measurements indicated that peak daily design requirements of 6 litres/person/day (bib taps) and 4 litres/person/day (spray taps) were sufficient, these being about twice the average daily requirement experience in the office blocks measured. The values are similar

Table 4.10.7 *Hot water usage in offices*

Period	Tap	Hot Water Usage Per Person (litres): ASHRAE Recommendation	Electricity Council Field Trial Data	Electricity Council Recommendation
Hourly Maximum		1·51		
Daily Maximum	Bib	7·57		6
	Spray			4
Daily Average	Bib	3·78	3·1	3
	Spray		2·0	2

to those recommended by ASHRAE (see table 4.10.7) and are about one third the value specified elsewhere.

The trials provided information of the annual comparative consumption, from which it can be shown that local electric systems are competitive on fuel cost alone. The results strengthen the case for using local electric water heaters particularly when these are used on off-peak tariffs. The lower water usage also has an important effect in reducing the size of storage required, particularly where local off peak units are involved.

4.10.4.2 Sizing procedure

The following simple procedure developed from the field trial research is based on the total peak daily requirement derived by adding the design water requirement at the tap to the system heat losses (in terms of litres/person/day) given in table 4.10.8. The procedure is somewhat different thereafter for off peak and direct systems, the prime consideration with the former being to size the store to cater for the peak day requirement, whilst in the case of the latter, the peak hourly requirement is the main consideration. The following shows by example (table 4.10.9) the procedures for local direct and off peak storage system for a 48 person office (say 4 basins) using bib taps normally occupied for 8 hours/day.

Table 4.10.8 *Allowances for system losses in sizing*

System	Circulation	Allowance for System Losses Litres/Person/Day
Local: Direct or	With Circulation	1·29
Off-Peak and Direct	Without Circulation	1·08
Local: Off Peak	With Circulation	1·58
	Without Circulation	1·36
Central	With Circulation	2·44

Table 4.10.9 *Example of Calculation of Hot Water Requirements for a 48 Person Office*

	Direct	Off peak storage
1 Water usage requirement	6 litres/person/day	6 litres/person/day
2 System losses (table 4.10.8)	1·08 litres/person/day	1·36 litres/person/day
3 Water capacity required	7·08 litres/person/day	7·36 litres/person/day
4 Total water capacity required (line 3 × 48 pers.)	340 litres/day	353 litres/day
5 Peak hourly requirement (line 4 ÷ 8 hrs × 1·5)	64 litres (128 litres in 2 hr peak)	–
6 Water replaced by 3 kW element during 2 hr peak	92 litres	–
7 Storage required	36 litres (line 5–line 6)	388 litres (line 4 × 1·1 to allow for dead area area under elements)
8 Minimum element power (assuming 7 hrs off peak charged and 15 litres/kW rating)	–	$\left\{\frac{388}{7 \times 15}\right\} = 3{\cdot}7\ \text{kW}$

In practice, of course, standard equipment having a specification close to the estimated requirement will be used.

Should the physical size of an entirely off-peak system present difficulty, then a compromise can be adopted making use of a smaller capacity cylinder and a 2 element arrangement. In this way most of the energy would still be taken by the low side entry element at off peak rates whilst the upper element would be available for day usage should the stored energy run out.

4.10.4.3 Equipment for steam raising

Electric steam boilers provide a reliable and economical source of steam at high efficiency, with a minimum of structural requirements and often with fully automatic control providing rapid response to fluctuating demands.

Steam raising boilers operate on a similar principle to hot water units but are also fitted with a pump and feed and condensate tanks. Small units are supplied as complete items of plant whereas larger units are often supplied as a number of separate parts to ease handling and allow maximum flexibility of installation. In view of the small size of the boilers it is often possible to locate the unit alongside the plant requiring steam and, where a boiler room is required this is small in size compared to that allowed for conventional plant.

4.10.4.4 Electrode boilers

An electrode boiler consists essentially of a steel tank containing water in which are placed three or more electrodes, connected to an a.c. supply. Current is passed between the electrodes through the water, which due to its resistance, becomes heated. An electrode boiler is about 98% efficient. It is more compact than an immersion-heater installation of equivalent capacity for loadings over 100 kW.

The boiler can be used on its own connected directly to the hot water system or it may be used in conjunction with some other equipment such as a thermal storage vessel. Where a storage vessel is employed, the boiler can operate during off-peak hours. A calorifier is also sometimes used with an electrode boiler in order to avoid the formation of scale from hard make-up water when large quantities of heated water are drawn off. For very large demands, the boilers can be operated from a high-voltage supply. Since an electrode boiler earths the installation attention must be given to the special clauses referring to this in the Electricity Supply Regulations and the IEE Regulations. (Fig. 4.10.8).

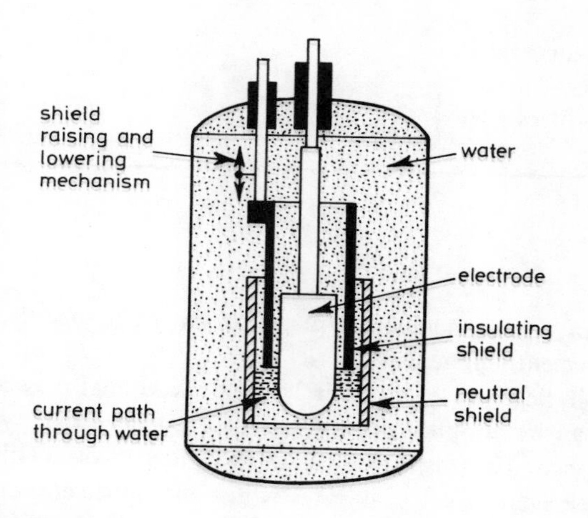

Fig. 4.10.8. *Electrode boiler*

4.10.4.5 Kitchen service

Experience has shown that kitchen requirements can range from 2·3–7·0 litres/meal depending upon the size of the establishment.

Specialist advice should therefore be sought on the sizing of the hot water service. Having established the design requirements, the storage capacity may be designed to meet the total requirements using off-peak energy. For example, if an establishment caters for 100 meals and the design level is 5 litres/meal the storage required is simply 500 litres. The element power required would be 4·8 kW. [i.e., $500/(7 \times 15)$]

If the physical size of this presented difficulties, then a compromise can again be adopted, again using the two element arrangement described earlier. The lower power would then be re-estimated by substituting the lower capacity installed whilst as an upper boundary condition the upper elements would need to meet the peak hourly requirement, probably around 1·5 litres/meal or 0·1 kW/meal, i.e., 10 kW in an establishment serving 100 meals.

4.10.5 References

4.10.5.1 British Standards (See also Appendix 6.2)

BS 699 and BS 3198 deal with copper cylinders for domestic premises, and BS 5617 with lagging jackets for these cylinders.

4.10.5.2 Bibliography

ASHRAE Guide (American Society of Heating Refrigeration and Air conditioning Engineers)
CIBS Guide: Book B (Chartered Institution of Building Services)
Technical Information Sheets (The Electricity Council):
Modification of Existing Hot Water Systems for Application on Economy 7. (EC 3883)
Hot Water Service in Offices (EC 4181)
Steam Raising by Electricity (EC 4149)
Hot Water by Electricity (EC 4150)
Research Report:
White Meter Water Heating (Environmental Engineering Section, The Electricity Council) (ECR R271)

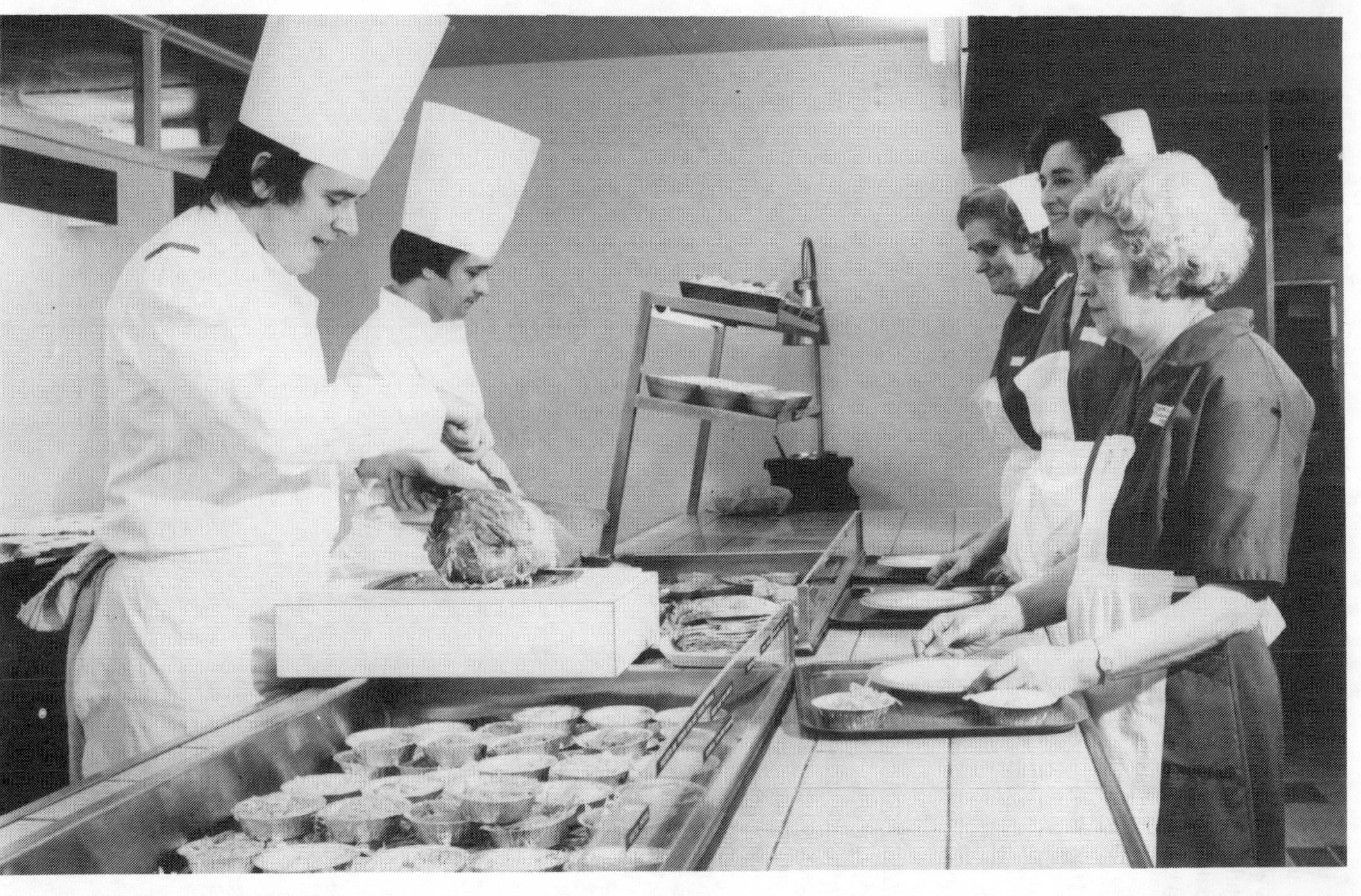

Waitress service counter in a hospital

Chapter 4.11

Food Preparation

David Taylor
Head of Electric Catering Group, The Electricity Council

4.11.1 Domestic catering

4.11.1.1 Introduction

Electricity is the most versatile power source in the kitchen, providing heat, light and motive power. The variety of food sources now available – fresh, frozen, chilled, canned, etc together with the increasing variety of electric food handling and cooking equipment gives the modern electric kitchen and the housewife the opportunity to achieve an efficient and attractive workplace.

4.11.1.2 Kitchen planning

Kitchen designs should aim to achieve an efficient relationship of working areas in a pleasant, clean and light environment. The kitchen as a workplace is a focal point in the house; a variety of tasks need to be accommodated in the kitchen, involving many activities other than food preparation.

The layout of a kitchen must be related to walls, windows and doors. Often the building constraints are such that an ideal kitchen design is impossible; the best is a compromise within the existing space. In many ways the flexibility of electricity can help to ease these constraints when planning food cooking and preparation layouts. Several styles of design are common for domestic kitchens, relating to alignment of the cooker, storage units and working surfaces.

The layout of a simple kitchen illustrated in Figs. 4.11.1, 4.11.2 and 4.11.3 should aim to achieve an easy ergonomic relationship between the housewife and the equipment and any dining area associated with the kitchen. Even in the smallest domestic kitchen design, it is useful to make a simple layout drawing. Graph paper of an appropriate scale together with cut-outs of the equipment, cupboards and work-tops can then be rearranged in the kitchen area, keeping in mind all the variety of tasks to be carried out in the kitchen. It is important to

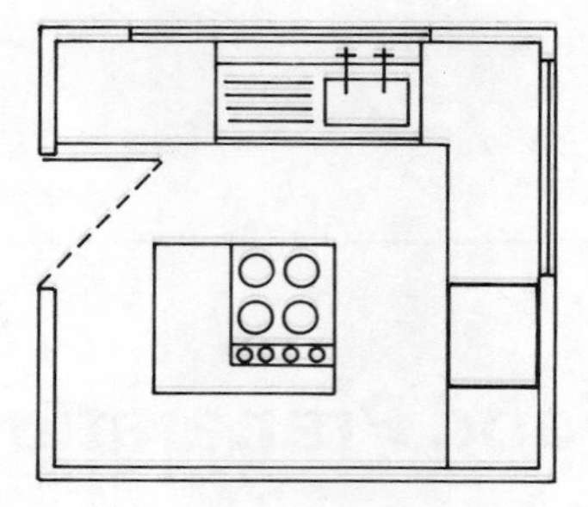

Fig. 4.11.1.

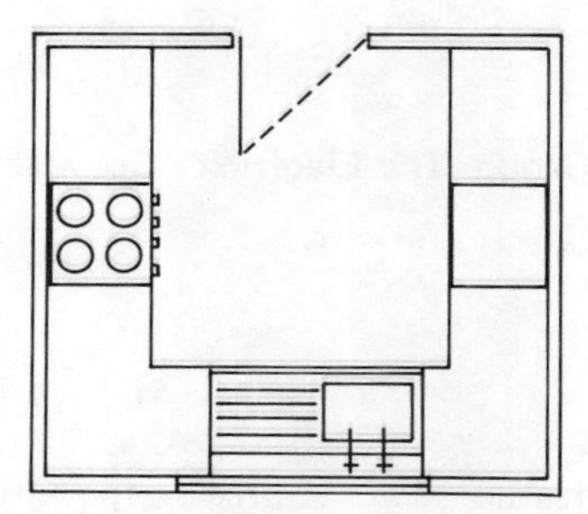

Fig. 4.11.2.

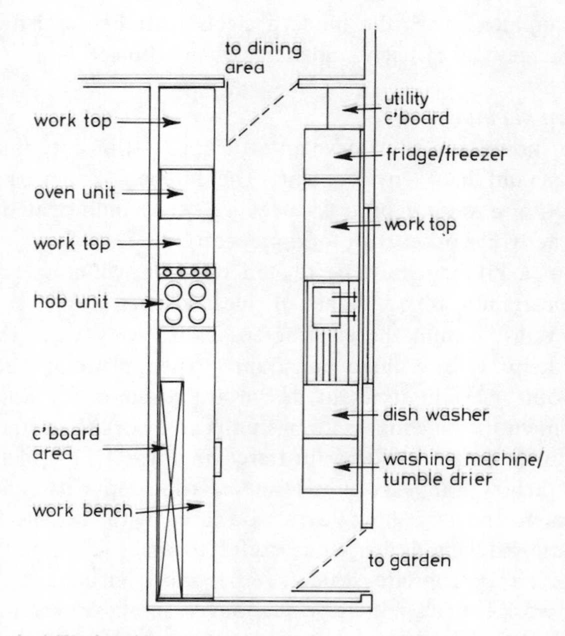

Fig. 4.11.3. *Typical Kitchen layouts*

appreciate the positions of various services, i.e. cooker point, socket outlets, light services, water supplies, drainage and ventilation. Other details to be considered are the opening of doors in relation to each other, the safety aspects of handling hot food from ovens or working with pans on the cooker hob and positions of switches. The main aim of a design should be to achieve the best arrangement possible within the constraints of the building, but not forgetting that the domestic kitchen is often required to function as a dining room as well as a workplace for general household tasks.

In preparing the layout, a number of aspects should be considered. A check list might be as follows:

(a) List of electrical appliances to be used in the kitchen. This could include any of the following: cooker, microwave oven, refrigerator, freezer, dishwasher and laundry equipment as major items, ventilation hood and exhaust fan to remove steam and smells, and a wide range of smaller portable appliances such as kettle, toaster, food mixer, liquidiser, food processor, slow cooker, electric fryer, all requiring 13 A socket outlets, and frequently in competition for a convenient supply point.
(b) Position of doors, windows, hatches and services.
(c) Basic shape of the room.
(d) Position of storage cupboards and door openings.
(e) A pattern of movement within the kitchen arrangement might be assessed, aiming to eliminate difficult equipment arrangements and the need to walk large distances between equipment.
(f) Avoid arrangements where working areas can be used as circulation areas and interference with passage-ways through the kitchen.
(g) In new kitchens try to avoid an excessive number of doorways into the kitchen, e.g., three doorways can create too much circulation through working areas.
(h) Avoid doorways between main preparation areas, i.e. cookers, sink and associated work-tops.
(j) Avoid outside and internal doors on opposite walls, to reduce draughts across cooking and working areas.

4.11.1.3 Kitchen environment

The best designed kitchen can be ruined if it is either too cold in the winter or steamed up with heat from cooking appliances during a busy day in the summer. The heating system in a house is sometimes linked to the kitchen, but it is common to find that the builder has expected the boiler to provide surplus heat to the kitchen and so does not provide any other heat source to the kitchen. The use of a wall-mounted infra-red heater or fan heater can readily provide direct rapid heat on a cold winter morning.

The atmosphere in a kitchen will benefit from fan-assisted ventilation or a ventilation cooker hood. Fans are available for fitting into windows and range in size from 125 to 300 mm diameter, and should generally be capable of achieving 10–15 air changes/hour. These can be highly desirable during active kitchen usage when large amounts of steam can be pumped into the atmosphere causing condensation problems on cold surfaces, windows or inside cupboards.

Packaged cooker hoods are available and generally incorporate a fan or filter system to remove volatile fats and grease, and a light to project over the cooker hob. This type of hood does not generally extract water from the atmosphere. A different design can be installed which is a true extraction hood taking the heat and volatile products through a grease filter and discharging the hot humid air outside the house.

4.11.1.4 Electrical safety in the kitchen (see also section 3.1.10)

Many accidents happen in the home and some 40% of these take place in the kitchen. Young children and older people can find the kitchen a hazardous place if care is not taken in the general safety aspects of the design and equipment layouts. Avoid placing the cooker or cooking hob across a traffic route or under a window where curtains or draughts might cause fire hazards. Care should be taken with floor coverings or surfaces to ensure they are properly laid to avoid tripping, or becoming slippery.

With the large number of electrical appliances now common in the domestic kitchen, a well sited ring main providing well placed 13 A socket outlets is very desirable. Inconvenient points requiring long lengths of cable are obvious hazards. Overloading sockets by the use of adapters is a common fault. The cooker will always need a separate circuit, of adequate capacity.

Adequate earthing of appliances, unless they are double-insulated, must be provided and, of course, they should be plugged into an earthed supply point. Appliances should not be interfered with or cleaned, particularly with damp cloths, if they are connected into the supply point, even if switched off at the time. Under no circumstances should an electrical appliance be immersed in water. The design of most appliances generally allows soiled parts to be removed from the appliances to avoid this problem, i.e. mixer blades or liquidisers. It is important to follow the manufacturers' instructions for operating and maintaining appliances.

4.11.2 Domestic cooking equipment

4.11.2.1 Electric cookers

A free standing cooker has an oven, a grill and a hob with boiling rings or heating areas. The door of the grill compartment usually opens to a horizontal position as a serving shelf for plates and dishes. An alternative type has the grill at high level, which frees space for a storage compartment below the oven.

A number of models have a second smaller oven for cooking small quantities of food. This is usually between the main oven and the hob or at a higher level. Double-size cookers have two ovens side-by-side. The grill is in one of the ovens, or above the hob.

Built-in cookers are designed to fit in with kitchen furniture for an attractive overall look and improved accessibility – and most leading makers of kitchen units provide for them. They are 'split level' with the oven/grill unit separate from the hob, which is placed in the kitchen work surface. The oven is higher than a free-standing cooker so that it can be used without stooping. Ceramic hobs are just one advance made in recent years. Improvements in insulation contain heat in ovens more efficiently, for economy of energy. The more sophisticated cookers have fully automatic electronic control of temperature and timing. Fan ovens are available to give faster cooking times and more even cooking throughout the oven.

Fig. 4.11.4. ***Domestic cooker with double oven and economiser radiant plates***

(Thorn EMI Domestic Appliances Ltd)

A cooker can be installed anywhere in the kitchen. The main requirement is a separate electric power supply, generally rated at 30 A. The majority of houses usually have this as a regular provision, otherwise it can be readily installed by a competent electrical contractor.

Typical standard cookers range in overall size from about 1300 mm high × 450 mm width × 555 mm depth. Depths of 550 mm and 610 mm fit in with standard kitchen unit furniture. Hob heights range from 860 to 920 mm. Cookers with second ovens are naturally larger with a typical overall height of 1640 mm, 717 mm width and 610 mm depth. The width of double-size cookers is up to about 1050 mm.

Most standard cookers are mounted on rollers and can be moved out easily for cleaning and access. Wipe-clean external surfaces make it simple to keep them looking good. For occasional, more thorough cleaning, the oven lining can be removed either in sections or complete in one piece. Most cookers have a 'stay-clean' or 'catalytic' coating in the oven. This vaporises splashes of grease as they fall on the lining, so only the shelves and door need regular attention.

4.11.2.2 Hobs

The most familiar type of hob heating is the radiant ring. Some rings have a dual circuit for heating either the whole ring or just the centre portion which conserves energy when using small pans or when simmering. Disc rings are a feature of continental hobs. On ceramic hobs the heated areas are marked in the flat, smooth surface. The elements underneath are radiant rings in insulated bowls, or infra-red quartz lamps.

All types of heaters heat up quickly and are accurately controllable. Control knobs have mechanical or illuminated indicators to show which rings are in use and the exact heat setting. Some hobs have precise electronic control which enables the heat to be increased or decreased by a light touch on the control panel.

4.11.2.3 Ovens

The electric oven is renowned for baking and roasting. It needs only a small vent for steam and so is virtually all-enclosed. It heats up quickly and then maintains the steady temperatures that ensure consistent results and even browning. The traditional designed oven has heating elements on both sides behind removable side panels. In some there is an additional low-loaded element at the top of the oven.

Fan ovens were introduced in the early 1970s. They provide even more uniform heating regardless of shelf positions and are especially useful for batch baking for the freezer and for thawing large quantities of frozen food. With the oven loaded to full capacity on up to four shelves, all the food will brown evenly. Food can generally be cooked at lower temperatures and cooking times can frequently be shortened. The latest electronic controls for cookers have accurate 24-hour digital automatic timers and precise touch controls. They also have a digital display of temperatures.

4.11.2.4 Grills

Grilling is done by intense radiant heat at close range. It is quick and provides even browning over the whole heated area. Some 'family-sized' grills have a dual circuit for heating either the whole area or only part of it, so that smaller meals can be grilled without wasting heat; both circuits have variable control. In some cases the grill chambers have additional heating elements which turn them into complete, full-heat auto-timed ovens when required.

4.11.2.5 Cooker control developments

Controls for adjusting the level of heat output from both the oven and the radiant heaters or the hob have shown themselves readily adaptable to developments in electronics over the last few years. Thermostatic control for ovens using thermistor or thermocouple sensors to trigger electronic switching circuits is a ready alternative to the electromechanical expansion thermostat, and electronic switching using thyristor devices can now be seen as an alternative to the bimetallic energy regulator traditionally used to control the hob and grill heaters. With the introduction of electronic controls, it becomes increasingly possible to combine these with a range of new functions such as touch controls, electronic timers and simple micro-chip memory systems, which could repeat cooking tasks once established by the operator.

4.11.2.6 Induction heating

Over the last few years developments in power transistors and thyristors have introduced a high frequency power pack capable of giving some 1·5 to 3 kW of power at frequencies in the range of 25 to 30 kHz. These power packs have already been introduced into commercial catering cooking hobs and these induction hobs are finding an expanding market on both the Continent and in this country. It is feasible that improvements in this technique and growing interest in its use in domestic cookers could see its introduction over the next few years as a real alternative to the resistance heater. The advantages of 'instant' control, high efficiency in use, i.e. power is only used when a pan is in contact with the induction area, no hot cooking surfaces to cause burning, no wasted heat from heater surfaces not in actual cooking use – all giving exciting possibilities for the technique in the future.

4.11.2.7 Microwave cookers

A microwave cooker looks simple. It consists of a supply unit which takes the normal domestic electricity power supply and passes it through a magnetron which generates electromagnetic waves of very high frequency (microwaves). These high frequency waves are carried into the cooking cavity or 'oven'. All components are contained in a cabinet on which the controls are fixed, and the front of the cabinet has a drop-down, hinged or slide-up door.

The internal measurements of the cooking cavity are carefully calculated to give the best use of the energy developed by the magnetron. The microwaves 'bounce' off and across the metal sides of the cavity in a regular pattern and, to make sure that all the food in the cooking space is heated as evenly as possible, a slow fan or 'stirrer' is fixed to diffuse the power evenly. Several models have a turntable on which the food is rotated through the energy field, achieving the same desirable even heating effect. Generally, there are no shelves inside a microwave cooker, but there may be a metal or glass base-plate on which the dish containing the food is placed.

Average external dimensions of domestic microwave cookers are in the range: height 320–410 mm; length 430–650 mm; width 330–600 mm. They are portable but quite heavy – weighing between 26 and 42 kg. The input of a domestic microwave cooker is generally in the range of 1 to 1·5 kW and it is normally connected to a 13 A outlet.

The main difference between microwave cooking and conventional ovens is in the timing of the cooking process. Most microwave cookers use time as the main control, unlike temperature thermostats in conventional ovens. Very short cooking times are normally required for microwave cooking and the time is set to switch the microwave power off after the required period. Times are usually calibrated in seconds up to some 5 minutes, then in minutes up to about 30 minutes. All models have a defrost control. Others include this in a variable power control which enables the user to reduce the output of the cooker. This is helpful in cooking some meat which requires longer, slower cooking and for some more delicate dishes. Most recent models are designed to include automatic timing, touch control, and recipe cards which are inserted into a slot on the control panel. Some also include a meat probe.

Microwave cookers are easy to look after. Because there is no heat inside the oven – only in the food – splashes of fat or liquid do not get burnt on to the oven sides, so are easily wiped off if they should occur.

Servicing of microwave cookers should be restricted to recognised service agents. Because of the complex circuitry and the safety systems designed into a microwave cooker, this aspect of servicing should be strictly observed.

Approved microwave cookers are safe to use. Always choose one which is BEAB approved (tested to the requirements of BS 3456) (See section 5.2.2.7) or has the Electricity Council Approved for Safety label, which is granted to catering appliances that have been tested to BS 5175 – several of the commercial models being quite satisfactory for domestic kitchens. Such models have been tested and comply with British Standards. (See section 4.11.5.15). The design of modern microwave ovens include features which include a positive series of door locks, seals and switches which make it impossible to operate the cooker without the door being tightly shut.

4.11.3 Commercial: introduction

All catering operations are made up of various activities ranging through a variety of food handling tasks. These stages of food handling may involve dirty raw materials preparation, through to complex dishes being worked to a fine degree of craft finish before presentation to a highly discriminating customer. Between these two extremes is a wide range of catering installation designs and a number of catering systems, which the caterer can use to produce his final product. The main point to be remembered at all times is that all the stages of catering are linked together by the food commodity, whatever system of catering is used or whatever style of kitchen installation is designed. Safeguarding the quality of the food material is of prime importance if the diner is to be satisfied with the menu served.

4.11.4 Catering planning

4.11.4.1 General

The planning requirements will vary according to the size or scale of catering operation. Solutions can range from simple low cost packages of lightweight equipment for small operations through to very large kitchen complexes where several thousand meals a day may be prepared. Whatever the size of the operation, it is vital that all stages of the food handling process be examined and planned in detail if a successful and cost-effective operation is to be achieved. Large volume projects involving large capital investment will require the services of a competent planning team to produce both feasibility studies and detailed layout designs and equipment schedules. Whilst the same amount of detail is not likely to be needed for small lightweight installations, the same disciplined approach is necessary to achieve a satisfactory design.

4.11.4.2 Simple packages

With any catering operation there will be variations of menu, number, times for service etc, but the disciplines arising from a cost-effective approach will begin to dictate some common practices in equipment, particularly in smaller catering operations. These equipment arrangements may well be termed 'packages'. The controlling factor is the simplicity of the menu. Hamburger, steak and pizza bars are examples of successful 'fast food' packages based on limited menus and equipment. But with staff feeding operations there is a danger that too strict an adherence to a package can cause 'menu fatigue', and so it is important to ensure plenty of flexibility for futher development to cope with changes in demand.

The basic equipment of a package will be a freezer and/or a refrigerator for storage of deep frozen or chilled foods, and a microwave or convection oven for single or multi-portion regeneration. The microwave oven is particularly suitable for night self-service of prepared dishes stored in a chilled display unit. The addition of a small dishwasher, boiling ring and hot drinks vending unit will make the package suitable for a daytime catering operation for up to about 30 covers.

Gravy, soup and custard are prepared on the boiling plates and the operator lays out fresh fruit, fruit juices, rolls, butter, cheese, etc on an appropriate display unit. The overall installed equipment load may range between 20–50 kW for this type of installation.

4.11.4.3 Larger kitchens

With the larger catering operation handling up to several hundred meals per service, substantial increases in storage, preparation, cooking, service and dishwashing facilities are likely to be required. In Fig. 4.11.5 this installation is aimed to produce up to 500 meals per service time. In this design there is increased freezer and refrigeration storage space and the cooking battery and the forward 'finishing' area have been combined and contain high-pressure steamers. These will quickly cook frozen vegetables to replenish counter containers against demand from a fast moving service counter. Pass-through holding cabinets are most useful in this size of operation or alternatively, a small complement of back bar equipment could be sited immediately behind the counter. Normally a single service counter run can handle about 250 people per hour. Thereafter, a double service counter arrangement may be required or alternatively, staggering of serving times will make better use of the single counter.

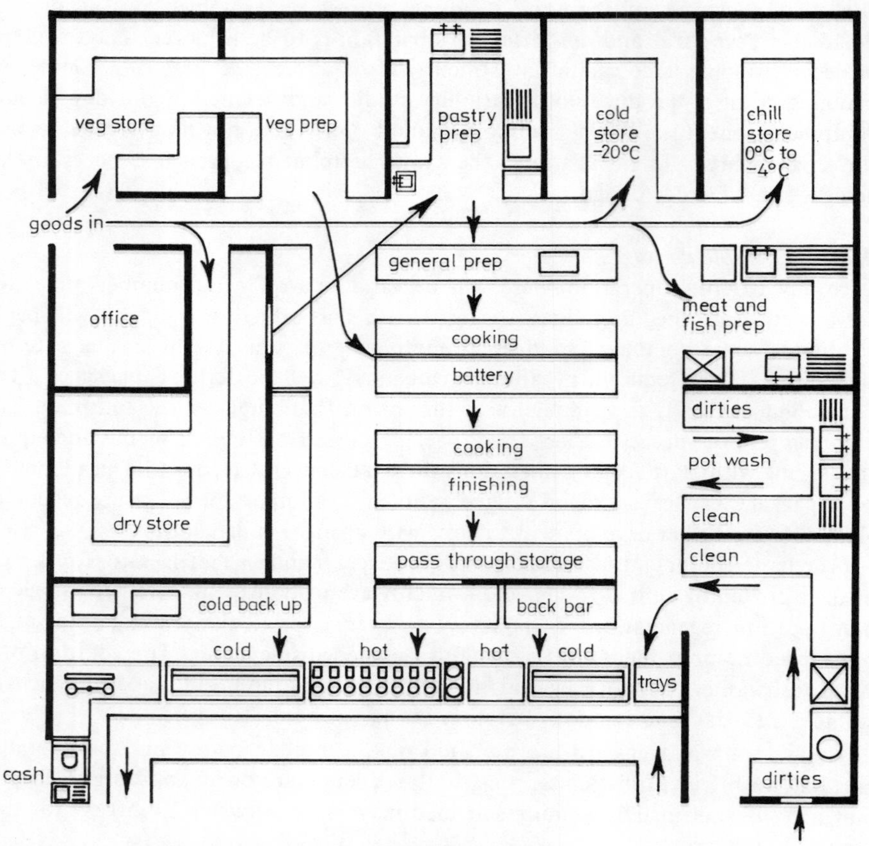

Fig. 4.11.5. *Layout of medium/large conventional kitchen*

4.11.4.4 Centralised cook-freeze or cook-chill systems

With the increase in food, energy and labour costs, traditional methods in large scale catering do not fully utilise the main resources of production, distribution and service.

Cook-freeze and cook-chill are systems of preparing and cooking food in economic quantities using rapid freezing (−18°C to −20°C) or rapid chilling (to 0–4°C) in purpose-designed equipment. This is followed by storage and service when and where required in peripheral areas or regeneration kitchens requiring minimal equipment and staffing.

One of the major departures from conventional catering operations is the regulated work pattern which a production kitchen can achieve. Since there are no immediate mealtime deadlines, output can be controlled to make the most efficient use of labour, equipment and space. Gearing production to a standard working week can also aid staff recruitment.

4.11.4.5 Peripheral service units: cook-freeze

Reconstitution of frozen foods can be carried out by a variety of equipment including: convection ovens, high pressure steamers, microwave ovens and boiling tops, depending on the size of the unit and number of meals served. Other equipment such as fryers and boiling tops might be required for the on-site preparation of salads, cold sweets, sauces, custards, gravies, chips etc. Sufficient frozen food storage capacity would be planned into the service unit to hold the deliveries of centrally produced menus.

Fig. 4.11.6. *Modular Back bar Equipment with readily accessible controls*

(Electricity Council)

4.11.4.6 Peripheral service units: cook-chill

Reconstitution of chilled foods in the peripheral or service units can be carried out with a variety of equipment, but the most successful technique is based on a wide range of radiant heat cavities. These units are compact and simple to use and reflect very efficient energy consumption against the high capacity regeneration which this equipment can achieve.

4.11.4.7 Storage areas
There are three basic storage requirements

(a) *Dry storage* for canned, bottled and dehydrated food. Also for general baking ingredients.
(b) *Vegetable storage* for fresh vegetables and fruit.
(c) *Refrigerated storage* for milk, butter, meat, fish poultry and cooked items.

The relative sizes of storage will depend on the following factors:

(a) Frequency of deliveries.
(b) Type and quantity of foods purchased (fresh, frozen, canned etc).
(c) Potential stock levels for bulk buying at discount prices.
(d) Density of packing (weight and size of foods and types of container).

Fig. 4.11.7. ***High speed cooking and fast regeneration using high pressure steamers***
(Electricity Council)

The following is a rough guide to approximate size allocations:

Dry Store. In small kitchens a cupboard may be adequate in a hundred-meals-a-day operation; allow 6 m^2 increasing to 12 m^2 for a thousand-meals-per-day output.

Vegetable Store. Since vegetables and fruit are perishable items, daily deliveries are preferable, which will keep space requirements to a minimum. For a fifty-meals-a-day operation, storage space is negligible; for a hundred-meals-a-day operation allow about 4 m^2 increasing to 10 m^2 for a thousand-meals-a-day output.

Refrigerated Store. Based on one delivery a week, allow 7–30 litres per person for cold storage ($-20°$C) and 9–35 litres per person for chilled storage (0–4°C).

In cook-freeze or cook-chill catering systems, the refrigerated storage requirements will vary from those required in a conventional kitchen. Cook-freeze installations generally aim for up to 4 weeks frozen food storage capacity in the central production unit with some 2–7 days local peripheral storage depending on the delivery frequency. In a cook-chill installation, the maximum shelf life for chilled food in catering is generally accepted as 5 days (DHSS Guidelines on Cook-Chill). Central chilled storage is, therefore, not likely to exceed that need to store 5 days production and in a similar way some 2–3 days peripheral storage capacity is needed depending on delivery frequency, allowing still for a maximum shelf life of 5 days in total.

4.11.4.8 Preparation areas

Safe food handling, with high standards of personal hygiene, is essential in the total catering operation and this applies particularly to preparation areas. Dangers of contamination between raw and cooked foods must be avoided. Wash-hand basins are essential in this area.

The need for preparation capacity and equipment will be greater in traditional catering operations than in newer installations such as cook-chill and cook-freeze. Space must be provided for the preparation of vegetables, pastry, meat, fish and general food items.

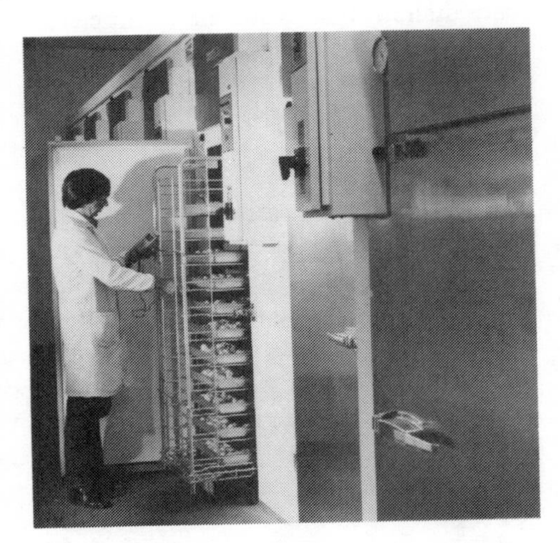

Fig. 4.11.8. *Bank of Blast Chillers in a Central Production Kitchen* (Electricity Council)

(a) *Vegetable Preparation.* Stainless steel sinks with large bowls will be required for vegetable washing. Mobile sinks are useful for transferring raw vegetables to the cooking area. Salads may be prepared within the vegetable preparation area but if the demand is large, salad preparation may merit a separate area nearer to the service point. Where fresh potatoes are used, electric potato peelers are available in sizes from 3·2–22·7 kg maximum capacity. Peel waste must be adequately trapped before liquid is discharged into the mains drainage.

(b) *Meat and Fish Preparation.* This area should be sited immediately adjacent to the refrigerated store. Separate fish lockers can be located within this preparation area or sited within the refrigerated store itself. Separate working surfaces are required for meat and fish, with chopping boards for cutting meat and suitable tops for fish preparation. In large-scale operations where meat carcasses are handled, electric bandsaws may be needed. For mincing and sausage making, separate machines, bowl cutters or mixer attachments are available.

(c) *Pastry Preparation.* The function of this area is the preparation of hot and cold sweets and pastry making for meat and fish dishes, and in some cases bread and rolls preparation. In large kitchens, a service cabinet for storing at least one day's supply of essential ingredients and a refrigerated dough retarder will also be needed. A mixer is essential. It is often advisable to cook in the same area and therefore a pastry oven and proving oven will be required, particularly if 'yeasted goods' are to be made.

4.11.4.9 Dishwashing

Hand Wash-up. For hand wash-up in smaller installations and for specialist pot washing in large areas, a minimum of two deep sinks, one for washing and one for rinsing, and adequate draining-boards for dirty and clean dishes are necessary.

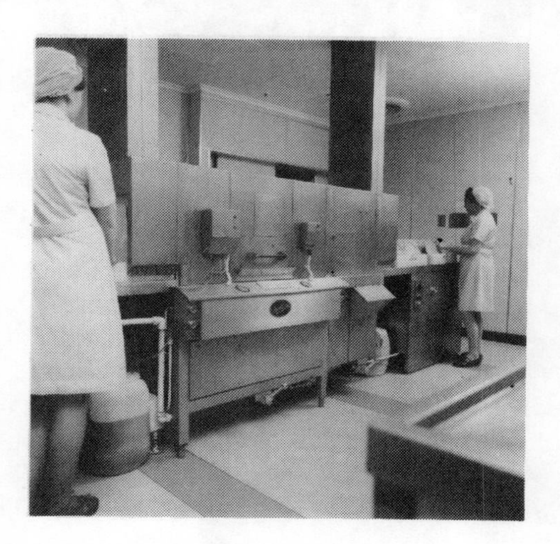

Fig. 4.11.9. *Central Continuous Belt Dishwasher* (Electricity Council)

A mechanical rotating brush for cleaning pots will be useful. The pot washing area can be sited adjacent to the dishwashing area or located nearer to the cooking and service areas from which most utensils arrive.

Mechanised Dishwashing. For the smaller installation a hand-loaded dishwasher with a loading of 6 kW is suitable. This provides a wash/rinse cycle of 1 to 3 minutes at 65°C and rinsing at 85°C. For medium installations a wide range of semi-automatic machines of the spray type are available. These vary in width from 1220 to 1850 mm and are capable of handling 2500 to 3000 pieces per hour (allowing 5 pieces per main meal).

For larger installations, 'flight' dishwashers become suitable. With this type, crockery is loaded directly onto a belt fitted with plastic or metal pegs which eliminate the need for baskets, except for cutlery. Lengths range from 4600 to 7300 mm and pre-rinsing is usually included in the larger models. Some models now include heat recovery devices to save energy using either heat pump packages or heat exchangers/condensers to recirculate waste heat back into the appliance. A new development is an air-to-water free-standing heat pump which can supply pre-heat water to the dishwasher by extracting environmental heat from the kitchen.

4.11.5 Catering equipment

4.11.5.1 Cooking: general

This area most reflects the great changes that have occurred in electric equipment and kitchen methods in recent years. New multi-purpose equipment has been developed to carry out many functions in both prime and end cooking, thus saving on time and space, and increasing productivity. This has called for new thinking on kitchen planning to ensure that the full potential of the equipment is achieved.

4.11.5.2 Bratt pans

These heavy duty deep pans are used for bulk cooking in large catering operations and are suitable for braising, stewing, shallow and deep frying, boiling, poaching and griddling. Smaller, shallow bratt pans are useful for griddling and shallow frying in fast food operations. The installed power requirement for this equipment ranges from 6–18 kW.

4.11.5.3 High-pressure steaming ovens

Steam applied from an external generator or from within the body of the unit provides these ovens with a rapid output. They are particularly suited to the prime cooking of fish and the rapid production of many kinds of fresh and frozen vegetables. (Power ratings 6–50 kW).

4.11.5.4 Fryers

As the electric fryer puts the heat where it is required, into the heart of the frying oil, a very rapid recovery rate is achieved. There is a wide range of sizes to suit all needs, which can now include refinements such as electronic/computerised thermostats and automatic basket lift action (Power ratings 2–30 kW).

4.11.5.5 Electric ranges

Now available with convection oven and solid or radiant boiling plate for general cooking. (Power ratings 10–18 kW).

4.11.5.6 Boiling tables

With the increasing use of specialised ovens without boiling tops, there is often a requirement for the separate production of sauces and gravies. Electric boiling tables are available with either solid or radiant rings and are fast, efficient and compact. (Power ratings 6–12 kW).

4.11.5.7 Induction cooking hobs

Over the last few years developments in power transistors and thyristors have introduced a high frequency power pack capable of giving some 1·5 to 3 kW of power at frequencies in the range of 25 to 30 kHz. These power packs have already been introduced into commercial catering cooking hobs and the induction hobs are finding an expanding market on both the Continent and in the UK.

A wide range of both cooker hobs and full electric oven ranges where the induction heaters have now replaced the conventional boiling plate, have been introduced by at least one continental manufacturer. This equipment gives the ideal electrical pan heating effects, i.e. speed of response, fine control, no heat spillage, no hot surfaces, no consumption of energy if not actually in contact with a pan. It is likely that improvements in this technique could see a wide application of induction into catering equipment ranges and boiling tables over the next decade. (Power ratings 2–8 kW).

4.11.5.8 Tilting kettles

A small, quick heating kettle ideal for the rapid reconstitution of small amounts of frozen food and the quick preparation of soups and custards in finishing kitchens. Floor or counter models are available. (Power ratings 8–40 kW).

4.11.5.9 Convection ovens

These ovens contain fans which ensure more rapid heat distribution with consequent quicker cooking and food sealing. Equally suitable for rapid defrosting or frozen foods, prime cooking or baking and regeneration of chilled foods. Models are now available using electronic control systems, programming capabilities and the ability to inject water to increase humidity during cooking. (Power ratings 3–150 kW).

4.11.5.10 Radiant heat regeneration

A wide range of models based on radiant heating are available from at least one manufacturer. This equipment is designed to operate in the cook-chill system of catering to regenerate chilled food delivered to service kitchens or service points. Food carefully prepared and finished for presentation, packed into stainless steel or ceramic containers is regenerated by this all-electric system in less than 30 minutes. The radiant heat units are compact, efficient and easily sited into either kitchen or non-kitchen areas. (Power ratings 1–15 kW).

4.11.5.11 Grills/Griddles

Grilling retains its popularity as a cooking method because of the distinctive flavour it imparts to food. The grill can also be used for 'flashing' completed dishes prior to service. The griddle is frequently used for the rapid preparation of 'grilled' chops and steak. Radiant heat (quartz sheathed elements) with micro-switch controls linked to the grilling shelf are also available to give rapid heating, linked to on-off switching to control energy consumption if no product is being cooked on the grill shelf. (Power ratings 3–12 kW).

4.11.5.12 Microwave ovens

These ovens can be used to advantage in either the cooking or service area. In traditional cooking terms the overall effect is nearer steaming than cooking, although new designs are being developed with branding plates which can give the traditional finishes of conventional ovens. They are particularly useful for producing single hot dishes or portions near the end of main meal periods. Alternatively, they can provide a complete hot meal service at any time because of their ability to defrost prepared frozen foods rapidly or regenerate chilled foods. (Power ratings 1–4 kW).

4.11.5.13 Microwave/convection

The combination of both microwave heating and forced convection air cooking has given the caterer equipment which combines the speed and flexibility of both techniques. Equipment available for many years has been used in a wide range of specialist areas where speed efficiency and a versatile tool is required. The combination is particularly suitable to 'a la carte' work where even larger dishes such as whole joints, ducks, or turkeys, can be cooked and browned in a fraction of the time taken by conventional cooking methods. Smaller capacity models are now being manufactured suitable for a wide range of medium and smaller installations. (Power ratings 3·5–9 kW).

4.11.5.14 Convection/steam

Over the last few years a wide range of equipment has been developed combining forced convection air with steam in various ratios and in either superheated state or at atmospheric boiling temperatures. This equipment is a very flexible extension of the convection oven linked to the heat transfer improvements obtained from increased humidity. Pressureless steamers, convection steamers, humidity injection convection ovens etc, may be regarded as members of a family of variations of this type of equipment now available to the caterer. The increased heat transfer characteristics, high efficiency and speed, combine to give this equipment increasing acceptance in the kitchen. (Power ratings 3–36 kW).

4.11.5.15 Safety approvals

The Catering Equipment 'Approved for Safety' Scheme was started by the Electricity Council in response to the increased use of electric catering equipment in commercial premises. The scheme now provides an authoritative reference on a wide and expanding range of equipment. The details of tested items which have received the blue 'Approvals' seal are published in the Electricity Council's publication 'Electric Equipment Approved for Safety by the Electricity Council' for use in catering and similar establishments.

4.11.6 Catering environment

4.11.6.1 Ventilation

The simplest system of ventilation is a canopy over the equipment, connected by ducting to an extract fan. The air must be discharged in a manner acceptable to the Environmental Health Officer and the Chief Technical Officer of the local authority. The passage of ducting through the building must be agreed by the Fire Inspector.

(a) *The Canopy.* This should be constructed of non-corrosive metal or other suitable materials and designed for easy cleaning. Obvious dirt traps should be avoided and a condensate channel with drainage should be provided around the edge. The canopy should be positioned approximately 2050 mm above floor level and project 250 to 300 mm beyond the sides of the equipment.

(b) *Grease filtration.* To prevent the dangerous build-up of highly flammable grease within the ducting, grease filters should be fitted within full view inside the kitchen canopy.

They will require frequent degreasing either by a maintenance engineer or the catering staff, and responsibility for this must be established at the outset. A fire damper with fusible link must also be incorporated at the entry to the ducting.

(c) *Fan and ducting.* The fan can be fitted either in the canopy end of the ducting or, preferably, at the discharge point in the wall or roof. The number of air changes required will depend on the design of the kitchen and the cooking equipment installed, but on average about 30 to 40 air changes per hour are required. This could, however, rise to 55 or 60 air changes if the kitchen is small and has a low ceiling. The advice of a heating and ventilating engineer should always be obtained.

4.11.6.2 Lighting

Lighting layouts for catering installation, particularly kitchen working areas should be designed to give the best light for the working task involved. Ventilation areas, ducting and canopies, may well provide problems to siting adequate lighting but efficient food preparation, cooking and serving all require good lighting levels to ensure high quality workmanship and satisfied customers.

The recommended level of task illumination of 500 lux is obtained in an average sized kitchen by an installation averaging about 30 watts of lighting per m^2 of floor area, using fluorescent lamps of a satisfactory colour. If filament lamp lighting is preferred, it is essential that enclosed fittings be used. The mounting height should not be less than 2·4 m above the floor, with fittings not more than 2·2 m apart. An allowance of approximately 80 W/m^2 of floor area will be necessary. Additional lighting is necessary under the ventilation canopies. The fittings must be able to withstand the atmosphere and it is usual to employ bulkhead type filament lamp fittings completely enclosed and sealed with gaskets. They shouuld be made in a non-rusting material, or provided with a galvanised finish. Screws and hinge pins, should also be non-rusting. Food service areas should be treated in the same manner as kitchens, using the same colour of lighting.

4.11.7 Service

The success of the whole catering operation is at stake in the service area. The following factors will be major considerations in shaping customer attitudes and must be taken into account at the planning stage.

(a) *Speed.* With limited time for lunch, waiting time in the queue must be kept to a minimum. Bottlenecks in the areas of drinks dispensing, cash-point and cutlery collection should be avoided. Self-service of gravies, custards and sauces away from the main service unit will also help. (During operation, good staff supervision is essential to ensure that food, cutlery etc, are quickly replenished at the service counter to maintain smooth customer flow).
(b) *Presentation.* The food must 'sell' itself. Attractive lighting combined with well designed ambient or refrigerated showcases will present food at its appetising best.
(c) *Quality.* This, of course, is vitally important, and the key to the maintenance of quality during service is temperature control – even the highest quality food can be ruined if it is not served at the right temperature. Heated and refrigerated storage and display cabinets to keep food in prime condition are essential.
(d) *Smell.* Stale cooking smells from the kitchen can ruin the overall effect – adequate ventilation is essential.
(e) *Hygiene.* This is as important in the service area as it is in the kitchen. Whilst all service equipment should be designed to be easily cleaned and maintained, the most important contribution to maintenance of hygiene must be the practice of good food handling, viz. personal hygiene, observing disciplined codes of practice and keeping all working areas clean and tidy.

4.11.8 References

4.11.8.1 British Standards (See also Appendix 6.2)
BS 3456 covers safety aspects of domestic appliances, and BS 5784 deals similarly with commercial catering equipment. BS 5175 refers specifically to the safety of microwave cookers.

4.11.8.2 Bibliography

Electricity Council Publications:
The Electric Catering Directory (EC 4271)
Electric Catering at Work (EC 3783)
Electric Catering for Leisure, Pleasure and Profit (EC 3510)
Electric Catering Equipment Approved for Safety (EC 4218)
Finishing Kitchen Planning Guide (EC 3445)
The Fitted Kitchen (EC 3679)
Freeze Production Catering Unit – Design Guide (EC 3194)
Planning for Cook-Chill (EC 3984)
"Understanding Electricity". (Series of Publications for Domestic Consumers)

Lifts and escalators

J. M. Lickley, M.A., C.Eng., M.I.Mech.E., F.C.I.B.S.,
National Association of Liftmakers (NALM)

4.12.1 Introduction

Items of equipment such as lifts and escalators are elements as vital in most building structures as the main corridors and stairways. (Stop them for whatever reason, and this is immediately apparent!) Adequate provision for them needs to be made at the earliest stages of planning a building. They are permanent features, difficult to shift or alter drastically once installed. It is important therefore for planners to have a good general appreciation of the standard range and capabilities of lifts – and where appropriate, escalators and passenger conveyors – so that the selection of equipment may effectively match the known or forecast requirements of the building.

Designs of lift equipment in the UK are strictly related to a number of British Standards of long standing, progressively updated, which refer to two vital matters, and reflect legal requirements:

(a) Safety in operation.
(b) Recommended dimensions related to load and speed, and based on the conditions for safe operation.

The vast majority of new equipment installed in UK by established lift makers conforms closely to the safety requirements for lifts defined in the British Standards. The safety record is high and this is reflected in the very small amount of official surveillance considered necessary over the voluntary maintenance of these safety standards within the Industry. Wide use of the BS recommended dimensions is important in a number of ways. It simplifies the planning of buildings and the selection of lifts and it helps the rationalisation of production, with benefits to producer and user alike.

While this chapter concentrates largely on the more standard aspects of new lift equipment, it is important to realise that there is a large business in the renovation of old lift equipment. There are over 100 000 lifts in service in UK and many of these are over 20 years old. When a building changes hands or is updated there is frequently the task of upgrading and modernising a lift within an existing lift well, as for structural reasons no further space is available. Such work as this, involving the fitting of new items of equipment into existing spaces or matching existing pieces of equipment, demands ingenuity of design and is very much of a custom-built nature, though the safety standards achieved must always be high, as high if possible as the latest standards applicable to new lifts.

4.12.2 Principal types of lift

Lifts may be classified into the purposes for which they are used or into the prime means of drive. From the user point of view the first classification is the important one. Generally he has little interest in the second. However at the initial planning stage of the building the second classification may be very important and the choice of drive can be severely restricted by structural features of the building. As a background to later discussion we will first define the types of drive.

4.12.2.1 Traction drive

This is the most common means of drive. The lift car is suspended from a set of steel wire ropes which engage, through friction, with Vee or U-shaped grooves in a traction sheave mounted overhead. The other end of the rope is connected to a counterweight which travels in the lift well in the opposite direction to the car. The movement of the car is effected by the lift machine rotating the traction sheave. Drive to the traction sheave is normally from a high speed electric motor through a worm-reduction gear box, though in high speed "gearless" lifts a slow speed motor is used, coupled directly to the traction sheave. To reduce power requirement, the counterweight is made equivalent to the weight of the lift car plus approximately half the rated load. A typical arrangement of a traction drive lift is shown in Fig. 4.12.1.

Depending on technical circumstances 2/1 roping is sometimes used instead of 1/1 roping, and sometimes the lift machine may require to be mounted at the side or the bottom of the lift well. In these cases the suspension ropes have to be diverted by appropriate additional pulleys in the well and/or on the car and counterweight. As the drive in all these cases depends completely on friction between ropes and sheave, there are strict limits on the relationship between dimensions of the ropes, sheaves, sheave grooves and the relative weight of car and counterweight so that there is no risk of uncontrolled slippage of ropes in sheave grooves.

4.12.2.2 Drum drive

An alternative means of rope suspension drive, which is used in a limited range of short travel applications, is so-called 'drum drive'. In this case the suspension ropes

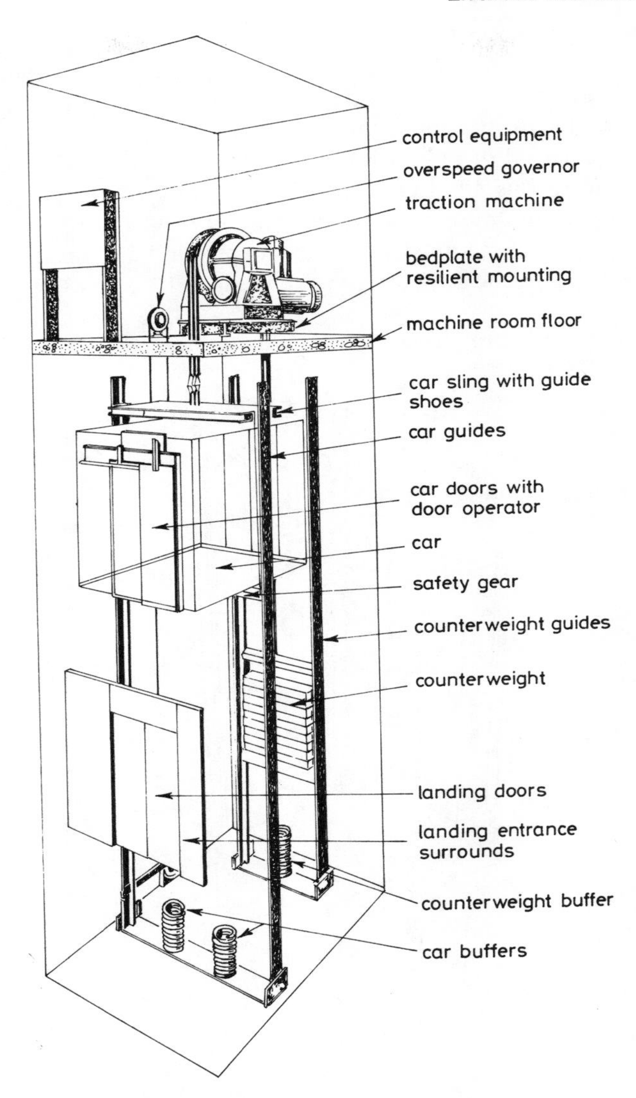

Fig. 4.12.1. *Traction lift installation* (NALM)

are wound on a drum at the top of the well, in the manner of a crane drive. The drum is driven from a high-speed electric motor through a worm reduction gear. There is no counterweight. As the lift car is not counter-balanced, more power is required of the lift motor than in the case of traction drive. Travel is restricted by the problem of effectively controlling the winding of multiple ropes on to the drum in long lengths.

4.12.2.3 Electro-hydraulic drive

This is the main alternative means of drive, suitable generally for short or medium rise lifts. The lift car is connected directly, or indirectly through rope or chain suspension, to a long stroke hydraulic ram mounted below the car or in the side of the lift well. Movement of the car is effected through flow of oil in or out of the hydraulic cylinder. This oil is provided under pressure from a power pack incorporating an oil pump driven by an electric motor, together with a sophisticated control valve to effect smooth starting and stopping in both directions of motion. A typical electro-hydraulic drive lift is shown in Fig. 4.12.2.

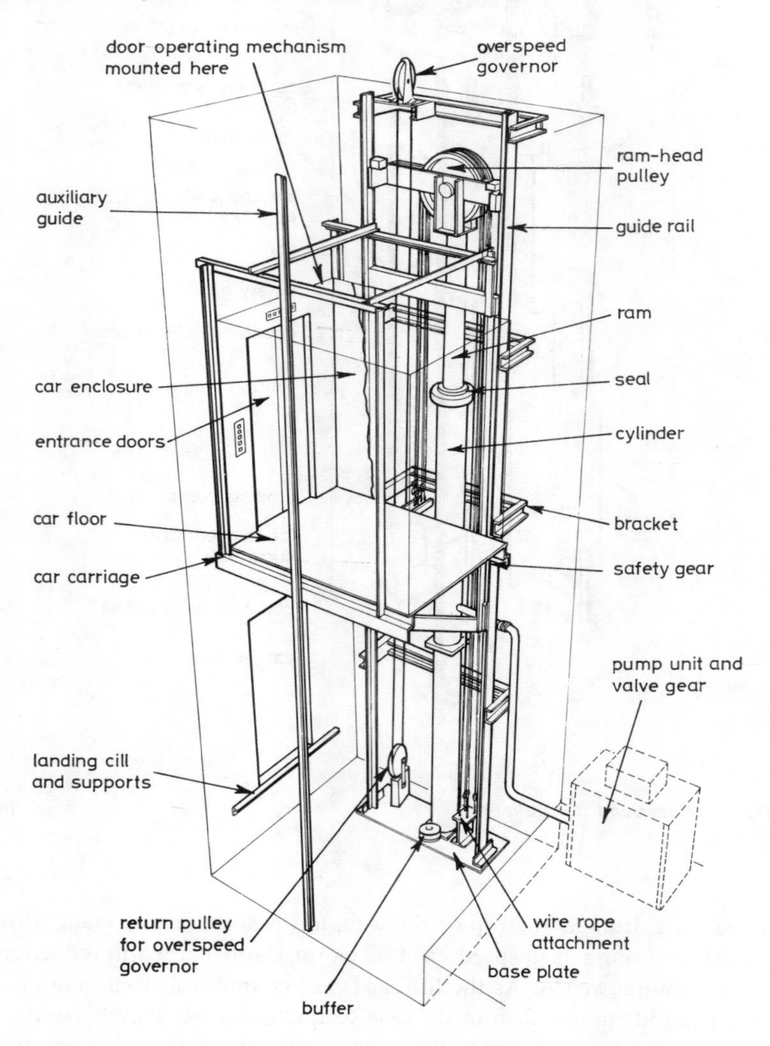

Fig. 4.12.2. *Hydraulic lift installation* (NALM)

For some applications this means of drive is more suitable than traction drive on grounds of convenience or building cost. The machine room does not, as with traction drive, require to be located above or immediately adjacent to the lift well. No significant loads are imposed on the lift wall structure or upper floors of the building, thus lighter means of building construction may be possible. On the other hand the load is not counter-balanced. Therefore the electric motor is considerably larger than for the corresponding traction lift, requiring heavier electric cabling.

4.12.3 Types of drive

While speed and comfort are strictly two different characteristic features of drive, in general practice they are closely related both to one another and to cost – the higher, the more costly.

Traction lifts and hydraulic lifts have different characteristics in this area, and therefore we examine them separately.

4.12.3.1 Traction lifts

Broadly speaking, the higher the building and the heavier the traffic, then the greater is the need for faster lift service. This is not merely a function of lift speed The subjective critical factor for prospective passengers is in fact 'waiting time', rather than actual 'travelling time'.

The mechanical characteristics of equipment components really establish the bounds of practical application. For comfort, convenience and safety the critical point is the approach of the car to a floor, its deceleration and stopping accuracy. In simpler lifts, stopping of the car is effected by switching off the motor and applying the mechanical brake, which is mounted on the lift machine. As with a motor car, a heavily loaded lift car travelling down takes longer to stop than a lightly loaded car, and in the absence of more sophisticated control, an acceptable compromise must be found between fierce braking which produces short stopping distance and gentle braking which produces long, but variable stopping distances, hence inaccurate floor levelling.

(a) *Single speed*

In general a single speed lift machine powered by a single speed a.c. motor can provide stopping within 35 mm of floor level from a running speed of about 0·5 m/s, and this is probably the acceptable limit in UK for such a lift used for light passenger duty.

Stopping distance and levelling accuracy for a lift dependent on mechanical braking for stopping, are related to the square of the speed at which the brake is applied. For more accurate stopping therefore, and greater comfort, it is necessary to reduce the speed of the lift electrically before applying the mechanical brake, and generally a levelling speed not exceeding 0·3 m/s is sought.

(b) *2-speed pole change*
The next stage of drive sophistication is the use of 2-speed pole change a.c. motors. These are double wound 3-phase motors having 2 synchronous speeds, generally in ratio 3/1 or 4/1. The higher speed is used for normal running and the lower speed is switched in electrically at a preset distance from floor level to provide a slower speed at which the mechanical brake is applied to stop the lift. Levelling accuracy of 10 mm is normally obtainable. The comfort of the speed transition from high to low speed can be adjusted and improved by a number of ways, both in the construction of the motor and in the electric circuitry to effect the transition. Lifts of this type are widely used for lift speeds up to 1·0 m/s, with carefully designed motors and control circuits.

(c) *Ward-Leonard*
Beyond 1·0 m/s we come into the region of higher buildings, generally office or hotel, where comfort, accurate stopping and short floor-to-floor times are essential features, and a satisfactory overall speed pattern needs to be established and maintained if the system is to work effectively. For many years the answer to the problem in this speed range has been found in the use of a d.c. lift motor controlled on the Ward-Leonard variable voltage principle from an a.c./d.c. motor-generator set. A d.c. motor is a variable speed unit in contrast to the fixed speed characteristics of the conventional single- or 2-speed a.c. machine. Therefore a smooth and flexible speed pattern can be established through suitable control equipment which can enable it to accelerate or decelerate smoothly at whatever rate is desired and to come to rest electrically, so that the mechanical brake can function merely as a holding brake. Geared lifts of this type are used up to speeds of at least 1·6 m/s. Levelling accuracy of 6 mm is obtainable. They are used also on lower speed lifts where a smooth ride is essential, even though considerably more costly than 2-speed a.c. A system now used as an alternative to a motor-generator set is a static convertor, which provides through thyristors an equivalent controllable d.c. power source for the lift motor.

(d) *Variable speed a.c.*
The alternative to d.c. drive for the same speed range is the variable speed a.c. motor, and this has become a common means of drive for higher-speed geared lift machines. This may be fed from controlled solid state devices. Typically a preset speed pattern is established electronically and monitored, normally by means of a tachogenerator driven from the lift motor. The power fed to the motor produces the necessary value of torque to drive the lift in accordance with the prescribed stepless speed pattern from start to stop. A geared lift machine of this type is shown in Fig. 4.12.3.

(e) *Gearless*
For the drive of gearless lift machines the principle of motor drive is d.c., similar to that for higher speed geared machines, though the control circuitry is generally more elaborate. Such lifts operate up to and beyond 7 m/s, though in UK few exceed 5 m/s as the height of buildings does not justify higher speeds. A typical gearless lift machine is shown in Fig. 4.12.4.

Fig. 4.12.3. *Geared Lift Machine* (NALM)

Fig. 4.12.4. *Gearless Lift Machine* (NALM)

4.12.3.2 Electro-hydraulic lifts
For hydraulic lifts, the speed depends directly on the flow rate of oil in and out of the hydraulic ram/cylinder unit. A constant speed pump, usually screw-type for smooth action, is driven by a single-speed a.c. motor for upward travel. Speed control is therefore effected completely by a hydraulic valve system which feeds the oil flow to the ram at the required rate and by-passes the surplus back to the storage tank. In some cases this may be monitored by a speed-sensing device which enables a predetermined speed pattern to be maintained under varying load conditions. For downward travel, the car descends under its own weight, the speed control system regulating the oil flow to the appropriate value. The levelling accuracy can be within the same range as for traction lifts.

4.12.4 Lift control systems

Control of lifts by the user is by means of push-buttons, mounted in the car and on landings. However the way in which the lift or group of lifts responds to a continual pattern of push button signals depends on the nature of the control equipment, varying from simple to considerable sophistication. A number of well-defined systems are used. The two most common are described below.

4.12.4.1 Automatic push-button
The lift is capable of receiving, storing and acting upon one instruction at a time. When the lift is standing at rest at a floor, a button pressed at a landing, or in the car, will cause the lift to travel to the required landing, stop there and await a further call. It cannot receive any other calls while it is travelling. Such a system is simple and generally adequate only for lifts where traffic is light and few landings are served.

4.12.4.2 Collective
In this system a lift is capable of receiving and storing calls while at rest or in motion. It then follows an established pattern of response. At each intermediate landing there are 'up' and 'down' pushes and at each terminal landing a single push. Registration of a call is normally indicated by illumination of the push. The car contains a full set of floor pushes. Pressure on a car push for a floor above the car, or an 'up' push on a landing, will cause the doors to close and the car to move upwards. On its way up the car will answer all registered landing calls for an 'up' direction, and any further calls registered for floors above the car. While the car is travelling up, the 'down' calls will not be effective to stop the car till 'up' calls ahead of the car have been answered, but they will be registered, becoming effective when the car has answered the uppermost call and reverses its direction of motion. Then a similar pattern of operation commences for dealing with 'down' calls and car calls registered for floors below the car.

A simplified form of collective control, 'down' collective, is employed in buildings where the bulk of the traffic is between the ground floor and individual upper floors, as in a block of flats, and there is little interfloor traffic. The system does not register 'up' landing calls, only 'down' calls.

Where the traffic requirements justify two lifts side-by-side, they are normally interconnected to form a duplex collective system. They share a common set of landing push buttons, and the calls registered in the system are allocated to one or other of the cars in a way which takes into account most effectively the position and direction of motion of each car. Typically one car, designated the 'parked car' will park at a specified 'home floor' with its doors in the open position. The second car will be a 'free car' and will park at the floor where it became idle. Initially only the free car will respond to any landing calls registered, but if after a predetermined time any landing calls remain unanswered the 'parked car' will be released to assist in answering landing calls. If a car call is registered on the 'parked car', it will immediately be released to answer landing calls. The direction of intended movement of the car on arrival at a floor will be indicated by an illuminated sign in the lift entrance.

The first lift to become idle will return to the 'home floor' and if on arrival no outstanding landing calls are registered, it will become the 'parked car' until such time as it is released again because of outstanding landing calls. If one lift is out of service for any reason, all landing calls will be routed to the operative lift. In normal operation both lifts will continue to respond to all landing calls, with either lift answering a landing call. Once a landing call has been answered by one lift, the call will be cancelled on both lifts.

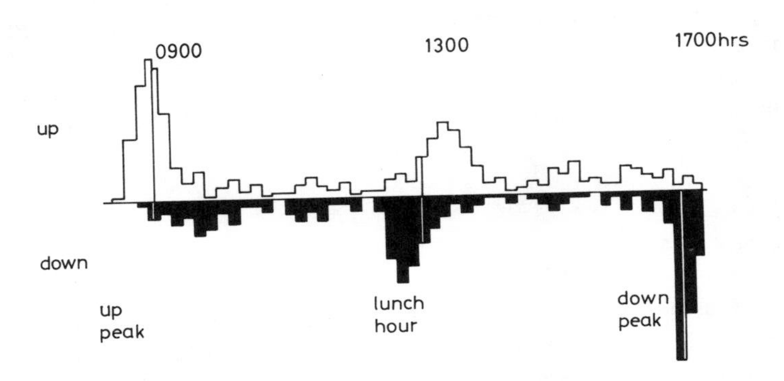

(NALM)

Fig. 4.12.5. *Typical traffic pattern in office building*

4.12.4.3 Group control

Three or more lifts may be interconnected into a collective system. With increasing number of cars and height of building the system of landing call allocation to individual cars becomes increasingly complex. For 3 cars a relatively simple extension of the 2 car system may be adequate, but for 4 to 8 cars (the practical limit) some form of supervisory system is used, nowadays often making use of micro-chip technology which can swiftly analyse all the relevant information and make decisions on landing call allocation, to optimise traffic handling continually. Such a system may also be capable of logging data on call response times, displaying call handling graphically on TV screens, and even detecting and logging intermittent deviations from optimum lift performance.

The design of lift control systems for heavy traffic in high buildings is a subject for the specialist, and much care is necessary in the selection of the size and number of lift cars and their speed. For preliminary guidance tables are available in for instance the British Standard CP 407:1972, but detailed design of the scheme depends on a thorough knowledge of the planned use of an individual building and the traffic handling capabilities of lift manufacturers' equipment. This needs to be studied at an early stage of the building project, as the number, shape and size of the lift wells is an important structural matter within the frame of a building. Fig. 4.12.5 illustrates the typical traffic pattern in an office building in the course of a working day.

4.12.5 Goods lifts

Goods lifts are driven and controlled in the same manner as passenger lifts. However the operational speeds are generally lower, though accurate levelling is very important for many applications, especially for wheeled traffic. While there is a British Standard range of recommended car sizes, it may be necessary to custom-build to meet special loading requirements, though still satisfying rigidly the BS safety requirements. Car and landing doors are usually manually operated. A popular form of landing protection is the collapsible steel shutter gate, which is very robust. Cars are usually of all steel construction. For very large cars vertically bi-parting shutter doors are often used. They may be power operated.

4.12.6 Service lifts

So far as UK is concerned a service lift is a small lift, so dimensioned that it is clearly not for the carriage of passengers. The majority of these lifts are in the load range of 50–100 kg. They are used for the handling of light and crated goods as in restaurants and bars, with sill level about 800 mm above floor level, and landing openings normally protected by rising shutters. Safety requirements for electric service lifts are strict, and covered by standard and statutory requirements. However they normally omit a number of features associated with the carriage of passengers e.g. car doors and safety gear. For certain standardised duties electric service lifts lend themselves to complete prefabrication. Car, guides and prewired steel lift well can be delivered as a small number of packaged units which can be quickly assembled on site.

4.12.7 Lifts for residential and personal use

In recent years considerable attention has been given to the needs of the elderly or disabled, to enable them to continue to live independently and maintain mobility within the home. The major handicap frequently is the staircase, and if this problem can be overcome by means of a simple and economical lift, then the need for continual home help attention, or alternatively removal to hospital, is eliminated or at least is postponed. Recent British Standards BS 5776, BS 5900 and BS 5965 lay down safety guidelines for the construction of simple lifts of this type and are being adopted quite widely by individual companies and by Local Authorities as a basis for a small but important section of the market. The range covered is quite wide, extending from a simple hand-operated installation to one which has many of the features of a standard general purpose passenger lift.

4.12.8 Needs of the handicapped (See also chapter 4.16)

There is increasing legislative requirement for physically handicapped people to travel freely within multi-storey buildings. So far as this concerns lifts, it has been established that the minimum convenient size of passenger lifts in UK is the standard 8 person lift, 1100 mm × 1400 mm inside with 800 mm clear entrance, for those in self-propelled wheelchairs, and standard car and landing push-buttons are in positions and heights suitable for the wheelchair occupants. Where there are special needs for the blind, then Braille symbols can be provided on push box face-plates, and for the severely handicapped, special low-level push boxes. In residential homes for old people, attention is necessary to the operating speed and sequence timing of the automatic doors, and special audible signals may be necessary.

4.12.9 Building work

A lift installation forms an integral part of the fabric of a building and it is very important from the beginning that the interface between lift maker and builder is recognised and their work of common concern is strictly defined and co-ordinated. The item of prime importance to the lift maker is the provision by the builder of an accurate and plumb lift well, with the landing entrances set plumb, one above the other. The lift car runs on a set of vertical guide rails from top to bottom of the well, and all the lift maker's dimensions refer back to these, including the position of the car, the car entrance and the landing entrances. Many dimensions shown on lift maker's drawings are specified for safe operational reasons, and generally cannot be reduced. In particular, lift well plan dimensions are minimum plumb dimensions. If they are too small, the lift car cannot be accommodated. Within the machine room there must be good access and adequate working space for equipment and for servicing personnel, and there must be appropriate lighting and temperature control, otherwise satisfactory operation may be prejudiced.

Lift wells are generally in concrete, and the lift maker requires to have metal inserts (usually channel section) in the walls of the well to attach guide brackets and landing door frames. The machine room floor is normally cast concrete with suitable cast-in holes for the passage of suspension ropes, electric cables etc, and the machine room itself requires to be of weatherproof construction. The lift maker does not usually commence site work until the builder has completed the construction of the well and the machine room, so that he has unobstructed access to a clear and dry working area for installation of the lift equipment.

The apportionment of work between lift maker and builder is generally in accordance with the recommendations of British Standard CP 407 and is clearly shown in the lift maker's drawings provided for the builder's use.

4.12.10 Dimensional standardisation and traffic handling

It is useful to manufacturer, architect and building manager to have some standardisation or preferred dimensions of lift cars and entrances. This helps towards safe and effective operation of a lift system as well as providing some cost saving through rationalisation of manufacture. BS 5655 part 5 is the basis for selection of a preferred range of lift cars, with associated well dimensions.

Car dimensions are based on an acceptable value of floor area and weight per person carried, persons being rated at 75 kg each, and for passenger lift duty a selected range of car entrance dimensions are standardised. The car and well dimensions satisfy the safety requirements of BS 5655 (and BS 2655 as appropriate) and the standard range is therefore a very satisfactory starting point in planning. Using these standardised values of car and entrance dimensions, and on the basis of practice and calculation the traffic handling capability can be estimated for a group of lifts in a building. This is increasingly important as the planned size and capacity of a building becomes greater. A slight deficiency in lift service in a 5 floor building may be unnoticed, but in a 25 floor building quite intolerable if the only alternative is to climb the stairs. Lettable value of the upper floors of a building is affected greatly by the effectiveness of lift service provided.

Good service embraces a number of related features, the basic number, size and speed of the lift cars, the position of the lift bank in the building, the logic system for handling calls, the floor to floor time (not merely high speed running time), the effective door operation (open, pause and close) and the signalling system to enable passengers to be directed effectively to the right car. In major building projects this requires close consultation between developer and lift maker in order to establish the most appropriate equipment to meet the needs of the building.

4.12.11 Escalators and passenger conveyors

Escalators have been in use for over 80 years, but only in the last 30 years have they come into widespread use in commercial premises. For interfloor passenger traffic they provide a high capacity, superior to a bank of lifts occupying the same space. Their styling provides an attractive architectural feature in many buildings, frequently incorporating glass panels and stainless steel or aluminium trims. They lend themselves to a high degree of prefabrication as a self-contained package so that speedy installation is often possible. The motor, gearing and control equipment are all totally enclosed within the steel frame which carries the endless step belt. For general duty store-type escalators the whole package generally requires support points at the ends only. Longer travel heavy duty escalators, as for railway stations, may require intermediate supports, but the construction is similar. Dimensions and safety features of escalators are highly standardised, and relate to established safety codes, in particular BS 5656. Fig. 4.12.6 illustrates the outline and typical dimensions of store-type escalators.

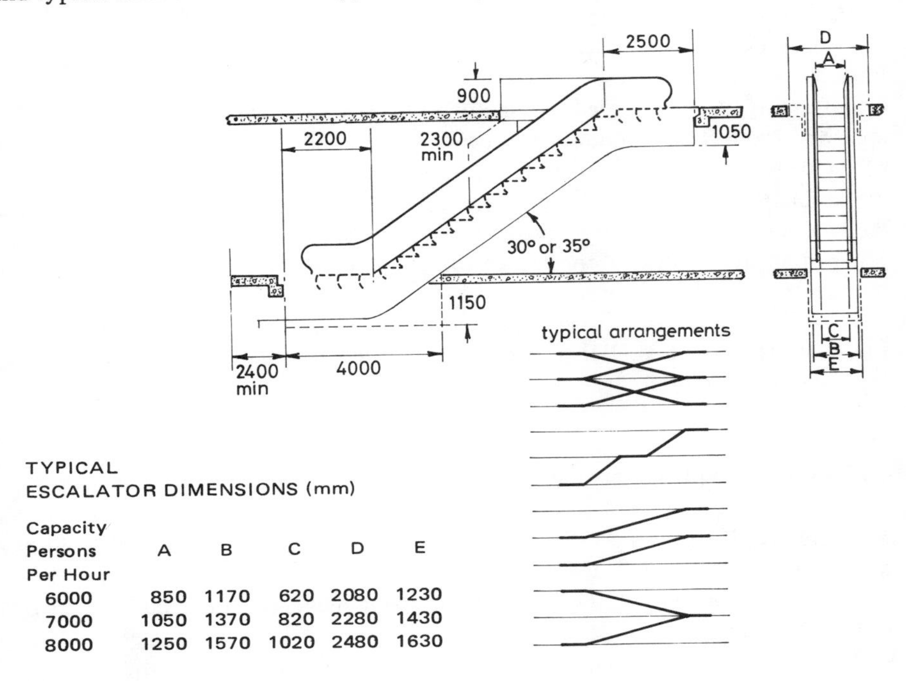

TYPICAL
ESCALATOR DIMENSIONS (mm)

Capacity Persons Per Hour	A	B	C	D	E
6000	850	1170	620	2080	1230
7000	1050	1370	820	2280	1430
8000	1250	1570	1020	2480	1630

Fig. 4.12.6. *Store type escalator: typical dimensions and arrangements* (NALM)

Passenger conveyors, seen mainly in airports and public areas, can be looked upon as flat escalators, and most of them are in fact constructed on the same principle, having metal pallets instead of metal steps. However they may also be made with endless reinforced rubber belts on the principle of the material-handling conveyor belts. Both types may be used on slight inclines, up to 12 degrees, and can accommodate certain types of shopping trolley, for instance in supermarkets.

4.12.12 Fire and emergency provisions

Lifts form a vital part of the transport system of a building. In a non-fire emergency, for instance failure of electric power in a building, it may be necessary to maintain vertical transport by at least a portion of the lift installation, and therefore it is now common practice in larger buildings and hospitals for the lifts to function on an emergency power supply network, which is switched on automatically if mains power fails. A number of operating systems are used, some of which restrict the number and speed of lifts remaining in service, possibly returning all others sequentially to the ground floor.

Legal requirements frequently need at least one lift in every building over a certain height to be reserved exclusively for fireman's use in the event of emergency. It has protected electrical supplies, it is in a fire protected lift well, and on operation of a special switch at the main lobby this lift returns to the lobby and is thereafter exclusively under fireman's control, with a special sequence of push-button operation.

Lift wells, if unprotected, could function very effectively as chimneys or fire spreaders from floor to floor in a fire emergency. In most modern buildings the risk of lift wells being firespreaders is very small however, as requirements for construction are strict. Both the lift well enclosure and the lift well entrances, which include landing doors and the frames must be of fire-resistant construction, being certified for $\frac{1}{2}$ hour to 2 hours according to local requirements. Lift entrances normally require to have half the fire resistance of the enclosure, with maximum 1 hour, since a fire would have to penetrate two entrances in order to pass from floor to floor. In the case of escalators, special fire-shutters triggered by heat sensitive links are sometimes required.

4.12.13 Inspection and servicing

A completed lift or escalator is subjected to careful check and running tests by the manufacturer before hand-over to the customer, and the form of test certificate provided is generally on the lines of the recommendations of BS 2655. Part 7 and/or BS 5655. Part 1.

To satisfy legal requirements most lifts (except mainly in private dwellings) require six-monthly checks by a competent person to confirm that the equipment is in safe working condition, with special reference to such items as lifting ropes and landing door locks which if defective could present hazards to the lift user. A prescribed form of report is used, which must be retained by the owner for possible Government inspection, e.g. in event of a dangerous incident. Apart from this legally-prescribed inspection many insurance companies require that lifts covered by their policies must be checked regularly by their own inspection engineers.

In order to keep lifts in good and safe operational order, regular servicing is necessary, and this is usually provided on a regular contractual basis, normally by the servicing organisation of the original lift installer. They provide as necessary the facilities for major and minor repairs and the ability to deal promptly, frequently on a round-the-clock basis, with lift stoppages however caused. They are able to report on the condition of the lift, recommend and provide equipment for the progressive updating of the equipment throughout the life of the building as the needs arise, and undertake the periodic examinations required by law.

4.12.14 References

4.12.14.1 Legislation (See also Appendix 6.1)

Building Regulations 1976
Construction Regulations 1961
Factories Act 1961
SI 715: 1962 Hoists Exemption order 1962
Health and Safety at Work etc Act 1974
Offices Shops and Railway Premises Act 1963
SI 849: 1968 Hoists and Lifts Regulations 1968
SI 863: 1968 Hoists and Lifts. Periodic Examination form for Lifts.

4.12.14.2 British Standards (See also appendix 6.2)

BS 2655 Lifts, escalators, passenger conveyors and paternosters. Parts 1–10. (NB. BS 2655 is being progressively superseded by BS 5655 but parts are still relevant for existing lifts).
BS 5655 Lifts and service lifts Parts 1 and 2. (Other Parts are in preparation.)
BS 5656 Escalators and passenger conveyors
Other relevant standards include
BS 329 Steel wire ropes for electric lifts
BS 476 Part 8 Fire tests in building materials and structures
BS 5606 Code of practice for accuracy in building
BS 5776 Specification for powerer stair lifts
BS 5900 Specification for powered home lifts
BS 5965 Specification for manually driven balanced personal home lifts
BS 6977 Spectification for insulated flexible cables for lifts
BS CP 407 Electric, hydraulic and hand-powered lifts.

4.12.14.3 Bibliography

Regulations for Electrical Installations (Institution of Electrical Engineers)
HSE Guidance Notes
PM 8 Passenger carrying paternosters
PM 26 Safety at lift landings
PM 34 Safety in the use of escalators
(Health and Safety Executive)

Console for private branch exchange handling voice and data (Plessey Telecommunications and Office Systems Ltd.)

Chapter 4.13

Communications

J. R. Pollard, M.A., C.Eng., F.I.E.E.
Head, Information and Publicity Services, Plessey Telecommunications and Office Systems Limited

4.13.1 Introduction

The topic of communications is treated in the broadest possible sense, from basic conventional telecommunications of the type provided by public communications authorities such as British Telecom (telephone, telex, data transmission) to private communication systems (intercom and direct speech), public address and sound reinforcement systems, video and closed circuit television systems, radio paging and other signalling systems. Also dealt with are the special problems associated in providing any, or all, of these services in a variety of building applications from flats and private houses, to office blocks, large factories, theatres and concert halls.

Having regard to the specialist requirements of communication systems, it is essential for new buildings that the basic communications requirements are specified and evaluated before major building work has commenced, so that the installation and operating aspects of such services can be included in the brief to the architect responsible for the work. This need arises from the increasing magnitude and complexity of communications installations, which means that substantial duct space will often be required e.g. for the telephone circuits in use in a single floor of an office block.

The duct space provided must allow for substantial growth in numbers of circuits (the initial installation should not occupy more than 50% of the available space). This is particularly true of video cabling, usually in coaxial form, where current uses may be zero or minimal but where growth over a decade might involve tens or even hundreds of video distribution circuits.

In a similar way, substantial areas of space may need to be reserved for the installation of complex sound reinforcement systems in theatres and other large auditoria, and for the control rooms associated with the operation of such systems. Moreover, the large amounts of electrical energy produced in the output circuits of substantial sound systems require safety precautions to be taken equivalent to those involved in the distribution of electrical energy.

4.13.2 Public communications networks

This title is used to indicate generically the groups of network services which have as their function the linking together of users who are dispersed geographically. Until recently, telecommunications services as a whole were almost entirely dominated by voice communication over the telephone. Such services historically were provided exclusively both within and outside buildings, factories and other premises, by the telephone administration of the country concerned, in UK originally the Post Office and now by British Telecom. Over many years, and in particular over the last decade, this situation has changed, and in some countries there are alternative public telecommunications networks even for long distance services. In these and other countries, services internal to buildings, factory and office premises may be provided by many competing companies, although they may still need to comply with specifications, equipment performance and interworking arrangements stipulated by, or on behalf of, the public telecommunications authority.

For the purpose of this chapter, therefore, reference to 'public communications' relates to denote those parts of the communications resources which are external to the building or other premises being considered, and the internal aspects are dealt with in later sections concerned with private communications systems. The distinction will vary from one country to another, according to national policy on telecommunications, and there will be instances of the public telecommunications authority continuing to provide internal private communications services, as will be the normal practice where this authority still retains monopoly powers.

In terms of this necessarily arbitrary distinction between public and private communications, building design and construction work to meet the needs of the relevant public telecommunications authorities (in UK, British Telecom, Mercury Communications; in Hull, the Hull Corporation, and in the Channel Islands, the Telephone Boards of Guernsey and Jersey, as appropriate) must be properly taken into account. Such needs will involve aspects of cable entry, and locations for the equipment for terminating circuits and service connections. This, as a minimum, will be some kind of distribution frame and possibly other items of apparatus located on customer's premises, together with the necessary interconnecting ducts and cables. For the more complex communications circuits and services it will often be necessary to incorporate significant quantities of equipment on the building premises. Advice on such aspects should always be sought, preferably at the initial planning stage, from the relevant public communications authorities. In addition, for office and business premises of larger sizes (say over 10 000 sq metres in total), consideration must be given to roof-top locations for the possible erection of small dish aerials for microwave and satellite links which will start to become commonplace over the next decade.

BS 6305 sets out the general requirements for apparatus for connection to the British Telecom public network, whilst British Telecom publish an informative booklet entitled 'Requirements for Telecommunications Distribution in Office Premises'. Also, BS 6301, BS 6312, BS 6317, BS 6320 and BS 6328 cover specific aspects of apparatus for connection to British Telecom networks.

4.13.3 Telex

The telex service provides a quick and effective method of transmitting and receiving printed messages from one location to another, which may be anywhere in the world. Telex machines are usually of the keyboard send and receive (KSR) type, in which a keyboard associated with the machine is used to transmit a message to the distant point, and messages in the return direction are printed out. When transmitting messages, the printing mechanism provides a local copy of what is being sent. Additional equipment is commonly used to prepare a perforated tape, which is then used to transmit the text at a continuous steady speed. This process is advantageous, either where the same message has to be sent to a number of locations, or where the cost of the telex call is high and where it is desirable to maximise the transmission speed by using tape, rather than sending by hand from the keyboard. The importance of the telex machine to the business community arises from the fact that world-wide it is normal to regard a telex message which has been authenticated by the sending and reception at both ends of the circuit of the answer-back code of the machine as the equivalent of a contractually binding document.

This gives such a message a significance and status far exceeding that of a spoken message over the telephone, and accounts for the widespread use of telex as a means of business communication. Identification by means of the answer-back code is a key element in the process. This code is generated within the telex machine, and is unique to the location in which the telex machine is provided. The answer-back code usually consists of the telex number, letters representing an abbreviated form of the name or identity of the company using the telex machine, and a final letter or letters indicating the country of origin. Such a code is set up inside the machine when first installed, and remains invariant unless altered by the telex service contractor on the instructions of the user of the telex machine. In this regard, it serves as a kind of mechanical signature for authentication.

With the trend towards integrated office systems there will be an increasing use of intelligent terminals (e.g. communicating word processors) which will be able to originate and receive telex messages, in addition to the centrally located telex service. There are also services which distribute a continuous flow of financial and other news, using telex principles, but on a broadcast one-way basis to receive-only (RO) terminals.

4.13.4 Private communication services

This section considers all the services, other than telex, which are internal to an individual building, a group of buildings, or a set of related premises. Originally such services were all speech messages over various kinds of telephone circuits, but many additional services are now involved and these are covered later in the section.

4.13.4.1 Speech systems

Dealing first with speech systems, there are three basic kinds of installations. In the first case, one or two individual telephone lines (each terminated on a telephone instrument) are commonly found in domestic premises and in the very smallest offices and shops. Secondly, and for larger office premises, it is customary to have some kind of switching equipment, occasionally manual but more commonly automatic. In older installations, this often takes the form of a local dial telephone service, having extensions at each point where telephone service is required, and these dial telephones are able to connect among themselves, but not to the outside world. Communications beyond the limit of the premises concerned are provided by an entirely separate group of telephones connected usually to a manual switchboard, with one or more operator positions, and serving to link into the external public communications services. The equipment used for providing the automatic internal only service is usually referred to as a private automatic exchange (PAX).

The third case is that of installations which make use of switching equipment which allows both internal calls within the premises and external calls to and from the public communications service. Originally, such equipment was invariably provided by the public communications authority and was regarded by such authorities as a branch of its own switching equipment, which led to the name private automatic branch exchange (PABX) and although such equipment is now freely available from many suppliers (in addition to the public communications authority) the name still remains.

For companies having a number of locations dispersed geographically, substantial economy in the cost of telecommunications services can be obtained by the use of private line circuits between the various locations. Such private line circuits are normally leased by the public communications authority, commonly by dedication of otherwise 'public' circuits to the exclusive use of one customer. Most modern PABX systems have the ability to provide least-cost routes by diverting calls automatically to remote locations over such private circuits instead of connecting via the public network. In addition to the main speech communication via PABX, use is often made in office and factory premises of networks of telephones of the office inter-communication, or 'intercom' variety, providing single push-button access between a limited number of individual stations. More advanced varieties of intercom include the 'Direct Speech' systems, affording hands-free loudspeaker intercommunication between the stations installed. Such stations are commonly installed on a kind of ring circuit to reduce cabling costs, but are seldom connected to the public communications services external to the building. Many variations of these voice communication systems are possible, and some are mentioned in later sections dealing with applications of communications to particular classes of buildings.

4.13.4.2 Paging systems

Many other private communications services exist; among them may be mentioned luminous paging signals, which are particularly attractive for hospitals and shop premises where a simple calling service is desirable without the nuisance value of telephone bells or loudspeakers. A further example of such a calling signal is a paging service, in which those needed to be contacted are provided with an individual paging receiver. The building is equipped with means of signalling by radio frequency induction into these paging receivers, with a selective calling arrangement so arranged that an individual recipient can be signalled by a 'bleep' from his paging receiver. Such a paging system (Fig. 4.13.1) can be extended to provide one-way or both-way voice communication using radio frequencies for transmission and reception between the central point and the individual paging devices, and this can be further extended to the provision of full radio communication using cordless equipment working either one to another, or to and from a base station. In this regard, it is important to note that the availability in many countries of a 'Citizens Band' radio service should not encourage serious users of communications to employ such equipment, since by its nature the quality of the service is poor, especially from the consideration that the frequencies are open to everyone suitably equipped, and there will both be interference from other users and loss of privacy.

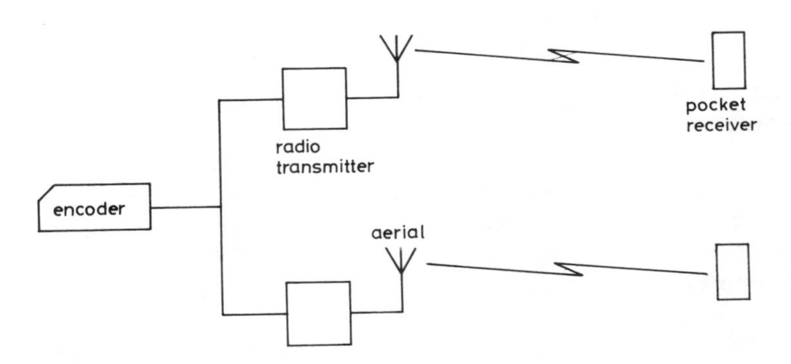

Fig. 4.13.1. *Radio paging system*

4.13.4.3 Integrated communications systems

Perhaps the most important development in private communications services has been that which has led to the emergence of the so-called integrated communications systems, or integrated office systems. (Fig. 4.13.2). Such systems are an important part of what has become known in the UK as 'Information Technology' (IT) and are also known as 'Télématique' in France. In these, common elements of cabling, switching plant, and other apparatus are used to provide not just voice communications, but data, text, facsimile and in some cases picture circuits as well.

Word processors, computers, computer and data terminals, visual display units (VDU), printers, workstations and many other items of office machinery are all now able to be interconnected by communications links, either over telephone circuits or with specially installed circuits such as coaxial cables. In many cases, coaxial cables in the form of a ring employing equipment of proprietary design may also be used, e.g. to link computers and peripheral devices.

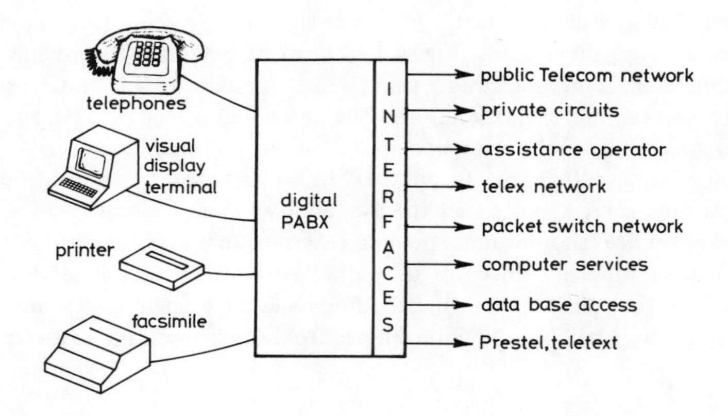

Fig. 4.13.2. *Integrated communications system*

4.13.4.4 Security communications

In addition to voice and data services described above, communications plant is often involved in such services as alarms, monitoring, access control and so on. (Chapter 4.14 deals in detail with intruder alarms and surveillance systems). There is, of course, a substantial communications involvement in many of these, since the high cost of maintaining a 24 hour watching service leads many companies to install intruder alarm systems which when intrusion is detected set up a call to an alarm centre service, or to the local Police Force.

For this protection to be effective, not only must the intruder detection equipment itself be of very great reliability, but in addition the circuit used to transmit the alarm to the operational alarm centre must itself be of great reliability, and so designed and located that accidental or deliberate interference with it is extremely improbable. Chapter 4.14 also deals more specifically with the problem of false alarms of one kind and another, but it is important for the user to realise that the effectiveness of his protection depends on the combination of the detecting devices he uses and the communications circuits used to relay the alarm to an appropriate distant point. It is self-evident that overhead wires which can easily be cut from outside the building would be unsuitable for this application, and close liaison between the user, a specialist contractor and the appropriate telecommunications administration is essential to ensure an adequate quality of service, reasonably free from false alarms.

4.13.4.5 Time systems

A further example of a communications-related system is the provision of clocks and time recorders. Traditionally, this has involved the installation of a master clock at some central point, with circuits extended to individual impulse type clocks, and to the printing mechanism of time recorders. Such a system has the advantage that the change from local winter time to summer daylight saving time, and vice versa, can be effected from one central point. A centralised system is therefore advantageous in the sense that all the time displays and time recorders will operate in exact synchronism, but only at the cost of an expensive central installation, and considerable cabling to the clocks dispersed throughout the premises concerned. It is now common for clocks to be provided which rely for their accuracy on a built-in quartz crystal oscillator with suitable dividing circuits to produce outputs at once a second, once a minute, and so on. These are then used to control stepping mechanism clocks co-located with the oscillator-divider circuits. These clock units are often cheaper than impulse clocks, and offer greater economies in wiring, but do need a visit to each clock possibly in a large area when it is necessary to make the change between winter and summer daylight saving times.

More complicated clock systems are often needed – e.g. to record flexible working hours, for individual job-costing and similar uses. In these, a terminal device is installed at a number of locations and cabled to a central installation which records events and activities, often in association with data-processing facility. The cabling and other installation aspects must of course be agreed with the equipment supplier, but generally will involve extra-low voltage telephone-type cabling and installation.

4.13.4.6 Broadcast systems

Previous sections have dealt with communications services which are mostly of a both-way nature. This section deals with communications which are of a unidirectional, broadcast variety. By far the most significant example of this is the use of amplification equipment for public address on a broadcast basis, or for sound reinforcement applications. All such installations (Fig. 4.13.3) consist basically of a source of input such as a microphone to convert sound into an electrical signal, an amplifier of appropriate power rating, one or more loudspeaker installations, and the necessary interconnection cabling. The range of equipment and applications is

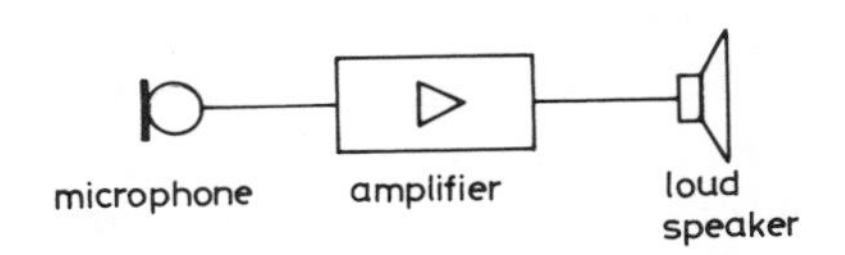

Fig. 4.13.3. *Simple sound system*

very broad, from the simplest consisting of an electronic megaphone or 'bull-horn' for crowd control, up to a sound installation embracing twenty or more microphones feeding a sound system of tens to hundreds of loudspeakers with amplifiers of output power ranging from a few hundred watts up to many kilowatts for large 'pop' concerts.

A typical application is shown in Fig. 4.13.4. It includes a number of signal

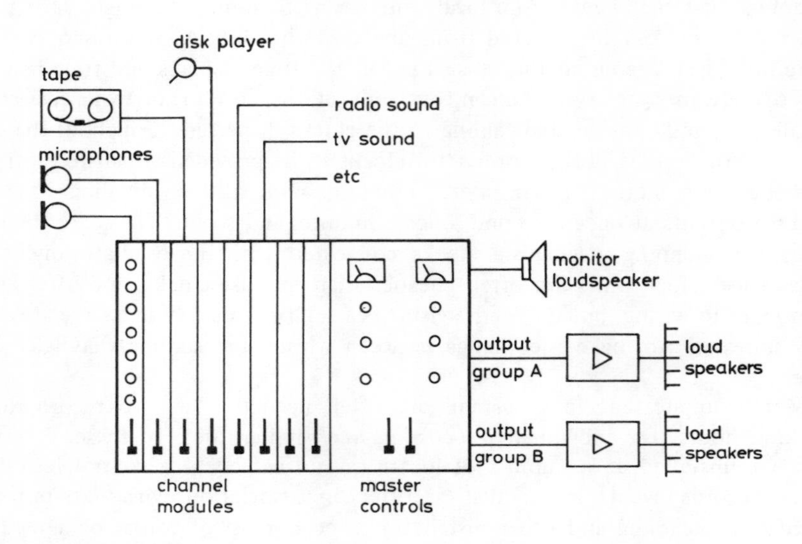

Fig. 4.13.4. *Theatre-type sound system*

sources, which can include microphones, cassette or tape players, record players, or inputs from radio and t.v. channels. The outputs from these are selected, the frequency response adjusted if necessary, combined in varying proportions into a number of output groups in a mixer, and the outputs from the mixers are taken to individual or groups of power amplifiers, which in turn feed loudspeakers.

For a simple installation of a loudspeaker system in a factory, it may be sufficient to provide a single microphone, a single amplifier and a single output circuit to one group of loudspeakers distributed around the factory premises. The amplifier will combine the power amplifier circuits which drive the loudspeakers themselves, and the microphone preamplifier which amplifies the very low level signal from the microphone. Between the microphone preamplifier and the power amplifier is a gain control, often of pre-set form, or even concealed inside the amplifier case. This control serves to vary the amplification or gain of the complete system in such a way that a suitable level of output can be obtained from the loudspeakers when the person using the system talks at whatever distance is convenient from the microphone. Such a control will normally be set on installation of the system and should not need to be disturbed unless local circumstances change.

Such an installation should be provided in the simplest possible form, usually controlled by a push-button or lever-key switch, which un-mutes the microphone or otherwise activates the system, which consists of the amplifier and a single circuit with a number of loudspeakers on it. Such an installation can obviously be extended in easy stages; the incorporation of additional microphone points, and extra switching to add blocks of loudspeakers can turn even an uncomplicated system like this into a very flexible installation.

Once a system is installed, a subsidiary use frequently made of it is for the broadcasting of background music, either continuously or at selected times through the day. For this it is normal to provide a second input to the amplifier, with the microphone switching so arranged that if the microphone is called into use when the music circuit is on, the input from the music circuit is over-ridden and replaced by the voice message from the microphone. On releasing the key, the circuit reverts to playing the music as before. Music used in this way will almost certainly be the subject of a number of copyright restrictions. These include the composer's copyright in the work being performed, the musicians' copyright in the performance, and the mechanical copyright in the recording itself. It is important that appropriate clearance is obtained for the use of music for the intended purposes to avoid breach of copyright.

At a more ambitious level, the installation incorporates a large number of input channels, of which some will almost certainly be microphones, and other inputs may come from cassette or open reel tape recorders, continuous loop cartridge players, a gramophone record player, radio circuits, t.v. sound, and so on. Such an installation would typically be provided in the entertainment area of a club, theatre or concert hall. In addition to the greater variety of input circuits, it is very probable that more than one output circuit will be required.

It is usual for each input circuit to have a control with which the signal level can be varied to suit the needs of the performance. In anything other than the most basic installation, a control which varies each signal provides the same function as the gain control mentioned earlier, and commonly consists of a potentiometer providing a suitable proportion of the input signal; the proportion varying according to the position of the slider on the potentiometer. In modern control desks the knob moves in a straight line and such a control is almost invariably referred to as a fader. In addition to the individual input circuit faders it is usual to provide one fader for each output group.

For reproduction of music under such conditions, as a minimum one would expect to find the output divided into at least two groups so that music which has been recorded in stereo can be reproduced using two separate channels. Mono signals can be reproduced by allocating the fader output to either the left or right stereo channel, or proportionately between them, if it is necessary to produce an apparently centred sound image.

For a large scale theatrical performance, such an installation would need to be further supplemented by microphones for individual performers, some of which may need to be radio microphones; directional microphones in a position equivalent to the footlights in a conventional theatre for general sound pick-up from the stage area, and possibly a number of microphones in the orchestra pit, for reinforcement of the musical accompaniment. It would not be unusual for such an installation to require some ten to thirty input channels and four or more output group circuits, each feeding a group of loudspeakers via a power amplifier. In such an installation, it would be normal to find that the mixing console for controlling the signal level from each microphone contained elaborate provision for adjusting the frequency response of each channel individually, and to deal with the acoustic problems often encountered in such buildings, it would not be unusual to find that each power amplifier was fed by way of an equaliser which enabled small adjustments to be made in the frequency response of the complete system, so as to offset any deficiencies in the acoustic properties of the auditorium.

By virtue of the fact that such equalisers contain a large number of individual controls moving in a straight line, profile of the control knobs after adjustment forms a rough visual map of the correction that has been introduced, and so such units are commonly referred to as graphic equalisers. In view of the complexity of such installations, and the possibility for achieving a variety of unsatisfactory results, the need for well trained and skilled operators is self-evident.

For some uses of such system, for example in concerts of 'pop' music, it is required to produce extremely high sound levels in the auditorium. In these circumstances, loudspeakers of considerable physical size, weight and substantial power handling capacity will be required in conjunction with amplifiers whose output may range from a hundred watts up to several kilowatts. In addition to the problem of finding enough space in which to install such a massive sound system, there are safety considerations to be borne in mind, both with regard to the high audio frequency power which is being used in relation to danger from electric shock, and the high acoustic power produced which may easily cause cases of substantial hearing impairment after only brief exposures to the very high sound levels which can be produced in this way.

Acoustically at the opposite end of the scale, the needs of those with already impaired hearing must be taken into account; conventional public address systems are of little help, since a hearing-aid worn on the body picks up a mixture of direct, amplified and reverberant sound, and the result to a listener with impaired hearing may well be confusing.

In these circumstances, consideration should be given to the incorporation into the auditorium fabric of an induction loop, which is driven with an audio frequency signal analogous to that being used to drive the loudspeakers. The magnetic field from the loop is picked up by a coil in the hearing-aid, amplified and thereby conveyed directly to the person with impaired hearing. The detailed design of such loops is outside the province of this present publication, and advice should be sought from such bodies as The Royal National Institute for the Deaf. (Ref. 1). In UK and many other countries a licence is normally needed for the installation and operation of an inductive loop system. (Such a licence is not usually needed for a loop on essentially domestic premises). (Ref. 2).

An important sub-set of public address installations is that used in lecture theatres, conference halls and similar locations for sound reinforcement. In this, a microphone picks up the speaker's voice, and after amplification, the signal is applied to loudspeakers, which will reproduce a magnified version of what is being said; thereby increasing audibility, especially towards the rear of the auditorium. There are a number of pitfalls in what is apparently a simple amplification installation. In the first place, both microphone and loudspeaker are in fairly close proximity, and there is, therefore, the difficulty of picking up sufficient acoustic energy from the person lecturing to produce a useful output from the microphone without the amplified voice from the loudspeaker itself generating so much signal in the microphone that acoustic feed back takes place and the system 'howls'.

This can only be overcome by appropriate care both in the design of the original installation, and in its subsequent operation. The problem usually arises in the use of buildings of highly inappropriate acoustic design. Microphones or loudspeakers having some degree of directivity can help to overcome the worst cases. Secondly, the performer may be encouraged to keep relatively close to the microphone which is picking up his sound, e.g. by a lecturer using a clip-on type microphone fastened to the tie or the lapel of a dress or coat. Thirdly, and this is often the only solution for particularly reverberant enclosures, a small element of frequency shift in the form of a cyclic variation of phase between input and output can be introduced so that an incipient oscillation cannot build up by virtue of the continuous variation of phase between the input and the output signals.

One of the problems with sound systems, whether for use in simple public address applications or for elaborate sound reinforcement installations, is that an otherwise satisfactory system does not realise anything like its full potential because inadequate provision has been made for its operation and maintenance. All too often, operation of the sound system is relegated to someone such as the building caretaker, or a hotel porter, who has been instructed by his predecessor to turn on 'this' switch and turn 'that' particular knob to position 5, and then to lock up so that no one can touch it! The importance of adequate supervision and skill in setting up and in operating such a system cannot be over-emphasized, and it is better to make no provision than to put in a system which is going to be incorrectly operated.

Even where a skilled operator is provided, it is desirable to have a periodic check made of the use of the sound system during an actual performance, so that it is possible to be sure all is well, and that it is being correctly used.

As with the sound-level problem in the auditorium, the reproduced sound level in a sound-proofed control room can also give rise to concern for the health and safety of the operators, if peak sound levels get too high. Both in this regard, and in respect of the high output power of the amplifiers, appropriate precautions must be taken to prevent danger to anyone using or being exposed to the sound system.

4.13.4.7 Video

Of increasing importance in new buildings, and also where it is necessary to add it into old buildings, will be the distribution of video signals. On commercial, business and other premises, and certainly in places of public resort and entertainment, use of video signals is becoming increasingly important. The block diagram of a typical video system is, of course, identical with that of a typical sound system; there are picture sources, combined and selected in a vision mixer, distribution amplifiers, and video displays. The sources to be used can be simple or complex cameras, video tape machines, monochrome or in colour, and vision mixing may vary from a simple control panel with push-button switching, to an elaborate installation with cross-fade, special effects, caption generators, image superimposition and a number of such services.

Ther is a need to anticipate additional video services – the reception of video signals over land lines, or as envisaged in Section 4.13.2 via microwave or satellite terminals. Some video services will be broadcast, other point-to-point; yet others may need to be both-way for tele-conferences, such as British Telecom's Confravision.

Video also includes closed-circuit television (CCTV) for surveillance, or for observing remote or hazardous processes, with signal distribution by coaxial cable, or optical fibre links as these come into more general use. With the increasing availability of microwave and satellite links for television services, the time is not far distant when at least some domestic premises, and most if not every hotel and conference centre will have such a receiving terminal to provide television signals from other countries, or will be connected by cable links to an organisation equipped with an earth station terminal. Such systems, originally known as community antenna television service (CATV) are now commonplace in North America, and are starting to spread into many other countries. This will inevitably mean that even more complex video signal distribution means will need to be provided in such places.

The image displayed to the viewers may be on individual monitors or displays (e.g. the practice of distributing signals by closed circuit to individual receivers located in hotel bedrooms). If required to be seen by a large audience, it may need a number of fairly large screen video monitors or, for the very largest auditoria, the image will be projected by some kind of projection television system. For many applications, what is needed is a high quality image with little or no need to record fast movements. In such cases, great economy in transmission costs can be achieved by a 'slow scan' technique in which electronic signal processing provides a high quality image up-dated only every 5 to 10 seconds. In this system the normal broad-band signal is replaced by data transmission over a voice-grade circuit, with obvious savings on long-distance links.

There is even more need for skill in setting up and operating with video systems than with sound systems, and the implications and costs of this must be kept in mind when such installations are being considered.

4.13.5 Communications planning

With the increasing magnitude and complexity of communications resources, and particularly having regard to the emergence of integrated communications systems for voice, data and other services, the necessity for adequate communications planning becomes self-evident. For public buildings, offices, factory premises, warehouses, department stores and so on, it is just as important to plan the communications resources in advance as it is to specify constructional techniques to be adopted, or the floor loadings to be specified. Later sections on installation matters go into this aspect in greater detail, and for the present it suffices to say that there must be, in any building project, an adequate understanding and specification of the communications requirements, so that they are properly taken into account, as must also be the need for maintenance, modification and extension certain to be required as communications facilities and needs develop over the years.

4.13.6 Installation considerations

4.13.6.1 Building aspects

Consideration is given in this section to two aspects of installations of communications apparatus, the first concerned with the building aspects, and the second concerned with technical matters.

Looking first at the building aspects, it is important to recall that the number, complexity and diversity of communications resources of one kind and another are such that very significant space may be needed for the equipment itself, as well as for the large variety both in number and size of interconnecting cables. The IEE Wiring Regulations, and similar Codes of Practice outside the UK, are planned on the basis that in the ordinary way communications equipment operates at extra low voltage and, therefore, poses no particular hazard. However, as noted earlier, loudspeaker-level signals commonly operate well outside the voltages permitted for extra-low-voltage telecommunications circuits and should be classified, segregated and installed as if they were circuits of the nature of the mains electricity supply.

The Regulations insist on proper segregation and separation of power wiring from communications circuits. As a minimum, this requires ducts which are internally divided, or the provision of separate channels and conduits. It is not unusual in a large administrative office block for there to be upwards of 1000 telephones, together with a rather smaller number of teleprinters, word processors, data terminals and workstations of one kind and another, all needing to be appropriately cabled to each other or back to the common apparatus concerned. This means that significant riser-duct space must be available which passes vertically through the building, preferably, in the case of a building of large plan area, in more than one location within the building. (Fig. 4.13.5).

If such ducts are incorporated in the basic fabric of the building, appropriate precautions must be taken where the ducts pass through the floors to prevent the spread of fire from one floor to another through the duct, and flame barriers should be incorporated especially in ducts built into high-rise buildings. In this regard, installation practice should be similar to, or identical with that prescribed by the IEE Regulations for power distribution.

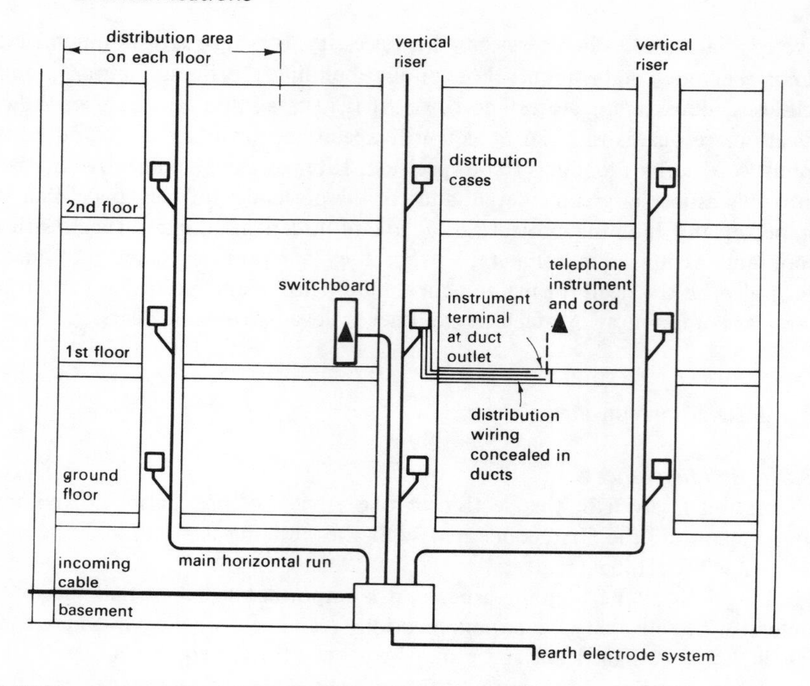

Fig. 4.13.5. *Arrangement of cables and equipment in large building*

In addition to carrying cables, such vertical riser-ducts are often used for the concealment of cable joints and for housing the distribution boxes used for cross-connecting between conductors of different cables. Such riser-ducts commonly pass vertically through the entire building, from basement to the ceiling level of the top floor, as shown in Fig. 4.13.6. The minimum clear internal dimensions of such risers should be 305 × 150 mm and in larger buildings these dimensions can with great advantage be increased up to 455 × 305 mm, both to allow more cables and for more space for distribution cases. Riser-ducts should be fitted internally with a 25 mm backboard, or with cable trays or bearers to facilitate installation and anchoring of cables and the fixing of distribution cases.

Risers must be incorporated into the permanent structure of the building (another reason for advanced planning of communications resources). Lift shafts and light wells must not be used because of the difficulty and danger encountered in installing, adding and maintaining cables etc. (In many territories such use would be excluded by local laws or regulations). Access to each duct is necessary at each floor level through which it passes, and is best afforded by a hinged door at a convenient height and of a size such as to give clear space through which to install or work on distribution cases located in the riser. Access can similarly be provided to the junction between the riser and any horizontal ducts used for local distribution of cables on the floor concerned (Fig. 4.13.7). The provision of adequate

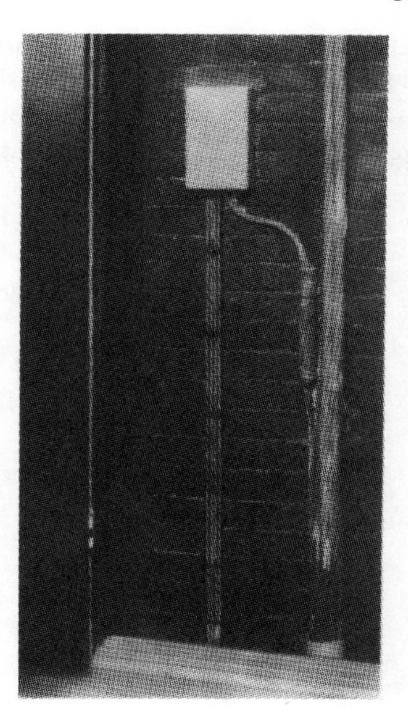

Fig. 4.13.6. *Riser duct and cable distribution*

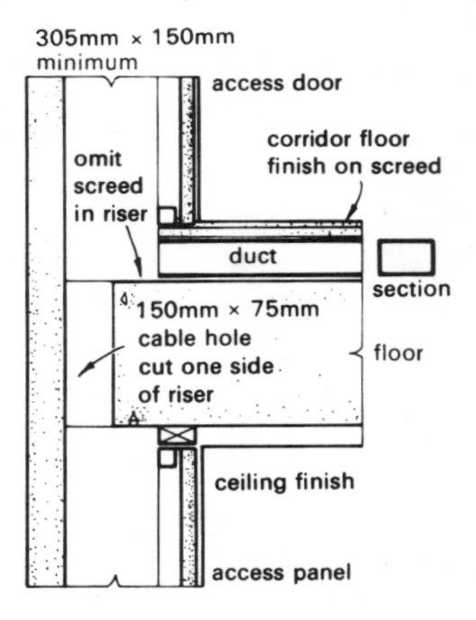

Fig. 4.13.7. *Access between vertical and horizontal ducts.*

duct and riser spaces and capacity will greatly speed up and reduce costs for installation, maintenance and modification of communications services and will similarly reduce turn-round time when new floor layouts are needed. Such activities will be futher facilitated by the provision of suitable socket-outlets for lighting and power use close to all access doors in permanent ducts and risers. To a certain extent, distribution in the horizontal plane is sometimes accommodated in voids above suspended ceilings, but access to such is difficult when the work-space below is in use. Circuits run in ceiling-space ought properly to be confined to those which need to be up there anyway, e.g. to loudspeakers mounted in the ceiling itself.

In the case of large open-plan offices, it is necessary to provide many telecommunications circuits, most of which will be ordinary telephone cables. In addition there may be a need for special circuits such as coaxial cables, and most office equipment dependent on communication links will also need mains power supply. This makes it inevitable that much cable distribution will have to be done at floor level.

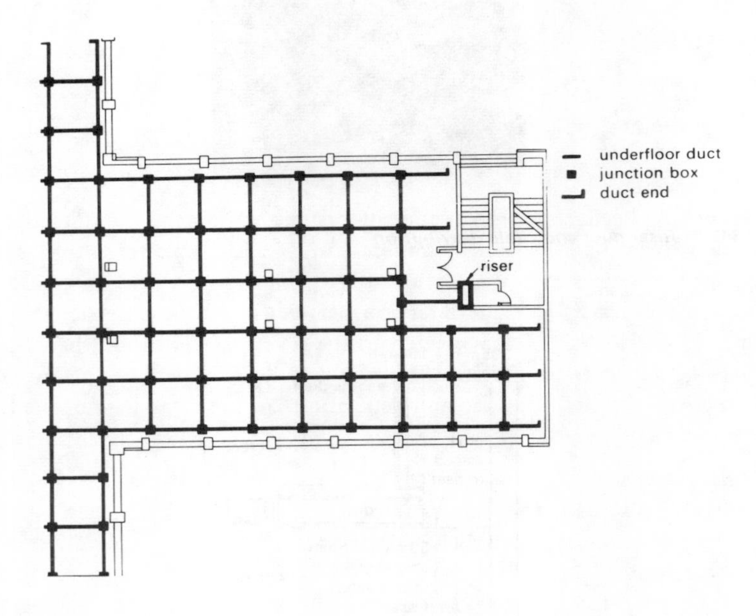

Fig. 4.13.8. *Grid layout of Floor Ducts*

The trend towards large open-plan offices and improved environmental conditions, e.g. close carpeting to the floor, makes it difficult to install floor level cabling without introducing a trip hazard, whilst ducts formed in the floor screed are too restrictive on layout changes. For such environments it is recommended that cabling in the horizontal plane be undertaken by carpet-depth trunking available in the form of lengths of extruded plastic with snap-on lids, which can be laid loose between individual carpet areas either as straight runs or in the form of a grid pattern, (Fig. 4.13.8) and which then allows access from the trunking itself to a desk, table or workstation placed over it, or by the way of a short length of subsidiary trunking at right angles, to a nearby wall for wall-located equipment and terminations. Photographs of such an installation are shown as Figs. 4.13.9 and 4.13.10.

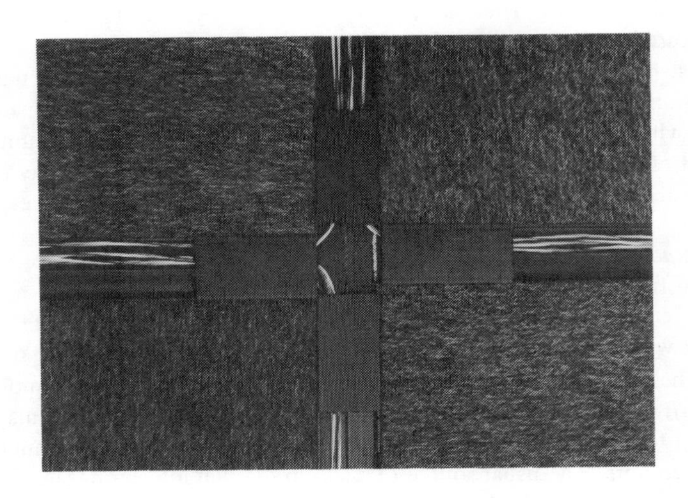

Fig. 4.13.9.

Fig. 4.13.10. ***Carpet depth trunking for communications cables***

(Plessey Telecommunications and Office Systems Ltd.)

No less significant then the need for adequate arrangements for cabling is the need for appropriate amounts and qualities of space in which to mount communications equipment. Unlike the old step-by-step and rotary exchanges, modern telecommunications systems for private communications service are relatively small and silent in their operation.

Accordingly, it is by no means essential to provide separate apparatus rooms for such equipment as PABXs, especially if they are realised in one of the modern electronic technologies. There are, of course, advantages in providing space which can be secured against accidental or deliberate intrusion, e.g. for cable termination points, distribution frames, and so on. Health and Safety legislation may require the provision of separate ventilated accommodation for power plant and storage batteries, where these are used to provide a back-up supply for communications equipment. The heat generated on modern systems is not large, but may need to be taken into account when assessing air flow amounts or air-conditioning capacity.

4.13.6.2 Radio frequency interference

Many industrial processes use radio-frequency energy, and computer installations commonly emit low levels of electrical radiation over a wide spectrum of frequencies, not in any way harmful to individuals but capable of being picked up on sensitive circuits. These circumstances, together with the increasing use of mobile radio transmitter/receiver units, radio paging, and Citizens Band radio, may require precautions to be taken to exclude possibly interfering signals from communications and audio circuits. The usual source of pick-up of such interfering signals is by the communications systems wiring or loudspeaker cables acting as an antenna and injecting the interference back into the communications or amplification equipments. A small amount of additional screening of cables locally is usually sufficient to exclude such stray pick up, but in difficult cases RF chokes or filters may have to be provided. In cases of particularly severe interference it may be necessary to enlist the services of the interference experts of the official radio licensing authority (in UK, the Home Office Radio Department), since effective elimination of severe interference will involve the (not always willing) co-operation of the equipment supplier or user responsible for the interfering radiation.

Additional sources of interference may arise where the main supplies themselves contain harmonics or other signals which can interfere with the communications equipment. As far as possible, communications apparatus, including terminals associated with communications links, should be operated from 'clean' mains supplies – that is, they should not be connected to circuits which also feed substantial loads which may be switched on and off at random times, e.g. lift motors, air-conditioning plants, or factory welding equipment. Indeed, as far as possible, such 'dirty' supplies should be kept out of the immediate vicinity of all communications apparatus. This problem is different from that dealt with in Section 4.13.6.4 which relates to the earthing of equipment, either from noise or on safety grounds.

Where the communications plant to be installed is substantial in either scale or complexity, it is important that the basic provision of risers, ducts, circuit distribution and equipment erection space be made as an inherent part of the building plan, rather than attempt to shoe-horn it in at a stage when the basic building work is complete and decoration is being done. However, the fact that modern switchboards are small in size and attractive in appearance means that they can be included as part of a front reception office for anything other than the very largest office block, thereby saving space and manpower.

4.13.6.3 Power supply

Turning now to the technical aspects of installation considerations, the most important is that of power supply. It is no use having a reliable, modern, digital switching system if it is dependent for its operation on an unreliable service from a mains supply network of doubtful survivability, which may be the case in certain circumstances overseas. It is equally important not to go to the opposite extreme so that a small, compact, modern switching system needs tens of square metres of storage battery space with special ventilation arrangements. The manufacturer, contractor or supplier of the switching equipment concerned is in the best position to advise on the size of reserve battery power to be provided, assuming it is needed at all. Generally speaking, it is sufficient to provide reserve battery power for no more than a few hours' operation, since a modern office installation will be paralysed if the electricity supply fails to computers, lighting equipment, air conditioning or ventilation plant, and so on.

4.13.6.4 Earthing (See also section 3.1.6)

Earthing of equipment often poses problems. It is essential that communications equipment which is operated from mains electricity must be either effectively earthed, or its supply be controlled by earth-leakage or current-balance type circuit breakers (in accordance with the wiring regulations for the territory concerned). However, it is important for the designer and installer of communications equipment to realise that an 'earth' which is provided for safety purposes may well have superimposed on it a great deal of electrical noise over a very broad band of frequencies.

In addition to the electrical noise which is present, there may well be significant potential difference between an earth terminal and the general mass of earth, because of the impedance of the earthing conductor. In some parts of the world there has been a practice of providing what are commonly referred to as a 'noisy' earth and a 'silent' earth, care being taken to keep these apart, and the 'noisy' earth being that which is associated with safety considerations of power supplies, armouring and shields on distribution cables, trunking and so on. The so-called 'silent' earth is associated only with signalling and communications plant, and thereby, it is claimed will be relatively free from noise. There are some instances where this practice has been adopted and has succeeded, but against these may be set a large number of cases where, for example, earth-return conductors are connected to the wrong earth, or the interference has persisted notwithstanding the duality of earth connections. It is accordingly essential that the designers of all the communications services must take proper account of the fact that the 'earth' terminal may not be electrically at a zero potential point, and may indeed have significant levels of audio or radio frequency interference on it, liable to cause malfunctioning of equipment not adequately designed to withstand such noise levels. Nevertheless, the practice of providing earth connections for telecommunications services must be observed, in view of the fact that many telecommunications and audio services operate at very substantial power levels, and an earth is needed on equipment frames, etc, to prevent accumulation of static potentials or other hazardous conditions.

The safety implications of the earthing problem need to be borne in mind in another respect. It is not unusual in the case of a large private switching system, for the battery which provides short-term continuity of supply to be of a few hundred ampere-hours capacity. One pole of the battery will be earthed, and such a battery at a typical telephone exchange voltage of about 50 V will have a short-circuit current of many thousands of amperes. If an earth fault or short-circuit were to occur at or close to the main supply busbar, the impedance is so low that this very high current will be reached in a few microseconds, long before a fuse is able to blow to limit the rise of current. The damage that can be done by such an electrical short-circuit is very considerable in magnitude, and the utmost precautions must be taken against the possibility of it happening.

4.13.6.5 Safety considerations

A further safety consideration which needs to be recalled because it is often overlooked, arises from the practice of distributing audio signals around buildings on a so-called 100 V line. In the traditional days of public address with small cabinet or horn loudspeakers, such a line would seldom carry currents of more than perhaps half an ampere, corresponding to 50 W into the loudspeakers. As noted earlier, public address and sound reinforcement installations commonly use powers up to a kilowatt, and this means that the voltage and current on such a loudspeaker line is more typical of a mains voltage distribution system than of a loudspeaker system, and appropriate wiring precautions must be taken, exactly as for mains wiring. In particular, it is essential to keep such wiring very well separated from communications circuits of a telephone kind and even more important to keep them separated from communications circuits of a low impedance, low level microphone kind.

Electrical interference and disturbance to electronic equipment can also arise from the static charges commonly encountered in buildings which are close carpeted with synthetic (man-made) fibre coverings. (See sec. 3.1.16)

In air-conditioned buildings this can be avoided by not allowing the relative humidity to get too low, and elsewhere care must be taken in the choice of floor coverings.

In addition to the inductive or capacitative transfer of energy from high level to low level circuits, a further hazard exists in large buildings which are equipped with induction loops for users of hearing aids, in that the magnetic field produced within and immediately adjoining the loop itself can produce substantial interference into the more elementary communications plant. The wiring for such a loop may itself also involve a voltage hazard, since a loop which is laid around the perimeter of a large auditorium, or a building such as a cathedral, may have an impedance such that to drive the typical 1 A magnetising current through it requires a few hundred volts of potential difference to be developed across the feeding point to the loop, and here again wiring practices and precautions equivalent to mains voltage distribution cables must be adopted.

Perhaps the most important aspect of installations, both in regard to cabling and equipment, is that the installation should be planned from the beginning on the assumption that it will require periodic maintenance, and it will certainly require to be updated, modified and extended during the lifetime of the building. Here again, the IEE Regulations provide good guidance on the provision of space in conduit and trunking. In addition, ducts used for distribution of services to office machines must be installed in such a way that cables can be added or removed, or the end of the cable be brought out at an entirely different point, at no more than a few moments' notice, so that a change in office layout in an open plan office can be accommodated with no more than a very brief period of delay, and little or no advance planning.

4.13.7 Communications applications

This Section covers in outline only the kind and class of communications services that may be required in various types of premises, and discusses briefly the problems that may arise in implementing them. Reference should also be made to Chapters elsewhere in this book which deal in general with the electrical services for particular classes of buildings.

4.13.7.1 Domestic premises (See also chapter 5.2)

Starting at the simple end of the problem, the first to be considered is that of domestic premises, both houses and flats. In these, and for the reasonably foreseeable future, the only communications services likely to be required are one, or perhaps two, telephone lines for a typical private residence, and the same for an apartment in a purpose built apartment block. There will, of course, be a few domestic premises where perhaps some kind of computer terminal might be installed, either for business or hobby reasons, but generally speaking such devices, and the use of a television receiver for videotext and similar access can make use of the conventional telephone line(s) provided.

Generally speaking, in new work, the cable entry bringing in external telecommunications services will be underground, and should be planned as part of the initial layout of the building development of which the particular building forms one part. A public telecommunications authority (in UK British Telecom) will always co-operate with building developers and architects in planning the layouts of suitable telecommunications services for such premises. British Telecom will also provide information on the best methods of distributing telecommunications service within a building. In view of the progressive adoption world-wide of telephone service by a number of plug points within the building, (so that the actual user of the telecommunications service plugs in the telephone, or other suitable piece of equipment) the need for advance planning becomes even more important but is easily accomplished.

In some blocks of apartments where significant levels of porter and maid services are provided, it is often the practice that telephone service is provided by way of a central switchboard, or PABX, serving the whole block of apartment; in this case the installation has more the characteristics of an office or hotel system.

Good planning of communications services for domestic premises suggests that as a minimum a telephone, or a socket for a telephone, should be provided in each of the principal 'living' rooms, including especially the kitchen and other working rooms, together with at least one or two sockets, or telephones, in the bedroom area of the premises concerned. In addition, for larger premises there may need to be a second telephone circuit, perhaps for staff, perhaps for children's use if the family is a large one, or an extension with intercommunicating facilities to separate buildings such as a garage, workshop, and similar premises detached from the main residence.

4.13.7.2 Office buildings (See also chapter 5.3)

At the opposite end of the scale, it is in office buildings that the greatest variety of communications services is found, together with the most rapid rate of change of use and application of those services.

In earlier sections, mention has been made of conventional telephones, intercommunication systems, direct speech, and similar voice facilities, and during the eighties the trend towards the introduction of communicating office equipment, as a means of improving office and management effectiveness, will grow rapidly. This applies equally to individual items such as data terminals, remote terminals, and job entry facilities for mainframe computers. In addition, account will need to be taken of packet switching systems for the more economic transmission of data to remote locations, facsimile machines for the remote transmission of text and graphics, together with the introduction of communications facilities to such machines as local small computers of the mini-computer, or micro-computer kind, word processors and a wide variety of office workstations, almost all of them based on a typewriter-like keyboard for individual use and a visual display unit on which to receive information.

Some of these will undoubtedly have printers associated with them where hard copy is unavoidably required. Over the next decade more and more office machines which hitherto have been stand-alone, will be interconnected by communications links of one sort and another. International standards are already being developed for the use of telecommunications circuits for digital traffic at a variety of data speeds, for the present day data traffic at 600, 1200 and 2400 baud using modems, to much higher speeds (9·6 to 16 kbits/s), using modems having a self-adapting capability so as to overcome deficiencies in the communications lines, to truly digital circuits provided by the Telecommunications authority which will offer data rates at 8 kbits/s and multiples thereof, 64 and 80 kbits/s, 2·048 Mbits/s and still higher capacities up to 140 Mbits/s.

With a general speed through the eighties of digital methods of switching and transmission in the public network, (in UK by the introduction of the British Telecom 'System X') such digital paths will be able to be extended to almost any distance, thereby providing a very large variety of data facilities more or less universally available. This will greatly facilitate mass information transfers – e.g. in setting up and manipulating data base information – and in direct links between computers or between computers and high capacity terminals. The ready availability of lower data rates will greatly simplify the introduction of remote data terminals of less demanding performance.

The office scene will also be enlivened by the introduction of workstations, which will integrate voice, possibly graphics, and certainly text and data services, into a single terminal having a telephone handset, a keyboard, a visual display unit, and possibly a printer.

Such workstations will be used as much by managers as by their staff, and will provide information direct to management, thereby avoiding the transmission of information in the form of pieces of paper through a large number of hands. This will improve both productivity and the decision making process, and greatly reduce the delays in taking management action to correct any shortcoming of a manufacturing or other operation. However, the greater use of visual display terminals (VDT) implied by this change in activity will impose new considerations of levels of ambient light, both direct and reflected, and of the colour and reflectivity of wall finishes behind VDT users.

4.13.7.3 Factories (See also chapter 5.1)

The situation in factories is likely to be similar to that in office buildings, but with communications resources rather more widely dispersed and in a less concentrated form. The telephone will always be an important medium, but such operations as purchasing and the wealth of activities embraced by production planning, are all likely to benefit by data terminals or workstations. These will derive their information from a database holding information and statistics relating to manufacturing operations. Planning, estimating and related activities will be similarly supported by data terminals having communication links. Factories are also places where extensive use will generally be made of mobile communications services, such as paging, or radio link connections, to enable thinly spread staff to be contacted for instructions, or in an emergency.

Public address systems will certainly be involved in providing relief from the number of monotonous and repetitious tasks which still may be undertaken in factories. This is likely to be occasional periods of music, rather than a continuous background, which is usually ignored after a short period.

4.13.7.4 Hospitals (See also chapter 5.7)
The communications requirements in hospitals are likely to be at least as complex as those in office buildings, but it is very probable that the communications channels will be relatively few in number because the terminals, telephones, etc, will be very widely dispersed over a large area, that is to say with a low telecommunications systems density. In the general nursing area of a hospital, there are likely to be one or two telephones in a typical ward serving a small group of patients, intended primarily for nursing and medical staff use. There will be a plug into which can be connected a trolley-phone for those patients who wish to make outgoing calls. There is already a tendency in some hospitals, at present mainly outside UK, to use communications links for calling up resources, facilities and services – e.g. the use of facsimile equipment to provide the equivalent of a signature authorising a particular course of treatment or medication – together with the use of scanning devices (light-pen) for reading bar coded labels to identify treatments, to record details of medical records, etc.

In view of the increasing trend in hospitals to encourage a degree of activity on the part of patients, it is very likely that existing radio program distribution services to earphones for each patient's bed will be supplemented by extra services providing more channels, including a locally generated hospital radio system, such as is commonly found in many large hospitals in the UK already, together with distribution facilities for video signals for teaching and diagnostic purposes, as well as possibly for t.v. entertainment in patient wards.

4.13.7.5 Computer communications (See also chapter 5.12)
It is in the field of computer installations that there will be the biggest impact of new communications services. Just as the development of computers in the 1960s and 1970s paved the way to an understanding of how better to organise telecommunications services in digital form with computer-like control complexes, so telecommunications is providing the means for computer to be linked to computer, to data terminals, and so on. Remote terminals on computers now appear to offer to their users all the facilities of a powerful mainframe machine in a desk top workstation, which can combine such diverse tasks as computing, sending and receiving messages, interrogation and display of database contents, word processing and computer-aided tuition, if required. It is in respect of computing services that there may for a time be a trend away from the universal adoption of telecommunications resources for the handling and distribution of information, since a number of computer manufacturers are planning proprietary specialist networks which will link computers and terminals together, using signalling and data transmission techniques different from those in use in the telecommunications industry. In the long term this is likely to be uneconomic to the user, in view of the universality of telecommunications circuits. Such specialist networks may continue in use for local and application-oriented use, however, even though they are likely to be superseded ultimately by more universal standards.

Some of these special networks are based on a ring-circuit construction, usually employing coaxial cables, provided at intervals with an access point to which a terminal can be connected and through which the terminal will send and receive data. Such a system can apparently offer higher data rates than a conventional telephone cable, but at the expense of a very considerable cost in wiring. This may well be justified in the immediate vicinity of a computer room, but may be less acceptable for a large installation spread over a plant covering some hundred hectares or so. As already noted, networks based on telecommunications digital technology are much more likely to be the long-term standard, especially with the move to low-cost transmission at high digit rates over optical fibre links.

4.13.7.6 Entertainment (See also chapters 5.9 and 5.14)
In the fields of entertainment, communications will play an increasingly important part. The trend towards smaller cinemas will almost certainly bring with it a widespread use of projection television systems for reproducing the image, supported in due course by terrestrial microwave links or perhaps via a broadcasting satellite. Theatres make comparatively little use of conventional communications in the telephone sense, but rely heavily on electronic communications as an aid to theatrical productions, where a number of ring-circuit intercommunication facilities have been developed specially for theatre use. Theatres are among the largest users of public address and sound reinforcing equipment, often employing complex installations of considerable capital cost. A particular point to be noted in theatre use of communications is that they involve probably the most adverse combination of circuits installed, from the standpoint of interference between separate communications resources. In particular, high level public-address systems or high level induction-loop systems will often produce annoying levels of interference on conventional telephones, intercom and ring-circuit systems. Considerable care is needed in planning such installations so as to segregate and separate circuits as completely as possible.

In theatres it is now normal for stage and auditorium lighting to be controlled by electronic dimming arrangements. Most of these systems generate significant harmonic components at multiples of the a.c. supply frequency and, unless carefully designed with suitable filtering, will induce noise at 'hum' frequency into communications services. Here again it is important to provide adequate separation between lighting circuits so controlled and audio or telecommunications service cables.

4.13.7.7 Concert auditoria (See also chapter 5.9)
Concert halls in many respects are similar to theatres. A great diversity of musical and other entertainments is presented in concert halls, from a small chamber orchestra needing no sound reinforcement whatsoever, to a 'pop' group relying almost entirely on electronic means of presentation. Here, it is most desirable to plan a sound reinforcement system which offers a close approximation to good domestic standards of high fidelity reproduction, together with a flexible control system and the potential to install a large number of microphone or other source

feeding points from the platform area to the control room. The same remarks apply to interference between services as are mentioned above in connection with theatre installations; concert halls are increasingly likely to require induction loops for the hard of hearing and this can, in the larger auditoria, produce induction and coupling problems between the substantial magnetic field generated by the induction loop and the extremely sensitive input circuits on the mixer which may have very long microphone cables attached to them. Here again, very careful attention to installation practices and the separation and screening of cables is essential.

4.13.7.8 Hotels and motels (See also chapter 5.5)
Hotels represent a particular challenge to the designer of communications services. More than almost anywhere else it is essential that the communications services be cost-effective so that, in as direct a way as possible, the cost of providing a communications service can be recouped from the hotel guests using it.

4.13.7.9 Room services
It is now universal practice to provide a PABX with a telephone extension per room. On a modern PABX the extension number can be made to coincide with the room number, thereby aiding guest recognition. In addition, common services such as the housekeeper, restaurant, room or floor service, need to identify the party calling them, and modern hotel telephone systems often also provide calling number identification to all service points within the hotel. The identification usually takes the form of a display of the calling room number, but in the more elaborate installations the name of the person booked into that room can be displayed so that the guest can be greeted by name.

In addition, hotels usually require the cost of calls made by guests from their rooms by direct dialling to be recorded in some individual way, so that they can be charged on the bill. Normal practice is to provide a call-charge meter per extension, so that charging signals from the public telephone exchange serving the hotel will be recorded on the meter, and the charge accumulated during a guest's period of residence can then be used for telephone service charging. With more modern PABX systems employing stored program control, it is usual to provide outputs which directly analyse the actual cost of calls made by the guest and do so in a form able to be fed directly in to the hotel's billing computer, including full details of the numbers called, the time and the duration of the calls made.

Some aspects of hotel service operations directly involve communications links and services, e.g. the use of data transmission techniques for the forwarding of information for guests' use of hotel services to the central data processing installation. Others include the use of electronically coded keys and locking systems to control access to residents' rooms; here again the communications service need is obvious, and still further increases the emphasis on adequate advance planning.

4.13.7.10 Conference facilities

Many hotels, in an understandable attempt to increase their room occupancy ratios, provide conference facilities which are offered on a package-deal basis to guests as an inducement to stay in the hotel. Some of the conference facilities are existing hotel reception rooms suitably adapted, whereas others are purpose built as annexes to the hotel, and in some cases complete conference complexes have been specially constructed.

For such conference facilities, the keynote for the communications installation must be flexibility. It must as a minimum be possible to provide basic telephone service, with a reasonable number of circuits available, in any of the conference rooms, thereby allowing for example a press conference to be set up. In addition, it is desirable to have facilities for the distribution of audio and video signals from a centre point to each of the conference rooms, and perhaps to the hotel as a whole. Each conference area will require to have sound reinforcement equipment with individual facilities, but so arranged that when partitions are opened up between individual conference rooms to provide a larger combined conference facility, the sound systems are easily able to be coupled to provide adequate coverage over the entire area. Because of the variety of room layouts that will be required, it is important that connection points for cables to microphones, and if possible also connection points for cables to loudspeakers, should be provided at several different locations in each part of the conference area, thereby not unreasonably constraining the kind of layout which can be provided in the conference facility. Care must be exercised to ensure that different plugs and sockets are used for the various services to avoid mistakes or actual damage (e.g. by plugging a microphone into a loudspeaker socket).

Controls for these sound and video services should be located as close as possible to the point of use. It should not be regarded as satisfactory, even in a simple combination of one or two microphones, an amplifier, and a couple of loudspeakers for everything to be permanently fixed in position, and fixed in volume setting, with the controls locked away in a remote service passage-way. There should always be some greater degree of flexibility both in operation and in use than this barest minimum, without going to the cost and complexity of a highly centralised arrangement needing a full-time professional operator.

As a minimum in a typical conference room, there should be a microphone available on a lectern, and one or more microphones available to be put on the table for session chairmen, or group discussion speakers. Additional microphone points in a larger room should be provided for microphones on long, trailing cables to be used for questions from the audience during discussion periods. The alternative, of using radio microphones, needs great care in planning so that the use of a radio microphone in one room will not cause an unacceptable breakthrough into a similar, but supposedly independent, system in a nearby room. In view of the very limited number of channel frequencies available for radio microphones, this requires very careful planning of communications resources. In addition, the problem of noise (hum) arising from electronic dimmers may be encountered, as in theatres;

adequate separation between lighting and communications circuits must be observed.

A final requirement which is already evident and is likely to increase, is the provision of video facilities to enable participants in a conference in one location to be addressed by a speaker in a different location using a remote t.v. link.

Such links are normally provided using spare t.v. channels of the type available for outside broadcast use by broadcasting authorities, and in a conference centre providing a full range of modern facilities, it will be essential to provide video termination arrangements to enable such links to be set up quickly and without a long period of advance notice. A particular manifestation of this is the teleconferencing service offered by British Telecom, at the moment only from fixed locations, and known as 'Confravision'. In this, some of the participants in the conference sit in a special studio in one British Telecom location, and the remainder sit in a studio elsewhere. Both way, high quality audio links are provided, and both way video, so that each group can see and hear the other.

In future, given proper availability of video terminating and distribution facilities in a well-equipped conference location, a tele-conference could be established in no longer a time than is taken to patch through the necessary links and to line up the terminal equipments – a matter of an hour or so, given one or two days' notice.

4.13.8 References

4.13.8.1 References in text

(1) Royal National Institute for the Deaf. (RNID) 105 Gower Street London WC1E 6AH
(2) Home Office, Radio Regulatory Department, Waterloo Bridge House London SE1

4.13.8.2 British Standards (See also Appendix 6.2)

BS 6305 sets out the general requirements for apparatus for connection to the British Telecom public network, whilst BS 6301, BS 6312, BS 6317, BS 6320 and BS 6328 cover specific aspects of such apparatus. Attention is also drawn to the following Codes of Practice: BS 6259, BS CP 3, BS CP 326, BS CP 413, BS CP 1013, BS CP 1020, BS CP 1022.

4.13.8.3 Bibliography

IEEE Standard Dictionary of Electrical and Electronic Terms. The Institute of Electrical and Electronic Engineers Inc, New York.

Regulations for Electrical Installations, 15th Edition published by the Institution of Electrical Engineers together with later amendments, and the Commentary (Jenkins) and the Guide (Whitfield). Peter Peregrinus Limited.

Telecom Users Handbook. Telecommunications Press.

A security control centre

Chapter 4.14

Electronic security systems

A. D. Matthews, B.A.(Hons.) M.Inst.M.
Chubb Alarms Limited

4.14.1 Introduction

Electrical and electronic surveillance systems, supported by efficiently controlled and trained staff, provide a basis for effective building security. The type of security system installed will obviously depend on the type of building concerned. Principles, however remain similar for all types of system.

We can define four types of electronic security systems

(a) Intruder alarm system
(b) Access control system
(c) Closed Circuit Television System (CCTV)
(d) Fire Protection system

One or more of these systems, may be installed in a building and they may be interconnected with one another. Each will be considered in turn. Finally, a combination of these, the

(e) Integrated security system will be considered.

A number of British Standards have been published which deal with specific aspects of security systems, whilst the January 1983 amendments to the 15th Edition of the IEE Wiring Regulations make reference to electricity supplies for safety services, including security systems.

4.14.2 Intruder alarm systems

4.14.2.1 General

The purpose of an intruder alarm system is to detect the presence of intruder activity, to process alarm signals and exercise control over them, in order to provide information on alarm activity. In response to alarm activity a warning signal is generated with the objective of either scaring off the intruder or calling for assistance in the hope of apprehending the intruder. Standards for the performance of equipment, installation, operation and maintenance of intruder alarm systems, are defined by BS 4737:1977. All major alarm companies install and maintain systems in accordance with this Standard and will issue a certificate of compliance on completion of system installation. The National Supervisory Council for Intruder Alarms (NSCIA) (Ref. 1) maintains a roll of approved installers, who as a condition of such enrolment, undertake to install and maintain alarm systems in compliance with BS 4737. In addition, the NSCIA maintains an independent inspectorate in order to ensure that its enrolled members comply with BS 4737. It is important to note that a number of police forces and insurance companies issue their own Codes of Practice for intruder alarm systems. Individual requirements may be complementary to BS 4737, but they do sometimes conflict with it and with one another.

4.14.2.2 Intruder alarm detectors

A wide range of detectors are available for different applications. The need for detection begins outside the building, in order to detect the approach of an intruder. Entry into the building or movement through it can be detected and monitored by various means. Table 4.14.1 summarises the main types of intruder alarm detection devices.

In order to ensure that the appropriate detection device is used for each application, a thorough and professional building or site survey should be carried out. This will ensure that effective detection is provided with a minimum of false alarms.

4.14.2.3 Installation of detectors

Intruder alarm detectors should be installed in accordance with BS 4737 and the surveyor's system specification, the detectors being grouped into circuits for ease of alarm (and fault) identification. A good practice is to allocate as few detectors as possible to each circuit. In fact an increasing trend is for each detector to be individually identified by its own circuit at the central control. Every detection circuit should be a double pole four wire circuit, or equivalent as in BS 4737. This four wire circuit provides both alarm signalling from the detector and intrinsic cable tamper indication. As an alternative for special security applications, line supervision can also be provided electronically. All circuit wiring must be supported by either conduit, trunking or adequate cable fixings. Installation requirements are fully detailed in BS 4737.

4.14.2.4 Multiplexing

In order to minimise the amount of cable installation, a multiplexed communication system may be used. This simply means that a number of detectors share a single cable. Each detector is scanned in turn, reporting its alarm status when scanned to the central controller. In order to ensure system integrity, the scanning

Table 4.14.1 *Intruder Alarm Detectors*

Alarm Category	Detector Type
Outdoor or Perimeter Detection	Outdoor microwave beams Outdoor infra-red rays Underground protection systems Microphonic fence protection Geophonic vibration detectors.
Trap Protection	Magnetic door and window contacts Closed circuit wiring for doors, windows and enclosures Pressure pads Infra-red rays and beams
Space Protection	Microwave detectors Ultrasonic detectors Passive infra-red detectors Capacitance detectors
Acoustic Detectors	Breakglass detectors Wall detectors Safe detector Strongroom detector
Deliberately Operated Devices	Personal attack button or key Footbar alarm Radio attack alarm

is carried out extremely rapidly and coded signal streams are used between detector and controller.

A typical configuration is shown in Fig. 4.14.1. Apart from the substantial cable savings that can be achieved for large systems, there are considerable additional benefits of flexibility and lower long term site disruption for additions and changes to the overall detection. Such system changes can readily be encompassed within the scheme without a need for additional main cable over the long distances. It is also apparent from Fig. 4.14.1, that a multiplex communication system may be bi-directional, so that it provides a remote control or command capability in response to alarm conditions. A more comprehensive description of multiplex communications can be found in "Handbook of Security". (Ref. 2)

4.14.2.5 Control equipment

Information gathered from detector circuits is processed and displayed by the control unit. In response to alarm activity external alarm signals must be despatched by the control unit, to audible warning devices or to summon assistance. High security installations may also be remotely monitored by a central station to ensure that they are set or unset at predetermined times. All control units should conform to BS 4737 and central stations to BS 5979: 1981. This will ensure that they are constructed soundly, operate in a secure and reliable manner and provide a protection against misoperation and tamper. A standby power supply must be an integral part of the control unit in order that operation is sustained in the event of a mains power supply failure.

An appropriate control unit is selected according to the size of the

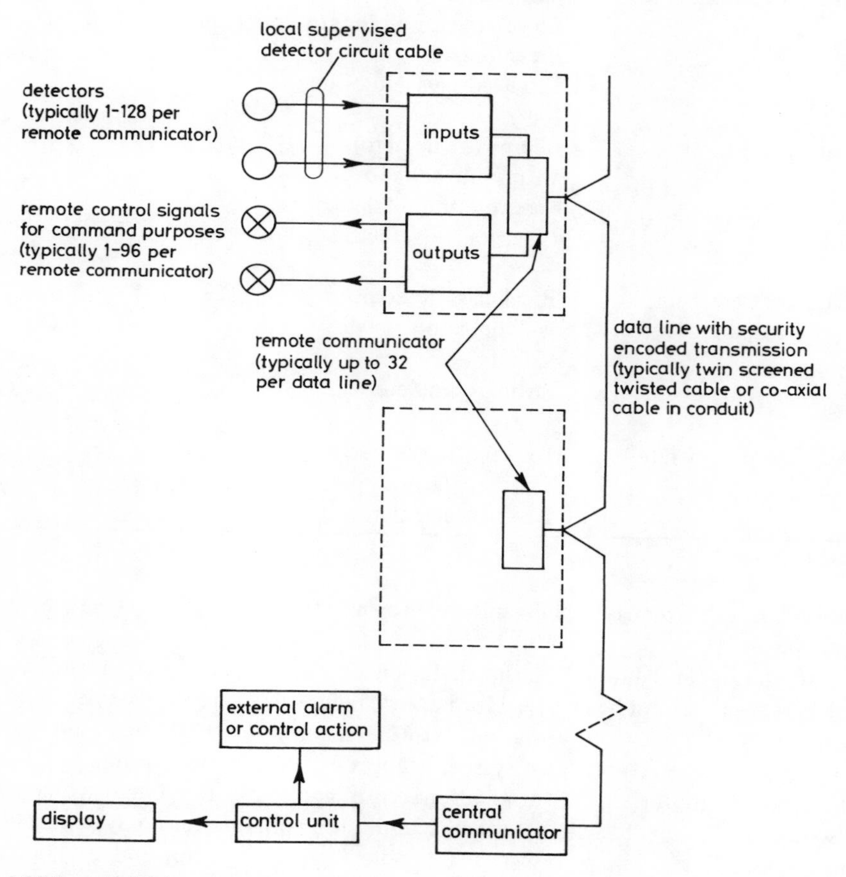

Fig. 4.14.1. *Multiplex signalling system*

system, the security requirements and the processing/display of alarm signals. Table 4.14.2 summarises a typical range of facilities provided. Most alarm control units now incorporate complex electronic circuits, including the use of microprocessor technology. Processing of alarm data may be provided in order to minimise false

Table 4.14.2 *Alarm Control Units*

Unit 1 Residential and small industrial/commercial applications	*Unit 2* Residential, industrial and commercial applications	*Unit 3* Bank installations and high security industrial/ commercial applications
2 Alarm circuits Personal attack alarm 1 Exit circuit 1 Tamper circuit	3 Alarm circuits Personal attack alarm 1 Exit circuit 1 Tamper circuit Entry Timer Alarm	4 Alarm circuits Personal attack alarm 1 Exit circuit 2 Tamper circuits Entry Timer Alarm Exit Timer Alarm
	Capable of extension by a further 16 circuits	Extension capability in units of 8 circuits
Actuation of internal and external sounders	Actuation of internal and external sounders	Actuation of many combinations of internal and external sounders.
Remote signalling of: Circuit alarms Personal attack	Remote signalling of: Circuit Alarms Personal attack System set/unset Late working Low voltage supply	Remote signalling of: Circuit alarms Personal attack Timer set Tamper Low voltage supply Power failure Shunt fault System set/unset Late working

alarm conditions. Emphasis is placed on ensuring maximum reliability and ease of maintenance.

4.14.2.6 External signalling

Alarm information may be relayed to audible warning devices (i.e. bells, or electronic sounders), to police stations or to private alarm central stations. Direct lines to Police Stations are obviously an effective way of ensuring a response to the alarm call. However, due mainly to police pressure of work, coupled with accommodation problems, many Police Station facilities are being withdrawn. Instead, alarm signals are transmitted to private alarm communication centres, operated under high security protocol by approved alarm companies, who then have the responsibility of calling for a police response when required.

The following types of remote alarm signalling are in use:

(a) Digital Dialler, using electronic transmission of digital information to a receiver at an alarm company central station.
(b) Direct Telecom line connection to Police Station or alarm company central station.
(c) Multiplex alarm transmission over Telecom lines to alarm company central stations.

For all types of alarm signalling a prime emphasis is placed on security and reliability of transmission.

4.14.2.7 Security system integrity
It is of course vitally important to ensure integrity of the security system itself and that no compromise occurs. This can best be achieved by working with a reputable alarm company, who screen all employees and maintain impeccable standards of discipline and operational procedures. Control should be maintained of all security information and system documentation so that this does not fall into wrong hands. System design should be such that it is self monitoring 24 hours a day and fully tamper protected.

4.14.2.8 False alarms
Any electronic system is, of course, prone to occasional failure, resulting in a possible false alarm. This risk can be minimised by insistance on high standards of equipment construction, installation expertise and regular maintenance. Problems may occur due to external influences, such as telephone line failure, used for external signalling. Due to the security risks involved, such failures must be regarded as suspected sabotage (until proved otherwise) and an alarm raised. There is likely to be a continuing conflict of objectives between the police on one hand – who wish every call on their services to be in response to a genuine alarm in order that they may arrest the offender – and insurers and the protected, on the other hand – who wish to deter or frighten off any criminal activity such that no potential criminal gains access to the protected area.

4.14.3 Access control systems

Access control systems complement an intruder alarm system by monitoring and controlling the movement of people and vehicles within or throughout a premises. In addition the access control system may be used to provide alarm monitoring and control facilities. Systems can be broadly categorised into two types:

(a) *Off Line* – Where an authorisation for entry or exit is provided by a reading mechanism at that location, without reference to any other control mechanism or information system.
(b) *On Line* – Where readers are connected either directly or by multiplex communications to a central device such as a microprocessor or a mini computer. An individual's request for entry or exit is despatched to the central unit which then

decides whether or not to grant this request, based on a set of stored criteria regarding personnel and their permitted movements within the premises. Such systems may also be used for management information purposes.

All systems work on a similar principle. A card or token is presented to a reader which then (either independently or with remote assistance) allows or prevents access and/or exit through doors or other barriers. Three types of readers are available for both "on" and "off" line applications:

(a) Readers requiring presentation of a valid token.
(b) Readers requiring entry of validification data, such as a personal numerical code.
(c) Readers requiring both a valid token and a personal identification.

Tokens may take a wide variety of forms. They are usually, however, cards encoded with data which is read by one or more of the following techniques – magnetics, radio, light or infra-red energy.

Systems may be programmed to allow access according to a person's status or only at particular times. In addition, ability may be provided to update a system, to add or delete cards or special user facilities. A printed record of all system activity may be provided and if desired, special reports may be printed. It is even possible for an access control system to monitor and control photocopier usage and petrol pump dispensing.

4.14.4 Closed circuit television (CCTV)

CCTV is an integral part of many security systems. Systems range from a single monitor with just one camera dedicated to it, through to systems with many internal and external cameras, connected via switching equipment to several locations for display. Often CCTV cameras are required to operate in total darkness, where floodlighting is impractical. This is possible, by use of infra-red lighting, which renders the scene under observation visible to the camera whilst it is apparently in total darkness to the naked eye.

Cameras may be fixed, or movable under remote control. Typically an external camera would be enclosed in a weatherproof housing. By remote control the camera can be panned, tilted, focussed, adjusted for exposure and have its viewing screen washed and wiped. All of these functions are carried out from a CCTV control panel; pictures from several cameras can be automatically sequenced and any desired picture held for display on that, or a second associated monitor.

In order to save installation cable and cost, pictures from several cameras can be multiplexed onto a single co-axial video cable, together with all of the signals necessary for remote control of the cameras, by means of telemetry. A permanent record from the television pictures can then be stored and replayed, by means of a video tape recorder.

4.14.5 Fire protection systems

4.14.5.1 General

The essence of successful fire protection is to ensure that fires can be detected and fought within a few moments of their breaking out. Early detection also allows more time for the evacuation of buildings and the protection of property, so that the fire can be controlled before it reaches unmanageable proportions. Fire protection systems can be divided into four main groups:—

(a) Automatic fire detection and alarm
(b) Portable extinguishers and related equipment.
(c) Automatic sprinkler systems.
(d) Special extinguishing systems.

Each has a vital part to play in preventing the ravages of fire which, if left unchecked, can cause total destruction of a business enterprise.

4.14.5.2 Automatic fire detection and alarm

In the event of an outbreak of fire, the fire must be detected before any action can be taken to protect people or property at risk. In many instances this can effectively be accomplished by an automatic fire detection and alarm system. An automatic fire alarm system consists of fire detectors wired to control and indicator equipment which provides a reliable power supply and actuates audible and visible warning devices. The most effective systems are connected directly to the fire brigade or to an alarm company central station.

Guidance on the performance and installation requirements for such systems is given in British Standard Code of Practice BS 5839. Under certain circumstances reduced insurance premiums can be obtained by ensuring compliance with the Fire Offices Committee (F.O.C) guidelines. (Ref. 3) Whenever the installation of a system is being considered the services of a reputable fire alarm company should be used and the fire brigade and insurers should always be consulted. For the purpose of the Fire Precautions Act 1972, the Factories Acts and the Offices, Shops and Railway Premises Act, alarm systems must, generally, be equipped for manual operation, as well as automatic operation, in order to give warning to persons within the premises.

4.14.5.3 Manual call points

Manual call points, such as break glass units, should be located such that no person need travel more than 30 metres from any position within the premises to generate an alarm. They should be located on exit routes, floor landings of staircases and at exits to the open air. The manual call points should be installed 1·4 metres above the floor, in accessible, well lit, conspicuous positions, free from obstruction.

4.14.5.4 Fire alarm detectors

Automatic fire alarm detectors are designed to detect one or more of three characteristics of a fire, which are heat, flames (radiation) and smoke. A wide range of

Table 4.14.3 *Fire Alarm Detectors*

Detector type	Detection characteristics
Heat Detectors	Expansion of a metal to close an electrical contact Differential expansion of a bimetal strip. Expansion of a liquid in a thin metal tube. Expansion of a gas (pneumatic detectors). Fusion of a metal alloy at a certain temperature. Melting of a heat sensitive insulation in a cable assembly to allow contact between two conductors. Release of mechanism caused by melting of a plastic cord. Release of pressurised gas caused by heat softening of a plastic tube. Thermo-electrical effect Change in electrical (resistance or capacitance) or magnetic properties. Chemical effect caused by heat.
Flame Detectors	Infra-red Ultra-violet
Smoke Detectors	Ionisation detection Optical detectors
Combined Heat and Smoke Detector	Infra-red light beam

detectors, summarised in Table 4.14.3, are available. The type of detector chosen must relate to the particular application and the experience of a skilled fire surveyor should be sought. In certain cases more than one type of detector may be used to protect an area. Detectors should conform to BS 5445 and BS 5446.

There are two main types of heat detectors

(a) Fixed temperature devices – in which an alarm is given when the detection element reaches a pre-determined temperature, and
(b) Rate of rise devices – in which an alarm is given when there is an increase in heat at a rate greater than a pre-determined value.

Often these two types of detection are incorporated within a single heat detector.

Flame detectors either detect ultra-violet radiation or infra-red radiation caused by fire. Both types use photo-electric cells, which react to direct radiation or when radiation is reflected on to them by mirrors.

Smoke is a suspension of small particles in air, resulting from combustion, and there are two basic types of device for detecting this:

(a) Ionisation detectors (sometimes known as combustion gas detectors) – which detect combustion particles, and
(b) Optical detectors – which rely on the obscuration or the scattering of light by smoke particles.

Some optical detectors employ both these effects.

The combined heat and smoke detector, illustrated in Fig. 4.14.2 and 4.14.3, uses an emitter, which generates a pulsed beam of infra red light, normally detected by a remote receiver. The received signal is analysed for either loss of strength caused by smoke obscuration ('a' in Fig. 4.14.3), or for changes in the air's refractive index caused by thermal turbulance ('b' in Fig. 4.14.3). Each unit provides coverage to 7 metres on either side of the beam, over a distance of 100 metres, making this type of detector particularly suitable for buildings with high ceilings, large open areas, cable tunnels or large ducts and the coverage of dangerous areas – such as above acid tanks or above machinery.

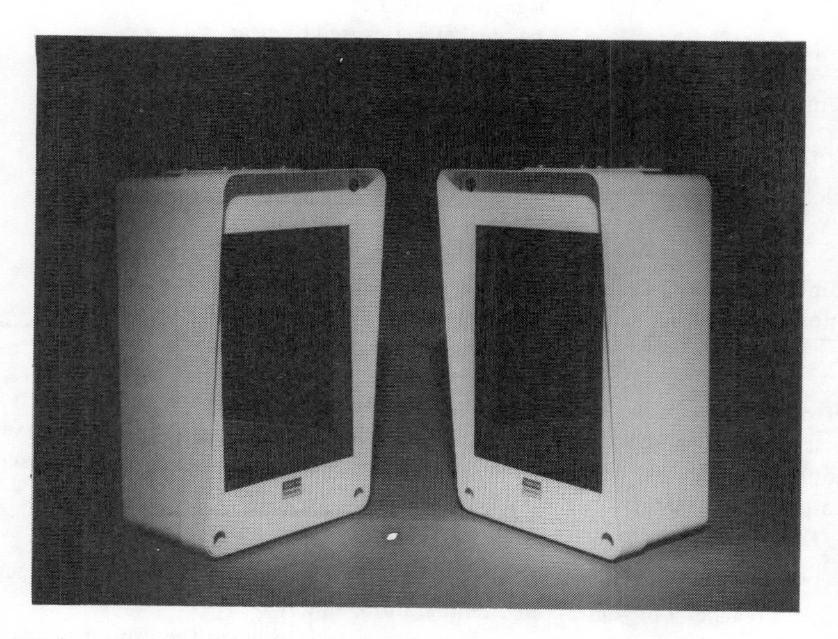

Fig. 4.14.2. *Combined heat and smoke detector* (Chubb Fire Security Ltd)

4.14.5.5 Installation of detectors

Detectors should be installed according to a fire surveyor's specification and in accordance with BS 5839 Part 1. Each type of detector has its own unique installation requirement in order to achieve effective protection. Manufacturers' recommendations must be followed at all times. Detectors should be grouped into zones in order to clearly indicate the source of a fire. These zones should conform fully to the requirements of BS 5839 Part 1: Section 7.

If p.v.c insulated cable is used for electrical connection of fire detectors it should be protected by conduit or trunking or installed in a duct or channel. If such protection is not available then mineral insulated copper sheathed (m.i.c.s.) cable should be used. Where m.i.c.s. cable is to be installed in damp or corrosive conditions, or underground, it should be p.v.c. sheathed overall. Wherever possible

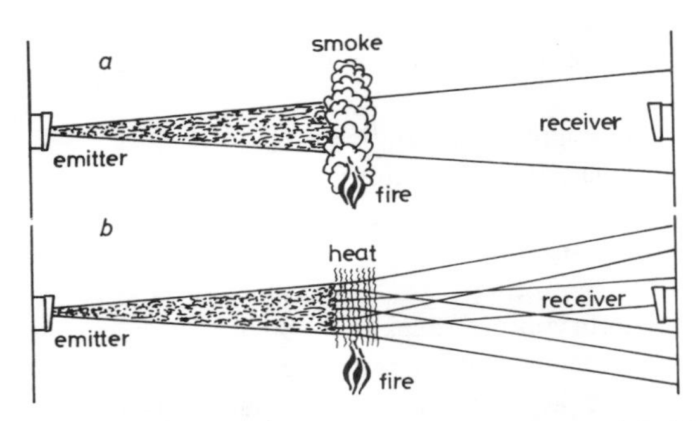

Fig. 4.14.3. *Operation of combined heat and smoke detector* (Chubb Fire Security Ltd)

cables should be routed in protected areas of low fire risk. A multiplexed communication system may be used provided that the reliability of the fire alarm system is not reduced by the sharing of the transmission by signals from other sources (such as intruder alarms).

4.14.5.6 Control equipment

Information gathered from fire alarm detectors is processed and displayed by the control unit which then takes action in response to the alarm conditions. This must clearly show the origin of the fire by zone indication. Where necessary an associated building plan or mimic diagram may be used. The control unit must also provide an integral warning of internal or cable faults, and all control units should conform to BS 3116 Part 4 in order to ensure sound construction and reliable operation; Table 4.14.4 summarises facilities provided by a typical multi-zone fire alarm panel.

4.14.5.7 External signalling

Alarm information may be relayed to audible warning devices (i.e. bells or electronic sounders), or to fire brigades, or to private alarm central stations. In most cases a reliable link with the fire brigade is vital, either directly or via a private alarm central station. Considerable economy in communication of alarm information may be obtained by sharing the same transmission media as for an associated intruder

Table 4.14.4 *Typical Control Unit Facilities*

	Typical Control Unit Facilities
1.	Identification of zone at fire or fault
2.	Keyswitch control to enable silencing of alarms, reset, test and evacuation procedures
3.	Two stage alarm activation
4.	Separate alarm output for each zone
5.	Relay equipment for external alarm, plant shutdown, discharge of fire fighting systems and/or fire brigade signalling.
6.	Repeat indication
7.	Flashing fire and fault indication, which becomes steady when the alarm is accepted.
8.	Zone power and mains failure indication
9.	Latching fire signal, overiding fault indication
10.	Latching or non-latching fault indication
11.	Low power consumption
12.	Flush or surface mounting
13.	Extension capability in multiples of 4 zones
14.	Power supply protection and monitoring
15.	Protection against false alarm caused by spurious signals
16.	Full circuit monitoring against short circuit, open circuit and low insulation resistance.

alarm system. Typically a digital dialler or multiplex alarm transmission system to a central station provides such a facility.

4.14.5.8 False alarms

False alarms may occur, whatever the system. Unless care is taken all systems may give alarms due to such causes as: mechanical and electrical faults resulting from inadequate maintenance; vibration, impact; ambient conditions and communication faults arising from maintenance and testing work or arising from outside activity on line plant. Fire detection systems are seldom called upon to operate, yet they must be fully operational when required. Routine testing should be carried out every week and servicing at least twice a year.

4.14.5.9 Portable equipment

Portable fire-fighting equipment is an essential complement to an automatic fire alarm system. Used at the start of a fire it can save thousands of pounds' worth of damage and prevent disruption of business. The main types of portable equipment are fire extinguishers, fire blankets, hose reels and water buckets. It is important that the correct type of extinguishing agent is used for the risk involved. Water should not be used on electrical equipment or flammable liquids. For fires involving flammable liquids, foam or dry powder agents should be used. For electrical and electronic equipment, carbon dioxide (CO_2) or vapourising liquids (such as Halon 1211) should be used.

4.14.5.10 Automatic sprinkler systems
Automatic sprinkler systems operate by means of a fire detector – such as a quartzoid bulb; chemical capsule or fusible element – releasing water onto the fire, when the temperature reaches a predetermined level. The F.O.C. Rules (Ref. 3) require the individual design of a sprinkler system for each type of occupancy. Whilst initial installation may be expensive, benefits arise from the possible reduction of insurance premiums and low maintenance costs.

4.14.5.11 Special extinguishing systems
Where there are high fire risks or where disruption of business could have serious consequences, for example in data processing rooms and chemical plants, a special extinguishing system may be installed. An automatic fire detection system, linked to the extinguishing system, releases an appropriate agent to flood the area at risk. The main extinguishing agents used are Carbon Dioxide (CO_2), Halon 1211 (also known as BCF), Halon 1301 (also known as BTM) and low, medium or high expansion foam.

Carbon Dioxide and halogen discharge systems are most effective on surface burning as opposed to deep seated burning. Early detection and discharge of the agent is vital for effective control and minimum damage. Since these gases totally flood the area at risk and in so doing inhibit oxygen, complete evacuation of the area is necessary in order to prevent risk to occupants. Foam is most frequently used in conjunction with smoke or flame detectors, to protect fuel tanker loading bays, warehouses, aircraft hangers, inaccessible basements and cable tunnels.

Expert advice should be obtained in order that the correct type of extinguishing agent is used, that it is correctly interfaced to the automatic detection system and that the whole is designed as a complete system matched to the environment involved. Care must also be taken to prevent accidental operation of the system due to false alarms. To minimise this risk, more than one detector may be required to operate before discharge of the extinguishing system.

4.14.6 Integrated security systems

An effective means of providing a total security system is to integrate intruder and fire alarm monitoring and control, command signalling, access control and CCTV into one building control system. Such systems are often computer controlled and can put at the disposal of a security guard and fire station information from anywhere on even the largest of installations. Many routine operations can be automatically programmed into the computer system, ensuring a speedy and efficient security response. An immediate reaction to fire can also be given, by sounding alarms at key points, automatically controlling lifts and ventilators and identifying required response from security or fire personnel. Even though these systems may be quite extensive in capability they are often more cost effective than installing several independent systems and can provide substantial savings in installation and manpower.

4.14.7 References

4.14.7.1 References in text

(1) National Supervisory Council for Intruder Alarms (NSCIA) St. Ives Road Maidenhead Berks SL6 1RD

(2) PETER HAMILTON (Ed) 'Handbook of Security', Section 7.2.9B. Kluwer-Harrap Handbooks

(3) Fire Offices Committee Aldermary House Queen Street London EC4P 4JD

4.14.7.2 Legislation (See also Appendix 6.1)

Factories Act 1961
Fire Precautions Act 1972
Offices, Shops and Railway Premises Act 1963

4.14.7.3 British Standards (See also Appendix 6.2)

BS 4737 and BS 5979 deal with intruder alarm systems, and BS 3116, BS 5445, BS 5446 and BS 5839 deal with various aspects of fire detection and alarm systems.

Fig. 4.15. *Arsenal Football Ground: metal halide floodlighting and undersoil heating* (Thorn-EMI Lighting Ltd)

Chapter 4.15

External heating

G. F. Hornby, M.C.I.B.S.
Director, Paterson Heating Limited

4.15.1 Introduction

4.15.1.1 Applications

External heating of external surfaces provides an effective means of raising the surface temperature above freezing to prevent hazardous conditions occurring due to the presence of snow and ice. The clearance of snow and the prevention of ice formation is important for roadways with a gradient, as well as access ramps and staircases. Sports grounds and race tracks can similarly be protected, thereby avoiding cancellations of meetings. Factory unloading and loading bays, domestic driveways and many other areas where the prevention of ice and snow is desirable can be fitted with electric heating elements. Although electric road heating may not appear to be cheap it is completely automatic and labour free, and controls can be arranged so that the surface can be heated before the formation of ice occurs and melt falling snow as it comes into contact with the heated surface.

With the increased use of motor vehicles and the provision for parking in elevated car parks the installation of heating cables in car parks is on the increase; in this particular application the heating cables can be installed during the general construction work thereby keeping the cost of the system to a minimum.

4.15.1.2 Construction

During the last 20–25 years a large number of road and ramp heating installations have been carried out, some of which have been monitored by the Transport and Road Research Laboratory and by some local authorities from which the following fundamental requirements have emerged:

(a) The system must operate efficiently and economically, these two requirements being affected by the electrical load installed and the type of control system employed.

(b) The installation of the system should be compatible with present day construction and road laying practices, thereby necessitating little or no change from normal techniques.
(c) Maintenance work, particularly on roadways, should be hampered as little as possible by the inclusion of the system. Repairs to the road surface could affect the heating elements but these are usually laid in well defined panels which helps to keep this problem to a minimum.

Two different systems have been developed, one using uninsulated steel mesh elements operating at voltages of up to approximately 30 V between conductor and earth, and the other using insulated heating cables operating at 240 V.

4.15.1.3 System capacity

The purpose of electric external surface heating is to maintain the heated area at just above freezing point, thereby preventing the formation of ice and being capable of melting any falling snow. The system should have sufficient capacity to do this under normal winter conditions; being able to cope with extreme conditions would necessitate higher electrical loads and would probably prove to be uneconomical as well as increasing the capital installation costs.

As the electrical loads associated with road heating are often large, an early approach to the Electricity Authority is desirable to ensure that a suitable electricity supply can be made available.

4.15.2 Systems

4.15.2.1 Mesh system

Expanded mild steel mesh is used and made up to form panels with the required electrical characteristics. Bus bars at each end of the panel are used for connecting the heavy feeder cables required to carry the high current. The mesh can be laid in place and held down by masonry nails or by pads of asphalt and can be covered directly by the wearing surface, although it might be advantageous to lay a sand asphalt layer first; this may prove an advantage during maintenance work.

4.15.2.2 Cable systems

Types of cable

(a) Cables commonly used are of two types, elastomeric and mineral insulated. Elastomeric cables usually have a stranded conductor insulated with crossed linked polyethylene (XLPE); these cables have a larger cross-sectional area for both conductor and insulation than the normal floorwarming variety and are able to stand up to the rigours of site treatment. A variation on this construction is to use the lighter floorwarming construction and cover this with a tinned copper wire braid and a further covering of high density polyethylene. (HDP).
(b) Mineral insulated cables usually have a solid conductor insulated with magnesium oxide and with a copper sheath covered with HDP.

The cables are supplied in lengths to provide a specific loading, e.g. 1·0 kW and 3·0 kW and are fitted with cold tails.

The length of the cold tail will vary on each installation and where excessively long tails are required an increase in the cross-sectional area on the conductor may be necessary to avoid excessive volt drop. The cold tails would be terminated in junction boxes provided at the edge of the heated area.

4.15.3 Installation: roads

4.15.3.1 Asphalt roads

The normal construction is for a sand asphalt carpet to be laid over the base concrete and then covered with the wearing course asphalt. The heating cables would be laid on the concrete and can be laid either across or along the run of the road.

Fig. 4.15.1. *Road heating installation*

Cables laid across the road may suffer some slight disturbance during the covering operation and for this reason it is usual to lay the mineral insulated cable along the run of the road and the more flexible elastomeric cable across the road. Before the heating cables are placed in position it is important that the surface of the concrete is swept clear of debris to remove any sharp objects which could damage the cables. A 20 mm thick sand asphalt carpet to BS 594 with nil aggregate should be applied over the heating elements at a temperature not exceeding 160°C. (Fig. 4.15.1)

Whilst the sand asphalt covering is being laid the heating cables have to be held in position and in the case of the mineral insulated cable this is achieved by fixing the cable to mild steel fixing tape with retaining tags pre-punched at 25 mm centres. The fixing tape can be held in position by masonry nails or by pads of asphalt if there is a damp proof membrane which must not be penetrated. The elastomeric cable is usually wound on to a jig formed by either a slotted plastic fixing strip or plastic discs pinned to the underlying concrete. Where there is a damp proof

Fig. 4.15.2. *Cable laying on a ramp*

membrane over the concrete which must not be penetrated, the plastic strip or discs are fitted to timber battens to form removable jigs. Removable jigs permit the cable to move after completion if there is any movement in the wearing surface. (Fig. 4.15.2)

In an unexposed unelevated situation the usual density of load would be between 110 to 160 W/m^2, the higher loadings being required in the north and the lower loadings in the south of Great Britain. In an elevated and very exposed situation these figures could be increased by 50%.

4.15.3.2 Concrete roads and ramps

The installation of heating cables into a reinforced monolithic concrete slab can be carried out in either of the following methods:

(a) The heating cables can be preformed by fixing to a light steel mesh which can then be laid on top of the reinforcement or the heating cables can be wired directly on to the reinforcing material. The concrete can then be placed in position to form a monolithic structure.

(b) The concrete can be poured up to the level of the top reinforcing material and the heating cables placed in position using removeable jigs. To ensure a sound monolithic structure it is essential that the remaining concrete is poured over the heating cables within an hour of pouring the first layer of concrete.

4.15.3.3 Suspended structures

Where a road or ramp is suspended it is usual to provide a damp proof membrane over the concrete structure, this usually consisting of approximately 20 mm of mastic asphalt. Obviously this membrane must not be pierced by fixings for the heating cables and the methods already described using removable jigs for restraining the heating cables whilst they are covered should be employed. Although it would be normal to apply the wearing course directly on to the mastic asphalt, a sand asphalt carpet would still be required to protect the heating cables from the aggregate contained in the wearing course asphalt. If the mastic asphalt can be laid at a temperature not in excess of 160°C then this could be used as a protective layer over the heating cables which would be laid on the concrete before the mastic ashpalt is laid, thereby doing away with the need of the sand asphalt carpet over the heating cables.

A suspended road or ramp will have an additional heat loss from the underside. The amount of the additional heat lost will depend upon the construction of the main structure below the heated surface. As a general guide therefore, the loadings indicated for roads in contact with the ground should be increased by approximately 25–30% to compensate for the additional heat loss from the underside of a suspended structure.

4.15.3.4 Pedestrian stairs and walkways

Concrete stairs can either be finished in Grano screed or sand asphalt and the heating cable can be fixed to the surface of the treads in the normal manner. As the area of tread is usually small, one heating cable will be sufficient to heat several treads, and it is necessary to ensure that a slot is cast into the riser so that the heating cable can pass from one tread to the next. Pedestrian walkways can be finished in either concrete screed, sand asphalt or paving slabs and the heating cables can be fixed to the underlying concrete in the normal manner; if there is a damp proof membrane on top of the concrete which must not be pierced then a removable jig must be used. The cables can then be covered with either concrete screed, sand asphalt or a thin screed over which would be placed the mortar bedding for the paving slabs.

4.15.4 Installation: sports grounds

Frost can make turf extremely hard and this can cause serious problems for football pitches, greyhound tracks etc. A few football pitches have been fitted with undersoil heating, the most notable being Murrayfield, Edinburgh. Quite a number of greyhound tracks (such as that at the White City, London) have undersoil heating as it is impossible to hold a race meeting if the ground is frozen due to the severe damage caused to the greyhounds' paws if they were to race on frozen turf. In these two applications the heating cables are normally installed by a mole plough pulled by a tractor, or by a self propelled specialized machine for inserting the heating cable approximately 150 mm below the surface. In the case of a football pitch the heating cable would run from one end to the other and back again to form a loop

Fig. 4.15.3. *Cable laying in a Greyhound Track using a Mole Plough*

with terminations in a suitable trench at one end of the pitch: in the greyhound track however, the heating cable would be laid along the run of the track for its full length, so that all heating cables would start and finish at the same point in the track. It is normal to install the heating cables at between 150 mm to 175 mm apart. (Fig. 4.15.3)

Experience has shown that an installed load of approximately 110 W/m^2 is adequate to provide frost protection for turfed areas as the heat loss from the surface is reduced somewhat by the natural insulating effect of the grass. The total connected load of a football pitch would be between 700 to 900 kW, and about 250 kW for a greyhound track.

4.15.5 Controls

4.15.5.1 General

Most road heating installations are controlled by sensing elements embedded in the road surface; pedestrian walkways and stairs and other small installations can be controlled by weatherproof air thermostats. Sports Tracks are generally controlled by two sensors, one sensing air temperature and the other ground temperature: these instruments usually indicate prevailing temperature so that groundsmen can override the automatic operation if required.

4.15.5.2 Road heating controls

It is essential on large heating installations that control of the system is precise, so that efficient use is made of electricity and that none is used when not required. The control system must therefore take into consideration surface temperature and the presence of moisture on the road surface and also be capable of snow detection.

These three functions can be provided in a composite housing, and suitable units are available commercially. They have to be very robustly constructed to stand up to stresses imposed by traffic and also small enough to be accommodated within the road surface.

The moisture detector usually consists of two electrodes flush with the road surface, moisture on the road surface being detected by a reduction of electrical resistance between them. The snow detector is similar in construction but it incorporates a small heater so that the snow is melted and the sensor can detect the presence of moisture. This type of equipment can also incorporate a setback facility to delay switch-on during dry conditions. For example, if the road surface sensor is set to switch the system on at 1°C the system would be energised at this temperature providing the road surface is wet, but if the surface is dry and the setback is set to 4°C below the surface temperature set point, the system would then energise at −3°C. This facility ensures that the structure temperature will not fall so low as to create a situation which could prove hazardous if rain or snow fell onto an extremely cold surface. It also permits more economical use of electricity by de-energising the system when snow or ice is unlikely.

4.15.6 Examples of installations

Notable road warming installations include some 1300 kW in the pavements and roadway of London Bridge, and 600 kW in White Lion Hill and 650 kW in Bridgehead, Blackfriars Bridge, in the City of London. In Scotland, the Kingston Bridge in Glasgow, the approaches to the Clyde Tunnel, and several access ramps to the urban motorway, should be mentioned.

In addition to the rugby pitch at Murrayfield, Edinburgh, the Arsenal pitch at Highbury, and that of Leeds United at Elland Road are examples of undersoil heating of soccer fields.

4.15.7 References

4.15.7.1 British Standards (See also Appendix 6.2)

BS 594 Rolled asphalt (hot process) for roads and other paved areas.

4.15.7.2 Bibliography

ESCRITT, J. R.: Reports on Electrical Soil Warming as an Anti-frost measure for Sports Turf. (J. Sports Turf Research Institute, Bingley. Vol. 8, no. 27, Vol. 8 no. 30, Vol. 10 no. 35).

WILLIAMSON, P. J. and HOGBIN, L. E. Electric Road Heating (LR 303, Transport and Road Research Laboratory, Crowthorne).

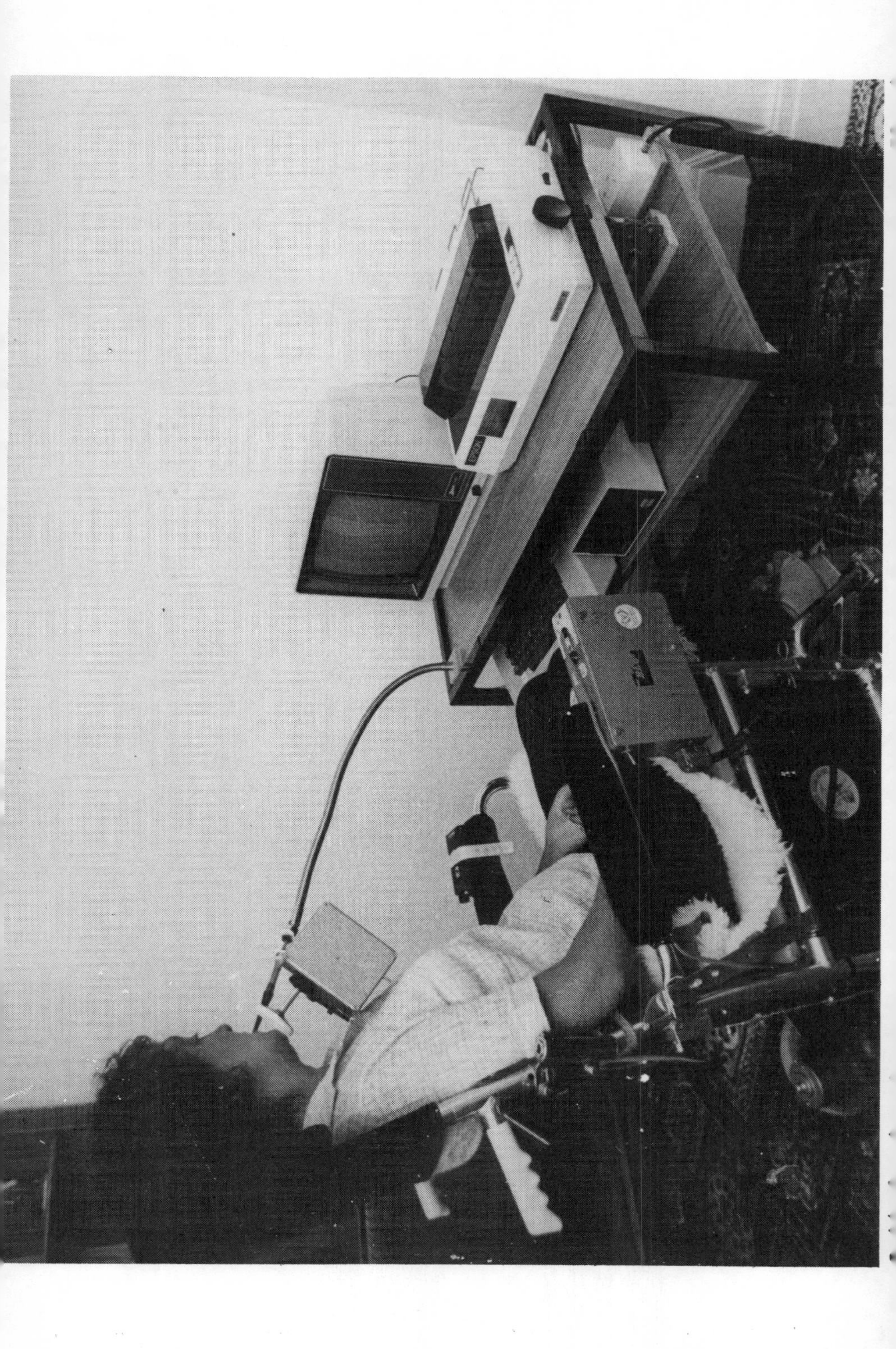

Chapter 4.16

Electricity and disabled people

Elizabeth Fanshawe, Dip.COT
Director, Disabled Living Foundation

4.16.1 Introduction

Although the causes of physical disability vary tremendously and each person's condition is unique, the actual major effects of disability can have several common factors. From the point of view of designers, architects and builders the most relevant effects are paralysis or weakness, lack of co-ordination, loss of a limb or limbs, cardio-vascular and respiratory failure, poor sight or hearing and the infirmities of old age. These will affect people to a greater or lesser extent and, because disabilities are not mutually exclusive, a person may have more than one disability. For instance a person may have a stroke with resultant paralysis down one side of his body and he may also develop cataracts which will impair his vision. The more severely disabled a person is, the less he will be able to do for himself. However, much of the handicap can be taken out of disability by the good design of his home and the wider environment, and by use of appropriate aids.

4.16.2 Aids used by the disabled

Many of the aids used by severely disabled people need to have a power source, and generally electricity is the most appropriate, either direct from the mains or by means of a battery. These aids fall into two main groups:

4.16.2.1 Equipment generally available

Equipment on the general market will include ordinary household appliances which, because they take the physical effort out of an activity, allow many severely disabled people to carry out a task. For instance the effort involved in handwashing clothes or going to a launderette, which is probably inaccessible anyway, can be drastically reduced by the use of a washing machine and spin dryer. As another example, a person with poor vision may be helped to see sufficiently to carry out a task by direct light over the area of activity such as the work surface of the kitchen, or persons who can't freshen their kitchen by opening a window can achieve the same effect by installing automatic ventilation.

4.16.2.2 Equipment specially designed

Equipment designed specifically for the disabled market includes the following:

(a) Electrically operated wheelchairs, (Fig. 4.16.1) used by those people too severely disabled to operate a self propelling chair. Electric wheelchairs obtain their power through a battery but this must, in many cases, be charged daily. Recharging facilities are of course essential for individual electric runabout vehicles used outdoors.

Fig. 4.16.1. *Power-chair for disabled office worker* (Vessa Ltd)

(b) Hoists – again the more severely disabled person may be unable to transfer from his wheelchair onto the bed, into the bath, onto the lavatory and so on. An overhead electrically operated hoist which traverses a track, whether suspended from the ceiling or on a gantry, will lift the person and move him from one site to another and on and off different pieces of furniture.

(c) Stairclimbers or home lifts (Fig. 4.16.2). – One of the greatest difficulties for disabled people is in negotiating stairs. In an ordinary house this generally means that the bedroom, bathroom and lavatory become inaccessible. One way of overcoming this problem is the installation of a stairclimber – which generally runs on a track at one side of the staircase, or a home lift which provides vertical access. (See also section 4.12.8)

(d) Specially designed environmental controls are available for severely disabled people. These will give control over most electrically operated devices such as telephones, radios, emergency bells, windows and doors (if these can be operated by a motor), and other equipment such as beds which may have a motor for adjusting the position. In effect they give a person control over his immediate environment, either by breathing down a tube or by a microswitch geared to the person's particular disability.

Fig. 4.16.2. *Stairclimber in use* (Stannah Lifts)

(e) Life support systems such as haemodialysis units for those with kidney failure and respirators. Electricity supply for such systems would need to be considered in conjunction with the medical authorities involved.

These are only a few of the aids or equipment that a disabled person may use which need an electric supply. Many of the others are small or portable, and from the designer's point of view the main thing is to provide sufficient conveniently sited socket outlets. When equipment is used in a bathroom, such as a hoist or a lavatory with an electrically operated wash/dry/flush system, appropriate transformers must be used, and the requirements of the IEE Regulations strictly observed.

4.16.3 Special reliance on electricity

4.16.3.1 General

It can be seen that in comparison with the general population disabled people rely far more heavily on electricity as a power source for equipment special to their needs and they also require more of the general benefits of heating, lighting and power. For example, it is more difficult for disabled persons to "make do" without light and heat than able bodied persons, and they may be at risk through hypothermia and suffer more if they cannot cope without light. Having established that electricity is more essential to disabled people than to the rest of the general public, it is up to those involved in the designing or building of any dwelling or public building likely to be used by disabled people that a sufficient supply is available, and that all switches and outlets are accessible. This means that any dwelling built to mobility or wheelchair housing standards (see bibliography) must have extra socket outlets, and these must be correctly sited. Related equipment such as meters, fuse boxes, and central heating and boiler controls must be easily accessible, whilst sufficient space must be available for split level cookers, freezers and other appliances. In any other dwelling these points are also desirable partly because they may allow people to remain in their own homes with minimum adaptation if they become disabled – and it is worth remembering that according to the Department of Health and Social Service Survey of 1970 there were then over 3 million disabled people in the UK – and partly because they are desirable features anyway. In public buildings and places of employment, again, many of the features essential for the disabled people who use these buildings are of benefit to all, particularly good lighting, good acoustics and the sensible siting of power outlets. People with visual impairment rely particularly on good lighting, both general and directional on the work area. For those entirely sightless, Braille or other raised indicators are necessary around controls.

4.16.3.2 Heating

The type of heating used needs consideration. Both direct and indirect heating should be available and many disabled people will need a higher level of heating if they suffer from poor circulation and are relatively immobile. Both forms of heating should be easy to control, and, it should be remembered that many disabled people are on low incomes and cannot afford large heating bills. The type of heating selected should take this into account and it may be advantageous to have a system which allows different rooms to be separately controlled so that at least the room in which the person spends the majority of his time can be kept to the necessary temperature.

4.16.3.3 Light switches

All light switches should be conveniently located, the recommended height from the floor being 1040 mm. Where ceiling switch cords are used, the knob pulls should be at 1040 mm above floor level and where the cord is adjacent to a wall it should pass through a screw eye to prevent it from swinging. For many people with hand impairment a rocker switch is easier to manipulate but if this is not supplied then the dolly should be not less than 10 mm across. (Fig. 4.16.3) An illuminated switch or surround identifying the switch position is often helpful and should certainly be considered in dwellings designed specifically for disabled people.

Fig. 4.16.3. *Light switch suitable for disabled persons* (Crabtree Electrical Industries Ltd)

4.16.3.4 Socket outlets

In addition to the extra number of socket outlets in any dwelling designed for disabled people the actual siting should be in places where they are most needed. As it is difficult for many disabled people to bend down, socket outlets should, wherever possible, be at the same height as light switches, i.e. 1040 mm, above floor level, but because this may present problems with trailing flex a lower level may be acceptable. However, this should be no lower than 500 mm above floor level.

4.16.4 Anthropometric dimensions

The anthropometric dimensions – that is, the measurements of heights and reach – of disabled persons and wheelchair users are published in "Designing for the Disabled" by Selwyn Goldsmith. These give designers and builders a guide for the siting of appliances. Dimensions of an average wheelchair are also available, indicating the space needed by a wheelchair user in front of, or beside, an appliance or power source.

4.16.5 Organisations

Organisations which can help with further advice include:

(a) Centre on Environment for the Handicapped 126 Albert Street, London NW1
(c) Special Equipment and Aids for Living (SEQUAL) 27 Thames House 140 Battersea Park Road London
(d) The Electricity Council 30 Millbank London SW1P 4RD
(e) The Royal Institute of British Architects 66 Portland Place London W1N 4AD

4.16.6 References

4.16.6.1 British Standards (See also Appendix 6.2)

BS 5619 Code of practice for design of housing for the convenience of disabled people.

4.16.6.2 Bibliography

SELWYN GOLDSMITH, 'Designing for the Disabled'. RIBA
SELWYN GOLDSMITH, 'Mobility Housing'. Occasional Paper 2/74. Room 1107 Beckett House 1 Lambeth Palace Road, London SE1 7ER
SELWYN GOLDSMITH, 'Wheelchair Housing'. Occasional Paper 2/75.
TERENCE LOCKHART, 'Housing Adaptation for Disabled People'. Disabled Living Foundation (Sales) Ltd 45 East Hill, London SW18 2QZ
JOHN PENTON (ed), Handbook of Housing for Disabled People. Housing Consortium West Group, 1122 Uxbridge Road Hayes, UB4 8JX.
'Lighting and Low Vision'. The Electricity Council (EC 4379)
'Making Life Easier for Disabled People' The Electricity Council (EC 3948)

Chapter 4.17

Houses of the future

M. R. Cowan, B.Sc., C.Eng., F.I.E.E.
Centre Director, The Electricity Council Research Centre

4.17.1 Introduction

In essence, every new house that is built is a house for the future because it will probably have a life in excess of 60 years and during that time will house several families with different lifestyles and different electrical equipment. In a 60 year period the availability and price of fuels will also change. It is important that the designer looks forward and endeavours to build homes that will be adaptable and economic for as much of their predicted life as possible.

4.17.2 Fuel and economics

A house designer in the 1920's probably assumed that there would be little change in fuel technology and economics during the life of his houses and his only decision on heating was how many fireplaces and chimneys to install. By 1980 central heating had taken over from the open fire, most commonly in the form of hot water radiators supplied from a central boiler fed by gas, oil or coal. The price escalation of fuels had caused attention to be given to improving insulation to reduce heat losses and fuel consumption, but this did not progress much beyond the provision of loft insulation.

In attempting to look ten, twenty or more years ahead a number of decisions have to be made and the most important are the cost of the house and the choice of fuel for heating. Electric heating systems are cheaper to install than pipe/radiator systems but unless they are supplied at off-peak tariffs are more expensive to run. When off-peak tariffs are used the technical features of the appropriate heating equipment are such that 24 hour heating is a semi-automatic corollary and to achieve maximum economy high standards of insulation are essential.

It will be seen that the choice of system is not straightforward. The future availability and price of competing fossil fuels are not known with precision but it is recognised that reserves of oil and natural gas are finite and the price of these two fuels will rise faster than inflation as they become less easy to extract. Long term prospects for the continuation of coal are better but its price may rise in line with oil and gas prices. A reasonably strong argument can be advanced to indicate that electricity prices should increase less rapidly than fossil fuels over the 60 year life of a house built today because electricity can be generated from several different feedstocks and because its competitiveness is likely to improve as more nuclear generation is commissioned.

However skilfully the analysis of future fuel prices and availability is carried out the key factor is whether the house can be sold when completed. The case for the electric house is strong but its perceived disadvantages are too numerous to anticipate its widespread adoption unless the house design incorporates good insulation, elimination of unwanted ventilation and the re-use of the "free heat" available, thus reducing running costs below those for competing systems.

4.17.3 The electric energy saving design

The following paragraphs and diagrams illustrate how a very low energy electric house design can be formulated.

Fig. 4.17.1 is a typical heat loss curve for a small semi-detached brick built house with conventional roof insulation. It can be calculated that the total heat loss over the year is 21 000 kWh of which 16 000 kWh are lost through the fabric and 5000 kWh are lost through ventilation.

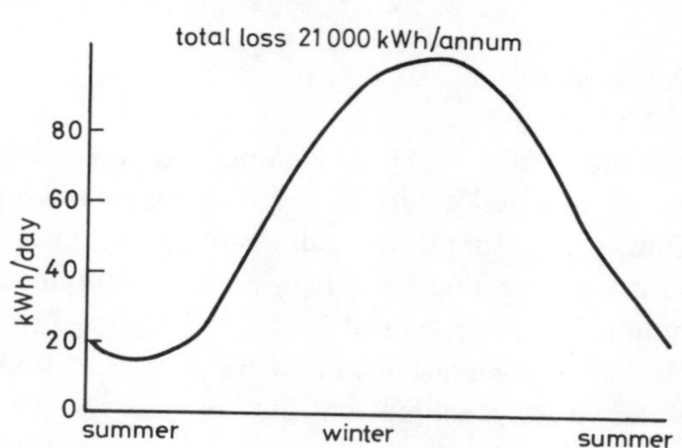

Fig. 4.17.1 *Typical Heat Loss*

Fig. 4.17.2 shows the free heat provided by solar gain and from the occupants and their use of appliances. Most of the free heat occurring in the summer is not useful but approximately 10 000 kWh/annum occurs in the winter, autumn and spring and should be included in the designer's considerations when determining the heating requirements for the house.

The envelope in Fig. 4.17.3 is the same as in 4.17.1 but the estimated 10 000 kWh of useful free heat has been shown. It represents almost half the total fabric loss. This emphasises the great change in the internal environment of modern houses compared with those of the 1920's. Then, there was very little free heat as the housewife did not have access to electric washing machines, cookers, dryers, kettles and irons. Lighting standards were low and television had not been invented. The coal fire was inefficient and required large quantities of air drawn in through doors and windows to maintain combustion.

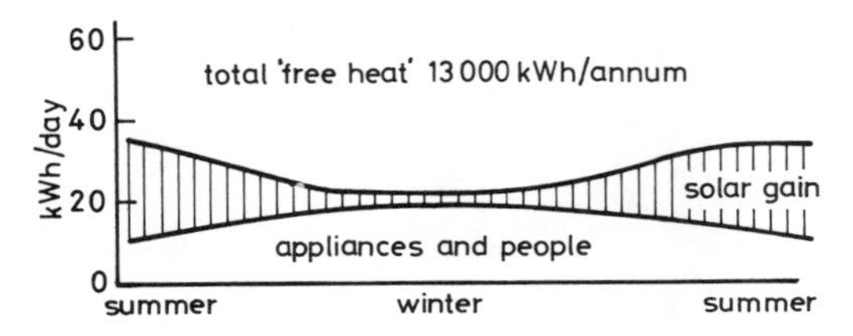

Fig. 4.17.2 *Free Heat Gain*

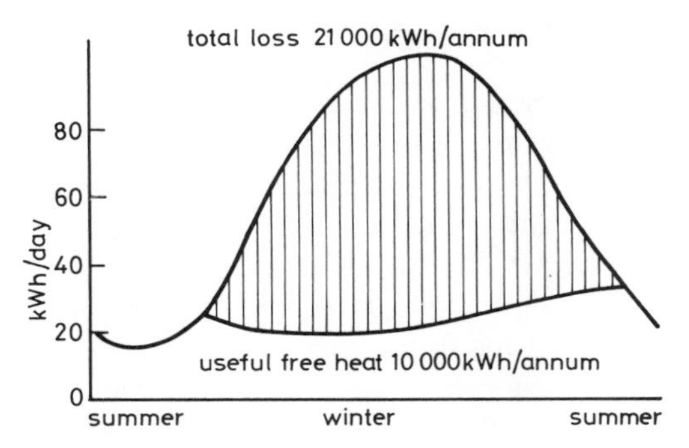

Fig. 4.17.3 *Useful Free Heat*

The 1970's house was much more efficient but still capable of great improvement. For example the inclusion of 100 mm of roof and wall insulation plus attention to unplanned conduction through window frames would halve the heat loss. Similarly if the house is sealed and mechanical ventilation is introduced the ventilation losses could also be halved.

Fig. 4.17.4 illustrates the heat balance that would result if the house designer redesigned the sample house in the manner described, i.e. a well insulated house, sealed to prevent unplanned ventilation and incorporating heat recovery within a mechanical ventilation system. The net heat requirement of 2500 kWh/annum would be only 25% of that for a similar size house built to 1970 design standards.

The first four houses to this design were completed in 1981 and 1982 and it is probable that this concept or similar ones will gain increasing favour as fuel costs rise. The heating system in such houses should be simple as the heat requirement does not justify the installation of hot water radiators. It is ideally suited to the characteristics of electric storage radiators with low capital and running costs and 24 hour heating. As the house must be reasonably air tight, chimneys and flues must be avoided and the products of combustion must not be permitted to leak into the environment. Again electricity provides the simplest answer to the designer.

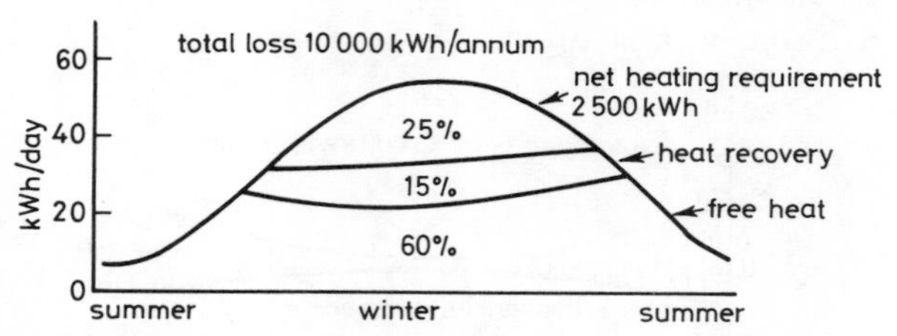

Fig. 4.17.4 *A Low-Energy Design*

4.17.4 Capital and running costs criteria

As stressed earlier a key decision factor is the price of the house because this will determine its acceptability to the buyer. Extra insulation, improved air tightness, mechanical ventilation and heat recovery represent additional costs which will not be completely off-set by the reduction of the capital cost of the heating system. The house buyer will be attracted by low running costs but may not be able or willing to pay a premium on the purchase price. This factor is impossible to determine theoretically as off-setting future running cost savings against an addition to the purchase price involves interest rates and the attitudes of building societies and house buyers. A very general guide may be that for a 50% reduction in annual space heating costs the house price could be increased by 5%.

4.17.5 Other electric loads

This description of one practical approach to a very low energy electric design for a standard house has of necessity only been an insight and has omitted detail. The description concentrated on the space heating requirements and it is important to note that the adoption of an energy saving concept will alter the balance of other loads and fuel usage. For example, the hot water fuel requirement will exceed the space heating requirement, perhaps accounting for 40% of the total fuel consumption compared with 25% for space heating and 35% for lighting, cooking, television, refrigeration and washing. This indicates that the designer will have to consider the water heating installation and perhaps conclude that showers should be considered as standard fittings.

Major changes in living styles occur by evolution rather than by planned design and just as the 1920's house had become inefficient and somewhat uncomfortable by the 1970's, so houses designed today will date. But it is probable that houses designed to minimise energy consumption and employing an electric solution will be capable of accepting most changes that can be envisaged without incurring the owner in major refurbishment because the addition or substitution of a new electrical device is generally simple and relatively inexpensive.

4.17.6 Heat pumps

In the U.S.A. and in countries with similar climates air to air heat pumps are common, their popularity deriving from their use for cooling in summer. Transposition of heat pump technology to operate economically for winter heating only is possible and it is worth noting that the introduction of mechanical ventilation as suggested can provide the possibility of retro-fitting a heat pump in the future. The loading of such a heat pump would be much less than that required with a house of more conventional design.

4.17.7 Information technology and its effects

The 1920's also saw the introduction of radio with the whole family gathered round a crackly set to catch the broadcast. Technology moved forward and later the children had their own transistor radios and then their own tape recorders. Meanwhile the single television set in the living room had become the focal point for family entertainment, but the invention of electronic games and video recorders increased the move towards the purchase of second sets and the continued separation of the activities of children and parents.

Future developments in electronics and information technology will include extension of cable and satellite television, home computers, shopping from mail order displays and direct debit banking in a cashless society. Telephone communication will become visual and available in every room. Householders will have the facility for central panel or remote control of everything from home entertainment to programming the electric blanket or the off-peak operation of their dishwasher. Probably each development will occur individually, with competing and different systems on offer.

All information technology systems require control and signalling systems and a wide variety of these will be employed. They will include broadcast systems as currently used for radio and television; telephone circuits, cable and optical fibre systems or even signalling over the Electricity Authority's mains. If the electric wiring in the home is used for internal signalling, filters or coding may be required to prevent stray signals trespassing into neighbouring premises and causing malfunctioning of equipment on these premises.

Consideration of the potential impact of future development of information technology provides pointers for designers and architects. Perhaps the most important is that different members of the household will have different interests and will want to enjoy them simultaneously. This suggests that two living rooms may be required in family houses with the added requirement that sounds originating in one room do not create nuisance in the second. Alternatively, better facilities may be required in children's bedrooms so that they can be used as both bedrooms and living rooms complete with appropriate facilities for information technology equipment which may become the successor to text books for studying and for homework. It is essential therefore that comfort standards are planned for the whole house to offer the required flexibility and to minimise the risks associated with the use of portable heating appliances particularly in children's rooms.

Because the pattern of living will change with greater use being made of more rooms a low energy approach to heating is highly desirable and, as has been suggested earlier, this should include attention to unplanned ventilation and the construction of air tight houses. This emphasises that considerable thought should be given to future wiring and cabling needs at the outset. In an energy saving house heat will be lost if occupiers or their agents drill holes for new wiring which then create passageways for unwanted ventilation.

4.17.8 Other changes

The traditional house comprises living quarters, bedrooms, kitchen and bathroom and there is no reason to assume a change in this basic pattern. The changes predicted in the section on information technology were changes in detail and other changes in detail will undoubtedly occur. They are difficult to predict but perhaps reduced working hours and greater leisure time will increase the importance of the garden and subsequently create a demand for electrical wiring in the garden to light it in the evening, to feed fountains and power tools or even to operate a visual display unit in a garden house. On a sombre note all houses may require improved security including burglar alarms and outside lighting.

To minimise fuel consumption and pipe losses, traditional plumbing may be superseded by single pipe, single tap operation with electric elements incorporated in the taps. If fuel prices escalate rapidly as oil and gas become less plentiful there could be an increasing swing towards showers and the eventual elimination of the requirement to provide a bath.

4.17.9 Summary

Significant energy saving can be achieved via improved insulation and by the use of 'free heat', and a low energy electric design can provide a low cost system that does not involve significant change in building practice or the appearance of the house.

In the electric house of the future the space heating bill will be small and probably less than a third of its total fuel bill. Internally the appliances, control systems and the occupants' living patterns will all change. But no major constraints on architectual appearance are foreseen although picture windows may disappear in the interests of fuel economy. The water heating load may become the largest individual load and this may lead designers to install spray taps, showers or even point of use single pipe dual purpose taps to reduce consumption. This trend will be accelerated if water authorities meter household water supplies and base their charges on consumption.

Finally the house of the future will be as similar to the house of today as the latter is to the house of yesterday. Appearance changes will not be determined by technical requirements, but integration of the design of internal services and the structure will become increasingly important as energy prices rise.

Factory main L V distribution board

(GEC Installation Equipment Ltd)

Chapter 5.1

Factories and warehouses

R. J. Briggs, C.Eng., M.I.E.E., M.C.I.B.S.
Director, Electrical Engineering, IDC Consultants Ltd

5.1.1 Introduction

As in other types of building it is now an increasingly widespread practice to adopt a formal approach to the design of industrial buildings in which all relevant factors are considered in relation to one another by an integrated specialist design team, the objective being to design an economical building to achieve optimum layout of production plant from raw materials input to finished goods output, with an environment which will enable the occupants to work throughout the day with maximum efficiency, at the same time ensuring the conservation and efficient use of energy and other resources.

The broad range of industry from heavy engineering through to food processing, pharmaceutical manufacturing and the electronics industry generally demand purpose built factories to suit the specific requirements of the particular manufacturing process. Buildings vary greatly in size and may range in floor area from perhaps 100 m^2 to more than 100 000 m^2 with a single storey height of from four metres to over twenty metres.

In addition to the production buildings, the factory complex may include ancillary buildings for raw materials and finished goods storage and despatch, inspection and quality control, offices and amenities, security control, central maintenance engineering, substations and an energy centre which may accommodate the main heat raising plant and associated distribution pumps, air compressors, process water treatment, standby generators, sprinkler pumps, effluent treatment and water storage tanks. The total site complex may require extensive external works including roadways, parking areas for staff cars and commercial vehicles and drainage.

When planning the factory layout, possible future expansion should be carefully considered with respect to function, probable size and time scale to enable the necessary provisions to be incorporated in the initial design where practicable and economical.

5.1.2 Service requirements

5.1.2.1 Allocation of space

The allocation of suitable space for services is a prime requirement for co-ordination. Initial considerations for space should take place at the inception stage but the more detailed evaluations will be made after functional requirements have been considered. These should include as appropriate, access for cleaning, inspection, maintenance and escape routes in addition to the dimensional requirements of the services plant and equipment. (Ref. 1)

Where heavily serviced building areas such as plant rooms can be separated from the remainder of the building design, it would clearly be an advantage for them to be designed as complete units, so that the building envelope is integrated with the services and the equipment within it. For maximum integration the full design team should consider such arrangements at the conceptual or outline stage of the building design. Early establishment of distribution zones for services will enable the design team to consider zone routings together with their ramifications on the space they are serving or through which they are passing. (Ref. 1) Particular attention should be paid to the following items which could have a significant effect on architectural and structural design.

(a) The production plant layout, including conveyor systems and overhead cranes and associated operational horizontal and vertical space requirements.
(b) Clearances required for lighting fittings, heating and ventilating equipment and other overhead services.
(c) Horizontal and vertical space requirements for electrical cables, ducts, conduits, piped services, ductwork and associated supports.
(d) Substation accommodation, which may be on the production area floor or on elevated platforms, or at the perimenter of the production building.
(e) Space requirements for plant rooms, switch and control panels, telephone equipment and battery charging areas.
(f) Energy centre space requirements.

5.1.2.2 Effects on structure

The effects of the services loads on the structure should be determined and additional steelwork for supports provided where necessary. The harmonization of the various services together with the building structure, should ensure a rationalized common support system as far as practicable to the benefit of the designer, installer and building owner.

Other aspects requiring consideration include:

(a) Access, handling facilities and foundations for transformers, switchgear, standby generators, pumps, air compressors and heat raising plant.

(b) Fire walls and barriers.
(c) Major holes for roof and wall ventilators.
(d) Floor ducts and trenches to accommodate incoming services and environmental and plant connections.
(e) Louvered ventilators for transformer and generator cooling, with automatic control being considered for the latter.
(f) Adequate space for installing and terminating heavy cables, pipework and ductwork.

Where suspended ceilings are to be provided in production and ancillary areas the ceiling tile layout should be designed at an early stage and fully co-ordinated with the lighting, heating, ventilating and fire protection services.

Adequate space should be provided above the ceiling to facilitate both the initial installation and fututure maintenance of the services.

5.1.3 Electricity supply

5.1.3.1 Supply and load details

The electrical energy demands in factories and warehouses may range from small light industry units with a load of perhaps 100 kVA to large industrial complexes where the demand may exceed 50 MVA. Small loads may be supplied direct at low voltage depending on the adequacy of the local 415 V network; larger loads will generally be supplied at 11 kV and will require an intake substation on the site. The supply may be by single feeder, duplicate feeders or ring main, depending on the local network, the factory load and degree of security of supply required.

The Electricity Authority should be notified at the earliest opportunity of the first approximation of load to enable the availability of supply to be assessed. The Authority will advise, on request, the supply voltage, substation requirements, prospective fault level, system earthing details, the limits for motor starting currents and other system disturbances, capital contribution and connection charges and tariff details. Full details of the total load should be confirmed as soon as available with a breakdown showing heating, motive power, catering and lighting loads and the overall load factor or periods of use.

5.1.3.2 Tariffs and metering

Tariffs for industrial premises are generally based on a maximum demand charge and rates per unit. The measured maximum demand may be kVA or kW with power factor adjustment; the charge being seasonally adjusted, with a higher rate in the winter. Special tariffs are available for off-peak heating and energy consumed at night.

Where the supply is taken at high voltage metering will normally be on the high voltage side; the consumer being responsible for the provision of transformers and the cost of transformer energy losses. Small loads supplied direct from the

Electricity Authority transformer, which may be located on or off the premises, will normally be metered at low voltage. Additional metering may be required by the user for internal audit purposes and voltmeters and ammeters may be required on important circuits to facilitate day-to-day operation and network analysis. Power factor indicators may be provided on the main switchgear or as part of the power factor correction equipment.

5.1.3.3 Power factor correction

There are clear economic benefits to be obtained from the appropriate use of power factor improvement plant, by direct reductions in energy costs and more efficient utilization of plant and equipment.

Power factor improvement equipment reduces the apparent power. In principle the power factor can be increased to unity but the amount of improvement that can be economically justified must be assessed in relation to the tariff under which electricity is purchased. For the majority of industrial applications the use of static capacitors with appropriate controls will provide a reliable and economical means of improving the system power factor.

Capacitors can be arranged for bulk correction at high or low voltage or individual correction by direct connection across motors and other equipment. The power factor correction equipment should not exceed 85% of the no-load magnetizing kVA when directly connected across individual motors.

In some heavy industrial applications power factor improvement may be obtained economically by the use of synchronous motors.

5.1.3.4 Standby generators

Standby supplies may be required to enable partial production to proceed during a mains power failure, or to maintain supplies to boiler plant and other services, or vital process plant which could be adversly affected by a sudden unscheduled loss of power. Generators driven by diesel or gas engines can be arranged to start automatically on mains failure or by push button control. The Electricity Authority should be notified of the intention to use private generation and the generator manufacturer advised of the proposed load details, particularly motor drives and starting current, and the acceptable voltage and frequency tolerances. Other items requiring attention include accommodation, heating, ventilating, noise and oil storage.

5.1.4 Environmental requirements

5.1.4.1 Space and water heating

Electric heating can be broadly classified into direct and indirect heating. Indirect or storage systems are operated during off-peak periods at significantly lower cost than the standard rate. Direct appliances which use electricity at the standard rate have the advantages of flexibility of performance, convenience and immediate response. The two systems can be used independently or may be complementary to one another to meet particular heating requirements. Electrical heating is clean, silent, requires little maintenance and is economical in builders' work as no flue construction and no fuel storage is needed.

Electrode boilers are ideally suited to industrial applications and can be operated during off-peak hours in conjunction with a thermal storage vessel. In this system, off-peak electricity is converted to heat energy and used to heat water which is transferred to well-insulated vertical or horizontal storage tanks. On completion of the charging period the storage tank should contain sufficient energy in the water to maintain space heating, and hot water supply until the next heating period.

Other types of off-peak heating systems available for the smaller factory or warehouse or ancillary buildings are:

(a) Storage radiators.
(b) Storage fan heaters.
(c) Centrally sited thermal storage warm air systems.
(d) Centrally sited thermal storage pipes/radiator systems.
(e) Hot water thermal storage vessel with radiators.
(f) Floor warming.

To be effective storage radiator heating must warm the entire building fabric and consequently operates most efficiently in a building of high thermal capacity.

5.1.4.2 Ventilation

Industrial ventilation systems should be designed to remove from the internal atmosphere undesirable airborne elements such as gases, vapours, fumes, mist and dust, and to supply clean fresh air to suit the needs of human occupancy and the manufacturing process. The supply air may be heated or cooled and humidity controlled to meet the particular environmental and process requirements. In order to conserve heat and to minimise the effects of toxic contaminants, local exhaust systems are preferable – the contaminated air being collected via hoods or canopies and exhausted through suitable filters.

Ventilation systems must be designed to comply with local regulations and the Health and Safety at Work etc. Act 1974 and subsequent amendments, both with regard to the internal environment and external pollution, in addition to any special needs of the manufacturing process.

5.1.4.3 Lighting

Lighting in factories and warehouses must offer sufficient illumination for maximum working efficiency and safety and promote a feeling of well-being amongst the operatives. Some of the factors which contribute to the quality of the lighting are freedom from glare and a balance of brightness and good colour rendering. The CIBS (formerly IES) Code for Interior Lighting (Ref. 2) recommends the quantity and quality of illumination for a wide range of industrial processes and warehouses.

Industrial illumination requirements vary widely from high bay manufacturing and warehouse areas to process plants with corrosive, damp, dust laden and potentially explosive atmospheres; food factories, pharmaceutical and electronic manufacturing industries each have their particular special lighting requirements. In general, the more detailed the task, the higher must be the illuminance level and freedom from glare.

Luminaires are available to meet the diverse requirements of industry. The suitability of a luminaire can be judged only in relation to its specific use but a large number of performance criteria apply. It should be mechanically secure and easy to install and maintain. Its robustness and the materials chosen for its components should be appropriate to the conditions under which it is to be used. The optical performance with respect to light distribution and glare should be appropriate for the particular environment and visual task. Luminaires which meet the special requirements of high bay narrow racking aisles in warehouses are available to provide good illumination in the vertical plane and the avoidance of dark patches at higher levels. In addition to good general lighting, supplementary lighting is often needed to satisfy local requirements for high intensity lighting or to compensate for obstructions to the general lighting distribution by plant and equipment.

Light sources used in industrial applications are generally tubular fluorescent or elliptical discharge lamps, the use of incandescent lamps being generally restricted to small amenity or special display areas. As an alternative to fluorescent tubes, mercury, metal halide and high pressure sodium discharge lamps offer the facility of compact luminaires with good optical control and are especially suitable for mounting heights of six metres and above.

Low pressure sodium lamps have a higher luminous efficiency but are generally unsuitable for internal industrial applications due to the yellow monochromatic light output. High pressure mercury discharge lamps take several minutes to cool down after switch-off before they will re-strike. Standby lighting is therefore necessary and luminaires are available with an integral relay operated tungsten halogen lamp to maintain safety lighting during this period.

5.1.4.4 Emergency lighting

Emergency lighting must be provided to ensure the safe means of escape for personnel in the event of a failure of the main lighting. The system should be designed in accordance with the requirements of BS 5266 Part 1. A minimum level of 0·2 lux is required in the horizontal plane at floor level on the centre line of the escape route with a uniformity ratio not greater than 40:1.

Illumination is required for:

Escape routes and direction signs,

Exit doors and emergency exit doors,

Fire alarm call points,

Fire fighting equipment,

Lifts,

Toilets of greater area than 8 m^2,

Each intersection of corridors,
Each change of direction,
Each staircase,
Every change of floor level,
Control and plant rooms,
Moving stairways and walkways,
Covered car parks,
External areas in the immediate vicinity of exit doors.

Luminaires may be powered by individual self contained batteries or from a central battery.

5.1.4.5 Transportation: battery electric vehicles

Battery operated vehicles provide a powerful, flexible, quiet, efficient and pollution free means of transport within the factory and warehouse complex. Vehicles and attachments are available to meet the majority of industrial materials handling and transportation requirements.

Fig. 5.1.1. *Battery-Electric Fork Lift Truck* (Electric Vehicle Association)

Large battery compartments provide high capacity ratings and extended time between charges. Multi-motor systems provide separate drives for travel, hoist and power steering functions. Vehicles normally provide excellent all round visibility and manoeuvrability is outstanding. Electronic controls facilitate automatic positional control and driverless operation, such vehicles being particularly suited to use in warehouse narrow aisle racking areas.

5.1.5 Process heating

5.1.5.1 Steam raising
Electric steam boilers are ideal for many industrial process applications. The equipment provides a realiable and economical source of steam at high efficiency with a minimum of structural requirements with fully automatic control, providing rapid response for fluctuating demands. (Ref. 3)

5.1.5.2 Waste heat
Regarded as a by-product, waste heat from process heating – whether from electricity or other function – can be utilised for space heating or will have to be removed by ventilation. The reject process heat can be recovered by using heat exchangers and transported in the form of hot water or steam to the point of utilization for space heating, thus affecting economies in operation.

Closely controlled electrical applications, whereby a minimum amount of localised heat is applied to the workplace, will materially reduce the amount of waste heat generated in production processes.

5.1.6 Automatic warehousing

Automatic materials handling systems enable the efficient handling, storage and retrieval of goods to be carried out with less personnel than required for manually

Fig. 5.1.2. *Automatic Warehousing: Four Dexion Storage and Retrieval Machines servicing Pallet Racking* (Stelrad Group)

operated warehouses. It is possible for the warehouse to operate without artificial lighting other than for maintenance access and, depending on the nature of the goods stored, only minimum heating may be required with consequent savings in energy.

The entire electro-mechanical system comprising aisle storage and retrieval and transfer stacker crane and conveyors is controlled by a central computer which also handles all management data for recording goods received, goods in stock and goods in despatch. The planning of the warehouse building, mechanical handling system and the control and data processing function requires close integration of the design team comprising building owner, architect, civil and structural engineer,

Fig. 5.1.3. *Automatic Warehousing: Dexion Courier Crane changing aisles on a transfer car* (Frigoscandia Ltd)

materials handling, environmental and electrical engineer to ensure that the complete system is tailored to suit the precise functional requirements of the user at the most economical constructional and operational costs.

5.1.7 Environmental control

5.1.7.1 Heat recovery

The cost of operating heating and ventilating installations may be much reduced by the use of heat recovery systems which involve the reclamation and redistribution of waste heat. Apart from the loss through the building fabric, heat is dissipated from natural ventilation through windows and doors, from ventilation exhaust air, from cooling towers and from process waste heat.

In order to be worthwhile, there must be sufficient waste heat of suitable quality to recover, and there must be a positive use for the heat once it has been recovered. The value of useful heat recovered must be greater than the cost of recovering it, taking into account both capital and running costs.

5.1.7.2 Noise

The control of sound levels is an important activity in the achievement of desirable environmental conditions. Certain industrial processes result in high noise levels which may require reduction not only for comfort, but to prevent injury; attenuation may also be necessary to meet local authority external environmental requirements. The acoustical treatment of interior spaces and the attenuation of items of plant will vary considerably throughout the wide range of industrial activity and will, in general, require specialist advice.

5.1.7.3 Effluent treatment

Under the Control of Pollution Act 1974 all discharges to rivers, streams, canals, etc require a Consent to Discharge from the appropriate water authority. Electroflotation can provide an efficient solution to the treatment of many industrial effluents and may be used alone or as part of a larger treatment process. In certain applications materials may be recovered for re-cycling.

Some examples of processes producing effluents which may be treated efficiently and economically by electroflotation are:

Emulsion paint manufacture,
Latex processing,
Fat and tallow processing,
Paper and board manufacture and processing,
Wool scouring,
Carpet manufacture,
Chemical and pharmaceutical manufacture. (Ref. 4)

5.1.7.4 Hazardous areas

Potentially hazardous atmospheres exist in many industries where flammable liquids, gases, vapours and dusts are handled or processed. Special precautions are necessary in such areas to avoid ignition being caused by normal operation of electrical equipment, or under fault conditions or by the discharge of static electricity. BS 5345 is the principal Standard dealing with the supply, installation and mantenance of electrical equipment in industrially hazardous areas; other references are included in Section 5.1.11.

5.1.7.5 Energy use

The complex nature of the interrelationship between the various factors affecting the environment outlined above means that an in-depth appraisal of the available alternatives is essential. To facilitate the process, computer programmes are available which enable an estimate to be made of the effects on energy consumption of the various building options as well as of different fuels and heating, cooling and heat recovery systems. The output of a typical programme may give the following:

(a) Details of input information.
(b) Design heat loss and heat gain in each zone.
(c) Design heat loss and heat gain of the total building.
(d) Monthly breakdown of the heating and cooling requirements of the building.
(e) Monthly and annual demand and consumptions of the heating, refrigeration, lighting and system auxiliaries for each design.
(f) Monthly and annual demand and consumptions of the heating, refrigeration, lighting and system auxiliaries for each design.
(g) Summary of the energy consumption and costs of the chosen design alternatives from which comparisons may be drawn. (Ref. 5)

5.1.7.6 Controls and energy management

A thermally efficient building free from infiltration of outside air which will allow the environmental services to act as a fine control and not as compensator for the poor performance of the building envelope is an essential pre-requisite for efficient energy control and management. The complete building needs to be operated as a unit with full integration of energy input, heat recovery and ventilation systems. Microprocessor based systems are available to link together the control of the various functions and provide economical central monitoring and control for the whole factory complex. Each system is designed to meet a specific need and the potential energy savings depend to a large extent on the flexibility and the degree of control required. Centralized monitoring brings together at one location all the status and alarm data from the plant giving instant warning of malfunctions and making available comprehensive performance data. Centralised control enables the system to be manually or automatically controlled from a remote central station with automatic feedback to the operator or maintenance engineer. The central monitoring and control system will encompass all the heating, ventilation and air-conditioning controls and additional features as follows:

(a) *Maximum Demand:*

Industrial electricity energy costs are generally based on a tariff incorporating a maximum demand charge per kW or kVA, and a kWh charge. Maximum demand equipment will constantly monitor the total load on the system and can be arranged to give early warning when a preset target value is reached to enable manual load shedding to take place, or pre-determined loads may be shed automatically on a sequential control basis to reduce the load to the target figure.

(b) *Lighting:*
The lighting may be automatically controlled on a programmable timed basis with photocell adjustments and manual override facilities if required. The centralised pre-programmed control of the lighting system tailored to suit the particular needs of industry offers the possibility of significant savings in energy.

(c) *Maintenance:*
Planned maintenance programmes provide data for the maintenance of plant and equipment on a pre-determined cyclical basis ensuring efficient regular maintenance and minimising unscheduled stoppages.

(d) *Computer-aided design:*
Computer-aided design programmes are available for many aspects of building environmental engineering to facilitate the design function and to enable rapid comparison of alternative systems.

Programmes include electrical power cable distribution, lighting, earth loop impedence, duct noise attenuation, heat and fluid flow, running costs of heating, ventilating and air-conditioning systems, heat pump energy balances, energy demand simulation, floor heating, radiator sizings, U-values for walls and roofs, duct areas for insulation, combined heat and power energy balances and cooling loads.

5.1.8 Electrical installation

5.1.8.1 Substation and switchrooms

Substation planning should be determined by the services electrical engineer in conjunction with the architect and production engineer. The ideal location is at the centre of the electrical load but compromise is often necessary to satisfy operational and aesthetic requirements.

The Electricity Regulations (Ref. 6) require that every substation shall be substantially constructed and so arranged that no person other than an authorized person can obtain access thereto otherwise than by the proper entrance, or can interfere with the apparatus or conductors therein from outside: and shall be provided with efficient means of ventilation and be kept dry. Further, substations should be constructed and arranged with the object of minimizing the effects of explosion or fire.

Wherever electrical equipment in a single location contains flammable dielectric liquid in excess of 25 litres, precautions shall be taken to prevent burning liquid and the products of combustion of the liquid (flame, smoke, toxic gases) spreading to other parts of the building. The precautions to be taken may include a drainage pit to collect leakages of liquid and ensure their extinction in the event of fire or installation of the equipment in a chamber of adequate fire resistance and the provision of sills or other means of preventing burning liquid spreading to other parts of the building, such a chamber being ventilated solely to the external atmoshpere.

Switchgear for the site distribution network will be provided by the consumer and may be oil circuit breakers, vacuum breakers, SF6, or fused switchgear. The switchgear and protection should be compatible with the Electricity Authority's switchgear with regard to fault rating, discrimination and physical characteristics.

High voltage switchgear should normally be located in a separate locked switch-

Fig. 5.1.4. *Duplicate 3000A busbars feeding factory main switchboard*

(IDC Consultants Ltd)

room with remote emergency tripping facilities adjacent to the transformers and low voltage switchgear. Access to switchrooms should be restricted to authorised personnel.

Transformer ratings and impedances should be selected to ensure that the system fault level is within the rating of commercially available switchgear. Additional transformer fittings include Buckholtz gas detector relays to provide an early warning alarm, which can be arranged to trip the supply in the event of gas being generated in an oil-cooled transformer under fault conditions, silica-gel breather to remove moisture from the air entering a transformer, and temperature gauge.

The system protection should be co-ordinated throughout from the incoming high voltage supply to final circuit distribution boards to avoid unnecessary interuption of supplies under overload or fault conditions.

Fig. 5.1.5. *Factory LV Distribution Board* (GEC Installation Equipment Ltd)

5.1.8.2 High voltage cable distribution

The extent of the high voltage cable distribution will vary from a single substation with the Electricity Authority incoming supply and local transformer connections only, to major industrial complexes with multiple substations strategically located around the site. The high voltage distribution network will be determined by the load characteristics and the security of supply demanded by the process. For many sites a simple radial system will be sufficient, but for more important industries duplicate radial feeders or ring main systems will provide greater security.

Where justified, ring main systems may be provided with pilot feeder protection automatically to isolate a faulty section, allowing the process to continue uninterrupted following a ring main cable fault. Similarly, duplicate radial feeders may be fitted with automatic isolation and bus section closure.

The planning of industrial high voltage distribution networks demands thorough engineering to ensure that the supply requirements of particular industries are provided on a sound and economical basis. The system voltage, prospective fault level, plant loading and installation requirements will determine the cable size and type.

Cable routes should be selected to minimise the risk of damage both during installation and throughout the life of the plant.

5.1.8.3 Low voltage switchgear

Low voltage switchgear may comprise oil or air circuit breakers, moulded case circuit breakers or fused switches. Switchgear should be selected to suit the system voltage and prospective fault level and to be compatible throughout to ensure

Fig. 5.1.6. *Overhead busbar with fused tap-off units* (GEC Installation Equipment Ltd)

correct fault clearance and discrimination. BS 5486 'Factory-built assemblies of switchgear and control gear' provides a sound basis for industrial switchgear design. Particular attention should be paid to the segregation between compartments and the facilities for terminating heavy cables.

5.1.8.4 LV cable and busbar systems

The internal wiring systems may comprise any or all of the following:

(a) Single core p.v.c. insulated cables in trunking or conduit.
(b) Pre-wired lighting trunking.
(c) Twin and multi-core p.v.c. insulated and armoured cables.
(d) Impregnated paper-insulated, lead sheathed and armoured cables
(e) Mineral insulated, metal sheathed cables.
(f) Metal clad bus bar trunking.

Power distribution may be by any of the above systems. Overhead busbar trunking is particularly suitable for supplying the power to production lines, especially where the layout of process plant is liable to be varied fairly frequently to suit production requirements. The individual items of equipment are connected to the busbars by tap-off boxes with integral fuses or moulded case circuit breakers.

Pre-wired lighting trunking with pre-wired socket outlets for direct connection to lighting fittings facilitates the rapid and economical installation of industrial lighting systems and the trunking may also be used for carrying other circuit cables.

Power cables are available with copper or aluminium conductors and the economics of these alternatives should be considered. Aluminium cables will generally be larger than the equivalent copper cable and special precautions may need to be taken at terminations to avoid corrosion by galvanic action. Where cables are enclosed in conduit or trunking or closely spaced on cable trays, care should be taken to apply the appropriate ambient temperature and grouping factors detailed in the IEE Wiring Regulations.

5.1.8.5 Control panels and motors

Environmental engineering involves motor drives for pumps, fans and air compressors ranging from fractional horsepower to several hundred horse-power for large air-conditioning systems. The selection of motors and associated control equipment should be co-ordinated to ensure that motor starting currents are within acceptable limits and the required starting torque, motor starter overload and back-up protection are compatible.

Large fans with high starting torque may not be suitable for star/delta or auto-transformer starting. Adequate facilities should be provided for terminating cables, particularly where 'over-sized' cables are specified for voltage drop reasons. Electronic and microprocessor monitoring and control equipment and wiring should be segregated and screened from power circuits to avoid induced noise causing system malfunction.

5.1.8.6 Socket outlets

Socket outlets supplying portable equipment should be supplied at 110 V; if the sockets are fed by means of a double wound transformer so arranged that the mid-point of the 110 V system is earthed, the effective shock voltage is reduced to 55 V. Such socket outlets should comply with BS 4343 and should not be interchangeable with socket outlets supplied from systems at other voltages.

5.1.8.7 External installations

(a) *Lighting*

Lighting may be required to enable external operations to proceed after dark; for commercial and private vehicle parking areas, roads and pathways and general security purposes.

A wide variety of equipment is available from wall mounted floodlights to street lighting columns and high mast towers which will illuminate vast areas from a single column. Such towers will accommodate multiple luminaire assemblies and may include an integral raise and lowering system to enable luminaire maintenance to be carried out at ground level.

(b) *Power outlets:*

External power outlets may be required for many purposes including overnight parking of refrigerated vehicles. Such equipment should be specially designed for external use with additional protection against driving rain where appropriate. All external equipment should have individual circuit earth fault protection by means of a residual current device.

5.1.8.8 System earthing

The earthing system must be compatible with the characteristics of the source of supply and the requirements of the IEE Regulations and CP 1013.

5.1.8.9 Lightning protection

The protection of structures against lightning is considered in detail in CP 326.

5.1.9 Communications

Telephones (public and private), public address, radio paging, staff location systems, time recording and data collection and processing are all important aids to communication and operating efficiency in factories and warehouses. Microprocessor systems are available to operate, control and interface all functions together with the environmental plant controls; the maintenance engineer may for example, be automatically radio paged and notified of a plant manfunction with consequent savings in plant down-time. Special equipment is available for noisy and hazardous industrial areas.

5.1.10 Security

5.1.10.1 Intruder security

Security systems for the detection and protection of personnel, property and equipment against fire and crime, offer a wide range of sophisticated electronic sensing devices, closed circuit television and security lighting. Systems and equipment must satisfy the requirements of each application and specialist advice may be necessary to correctly assess the risk and apply an optimum and economical solution. Protection devices include simple door and window contacts and/or infra-red beam, microwave and ultrasonic detectors and/or closed circuit television monitoring. Electronic card access systems restrict the movement of personnel to authorized areas. A central micro-computer based control console will monitor the whole alarm and personnel access system.

Security lighting covering the perimeter fence, open external areas, building facades and interior security routes will deter the prospective unauthorized intruder and assist detection by security staff. (Ref. 7)

5.1.10.2 Fire precautions

The Factories Act 1961 requires that in every building which is, or forms part of a factory, effective means shall be provided and maintained for giving warning in case of fire which shall be clearly audible throughout the factory, and the Shops, Offices and Railway Premises Act 1963 requires audible or visual warning in the premises covered by the Act. BS 5839, Part 1: 1980 provides recommendations for the planning, installation and servicing of fire alarm systems in and around buildings Compliance with the Standard will normally satisfy the requirements of the above Acts. The Standard includes recommendations for system zoning, location of call points, siting of alarm sounders and the audibility required, control and power supply equipment. In addition to manually operated audible alarm systems required by the Acts, BS 5839 also makes recommendations for the provision of automatic alarm systems by means of heat and smoke detectors. Automatic detection may be required to provide protection during unoccupied periods and to meet the special requirements of the insurers.

Rules for automatic fire alarm systems are also provided by the Fire Offices Committee (FOC) and insurers may require compliance with these rules, whilst the FOC Rules for sprinkler installations also contain specific requirements regarding the electrical installation.

5.1.11 References

5.1.11.1 References in text

1. MICHIE, ADRIAN, and OGLE, JOHN: 'Co-ordination of Building Services – design stage methods'. Technical Note TN1/82. Published by Building Services Research and Information Association.
2. The 'Code for Interior Lighting'. Published by the Chartered Institution of Building Services.
3. 'Steam Raising by Electricity' Technical Information Sheet IND 36 1981. Published by the Electricity Council. (EC 4149)
4. 'Electroflotation for Effluent Treatment'. Technical Information Sheet IND 13 1975. Published by the Electricity Council. (EC 3405)
5. 'Energy Management in Commercial Buildings'. Published by the Electricity Council, (EC 3325).
6. 'Memorandum on the Electricity Regulations'. Factories Act 1961 (SHW 928). Health and

Safety Executive. (HMSO)
7. 'Essentials of Security Lighting'. Published by the Electricity Council. (EC 4131)

5.1.11.2 Legislation (See also Appendix 6.1)

Electricity Supply Regulations 1937, and Explanatory Notes.

Electricity (Factories Act), Special Regulations 1908 and 1944, and explanatory memorandum.

Health and Safety at Work Etc. Act 1974 and subsequent amendments.

Building Standards (Scotland), (Consolidation) Regulations 1971 with Amendment Regulations 1971–1980 and Explanatory Memorandum.

Local Authority Building Regulations, (Note: Local Regulations may vary and should be checked for each area).

Control of Pollution Act 1974

The Highly Flammable Liquids and Liquified Petroleum Gases Regulations 1972.

The Petroleum (Consolidation) Act 1928.

5.1.11.3 British Standards (See also Appendix 6.2)

Amongst relevant British Standards are the following: BS 5266, which deals with emergency lighting, BS 5345 with electrical apparatus in potentially explosive atmospheres and BS 5839, which refers to fire detection and alarm systems. BS 5486 covers LV switchgear and BS 5997 is the Guide to BS Codes of Practice for Building Services.

BS CP 326 deals with lightning protection, BS CP 413 with ducts for building services and BS CP 1013 with earthing. BS CP 1017 covers the distribution of electricity on construction sites and BS CP 1018 deals with floor warming systems.

5.1.11.4 Bibliography

BEEMAN, DONALD, 'Industrial Power Systems Handbook' (McGraw-Hill Book Co.)
DRURY, JOLYON: 'Factories; Planning, Design and Modernisation'. (Architectural Press)
LYTHALL, R. T.: 'J & P Switchgear Handbook' (Butterworth)
ROLLS, T. B.: 'Power Distribution in Industrial Installations' (Peter Peregrinus)
SEIP, GÜNTER G.: 'Electrical Installations Handbook' (2 volumes) (Siemens Aktiengesellschaft, Heyden and Sons Ltd)
STIGANT, S. AUSTEN, and FRANKLIN, A.C.: 'J & P Transformer Book' (Butterworth)
YOUNG, R. E.: 'Control in Hazardous Environments' (Peter Peregrinus)
"Electrical Safety in Hazardous Environments' (IEE Conference Publications Series) (The Institution of Electrical Engineers)
'Protective Relays Applications Guide' (GEC Measurements, Stafford)
'Industrial Ventilation' (American Conference of Government Industrial Hygienists, Lansing, Michigan, USA)
'Explosion Protection Manual' (English Brown Boveri, Coventry)

Modern Living Room (George H. Scholes plc)

Chapter 5.2

Electricity in the home

Home Economics Department, The Electrical Association for Women

5.2.1 Introduction

Electricity makes a major contribution to living standards in every home by providing heating, lighting and motive power. Over the past decade the household applications of electricity have increased considerably and, as a result, the need for fully adequate and well-planned electrical installations in homes is greater than ever before. Moreover, there are many homes in which the electrical installation is inadequate to meet the demands made upon it and, in many instances, modernisation is urgently needed to handle the increases in electrical usage.

While old habits have led to our becoming wasteful, the effects of increased fuel prices, diminishing material resources, and environmental considerations are now heightening our awareness of the need to economise. Careful overall design of houses and flats is needed to ensure a well-insulated environment with adequate ventilation and full facilities for the efficient use of electricity.

5.2.2 Electrical appliances in the home

5.2.2.1 General

The increased use of electrical appliances in and around the home has escalated rapidly with the advent of the food freezer, automatic washing machine, tumbler dryer, colour TV, hi-fi, lawn mower and so on. These appliances have all become an integral part of modern living and are taken largely for granted. Careful planning, of both the wiring installation and the installation of appliances around the home is, therefore, very important.

5.2.2.2 Kitchen

The major appliances used in the kitchen, such as the refrigerator, food freezer, dishwasher, washing machine, tumbler dryer, and split level cooker are designed so that they may be built-in. Consideration therefore needs to be given to their siting and the provision of an adequate electrical installation to ensure their safe operation. In some instances it may be possible to site laundry equipment in a specially designed laundry or utility room. Because of the increased use of small appliances, an adequate number of socket outlets is necessary either immediately above the work surface or set into them. Small appliances include a microwave oven, slow cooker, contact grill, toaster, food mixer, kettle, deep fat fryer, knife sharpener, coffee maker and food processor, to name but a few. Ideally, the work surfaces should accommodate the more popular small appliances but adequate storage space should also be provided for those used less frequently. An extractor fan is a useful supplement to natural ventilation.

5.2.2.3 Living room

The boom in home entertainment calls for an adequate number of socket outlets for the television, video recorder and audio systems in addition to those needed for fuel-effect fires, table and floor based lamps. In a dining area, provision should also be made for a heated tray or food trolley.

5.2.2.4 Bedroom

Again, adequate socket outlets are necessary for electric blankets, an automatic tea maker, electric clock radio, bedside lights, beauty care appliances, and possibly a television.

5.2.2.5 Bathroom

The use of appliances in the bathroom is limited to an electric shaver and an electric toothbrush. These must be operated through a special shaver socket outlet in which a transformer is incorporated to isolate the socket from the mains supply. This eliminates the possibility of shock. Other socket outlets are not provided in the bathroom.

5.2.2.6 Garage and garden

The range of equipment usable outside the confines of the home has widened, and it is essential to have adequate socket outlets conveniently situated. Equipment used in the workshop/garage may include power tools, soldering equipment, battery charger, special lighting equipment and perhaps automatic garage doors. Appliances which may be used in the garden include television and small cooking appliances, as well as power tools, lawnmowers and hedgetrimmers. Permanent installations may include decorative lighting, fountain, and waterfall pumps. In both the garage/workshop and garden, special emphasis needs to be placed on safety and adequate protection from electric shock. (Section 5.2.13)

5.2.2.7 Safety certification

When choosing household appliances, it is important to ensure that they are safe to use. The British Electrotechnical Approvals Board (BEAB) is the UK national authority which tests and approves household appliances for safety, and award of the BEAB Mark (Fig. 5.2.1) is an assurance of the safety standard of the appliance concerned. BEAB tests to BS 415 for sound and vision equipment used in the home, and to BS 3456 for most other household appliances.

Lighting fittings and their components, and industrial/commercial equipment often found in the home such as portable tools and small office machines, are certified for safety by the British Standards Institution. In such cases look for the BSI Kitemark or Safety Mark. (See Appendix 6.2). Wiring accessories, and the fuses in consumer units, fuse boxes, and plugs, may be certified by the Association of Short-circuit Testing Authorities. (ASTA).

Fig. 5.2.1. *BEAB Marks*

5.2.3 Thermal insulation

5.2.3.1 General

For efficient and economic use of energy, particularly for space heating, there must be adequate thermal insulation, the cost of which is reflected in lower electricity consumption and hence costs.

Minimum standards of thermal insulation for dwellings are laid down in the latest amendments of the Building Regulations. The Building Regulations also give the maximum amount of heat loss through walls, roofs and floors. (See also section 4.2.2.5)

These minimum standards of thermal insulation are further increased in the Medallion Award Scheme. (Section 5.2.4.1)

5.2.3.2 Methods of insulation

For the householder the priorities for various methods of insulation are:

(a) *Draught excluders*, a cheap and effective means of eliminating draughts around doors and window frames. Adhesive foam strips or metal strips may be used, as well as more specialised products such as a letterbox draught excluder.
(b) *Loft insulation* may be carried out by the handyman and can usually pay for itself in about two years. Up to one quarter of the heat can be lost through the roof, but this loss may be reduced by laying 80 mm glass fibre insulation between the joists.
(c) *Cavity wall insulation* can reduce heat loss by up to two-thirds. It involves pumping ureaformaldehyde or expanded polystyrene beads into the cavity. In situations of exposure to severe weather, such as on high ground or on the coast, mineral fibre or rock wool insulation are recommended. The cavity fill material should either meet BS 5617: 1978 or have an Agrément Certificate. (Ref. 1) A firm should be chosen which has either received an Agrément Board registration certificate of competency to install, or is registered with the British Standards Institution. It may be necessary to obtain planning permission before this work is carried out.
(d) *Double glazing* is an effective means of reducing heat loss through windows, and it offers the additional advantages of cutting down both condensation and noise. Double glazing may be installed using complete factory sealed window units. Alternatively, secondary frames may be fixed inside the existing windows. The hermetically sealed air space between the two sheets of glass is normally 10–15 mm.
(e) If chimneys are no longer being used they should be sealed with a suitable ventilation grille and a ventilation cap fitted to the top of the chimney stack. A layer of glass fibre may be placed under floor boards. With concrete floors, an underlay and a thick carpet can help save heat.

5.2.4 Award schemes

5.2.4.1 Medallion Award Scheme

The Medallion Award Scheme was introduced in September 1977 by the Electricity Boards in England and Wales. For new homes in the private sector it has two provisions which particularly relate to operating costs:

(a) an improved level of thermal insulation (External Wall Maximum 'U' value = $0{\cdot}6\,W/m^2\,{}^\circ C$; Roof = $0{\cdot}32\,W/m^2\,{}^\circ C$)

(b) design and control of the water heating and space heating is such that at least 50% of the energy for these services will be used during the night when electricity is supplied at a cheaper rate.

5.2.4.2 Civic Shield Award Scheme

The Civic Shield Award Scheme is the Local Authority equivalent to the Medallion Award Scheme. It applies to existing properties being upgraded or renovated as well as to new homes. The schemes differ in that, whereas the Medallion Award Scheme is for all-electric homes, in the Civic Shield Scheme cooking need not be by electricity.

Fig. 5.2.2. *Microwave Oven* (TI Creda Ltd)

5.2.5 **Cooking** (See also chapter 4.11)

It is possible to cook food using a wide variety of electric cooking appliances. The main appliance is the cooker which may be a free-standing or built-in model, or in special situations a table-top model. A free-standing cooker comprises an oven, which may be fan-assisted; a grill inside a compartment which may double as a second oven; and usually, four radiant rings or a ceramic hob. A built-in model consists of two separate units. One is a hob with four radiant rings or alternatively a ceramic hob. The other is a separate oven unit which may have two ovens (of which one may be fan-assisted), and a grill compartment. 'Stay clean' oven linings, and autotimers are standard features on electric cookers.

Smaller table top cooking appliances are popular and, although they are not designed to replace the conventional cooker altogether, they have advantages in

Fig. 5.2.3. *Electric cooker with ceramic hob and turbo-fan oven* (Belling and Co. Ltd)

economy and convenience. In a microwave oven high frequency electro-magnetic waves cause heat to be generated inside food. The microwave oven has a high speed of operation which, together with an economical use of electricity, has increased its popularity. The oven can be situated on a work surface (or, in the case of certain models, may be built-in) and can be operated from a 13 A socket outlet. A microwave oven is an ideal adjunct to a food freezer since the majority of models incorporate a defrost facility which 'pulses' the microwaves to ensure even thawing of the food.

The slow cooker is a low temperature cooker with an internally glazed cooking pot and lid. Within the sides are circular heating elements. These have a low loading and again may be operated from a 13 A socket outlet.

The contact grill consists of two heavy aluminium heating plates which make direct contact with the food, cooking the food rapidly by conduction and penetrating radiant heat. Some models have a 'lift and lock' height adjustment to enable a shallow baking tray to be placed on the plates. This extends the use from grilling to include baking and braising. Some models also have detachable plates and special plates for waffle and sandwich making.

The multi-cooker is shaped like a frypan with a sealed thermostatically controlled element underneath. As well as frying it will also stew, roast and bake. Again it is economical to run and may be used in place of a conventional oven. The deep fat fryer enables frying to be carried out safely as the oil is thermostatically controlled. Some models have a filter system in the lid to reduce the escape of steam and smell. Finally, a cooker hood, either self-contained or ducted to the outside air, is a useful supplemental aid in removing cooking odours and steam.

5.2.6 Refrigeration and food freezing

Consumers' needs have altered over the past ten years, so there have been changes in the range of appliances designed to preserve or store food by the reduction of its temperature. The principles of refrigeration and food freezing are still the same, but the choice of appliances also includes fridge/freezer and larder refrigerator (with no ice-making compartment) as well as chest and upright food freezer and refrigerator. The temperature inside the cabinet of a refrigerator is maintained at below 8°C (47°F) and there are two types of refrigerator available – the compressor type and the absorption type. The former is most common, whilst the latter has the advantage of no moving parts and so is quieter in operation, but size for size uses more electricity. Star markings on the evaporator compartment indicate the length of time that commercially frozen food can be stored in the evaporator and are linked with the markings on packages of commercially frozen foods. In some refrigerators defrosting has to be done manually, but in certain models there is a semi-automatic facility which requires setting, or there may be fully automatic defrosting at frequent intervals so that there is no build-up of frost.

The food freezer is designed to operate at temperatures at or below −18°C and can freeze fresh foods as well as store them. The chest freezer has a top opening lid, whilst the upright freezer has a front opening door, and takes up less floor space. Larger models may have two doors. The combination refrigerator/freezer has an upright freezer and refrigerator normally housed in the one cabinet. Defrosting of the chest freezer should be done manually once or twice a year. An upright model needs to be defrosted two or three times a year, again this is done manually but there are some models that have a special 'frost-free facility', to eliminate the need for defrosting.

5.2.7 Laundry

There are two types of washing machines available – the twin tub and the automatic model.

The capacity of a twin tub is smaller than that of a larger automatic, but it does provide economy in use i.e. the wash water can be used more than once if desired. The spin speed of twin tubs will vary and can be as high as 3100 rpm. This machine is normally operated manually by wash time and temperature controls.

Automatic washing machines have the advantage of being almost 'set and forget'. There is a choice of top or front loading models, each offering a wide range of wash programmes. Automatic models should be plumbed in to the water supply and, depending on the model of machine, may be hot and cold fill or cold fill only. Other facilities include a variance in capacity – from 1·8 kg to 5 kg dry weight of cottons and spin speed – dependent on wash load as well as various 'economy' options.

The combined washer/dryer is ideal for the smaller kitchen or laundry room. Otherwise, where space permits, a separate tumbler dryer may be installed. Adequate ventilation must be provided for this either directly through an external wall or through an adjacent open window. Although tumbler dryers are designed to be floor-standing some smaller models may stand on a work surface or be wall mounted. Stacking kits enable dryers to be stacked on top of a matching washing machine.

Irons may be of the dry or steam type and will vary in weight and wattage. Their temperature settings are generally in line with symbols that match those given on clothing labels as devised by the Home Laundering Consultative Council (Ref. 2). Rotary and flat bed ironers are also available.

5.2.8 Space heating (See also chapter 4.8)

5.2.8.1 General

Heating systems should be designed to maintain comfortable temperatures, even when there are adverse weather conditions outside. The advantages of electric space heating are that it is efficient, requires little maintenance and is completely free of noise, dirt or smells. It is also capable of fully automatic operation and, since there is no need to provide chimneys or an area for fuel storage, building costs are reduced.

There are two broad types of electric space heating equipment – thermal storage systems which operate on cheaper off-peak supplies and direct acting systems which may be switched on or off at will.

5.2.8.2 Storage heating systems

Storage heating systems are a popular method of providing central heating. They are economical in operation, and take advantage of off-peak electricity.

5.2.8.3 Storage heaters

Storage heaters consist of a metal case containing bricks of a high thermal retention, between which heating elements are placed. Improvements in design have meant that the heat-storage requirements can be obtained during the night period only. These heaters are known as 'slim-line' heaters. The supply to the heaters is automatically switched on during the off-peak period by the time-switch provided and set by the Electricity Board. A thermostat or 'charge controller' is incorporated

Fig. 5.2.4. *Storage Radiator* (TI Creda Ltd)

in the heater so that the input during the charge period can be regulated by the user. Ideally the user should adjust the control to allow for the considerable variations in heating levels necessitated by changes in weather conditions.

A newer type of automatic control has been extensively field-tested and has shown savings of 15% on average space-heating consumption compared with manual control. The new control consists of a close differential room thermostat which operates an extra-low-voltage switching unit. A room thermostat senses the overnight temperature and this provides a basis for automatically controlling the heat input. With the advent of the silicon chip a new generation of control systems is being developed which will give even greater flexibility of application.

The construction of storage fan heaters is similar to that of storage heaters, but with a greater thickness of insulation, so that the heat is dissipated more slowly. The rate of heat output may, however, be increased by the use of the fan incorporated in the heater. Although more expensive to purchase than storage heaters, these can provide more flexible control. Storage fan heaters would normally be used where an increase in temperature may be required quickly.

Fig. 5.2.5. *Electricaire Unit* (TI Creda Ltd)

Initial costs of these systems can be comparatively small compared with other heating systems, because additions to the number of storage heaters originally provided can be made later, as required.

5.2.8.4 Electricaire

The principles of Electricaire heating are the same as those of storage fan heaters but, instead of separate heaters in each room, one central unit is provided in a convenient position. Warm air is then conveyed by a system of ducts from this position to each room in the house. The ducts are concealed, and two small grilles provide the only visible sign of the heating system in each room. These are the inlet and return ducts, measuring about 255 mm by 200 mm. The input of heat can be regulated manually or by weather sensing control whilst the amount of heat given out is controlled automatically by the room thermostat, which can be adjusted by the user. Fan speed may be increased to circulate the air more quickly and thereby rapidly increase the room temperature if, for any reason, the heating system has been turned down. The Electricaire system is best suited to new properties, unless a considerable amount of installation work is acceptable.

Fig. 5.2.6. *Convector Heater* (Dimplex Ltd)

5.2.8.5 Floor warming

This is a relatively cheap method of installing space heating in new buildings and extensions, and has been commonly used in blocks of flats. Suitable only for concrete floors, it consists of a special cable embedded in the mass of the floor with a sufficient thickness of cement screed on top to ensure adequate heat storage capacity. It is essential to insulate the heated slab from the ground, and also the surrounding structure.

Floor warming is operated in conjunction with an off-peak tariff, and is controlled by time switches and thermostats so that circuits for different rooms may be switched independently.

5.2.8.6 Direct acting heating

Direct acting heating appliances include convector heaters, radiant heaters, radiant convector heaters, fan heaters, oil-filled radiators, panel heaters, tubular or skirting heaters and ceiling heating systems. Of the heaters available, some are more suitable for certain situations than others, therefore, it is wise to seek specific advice before purchasing.

5.2.9 **Water heating** (See also chapter 4.10)

Hot water on demand is a basic requirement for domestic premises. An advantage of electric water heating is that is possible to place the element in the water so that the efficiency of such a heater is nearly 100%. The water heating process is completely automatic, being thermostatically controlled, and it does not need maintenance. The water is heated in an insulated tank or cylinder fitted with one or more immersion heater elements, which may be positioned in the top or the sides of the cylinder.

Fig. 5.2.7. *Fuel effect Fire* (Berry Magicoal)

A storage water heating system can take advantage of off-peak electricity, but to gain maximum benefit there must be a tank large enough to provide for normal family needs. The cylinder has two separate thermostatically controlled heating elements. One, fitted close to the bottom of the cylinder, is switched on automatically during off-peak period. The other element, with a thermostat set at a lower temperature, is fixed at a higher level in the tank to heat a daytime reserve if the total demand for hot water has been exceptionally high. This second immersion heater may be switched on manually. Special controls are available which reduce the use of daytime electricity to a minimum. Other types of water heaters include point-of-use water heaters, for instance over (or under) the sink; storage heaters; instantaneous heaters; wall-mounted kettles; and instantaneous showers. These heaters may prove more economical if the pipe-run from the hot water cylinder to kitchen, sink or wash basin is unduly long.

In all instances, loss of heat from the water tank and hot water pipes must be minimised. In purpose-made electric water heaters the lagging will be an integral part of the design but other tanks will need to be fitted with an insulating jacket. The minimum thickness of this jacket should be 80 mm. Hot water pipes should be lagged wherever possible.

5.2.10 Lighting (See also chapter 4.9)

Lighting in the home is used for two purposes; for seeing and for effect. For visual tasks it is essential that the lighting is sufficient to prevent eye strain. Lighting for effect is decorative and is used to add interest to the home and enhance the appearance of the furnishings and decor. In winter-time lighting provides the bonus of additional warmth because the energy used for lighting is released as heat. Most home lighting needs are met by filament lamps of 40, 60, 100 and 150 W which have a working life of about 1000 hours. Double coil or 'coiled coil' lamps give more light but cost slightly more. 'Long life' lamps that will last about 2000 hours are available, but they are more expensive and give about 7% less light. Filament lamps include pearl lamps, which have a frosted finish inside the glass, which gives a softer light and suits most fittings. Mushroom lamps are more compact, and clear lamps are especially suited to glass fittings where they help give extra reflective sparkle. In kitchens and other utility areas, an opal or prismatic enclosure is aesthetically pleasing. In other rooms they can be built into recesses, pelmets or behind baffles to provide feature lighting.

Fluorescent lighting can be used for seeing or for decorative lighting. Fluorescent lamps, which give about four times the amount of light given by a filament bulb of the same wattage, are therefore more economical in use. Fluorescent lamps are also available in U shapes and circles.

Complete fluorescent fittings can be used in many situations. Practical tube sizes range from miniature tubes 150 mm long up to 2400 mm. Suitable colours for home use include Warm White de luxe and Softone. The new SL type of lamp works on the fluorescent tube principle, but will fit into normal light sockets. SL lamps have low power ratings, of 9, 13, 18 or 25 W, and produce the equivalent lighting of 40, 60, 75 or 100 W bulbs respectively.

As well as general lighting, focal decorative lighting may also be needed for effect. There are various designs of lighting fittings available, and wall and ceiling fittings are generally used in conjunction, together with free-standing table lamps or 'spot lamps'. Lighting control is normally by on/off switch, but dimmer and time control switches are available, assisting in both security and economy measures.

Exterior lighting is effective for security purposes, and may also be used to highlight particular features of the home or garden. Outside lighting may be controlled by either a 24 hour time switch, or one which incorporates a photo-sensitive cell. This will automatically switch the lights on as dusk falls throughout the year without the need for regular adjustment. From the safety angle good lighting is vital to illuminate steps and other obstacles.

5.2.11 Ventilation

Although thermal insulation is important there is still a need for adequate ventilation. Air change is essential in achieving a required comfort level. It also reduces condensation to a minimum. Levels of ventilation have to comply with Building Regulations, and are at present concerned with the window opening areas in relation to the floor area.

Houses and flats are sometimes provided with internal bathrooms, toilets and shower rooms. These need adequate ventilation which can be achieved by a ducted fan. These are delay switch controlled, and operate when the light is switched on, stopping approximately ten minutes after the light is switched off.

5.2.12 Providing for the disabled (See also chapter 4.16)

The implementation of the Chronically Sick and Disabled Persons Act 1970 has resulted in increased focus on the personal and national advantages of rehabilitating disabled people in their own homes. Electric domestic appliances can play a large part in helping the disabled to be independent. Special appliances are often not necessary, but any electrical appliance should be placed or fixed so that full advantage may be gained from it. The automatic controls, available on such items as electric cookers, laundry equipment, space and water heaters and electric blankets, can be of great help.

It might be necessary to adapt or replace the conventional control knobs or switches, as these may cause problems for people with disabled hands. Special switches available include coverplate switches which require only a light pressure from hand, elbow, knee or even walking stick. Simply fixing a large ring to pull-cord switches may make them easier to use. Other more sophisticated methods are air switches, which can be operated by a light touch from hand or foot, or even a puff of air from the mouth. These switches may need to be situated at a low height, accessible from a wheelchair. Simple intercom or alarm systems are available for bedridden or chair-bound people to summon assistance.

Electric cookers may be adapted to meet some needs of disabled persons. Their automatic features, such as timers and thermostatic controls, are complemented by stay-clean linings. Split-level cookers allow the hob and oven to be placed in the most advantageous position for operation from a wheelchair. Microwave ovens and other small portable cooking appliances can be used on any surface at a suitable height. For the blind the control knobs of appliances may be replaced by knobs with braille markings.

5.2.13 **Electrical installation** (See also chapter 3.1)

5.2.13.1 Notes on wiring

The supply to domestic consumers in the UK is normally single phase 240 V, at a frequency of 50 Hz. The supply enters the house at the service entry point, then passes through the house service cut-out which contains the main fuse and meter. In new properties these may be situated in special boxes on the exterior of the house, while in flats they may be communally sited for ease of reading by the Electricity Board staff. The distribution of electricity to all circuits in a house is controlled by a consumer unit, incorporating a main switch to isolate the supply. Each circuit inside the house is connected to its own terminal, with a fuse or preferably miniature circuit breaker matched in rating to the circuit it protects.

Every modern home has the following circuits:
Fixed Lighting (5 A)
Water Heating (15 or 20 A)
Ring Circuit (30 A)
Cooker Circuit (45 A)

In a house there may be two fixed lighting circuits and two ring circuits, one of each for both upstairs and downstairs. A single 30 A ring circuit may serve a floor area of up to 100 m^2, but consideration should be given to the loading in kitchens, which may require a separate circuit. In addition to the ring circuit there is the multi-socket radial circuit. Both circuits have BS 1363 13 A socket outlets for use with 13 A fused plugs. Table 5A of the 15th edition of the IEE Wiring Regulations gives details for ring and multi-socket radial circuits. These include cable sizes, fuse ratings, the floor area they serve and the type of overcurrent protective device which must be used.

It is unlikely that all appliances in the home will be in use at any one time and so a 'diversity factor' can be employed. This means that the wiring, fuses and appliances are planned on the basis that not all the potential, or possible, loading will occur at once. The diversity factor should be calculated by the engineer responsible for designing that particular installation. Appendix 4 of the 15th edition of the IEE Wiring Regulations gives notes on the application of the diversity factor for final circuits, stating how this may be assessed for differing types of premises.

Often it is not fully appreciated that an adequate number of socket outlets must be provided if an installation is to be safe under all conditions. Apart from the convenience of being able to use appliance in any required position, a reasonable number of socket outlets will eliminate lengths of trailing flex and other dangers.

In the event of a fault occuring in an installation, whether in an appliance or in part of the wiring, it is essential that the faulty section be disconnected from the supply immediately, although the remainder of the system should remain in operation. This can be achieved by an adequate system of fuses or miniature circuit breakers, and by the provision of earthing.

The 15th edition of the IEE Wiring Regulations advocates the use of a residual current device with a rating not exceeding 30 mA to give additional protection. A residual current device is designed to sense very small fault currents which are well below those needed to blow a fuse. The Wiring Regulations also state that a socket outlet likely to be used for portable appliances outside a building or in a garage/workshop must be protected by a residual current device. This means that any equipment such as a lawnmower, power tool or hedge-trimming device, used from a socket outlet situated in a shed or garage, should be so protected. These may be permanently fixed as a socket outlet combined with a residual current device; or as a unit like an adaptor, which plugs into the socket outlet; or as an extension lead, with an incorporated residual current device; and lastly as a unit which replaces the 13 A plug and is connected to the flexible cord of the appliance.

5.2.13.2 National Inspection Council for Electrical Installation Contracting

Reputable organisations concerned with electrical installations ensure that their work is carried out in accordance with the IEE Regulations. When looking for a reliable electrical contractor to carry out electrical work, always select one from the Roll published by the National Inspection Council for Electrical Installation Contracting (NICEIC). This is an organisation for the protection of electricity consumers against faulty, unsafe or otherwise defective electrical installations. Copies of the NICEIC Roll are available for reference in Citizen's Advice Bureaux, Consumer Advice Centres, Electricity Board Shops and Public Libraries. Members of the Electrical Contractors' Associations, and Electricity Boards, are approved contractors on the Roll of the NICEIC.

5.2.14 Communications and security

Provision should be made in the early stages of design for the installation of communications and security systems. These would include door bells, TV aerial points, telephone wiring, entryphones, baby alarm, intruder detector alarms and smoke detector and fire alarms.

5.2.15 Tariffs

In Great Britain each Area Board offers a standard domestic tariff for unrestricted use, which has a two-part structure with a quarterly standing charge and a kWh rate for units consumed. In the South of Scotland a block of higher priced primary units replaces the quarterly standing charge. In addition all Boards offer day/night tariffs which allow consumers to purchase electricity at two different rates; one rate applicable during the day-time period and a much lower rate for those units consumed during a specified night period. A kilowatt hour meter with two registers is installed; one register records units consumed during the day-time period, and the other records units used during the night. An associated time switch automatically arranges the change-over from one register to another at the specified times.

The main day/night tariff offered by all Area Boards in England and Wales is called Economy 7, and this has a lower unit rate for seven hour night period. The tariff comprises a quarterly standing charge, a day unit rate and a night unit rate which is applicable to all electricity consumed during a 7 hour night period regardless of use. This means that all electricity used during the seven-hour period is recorded at the lower rate and hence, by installing suitable control equipment, appliances such as dishwashers and washing machines can be programmed to operate during the night. Economy 7 is particularly suitable for those homes with electric storage space heating, and those who heat water mainly by electricity. Using this tariff it is possible both to maintain a good standard of space heating using storage heaters and, with a reasonably-sized well-lagged tank, to heat a full tank of water at the night rate and only use day-rate electricity for top-up purposes if required. The Economy 7 tariff may also be the most attractive option for consumers without any storage space heating but a larger than average consumption, provided they are prepared to change slightly their pattern of electricity demand to exploit the low night rate.

Because so much depends on individual use it is best to seek the advice of the local Electricity Authority, in the UK and in other countries.

5.2.16 References

5.2.16.1 References in text

(1) The British Board of Agrément PO Box 195 Bucknalls Lane Garston Watford WD2 7JR
(2) The Home Laundering Consultative Council c/o Clothing and Footwear Institute Albert Road Hendon NW4 2JS.

5.2.16.2 Legislation (See also Appendix 6.1)

Chronically Sick and Disabled Persons Act 1970
Building Regulations 1976 and subsequent Amendments

5.2.16.3 British Standards (See also Appendix 6.2)

BS 415 Safety of electronic apparatus used in the home
BS 1363 13 A Plugs and Sockets
BS 3456 Safety of household appliances
BS 5617 Cavity wall insulation

5.2.16.4 Bibliography

'Essential Electricity – A Users Guide'. Tenth Edition of the EAW Electrical Handbook. Hodder and Stoughton.

Regulations for Electrical Installations (Institution of Electrical Engineers)
The International Textile Care Labelling Code. (The Home Laundering Consultative Council)
The Electricity Council continually produce new publications concerning electricity in the home. Amongst those of particular interest are
"Reducing the energy cost of electric space heating and hot water systems". (Technical Information Sheet DOM 4)
"Improved Control for Storage Heaters". (Technical Information Sheet Dom 11)
"Electricity in Your Garden" (EC 3458)

Low rise office building

Chapter 5.3

Offices

Derek S. Ball, C.Eng., M.I.E.E.
Project Director, Ove Arup & Partners

5.3.1 Introduction

It is most important that the design brief for electrical installations in offices should define whether the offices are to be designed for a specific tenant, in which case his business needs and method of working will be known, or if the development is to be speculative, in which case the designer may have to take the initiative in preparing sketch or scheme stage proposals for approval. Common to both categories will be the need to maximise net lettable or usable area. This may be helped by careful planning and siting of plant rooms, services risers, distribution cupboards and core areas to make the best use of space. To limit building height and hence cost, the ceiling void depth for electrical and mechanical installations should be minimised consistent with sensible facility for installation and subsequent maintenance access of services through the life of the installation.

Flexibility should be the keynote to account for future changes in office layout, such as partitioning, and new equipment as this comes onto the market. This is particularly relevant in a speculative development where tenants' business needs may be quite unknown at the onset of design. However, high on the list of design priorities will probably be the need to minimise capital expenditure. This should be seen to be compatible with the standard of environmental services required and the degree of flexibility to be provided in the installation since there is usually a premium cost to be paid.

Office accommodation today tends more to open plan arrangements with moveable chest high partitions to form work stations. Here, particular care should be taken to avoid the depressing appearance of large areas of flat ceiling. This can be countered by the form of the structure, for instance using coffers or by architectural treatment of the ceiling to provide vertical modelling. The use of properly designed louvred luminaires will, for instance, not only provide visual interest but also direct light downwards to avoid glare and unwanted reflections.

The electrical design issues should focus primarily on the interactive considerations of how the building is to be illuminated, the depth of rooms or floors, clear ceiling height, services corridors and risers, internal climatic conditions, heat transfer and the extent that daylight is to be allowed into the occupied space. An early decision is needed on the degree of artificial supplementary lighting required or indeed whether total reliance is to be placed on lighting as in deep plan offices. Too much natural light in occupied spaces should be avoided since the penalties are usually high in solar gain, which is costly and difficult to deal with, glare and harsh contrasts in illuminance.

There is much environmental variety in buildings expressed in light, sound, heating, cooling, ventilation and modelling. It is fundamental, but not always understood, that buildings should be designed with all these factors in mind, particularly the thermal characteristics which should be suited, if necessary, to the use of air conditioning rather than needing air conditioning due to failure in the architectural treatment to acknowledge the environmental needs of the occupants.

5.3.2 Electricity supply

5.3.2.1 Supply details

Having established the design brief for environmental services and office electrical equipment and hence the approximate electrical energy demand, the next step will be in discussion with the Electricity Authority to determine the method of supply, point of entry, sub-station accommodation if required, metering and appropriate tariff for the incoming electricity supply. As an initial rough guide, a figure of 100 VA/m^2 of gross floor area may be taken as the maximum demand, being about half the total connected load for a typical air conditioned office building in the UK. Supply will be provided normally at 415 V for loads up to about 300 kVA and exceptionally up to 1 MVA depending on the system characteristics and for larger developments at 11 KV.

The Electricity Authority will require 24 hours uninterrupted access from the street to any sub-station housing their high voltage equipment. This may pose problems of security, particularly in multi-tenancy situations, which should be worked out in the early stages of design.

5.3.2.2 Metering

Single tenancy developments normally require only one meter whereas multi-tenancy offices usually require the incoming supply to be separated into metered circuits for landlord's supplies and unmetered circuits for tenant's rising mains. The latter can comprise either bus-bars and tap off units or cable risers feeding sub-distribution boards, sealed by the Electricity Authority. Metering is then provided on a floor by floor basis, the energy costs being recovered directly by the Electricity Authority.

Alternatively, the landlord may install tenants' sub-metering but he will then be responsible for the administrative costs of meter reading, billing and collection of monies, which is not generally favoured by developers. Yet a further possibility is for the landlord to assess tenants' electrical energy consumption on the basis of installed environmental services and office electrical equipment and include this as an 'all in' inclusive charge in floor rental. This alternative has the merit of a simplified and hence lower cost electrical distribution system but tends to suffer from extravagent use of 'free' energy by the tenant.

5.3.2.3 Tariffs

Electricity Authorities offer a choice of tariffs each suited to a range of consumer usage patterns. The most appropriate for office development will be framed normally on a two part structure, one element as a maximum demand (MD) charge and the other as a charge for units (kWh) of energy consumed. The MD element of the tariff relates to power factor (p.f.) of the load and penalises consumers who fail to maintain the required minimum value, usually 0·9 to 0·95 lagging.

The electrical load cycle and power factor of the installed electrical load can vary significantly in an air conditioned office building, being particularly affected adversely by low power motive drives during periods of light duty. The cost of installing corrective static capacitors will be recovered normally in reduced energy costs within one or two years.

Alternatively, consideration should be given to the cost effectiveness of installing synchronous a.c. motors instead of induction motors where, for instance, large individual drives for chillers are required for an air conditioning installation. These machines offer the inherent characteristic of operating at a leading power factor which provides an opportunity for correction to the building electrical system. Whichever corrective arrangement proves the most commercially viable should also be made fully automatic.

5.3.2.4 Standby plant

Standby power plant, normally in the range 30–1000 kVA may be needed to maintain essential environmental services in the event of interruption in mains supply so that normal business activities can continue. This is particularly relevant to mechanical ventilation in window sealed, air conditioned offices where, for instance, an alternative supply is mandatory in buildings subject to Section 20 of the London Building Acts (Amendment) Act 1939. Other essential circuits will often include office and circulation area lighting, at least one lift, particularly where this is designated a fireman's lift, water and/or fire booster pumps, office business machines and computers with their associated air conditioned peripherals. The tolerable environmental limits of temperature and humidity associated with computers have to be maintained normally within close limits if damage or malfunction is to be avoided. The size of standby plant is often limited to 50% or less of the maximum demand by constraints of cost and physical space. An early judgement at sketch or scheme stage should, therefore, be made to test the commercial viability in providing this added security, since it is considered by some developers to enhance materially the value of lettable office space.

Having identified certain plant or equipment items and engineering services as 'essential', the appropriate machine rating, class of governing and voltage regulation will be determined by reference to the expected maximum demand, the incremental size of applied loads and the limiting variations of voltage and frequency related to the nature and sensitivity of the connected load.

Provision is sometimes required for a 400 Hz and/or 50 Hz frequency stabilised 'no-break', uninterruptable power supply (UPS) to maintain an on-line computer and associated peripheral equipment where the system does not have facility to 'power down' without loss of data in the event of a power supply interruption. Computers are run generally on a double shift basis to maximise return on investment so that absolute continuity of power supply is essential.

The equipment may take the form of a static battery/invertor or, alternatively, a continuously rotating machine capable of sustaining the load for typically three minutes. Both arrangements require the back-up of auto-start diesel-electric plant to take up the load quickly, within the short time span provided by the 'no-break' system.

5.3.3 Controlling the environment

The more enlightened owner/developer will expect proper consideration of cost in use in the design of building engineering systems. This should include the specification of energy efficient plant, as, for instance, heat recovery from ceiling mounted luminaires and exhaust air, two-speed fans to match high and low load conditions, high efficacy lighting and low maintenance plant. An energy conscious design for an air conditioned office building should, as a first approximation, achieve something in the order of 180 kWh/m^2 per annum in the UK, a particularly significant criteria considering that energy costs at the present are typically 20 to 25% of the total operating cost of the average commercial building.

Against this background, building engineering systems installed in modern commercial buildings are becoming progressively more complex. For efficient plant operation, management, control and maintenance, a micro-processor programmable controller based building automation system (BAS) offers many opportunities and advantages over the limited facilities provided by the hard wired systems used largely a few years ago. The BAS is capable of performing a wide variety of functions. The degree of sophistication and type of energy optimisation or management program appropriate to a particular project will be determined generally by the size and complexity of the building services installations. Equally, a cost benefit evaluation will be required to determine the optimum return on investment with a pay back period not normally extending to more than 2 or 3 years. Control equipment now available may prove cost effective in maximising the efficient use of plant and minimising recurring energy costs, even in smaller office buildings which would not, for instance, support the employment of full time skilled maintenance staff. (See also section 3.5.13)

5.3.4 Lighting

5.3.4.1 General lighting

Energy consumed by lighting in offices can be as much as half the total electrical load and in the present climate of energy conservation there is now a strong incentive to limit demand and cost by increasing its efficient use.

Energy conscious design solutions are now making use of new technology and new techniques. For these to be successful in achieving a pleasing and efficient working environment over a diverse range of applications, thought should be given not only to the more obvious considerations of design illuminance and high lamp efficacy but to the signficant visual effects of source intensity, direction and quality. In this context, for instance, the spectral distribution of light may vary signficantly from one source to another. This will be manifest not only in the source colour appearance but more importantly in its colour rendering of chosen furnishing, fabrics and finishes which may be modified or enhanced dramatically.

The CIBS (formerly IES) Code for Interior Lighting recommends the following task and building service illuminance in offices:

offices:	Lux
filing, printing and circulating areas	300
clerical work	500
drawing and deep open office areas	750

Office lighting can be provided either:

(a) direct from ceiling mounted luminaires using some form of reflector with further optical control by diffuser, louvre or prismatic lens.
(b) indirectly from the ceiling by luminaires placed in furniture or floor standing below.
(c) task lighting.

Ceiling mounted luminaires can in general be arranged to provide nearly uniform illuminance, to satisfy the most demanding task, over the whole working area. This has the principal advantage that work and funiture can be arranged anywhere but suffers a disadvantage than non-work areas will be illuminated to an unnecessarily high level, with consequential waste of energy. The arrangement is, however, particularly suited to speculative development using conventional fluorescent tubes where a typical lighting load for an office illuminated to 500 lux will be about 21 W/m^2. By using luminaires developed for use with T8 krypton filled tubes, large open plan offices can be similarly illuminated using only 13 to 14 W/m^2.

A variation on this theme, which conserves energy and may provide more visual interest, involves localising luminaires in an arrangement grouped around work stations to provide the required task illuminance whilst lighting other non-critical areas, including circulation space, to a lower level. Typically a task illuminance of 500 lux would require a background illuminance of 200 to 300 lux. Conversely lighting of work stations containing visual display units (VDU) requires only about

350 lux from luminaires designed to provide good directional control to avoid unwanted reflection in the screens. Less flexibility is provided with this arrangement when the luminaires are integrated with the office layout, but it is particularly suited to custom designed offices.

A development of luminaire design of particular application to offices is the uplighter, an indirect, energy conscious system employing highly efficient, high intensity discharge (HID) sources which may provide, by careful siting close to the work station, both task and background lighting. Such an arrangement, which provides increased light where it is most needed and less light for circulation and non-critical areas, can achieve a task illuminance of between 500 and 700 lux with an electrical load as low as 13 W/m^2 or better. The total upward emitted light is reflected from the ceiling, where the aim should be to achieve about 80% reflectance, and upper area of walls onto the working plane. This provides a good quality of light containing a significant horizontal component producing relaxing and comfortable conditions with none of the problems of glare and shadow often associated with direct lighting schemes. Uplighters may be wall mounted, ceiling suspended, free floor standing which provides a very flexible and adaptable arrangement, or form part of an architectural element integrated into the office furniture. However, the discharge lamp requires a run up time of anything from 2–10 minutes, depending on size and type from switch on to 90% full light output. Similarly, in the event of momentary mains supply interruption, the lamp has to cool down before it can re-strike and regain full brightness, normally in the order of 4–10 minutes, except the high pressure sodium lamp which will only take 1 minute. Back-up lighting is therefore usually required in offices to provide some illumination during the 'blackout' and this may take the form of compact source tungsten or tungsten halogen lamps often incorporated within the body of the luminaire or alternatively in separate fluorescent luminaires. These should be arranged to switch on automatically on loss of supply and remain in circuit until the HID lamp reaches at least partial normal rated output.

High Intensity Discharge lamps such as metal halide (MBI and MBIF) and the more efficient high pressure sodium (SON de luxe) are both currently used in commercial luminaires. The preferred source for offices is, however, the MBIF lamp which provides a pleasant, cool to intermediate colour appearance (4000 K) coupled with a satisfactory colour rendition blending well with daylight.

5.3.4.2 Task lighting

Local or task lighting brings the luminaire to the task and is mounted on or adjacent to the work surface. Here the separation of task lighting from general office lighting is quite distinct and independent installations are provided and controlled for each function. Depending on the task, local illuminance varies normally between 500 to 700 lux against a background illuminance of 300 lux to provide an acceptable brightness ratio between the task and surroundings. The principle advantages are the ease of adjustment and relative cheapness. Disadvantages include lower luminous efficacy, possible discomfort in the form of waste heat, possibility of mal-adjustment and shorter lamp life. These luminaires have to be positioned carefully to minimise reflected glare and the area of adequate illuminance may be insufficient if larger than double A4 size papers are dealt with or if tasks involve looking at several points on the work surface.

5.3.4.3 Lighting control

Since lighting may account for up to half the total energy input to an air conditioned office building, a control system which can automatically reduce this demand substantially and which will also thereby reduce the cooling load, deserves serious consideration.

Economy can be achieved by a planned energy programme employing selective and controlled switching of lighting circuits to optimise the use of energy without necessarily lowering standards. For instance, there may be no need to energise luminaires adjacent to windows in the perimeter zone where supplemented by daylight to the working plane. Similarly all, or a substantial part, of the office lighting can be switched off during the lunch break. Lighting may be switched off or on progressively as daylight increases or decreases. Switching can be effected manually or automatically but reliance on the human element is unlikely to achieve the right judgment at the right time since experience shows that lights are generally left on. An automatic programmed control can, on the other hand, be set to function at pre-determined times and at pre-determined ambient illuminance to suit office regimes and to respond properly to available natural daylight. At the close of office working all luminaires can be switched off automatically except those 'essential' circuits providing background lighting required for safety, office cleaning and/or security patrols. Local on/off control for individual offices can still be retained if required by means of additional control circuit wiring.

The control equipment will employ typically a pulsed on/off relay function using a combination of time switch, photo relays and similar inputs as a discrete system or as part of an overall building services energy management system of control. Development work is in train for more sophisticated switching using mains cables for signal transmission to uniquely addressable micro-processors mounted within the luminaires.

5.3.4.4 Emergency lighting

The requirement for emergency lighting in office buildings, as distinct from standby lighting (para 5.3.2.4), stems from interpretation of legislation but most design work is now accepted by enforcing authorities on the basis of BS 5266: Part 1: 1975 "Code of Practice for Emergency Lighting of Premises". However, design for any particular installation will be subject to local variations in interpretation of the legislation concerned with safety of people in or escaping from a building in the event of complete electricity supply failure, or localised circuit failure where the loss of lighting would present a hazard. The relevant enforcing authority should be consulted during and on completion of the design stage.

The Code requires a minimum of 0·2 lux at floor level along the centre line of escape routes, intersections of corridors and changes in direction, highlighting any obstructions and emergency equipment, such as fire alarm call points and extinguishers. Illuminated exit or emergency exit signs as appropriate are required above all exits and illuminated directional signs at any point on an escape route where an exit or emergency exit sign is not in direct sight. Emergency lighting is also required in lift cars, moving stairways and walkways, toilet accommodation exceeding 8 m^2, covered car parks and plant rooms.

Whilst 0·2 lux is defined as the minimum luminance under working conditions assuming for instance, a nearly exhausted battery at the end of its rated discharge period, it is not suggested that systems should be designed down to this figure.

When considering escape lighting illuminance in relation to 'normal' illuminance of say 300 lux, it would be more appropriate to design for a related minimum value of say 1·0 to 1·5 lux with commensurate values for higher 'normal' illuminance.

Fig. 5.3.1. *Large open plan office* (Philips Lighting)

This argument for a higher minimum value will be particularly relevant in the presence of fire and smoke, since a change in illuminance values in the ratio of say 1500 : 1 at the moment of mains supply failure may detract seriously from fast eye adaption to the emergency illuminance. The British Standard requires the diversity ratio i.e. maximum to minimum illuminance to be no greater than 40 : 1 which is another practical consideration for thinking in terms of higher than minimum illuminance.

A typical system will be powered independently of the mains supply from a central source (battery, battery/inverter or generator) or from individual luminaires, each incorporating a self contained battery charger/battery or battery inverter arranged to energise the lamps instantaneously on mains failure.

Where some or all of the normal mains lighting circuits are backed by automatic start standby power plant, consideration can be given also to using these circuits for escape or emergency lighting. In this event the British Standard requires the lighting to be operational within 5 seconds of mains lighting failure except when the population is familiar with the building, as in offices, when the interval may be relaxed to 15 seconds subject to local authority agreement.

Fig. 5.3.2. *Small open plan office*

The appropriate choice of system or systems, as defined in BS 5266, will be dictated by the number of luminaires involved, the circuit route distance, the relative installation costs and the particular needs or risk classification of the building which will also determine the battery duration period of 1, 2 or 3 hours as appropriate. Each building has to be considered on its own individual needs and no generalisation is really practical in giving guidance as to the most appropriate arrangement.

The IEE Regulations require emergency lighting wiring to be separated physically from other wiring circuits and protected by a continuous metal enclosure or sheath.

5.3.5 Electrical installation

5.3.5.1 Switchboards and mains distribution

Fire rated and ventilated space must, apart from any sub-station required by the Electricity Authority, be allocated to low voltage switchgear to control the distribution of electrical energy through feeder cables and/or bus-bars, to subsidiary distribution panels located at load centres in various parts of the building.

Larger electrical loads may be connected directly to the main switchboard. For example, computer installations have power requirements ranging typically from 40 kVA to 400 kVA for the larger equipments. These are usually supplied by a discrete feeder which will provide a 'clean' supply to this type of equipment, which is particularly sensitive to fluctuations in voltage, harmonics and transient voltage disturbance generated by other equipment. Similarly, a separate 'clean' earth system may also be required which should be installed outside the effective zone of influence of the building electrical system main earth electrode.

5.3.5.2 Floor access systems

The most commonly employed point of electrical connection to office equipment is the 13 A socket outlet. The number and arrangement of these outlets should be determined by the office equipment to be installed and the required flexibility in use.

Alternative arrangements providing increasing flexibility in ascending order are:

(a) individual fixed outlets supplied by conduit and/or trunking.
(b) outlets fixed on or in skirting trunking.
(c) outlets connected from a fixed grid of under floor trunking.
(d) outlets connected into a variable grid open top trunking system.
(e) outlets connected into a cavity floor system.

A comprehensive underfloor trunking system should allow a flexible arrangement of office furniture and office electrical equipment so that connections can be made without recourse to long flexible cords trailing across the floor. Trunking will normally accommodate outlet boxes comprising mains supply socket(s), telephone outlet and data transmission entry/outlet point associated with desk computers, input and output terminals, VDU's and the like. In order to satisfy the safety standards prescribed by the IEE Regulations and Telecom requirements in particular, circuits must be segregated within the trunking by continuous metal dividers. The outlet boxes must provide separate and properly designed points of exit with cord clamps for mains and telecom flexible cords.

Floor trunking is arranged principally in two different ways, by providing an interconnected grid, usually at about 2 m centres, which is the most flexible and suited particularly to open plan offices or the feeder and branch arrangement. The latter employs a central feeder trunking with branches off best suited to partitioned offices with the central feeder along a corridor.

Built in flexibility to accommodate changes in office layout and/or function of

Fig. 5.3.3. *Drawing office*

work stations is costly. However, when this is not provided, the cost of later disruption to floors and work places, which takes place typically every five years, and where alteration and/or increased capacity are required, may well exceed the initial cost of installation. This can prove a significant consideration in the choice of premises by a prospective tenant. There are three basic types of floor access:

(a) Underfloor system – this is laid normally on the structural floor slab prior to any finishes being placed. The maximum depth of trunking will be determined by the thickness of floor finish. Changes in direction and intersections in the grid arrangement are accommodated in junction boxes which preserve the physical separation between circuits. Wiring outlets are provided in each compartment at pre-determined centres on the trunking run within the floor finish. The main advantages of this system are its relative low cost and minimal dimensions where only a shallow screed is available. However, it offers less flexibility in accommodating major changes in office layout except by accepting the need to damage floor finishes in gaining access to the buried outlets for connection of above floor terminal boxes.

(b) Flush floor system – this is similar to the underfloor trunking except it is fitted with removable covers along its length designed to accept the floor covering. This type offers greater flexibility since flush floor outlet modules can be added or removed at any time to suit changes in office layout with the minimum of disturbance to the floor.

(c) Cavity floor system – floors are supported by adjustable steel jacks and often designed with a grid of removable access panels over the whole area. This arrangement provides a high degree of flexibility in the positioning of service outlets and electrical cable inter-connections such as are required in computer installations, telephone equipment rooms and under floor air conditioning systems. The cavity is used normally as a plenum to supply essential cooling air through grilles to the equipment above. However, the building height is increased, due to the floor void, resulting in higher building cost and the system is therefore limited generally to high technology areas.

A Code of Practice for electrical systems in office furniture and screens has been published by the BSI (BS 6396: 1983)

5.3.5.3 Lightning protection

The need, or otherwise, of a lightning protective system can be assessed quantitatively by reference to BS CP 326, although this risk index assessment should be applied with judgment and practical experience.

Principal factors in this consideration, particularly in tall office buildings, include the incidence of lightning in the geographical area of the building, extent of isolation from other buildings and topography, type of structure and content and height of building. The structural steel frame or steel reinforcement in a building may, to advantage, be used as part of the protective system. In particular, this may permit the omission of down conductors, provided the steel conducting path is electrically continuous and suitable bond points are established at roof and ground level for the connection of an air terminal network and earth electrodes respectively.

5.3.6 Communications

Communications technology generally is undergoing a major technological revolution which in its turn has brought economic confusion. Increasing competition in the supply of hardware and software network services requires careful and well informed technical consideration in the choice of any new communication infrastructure. Rapid advance in digital techniques is removing the demarcation between the voice switching function of modern telephone equipment and many forms of computer data processing.

Equipment currently available is capable of handling both functions, and cabling facilities within buildings should be designed to accommodate not only the present systems but provide for future developments involving, for instance, the use of communications satellites.

Communications presently includes telephones (voice), electronic message systems (including telex and teletext), computer data and image transmission.

The developer may consider providing any one of a number of alternative telephone equipments ranging from a simple house system (PAX) to a stored program controlled (SPC) private automatic branch exchange (PABX) in advance of his having let part or all of the building. Such a capital commitment could be seen as enhancing the value of lettable space since it would avoid delay otherwise implicit in ordering and installing a specified telephone system once a tenant has contracted to rent space.

In this circumstance, the sophisticated stored program controlled equipment in particular, offers many facilities including the opportunity of partitioning the system to provide separate circuit facilities for multi-tenant occupation, and adding various software packages to suit the particular requirements of different tenants.

Early discussion with the Telecom Authority regarding any proposed system is, however, advised. Work undertaken by a contractor will be subject to the Telecom Code of Practice and the installation will be subject to approval before connection is made to the public switched telephone network (PSTN).

However, apart from significant cost, it is often impossible to predict with any accuracy the telephone system needs of prospective tenants and the developer may settle for providing block wiring during building construction. This not only facilitates speedy wiring connections to telephone equipment as soon as it is delivered to site, but does so whilst avoiding damage to finishes, ceilings and floors otherwise posing much difficulty in wiring after occupation. Whatever form of PABX is used, they all require suitable space for an operator console. The larger the PABX, the more consoles are required, one being adequate for up to around 150 lines and two being able to serve up to around 300 lines.

Cables from the main distribution frame at the termination of the exchange lines may be routed vertically up risers on cable trays and/or in cable trunking and conduits located, as far as possible, centrally with respect to the distribution area they serve. Horizontal run-outs from intermediate terminal boxes will usually be afforded by a floor access system of trunking and conduits with floor outlets. Segregation of communication circuits from mains cables in risers, on trays and in ducts or conduits must be maintained to satisfy the safety and technical standards prescribed by the IEE Regulations and Telecom Codes of Practice. The current trend towards the paperless office is to disseminate more information through electronic work stations rather than by the written or typed word and as this practice advances with time, more accommodation may be required for interconnecting cable links adding emphasis to the need for an adaptable system of under floor communication.

5.3.7 Transportation systems

5.3.7.1 Lifts

An adequate and properly planned passenger and goods lift (and/or escalator) installation is essential to the efficient functioning of a multi-storey office building. An unsatisfactory installation is, conversely, difficult, disruptive and costly to remedy and may detract from letting in a speculative office development.

The requirements of local authorities vary but for example, buildings which fall within Section 20 of the London Building Acts (Amendment) Act 1939 have to be provided with a designated fireman's lift. This is required to be sited near the main entrance, to open onto a smoke lobby at each floor, be contained within a 3 hour fire zone and be capable, by switch operation, of being put under sole control of firemen during an emergency.

5.7.3.2 Document transmission

Automated conveyance systems are provided in different types of buildings to perform a variety of tasks. In offices they are used principally for distribution of mail and documents.

Available equipment can be classified broadly into pneumatic tube systems, document lifts, V-trough conveyors and electric transporters.

Provision of any of these systems is not made normally in speculative office buildings. However, where a specific need is demonstrated, great care should be exercised in selection of equipment most appropriate to the nature of the business and compatible with constraints imposed by the building structure.

(a) Pneumatic Tube Systems: carriers are transported in p.v.c tubes by either exhausting or blowing air from a central plant. The tube size varies typically from 50 mm to 275 mm with carrier capacities from 50 g to 10 kg. The carriers, being cylindrical, are not suitable for transporting bulky files or similar large inflexible objects. The speed varies at which carriers are transmitted and can be as high as 4 m/sec.
(b) Document Lifts: several types of document lifts for vertical distribution are available. They can be simple systems where control is exercised from a central location, such as a registry in a large office, to fully automatic systems which permit despatch and receive controls at all floor landings. The maximum carrying capacity of a typical system is 300 containers per hour with each addressable container able to carry a load of 8/10 kg.
(c) V-trough Conveyor: this system is suitable for carrying single sheets of paper or pocket files between series of desks. The principle application is in offices where routine processing is required or operations rooms where messages have to be conveyed from receiving areas to action areas.
(d) Electric Transporters: this system comprises tracks and electric cars made up of drive units and detachable containers designed to carry bulky documents. The system is suitable for transporting heavy and frequent traffic horizontally and vertically throughout any building. The cars can also travel hung vertically downwards from the tracks. Full intercommunication between all the send/receive

stations is achieved by setting address selector switches on the drive unit to correspond with numbers allocated to the required destination. The carrying capacity of each container is typically 8/10 kg and the speed of travel about 0·5 m/sec.

All systems require significant builders work which may be accommodated relatively easily at the building design stage but which may vary from the difficult, disruptive and expensive to the impossible after building construction is complete.

5.7.3.3 Window cleaning systems

Modern high rise buildings equipped with efficient air conditioning systems have made possible an increasing use of vast areas of sealed windows. Even where such windows are openable, manual cleaning is labour intensive, can be hazardous and cause disruption and loss of privacy to the occupants.

BS CP 153: Part 1: 1969 recommends that manually operated window cleaning systems may be employed for buildings no more than 45 m high, and on buildings taller than 30 m high, the gondolas which carry cleaning personnel should be restrained against the building facade to prevent sway resulting from winds. For buildings higher than 30 m, having an area of more than 500 m^2 per floor and windows exceeding 50% of the external envelope, consideration should be given to the provision of power operated gondolas restrained against the building, and for very tall buildings, an automatic window cleaning system. Both systems require tracks on the perimeter of the roof on which the roof car can run and exterior mullion guides for the full height of the building to restrain the gondola and/or the automatic window cleaning machine against the building.

Where an automatic window cleaning system has been installed, a gondola should also be provided for manual inspection of the building and for maintenance of items such as advertising signs, aircraft hazard lights and floodlighting.

On the basis of a monthly cleaning cycle, two to three cleaners operating from one gondola can clean about 4000 m^2 of windows per month, giving a cost factor of £10–12 per m^2 per year. Power operated gondolas require about 15 kW of power when in use. Automatic window cleaning systems are 8–10 times faster than manual cleaning and require about 20 kW of power when in use.

5.3.8 Security

5.3.8.1 Intruder security

A security system may be as simple as a magnetic proximity switch on a door to as sophisticated as a closed circuit TV system (CCTV) and/or electronic surveillance. Normally such complex systems are designed by specialists but wiring accommodation and wiring systems to communicate for instance with a security room require careful consideration in the overall services design stage. Particular care must be taken to preserve the physical separation and segregation of communications wiring from mains voltage circuits as required by the IEE Regulations.

5.3.8.2 Fire precautions

Mandatory requirement in the UK for fire precautions applied to office buildings are well documented. The complexity of a detection and alarm system should reflect the assessed fire hazard posed by the nature of the work and type of materials used in the building. For offices this will generally be relatively straightforward. The system should provide audible warning to protect life and minimise financial loss by initiating action, and additionally where appropriate, be able to identify the location of a fire.

The Building Regulations require physical separation of large buildings into discrete fire zones to limit the spread of fire, so that any detection and alarm system should be arranged similarly to serve each zone. This will minimise disturbance to the occupants of a large building and identify the location of the fire so that it can be dealt with quickly.

The most appropriate form of detector and its operating range and sensitivity characteristics should be chosen carefully by reference to the nature of the fire hazard and the constraints of the building structure. Oil and other flammable liquids and gases for instance, will generally be best protected by flame detection equipment whilst the building fabric at large would be protected by an appropriate form of smoke detector to signal the early stage of an outbreak of fire. Plant rooms containing mechanical and electrical equipment are often better served by heat detectors where a rapid rise in temperature may be the first signal of a fire condition.

A particular requirement should be noted for offices subject to section 20 of the London Building Acts (Amendment) Act 1939 for ceiling voids not wholly formed of non-combustible materials, or containing other combustible materials, exceeding 0·8 m in depth measured between the roof soffit and top of the ceiling, which must be protected by detectors.

A comprehensive system of fire detection will be normally required for computer rooms, including ceilings and floor voids in which fire could be initiated or through which it could spread. Conventional methods include sprinklers or total flooding by CO_2 or halogenated gas. CO_2 is hazardous and may cause damage to the equipment it protects due to the rapid drop in room temperature when discharged. Of the halogenated gases, Halon 1211 (BCF) and Halon 1301 (BTM) are used for fire protection, the latter being more popular. These gases pose minimal hazard to life and take far less storage space than CO_2.

5.3.9 References

5.3.9.1 Legislation (See also Appendix 6.1)

Building Regulations 1972 and Amendments
Electricity (Factories Act) Special Regulations 1908 and 1944
Electricity Supply Regulations 1937
Fire Precautions Act 1971

Health and Safety Act at Work etc Act 1974
London Building Acts (Amendment) Act 1939

5.3.9.2 British Standards (See also Appendix 6.2)

BS 4211: 1967 Steel ladders for Permanent Access
BS 5266: Emergency lighting
BS 5655: Part 1: 1979. Lifts and Service Lifts. Safety Rules for the Construction and Installation of Electric Lifts.
BS 5839: Part 1: 1980. Fire Detection and Alarm Systems in Buildings
BS 6396: 1983. Code of Practice for electrical systems in office furniture and screens
BS CP 3: Chapter IV: Precautions against fire. Part 3: 1968 Office Buildings.
BS CP 153: Part 1: 1969. Windows and Rooflights – Cleaning and Safety.
BS CP 326: 1965. The protection of structures against lightning
BS CP 407: 1972. Electric, hydraulic and hand powered lifts.
BS CP 1013: 1965. Earthing

5.3.9.3 Bibliography

Regulations for Electrical Installations (Institution of Electrical Engineers)
CIBS (formerly IES) Code for Interior Lighting
Fire Offices Committee: Rules for Automatic Fire Alarm Installations
Home Office Guide to the Fire Precautions Act 1971: no. 3 'Offices, Shops and Railway Premises'. (HMSO)
'Guide to Permanent Suspended Equipment' Suspended Access Equipment Manufacturers Association (SAEMA) 82 New Cavendish Street London W1M 8AD

Interior of Department Store (Thorn-EMI Lighting)

Chapter 5.4

Shops

G. N. Kent, C.Eng., M.I.Mech.E.
Chief Engineer, Barkers of Kensington

5.4.1 Introduction

In the economic cycle of society, shops and stores provide the final link in the distribution chain from grower, or manufacturer, to the consumer. It is necessary for the retailer to provide this link as efficiently as possible and that means keeping down the cost of the operation. The retailer recovers his cost by making a 'mark-up' on the goods he sells and this will vary from one trade to another.

Out of the mark-up, the retailer has to recover costs of labour, rent and rates, holding stock, storage, insurance, accounting, heating, lighting, security, mechanical services and display. The last five mentioned items and possible the sixth will, without doubt, involve the use of electricity as the energy source. Electricity may not be the major part of the retailers' expenses, but it is one part over which he has the best chance of exercising control. It is easily switched on and off, and with the advent of modern control systems, can now be more readily regulated. It is a vital part in this final link of the economic chain.

The premises used for shops and stores vary considerably, from the tobacconist's kiosk, where the customer does not cross the threshold, to the department store, where a large part of the floor area is open to the general public. To attract customers to such a shop every effort is made to make the internal environment agreeable both to customers and staff. Most shop premises nowadays are purpose built. The developer, his architect and consultants may be preparing a site for a specific client, such as one of the large chain stores, in which case he will be greatly assisted by his client's own experience and specialist staff, but in the majority of cases of small individual shops, he will be providing premises with little knowledge of their final occupier. Basically, a shop consists of four main areas: sales, stockrooms, staff amenities, and space for engineering services and plant. Each of these areas calls for its own special treatment.

5.4.2 Electricity supply

5.4.2.1 Provision of supply

For the majority of smaller premises in the UK the electricity supply will be at 240 volts single-phase, and for larger premises, at 415 volts three-phase. In a few very large premises supply may be taken at high voltage and transformed down by the consumer, to the usual 415 volt three-phase system. This will require provision for the installation of a substation and switchroom on the premises.

Single-phase is used for all lighting circuits and as a rough guide, for heating circuits up to 7 kW, and for mechanical services up to about 750 W. Single-phase may be used for electric motors above 750 W, but, size for size, the three-phase motor is smaller and more compact, and starting currents not so heavy.

With the electrical supply playing an ever widening role in the operation of shops and stores, it is advisable, when planning a new installation, or modifying an old one, to consider the need for ensuring a continuation of supply, even to the extent of installing a standby generator. However, it should be borne in mind that the Electricity Authority have great experience in maintaining a reliable supply, and where interruptions do occur they are far more likely to be of a local nature but these of course can be just as inconvenient. It is therefore prudent to plan circuits so that equipment, such as check-out tills, scales and slicers, are not all controlled by one local fuse or circuit breaker. It is better to spread the electrical supply to a row of check-outs over a number of circuits.

For larger installations with a good deal of inductive load, such as motors, it is often worthwhile considering the question of power factor correction. The desirability of fitting power factor correction equipment depends upon the type of electrical equipment installed, the tariff charged for electricity and the cost of the correction equipment.

5.4.2.2 Tariffs

Smaller shops will probably take supply at a block tariff, but consideration should be given to a maximum demand tariff if the call for electricity is reasonably constant for at least eight hours in each day.

If a substantial proportion of electricity is used during the night hours, it will be worthwhile examining the benefits offered by a night and day tariff.

5.4.3 Environmental considerations

5.4.3.1 Air conditioning and heating

For heating, there are statutory requirements under the Offices Shops and Railway Premises Act 1963, which specifically states that a temperature of less than 16°C after the first hour shall not be deemed to be a reasonable temperature while work is going on. It further specifies that the method of heating shall not produce fumes which are likely to be injurious or offensive to persons. To the efficient retailer this figure of 16°C has little significance except to set a minimum. If a retail outlet is to prosper, the staff must be alert and cheerful, and customers must be kept comfortable. Heating is only one aspect of the internal environment and the store operator has to consider also the humidity and number of air changes per hour.

In considering a scheme for controlling the internal environment of a shop, it is important for the designer to take account of the amount of heat generated within the building itself – by the staff and customers, the heat from the lights and machines and, in food shops, from refrigerated cabinets, unless the compressors for these are installed outside the shop.

Control of humidity is perhaps the most difficult to achieve, if not actually impossible with straightforward ventilation. The amount of water to be added or extracted from the air, even for a small shop or store, can be substantial. However, with air conditioning the task becomes a more practical proposition. Here the air within a store is recirculated, through filters to cleanse it, but conserving its temperature and humidity. A variable proportion of fresh air is added to suit conditions outside but, in order to replace the oxygen it is not normally less than 10%.

The ventilation requirements of the Act are not precise in that it merely calls for the circulation of an adequate supply of fresh or artificially purified air, the interpretation of 'adequate' being left to the inspector appointed to enforce the Act. For smaller shops, a simple input and/or extract fan to give four to six air changes per hour would satisfy the Act but, in medium or large stores, something more elaborate is required. In the latter, heat gains from the high level of lighting and other heat sources will necessitate the installation of a ducted input and extract ventilation system. Mechanical ventilation provides air movement but, its ability to provide comfortable conditions depends entirely on the temperature and humidity of the external air, together with the degree of heat gain within the building. With today's marketing techniques which call for more selling space per square metre, and higher customer densities, the need for air-conditioning has become generally accepted.

Where air-conditioning is installed there will be little need for additional heating, except for preheaters and perhaps, in the area of doorways. This area is potentially a source of great heat loss and the cause of draughts, particularly when the doors are left open; (a normal trading policy is that an open door attracts customers into the store). Some stores fit revolving or double sets of doors to form an air-lock but, where single rows of doors are used it is the practice to provide an air curtain usually blown vertically downwards from heaters mounted over the door head. A typical air curtain would have a fan air velocity of some 5 m/s to provide an effective throw and a leaving air temperature of 50°C. Even in stores without air-conditioning, air curtains may well provide part of the anwer for winter heating.

5.4.3.2 Lighting

All shops require artificial lighting at some level, ranging from the antique shop in which a comparatively low level of illumination may suffice, commensurate with safety for staff and customers, to supermarkets which aim for a much higher level of lighting to aid display and the selection of goods. At one time some of the larger supermarkets aimed for a lighting level as high as 1000 lux with the objective of attracting customers, but a typical level is perhaps nearer 600 lux. The level recommended in the CIBS Code is 500 lux.

In medium and large stores, air-handling fittings can be used to advantage as part of an integrated lighting and heat recovery system. There are several types of ventilating fitting but basically they all draw air from the occupied space through the fitting so that it passes over the lamps and control gear, extracting heat from them. This maintains fluorescent tubes at their optimum operating temperature, giving more light per watt of input and keeping control gear cool, thereby reducing the risk of failure due to overheating. The heat recovered can be used for heating

Fig. 5.4.1. *High class men's wear* (Osram-GEC)

other areas instead of being wastefully dissipated. In this way heat is prevented from entering the occupied sales areas and cooler conditions can be maintained during the summer and fresher conditions during the winter. The recovered heat can be used for providing some or all the heating requirements of stockrooms or other back areas of the shop. Whatever the type or design of lighting, care must be taken to ensure that the installation can be serviced and kept clean in order to maintain the designed level of illumination. It is uneconomic to install high levels of lighting only to lose possibly one third of the available output through inefficient cleaning and maintenance. In addition to a general overall level of illumination, many shops and stores will make use of special displays using fascia or spot lights to highlight particular merchandise.

In the case of spotlights, a degree of flexibility, perhaps using lighting track, will be sought to cope with changes in display and for special promotions.

Fig. 5.4.2. *Display cabinet* (Concord Lighting)

5.4.3.3 Emergency lighting

In most shops, particularly the medium and larger ones, it is necessary to provide a separate source of lighting for use in an emergency (e.g. a power failure), which will automatically switch on if the mains supply fails. There are various forms of this, a common system being battery-operated, with automatic charging facilities so that the batteries are kept available for service. The main purpose of the emergency lighting is to enable the building to be evacuated, therefore the lamps must be so placed that all exit routes are adequately illuminated. However, consideration should be given to providing a reasonable level of illumination in the area of tills or small valuable stock to prevent opportunist thieving in the case of a failure of the mains supply.

5.4.3.4 Stock rooms and staff areas

Lighting in stock-rooms should be designed to give a good level of illumination and with local switching so that lights in unoccupied areas or by windows can be turned

Fig. 5.4.3. *Hypermarket interior* (Osram-GEC)

off when not required. Heating will be required in office areas and rest rooms and to a lesser extent in stock-rooms. Some stock-rooms, as would be found in food shops, florists and furriers, may need to be refrigerated. In addition to lighting in toilets, an electrical supply may be necessary for ventilation, heating water, running hot-air dryers and other facilities.

5.4.4 Service facilities

5.4.4.1 In-store requirements

Food shops and the food departments in larger stores call for a reliable electrical supply to run equipment such as scales, refrigerated displays, food slicers, coffee grinders, meat mincers, and more recently in supermarkets, bakery ovens to provide the customer with fresh baked bread.

Special promotions in shops bring with them need for an electrical supply. A microphone, an amplifier, and two or three loud speakers may be used to aid a demonstrator to reach a wider audience. In recent years video tape and a television screen have frequently been used to replace the demonstrator.

If the shop is on more than one floor, lifts are required for stock movement, and escalators for customers; if on more than three floors, lifts may well be required for customers as well as for stock. As the store becomes larger, so the mechanical services become more extensive and varied.

Most department stores now offer their customers some facility for refreshment, ranging from automatic vending machines and facilities for serving refreshments and snacks to full restaurant service, with provision for cooking and all the attendant extract ventilation, washing-up, and food storage.

Fig. 5.4.4. *D.I.Y warehouse* (Philips Lighting)

5.4.4.2 Checkout facilities

Here a cashier, seated at a till and often aided by a motor driven conveyor belt, will check each item and take the customer's money. Both till and conveyor belt will require an electrical supply. Given the unit price, scales will weigh the purchase and display the weight and the price. In some cases a small additional piece of equipment will print a label to be attached to the package.

A newcomer to the shopping scene is the computerised till, which under the control of a trained operator, will take a customers' money, print a receipt, — sometimes listing the purchases, – tell the cashier how much change to give, and at closing time, print out a list of the day's transactions. In larger stores, a more sophisticated version of the computerised till, is the 'terminal'. This forms part of an integrated system of credit and stock control. In addition to taking cash and providing information on stock movement, it can charge an account, credit a specific department, warn if the account requires special sanction and tell the operator if a credit card is on the list of stolen or lost cards. More recently still, these terminals can be linked into a banking system and the customer's account be debited at the time of purchase.

Computerised tills, terminals, and similar electronic equipment have an electrical requirement different from other electrical equipment, insomuch as they require what has become known as a 'clean' earth. This is an earth connection clear of any stray currents from other equipment and wired independently back to a base earth. Where larger stores have an integrated system of terminals, accounting and stock control, a communications cable will take the impulses back to either a central computer or via a concentrator through a telephone link to a computer in premises elsewhere. All computerised equipment should have an electrical supply available twenty-four hours a day, seven days a week. Although most will have a built-in battery back-up to hold memory over short periods, usually eight hours, it is not advisable to interrupt the electrical supply. The batteries are designed only to hold memory, not to operate the equipment.

5.4.4.3 Illuminated signs

Illuminated signs are a powerful aid to advertising, widely used by the retail industry. The illuminated fascia and projecting box signs proclaims the identity of a store and is designed to attract customers. The purpose of a sign is to transmit a message and, apart from a good light source, its design involves the size and proportions of the letters, and the spacing between them. A strong contrast between the letters and their background is recommended and the sign should be readable at a distance and at angles. The light source can be hot cathode (fluorescent lamp) or cold cathode (high voltage neon) each of which has advantages and disadvantages. Selection depends on the intensity required which may, in turn, depend on the area, local by-laws, the size, shape and colour of the sign, and the cost of the lamps and wiring, together with running and maintenance. Expert advice and guidance can be obtained from a member company of the British Sign Association. (Ref. 1). Internal department, point-of-sale and obligatory signs (such as for emergency exits) are usually hot cathode and range from tablet signs indicating the location and the merchandise available in the various departments, to simple directional box signs.

5.4.5 Electrical installation

The type of supply and method of internal distribution depends on the nature and size of the store (i.e. single-or three-phase). For small shops or lock-up units, the electrical requirements are similar to those for a domestic supply; a single-phase connection to feed lighting, hot water, and possibly space heating, is all that is necessary to satisfy the requirements of the Offices, Shops and Railway Premises Act 1963.

From the medium-sized store upwards, a three-phase supply will be distributed throughout the building in a number of main circuits. A little forethought given to the initial layout and planning of these circuits can provide for such features as remote control, in the event of fire, or clock control, to ensure the economic use of an expensive energy source, and to provide duplicate circuits in sensitive areas where failure of one circuit could be more than just a little inconvenient. These circuits can be arranged for power, general service, essential services, and heating and ventilation equipment. The power circuits serve such items as lifts, escalators, conveyors, waste paper baling machines and other equipment with motors larger than 750 W or so. The general services circuits serve overhead lighting socket outlets for vacuum cleaners or other floor cleaning machines, departmental and point of sales signs and so on. Separate display lighting circuits can be installed for services only in use while the store is actually trading. Special circuits are needed to serve such essential items as clocks, refrigerators, police security lighing, fire, smoke and burglar alarms, and other specialist equipment requiring an electrical supply twenty-four hours a day. Illuminated fascia and external box or neon signs which are in use outside normal trading hours may have a circuit of their own time clock controlled, or be incorporated in with the essential services circuit.

It should be noted that where three-phase supply is available in a shop, circuits for lighting and socket outlets in the vicinity of one another must not be taken from different phases, as this could give rise to the potential between adjacent fittings being 415 V.

The type of cable used for internal distribution is a matter of choice and provided that the cables are of the correct size and installed in accordance with the IEE Wiring Regulations, either p.v.c. insulated and sheathed or mineral-insulated metal sheathed (m.i.m.s.) cables can be used. For mechanical protection, p.v.c. cables can be armoured or carried in steel conduit or trunking. Steel trunking is usually more expensive than conduit but has the advantage of flexibility, as additional cables and outlets can be provided with relative ease. Emergency lighting circuits should not be run in the same conduits or trunking as general lighting circuits.

The main switch panel should incorporate the correct excess current protection and it is common practice to use circuit breakers of the correct current carrying capacity for boards feeding lighting and so on. All the power circuits e.g. lifts escalators, conveyors, fans, compressors, boiler plant, should be provided with suitable switch fuses and isolators adjacent to the plant, clearly marked if necessary.

5.4.6 Security and fire precautions

With the public having access to so much of the premises, the shop or store operator has a problem with security, not only of his staff but of customers who may range from the very young to the old and infirm, whilst on the premises and during emergency situations. Staircases must be adequately lit, escape routes clearly marked and there must be a means of raising an evacuation alarm without causing panic. Many stores now prefer to use a public address system in contrast to the clanging of fire bells. With the advent of the Health and Safety at Work Act, the administration of safety precautions comes under the local Chief Environmental Health Officer who is always willing to give advice on such matters.

Security of stock and of the premises is another aspect and one which is having to receive increasing attention. Smoke detectors and intruder alarms may be used to protect the premises whilst unoccupied but during trading hours, displays designed to be attractive also become tempting to those unable or unwilling to pay at the check-out. Good security of stock can be achieved by placing it in view of staff and this can be extended by the use of television cameras. With the aid of video-recorders security staff can play back recordings of problem areas and on occasions recognise shop-lifters. Another method of securing stock is to use a magnetic stock control tag; this has the dual purpose of aiding stock control and if not removed by the cashier, will raise an alarm when taken through sensors placed at exits.

5.4.7 Referenes

5.4.7.1 Reference in text

(1) British Sign Association PO Box 4 Beckenham Kent BR3 3NW

5.4.7.2 Legislation (See also Appendix 6.1)

Health and Safety at Work, etc, Act 1947
Offices Shops and Railway Premises Act 1963

5.4.7.3 Bibliography

Regulations for Electrical Installations (Institution of Electrical Engineers)
CIBS (formerly IES) Guide for Interior Lighting

Brightly lit hotel entrance

(Raymond J. Tooth)

Chapter 5.5

Hotels

Raymond J. Tooth, M.C.I.B.S.
Principal, Raymond J. Tooth and Associates

5.5.1 General

5.5.1.1 Introduction

Hotels and motels should be designed to provide a wide variety of accommodation and services to meet the needs of modern day living for both business and leisure purposes.

Generally the location of the hotel will dictate the form it will take, i.e. a green field site will lend itself to low rise development with good car parking, whereas in city centre sites where land is at a premium high rise structures will probably be favoured.

The size and type of building will vary but every hotel comprises three main areas: public and circulation areas, living and sleeping areas, and service areas.

5.5.1.2 Public and circulation areas

Public and circulation areas comprise reception, where good access for incoming and outgoing traffic is required, lounges, bars, dining rooms and conference/meeting rooms. Lifts where required should be close to reception. Other facilities such as shops, swimming pools and other recreational and leisure activities are also sometimes provided. Where facilities may be used by casual visitors as well as residents, alternative entrances may be required.

5.5.1.3 Bedroom areas

The layout of bedroom areas is usually repetitive, comprising single and double units, usually with an integral bathroom. Provision is sometimes made for interconnecting bedrooms to form suites. At least one bedroom should have special provision for use by disabled persons. Within the bedroom block facilities should be provided for housekeeping, room service and utility rooms. Some hotels may require the inclusion of basic facilities to allow residents to cater for themselves to a limited extent.

5.5.1.4 Service areas

The main service facility in hotels is catering, which involves kitchens and associated preparation rooms, washing-up areas and cold stores. There may be more than one restaurant or dining room, served by one or more kitchens; small kitchens or serveries may also be required at various points to provide room service. Accommodation within the service areas is also required for laundries, heating and ventilation plant, switch rooms, telephone equipment, lift motor rooms and car parking.

Where car parks are located inside the building special requirements regarding ventilation are necessary, and where required special consideration may need to be given to the siting of a substation on the premises.

Fig. 5.5.1. *Reception Area* (Raymond J. Tooth)

5.5.2 Environmental requirements

5.5.2.1 Comfort

The environment of a hotel should be designed to ensure the well-being of the occupants, as it is often used as a criterion when comparing one hotel with another.

Table 5.5.1

Type of building	°C
Hotels:	
Bedrooms (standard)	22
Bedrooms (luxury)	24
Public Rooms	21
Staircases and corridors	18
Entrance halls and foyers	18

(CIBS)

The mechanical and electrical services actually create this environment and should therefore be carefully designed in conjunction with the interior of the building.

Heating and ventilating systems should follow the requirements laid down in the CIBS Building Services Manual, but it is important to note that these are recommended design values only and systems should be designed within the parameters laid down by current Statutory Regulations for non-domestic dwellings.

Table 5.5.1 is an extract from Table A1.3 of Part A1 of the CIBS Guide, "Environmental Criteria for Design".

5.5.2.2 Air conditioning

The use of air conditioning or ventilation system may be dictated by the location of the hotel, e.g. in areas where high solar gains are experienced, or in noisy situations, where sound proofing by the installation of double glazed windows is necessary. An alternative method of providing ventilation where full air conditioning is not necessary is to use window heating/ventilation units fitted with sound attenuators. When air conditioning is provided by individual window units provision should be made for easy replacement and maintenance of all component parts.

5.5.2.3 Mechanical ventilation

All internal bathrooms should be mechanically ventilated. Adequate ventilation and/or air conditioning is also necessary to remove contaminated air in bars, restaurants, conference rooms and other areas where smoking occurs. Separate ventilating systems should be provided for bathrooms, public or circulation areas and sevice areas. Where oily fumes or dust are conveyed, equipment must be provided to removed these contaminants before exhaust air is discharged. Kitchen ventilation systems must incorporate grease filters and fire dampers. In these systems, large quantities of air are extracted and it is advisable to provide a mechanical ventilation system to introduce warmed replacement air. Internal and basement car parks require extract equipment with standby facilities to ensure continuous operation. Utility rooms and housemaids' cupboards require extract ventilation if they are situated internally.

5.5.2.4 Lighting

A high standard of lighting is very important. It enables people to move about easily and safely and contributes to the creation of a pleasant environment. The best results are achieved when the architect and the lighting engineer work together from the start of the project. The interiors of all buildings, and especially hotels, can be divided into three main areas which call for differing lighting requirements: working areas, general non-specific areas, and circulation areas. For all these the lighting should be free from glare and should provide sufficient light without excessive contrasts.

The CIBS Code for Interior Lighting makes the following recommendation for minimum illumination levels in hotels.

Entrance hall	200 lux
Public rooms	200 lux to 400 lux
Bedrooms	100 lux to 200 lux
Kitchens	200 lux to 400 lux
Service areas	100 lux to 200 lux

Fig. 5.5.2. *Small Conference Room* (Raymond J. Tooth)

For ballrooms, conference rooms and so on, the lighting should be arranged so that a variety of effect can be obtained, e.g. subdued for dances, high for conferences. If a stage is provided, spotlights and stage lighting with dimming and colour control will be required. The light fittings should be carefully chosen for the areas in which they are to be used e.g. vapourproof fittings in kitchens, waterproof fittings for outdoor illumination. Corridors should be well illuminated with increased lighting to emphasise bedroom doors, stairways, lifts and lobbies. Switching should be arranged so that a reduced level of illumination can be provided at night. Provision should be made for external lighting, e.g. floodlights, illuminated signs and so on, preferably with photo-electric cell controls.

Consideration should be given to use of 'low energy' lamps and effective use of light switching methods either by using sound sensors, or daylight sensors, designed to switch off lighting in unoccupied rooms or when sufficient natural light is present.

5.5.2.5 Water heating

Hot water demand is high, with baths and showers in bedrooms and heavy usage within the kitchen areas, therefore ample storage should be available to meet peak demands. A central hot water system is normally employed. Valves should be provided near every outlet to facilitate maintenance. For high-rise buildings, it may prove necessary to provide a series of calorifiers and booster plant in order to distribute the water. Where hot water is provided by central plant, duplication of essential equipment is vital to provide a reasonable measure of standby in the event of plant failure.

5.5.3 Installation considerations

5.5.3.1 Need for reliability

Over recent years there has been an increasing tendency to reduce to a minimum the number of staff employed in hotels, frequently achieved by the introduction of automation. All services, plant and automatic equipment should, therefore be designed, chosen and installed to provide a high degree of reliability and minimum maintenance. Accessibility is essential to ensure the minimum interruption and inconvenience to guests in the event of a breakdown or supply failure. Sometimes, therefore essential plant is duplicated or standby facilities provided to enable maintenance to be carried out.

5.5.3.2 Installation of systems

All heating, ventilation or air conditioning systems must be rapid in response in order to control the rapidly changing internal conditions resulting from fluctuating occupancy and use.

Electrical heating can be installed in hotels in a number of ways, one of which is by using a central heat generating plant (i.e. an electric or electrode boiler). The boiler can be installed in the basement or sub-basement, or at the top of the building. If it is sited at high level, it can often be housed with the ventilating, air-conditioning and cooling plant in the roof areas. At least two boilers should be provided so that one can be taken out of commission for repair and maintenance at any time. Other items of essential plant such as pumps and fans, should be duplicated to provide an adequate standby. Where boilers are used, the heat transfer system may be steam, high pressure hot water, low pressure hot water or air. Hot water at low pressure is the most commonly encountered but hot water at high pressure is used in larger hotels. Terminal units should be carefully chosen to provide maximum thermal comfort for the guests. In general, radiative fittings will be more satisfactory than convective ones but they are less responsive to controls.

The equipment in each bedroom should have controls to enable the temperature to be reduced at night or times of non-occupation. In addition override facilities should be provided, located in reception, to isolate sections or zones of the hotel during periods of low occupancy. Where central plant is employed it is sometimes difficult to meet individual room requirements particularly during the summer period. Each hotel should stock a number of portable electric heating appliances which can be used to meet individual heat requirements in excess of the design condition at times when the central plant is not operating. An alternative to central plant is individual convective or radiative heaters in each bedroom but it is essential that some form of thermostatic control is provided along with the facility to isolate unoccupied rooms from reception of heat.

In order to house the mechanical and electrical services in a multi-storey building it is necessary to provide a system of vertical ducts. These should be accessible from the corridors wherever possible and located between 'back to back' bathrooms. Suspended ceilings will be needed in public areas to house ventilation ducts, cable routes and recessed lighting.

Lift shafts are required for passenger, goods and service lifts and hoists.

5.5.3.3 Noise

Care should be taken to reduce noise transference especially in bedrooms and conference areas. In certain locations it may be necessary to reduce the ingress of external noise by the introduction of some form of secondary glazing, but this can result in a ventilation problem. Noise from engineering services can be extremely annoying, therefore the ventilation and plumbing systems should be designed with this in mind.

5.5.3.4 Operational costs

Whenever possible consideration should be given to the inclusion in the overall design of equipment which has low operating costs. In some cases heat reclamation plant e.g. heat pumps, heat recovery equipment etc., can be incorporated, if economic payback periods can be obtained on the original capital costs.

5.5.4 Electrical installation

Most hotels or motels take power at 415 V three-phase although a large installation requires a high voltage service with a transformer substation on site. In the largest hotels, one or more substations at suitable positions on site can feed the distribution centres. The distribution boards should be located in switchrooms at suitable load centres, interconnected where possible to reduce the effect of a possible supply failure.

The maximum demand and the total installed load, which may be as high as 2000 kW and 3000 kW respectively, determine, to a large extent the capital cost of the system. Peak loadings probably only occur a few times a year, when maximum power and lighting demands coincide. If these peak loading periods can be adequately obviated, either by a maximum demand warning system or some form of load-shedding equipment, economies can be made in the sizes of cables and switchgear. The power supply to services and service areas should be installed independently of other areas. This includes lifts, air conditioning plant and car parks. These circuits are normally three phase and terminate in separate control panels within the plant room. A composite control panel should be provided in the kitchen area with a separately controlled circuit for each main item of equipment. This enables equipment to be isolated in the case of emergency and for cleaning purposes.

Distribution to bedroom areas should be a single phase 240 V ring main. Corridor and bedroom lighting circuits should be interconnected to provide security of supply should a fault occur in any one circuit. Bedroom/bathroom units can be connected in pairs to a conventional consumer unit installed in a vertical service duct between them. Excess current protection should be provided by miniature circuit-breakers to ensure a minimum of delay in the restoration of the local supply. Socket outlets are required in each bedroom to cater for portable appliances. Shaving sockets are normally required in each bedroom or bathroom. These must be of the type approved by the IEE Regulations, and conforming to BS 3052: 1958. Socket outlets must be provided in all areas, for cleaning equipment used in servicing the hotel.

The distribution cables from main switchgear sub-switchboards should be accommodated in vertical ducts where possible, with the horizontal distribution located in false ceilings or floor ducts.

For kitchens, food preparation areas, plant rooms and the like, the electrical installation should be carried out in corrosion-proof materials, e.g. galvanised conduit, trunking and fittings, m.i.c.s. cables. In studio-type bedrooms, much of the wiring can be accommodated within the fitted furniture. For public areas, particularly bars, restaurant and ballrooms, the installation should be so designed as to allow for future modification. Large or prestige hotels invariably require some type of generating plant to reduce the inconvenience of a supply failure e.g. a stand-by generator. Earthing of supplies should be in accordance with current regulations and all equipment and distribution boards provided with adequate labels for identification purposes.

5.5.5 Communications

5.5.5.1 Telephones

Public and private internal telephones facilities must be provided. Accommodation is required for the switchboard and the exchange equipment, the type and extent of which will depend upon the nature and size of the hotel. Telephone instruments can be of the type which incorporate an illuminated indicator to advise residents of messages taken. Public call boxes should be provided in circulation areas and socket outlets for telephones in public rooms which may be used for exhibitions and conferences. Direct speech systems can be employed, particularly in the catering and kitchen areas. These are very useful in conjunction with the operation of small hoists.

In addition, hotels usually require the cost of calls made by guests from their rooms by direct dialling to be recorded in some individual way, so that they can be charged on the bill. With modern PABX systems employing stored program control, it is usual to provide an output which directly analyses the actual cost of calls made by the guest, and does so in a way which includes details of the number called and the time and duration of the call which was made.

5.5.5.2 Public address

Public address systems should be installed throughout the public and circulation areas and can be used for paging or broadcasting music. The main control can be from a receptionist or switchboard operator, with local control facilities in all areas.

Most modern hotels provide conference facilities and therefore the communications systems must be totally flexible.

In addition to normal telephone and public address systems it is desirable to have facilities for the distribution of audio and visual signals.

5.5.5.3 Radio and television

Relayed radio and television, with a selection of programmes, can be provided in bedrooms and lounges. In addition to normal television broadcasting channels, in-house movies can also be provided from a centrally located video recorder. In some cases teletext services may be required. A small radio transmitter can be used to provide a staff location system. Each member of staff is equipped with an individual pocket receiver, under the control of a telephone operator or receptionist.

5.5.5.4 Room management systems

Developments in micro-computer technology have enabled systems to become available which can not only provide room status information but also give morning call alarms, advice of a message waiting, and control of room heating, all from a central station usually located in reception.

5.5.6 Security

5.5.6.1 Intruder security
Security Systems

Computer based guest check in facilities can be used not only to record and issue accounts but also to provide accurate means of checking security in occupied rooms, either for guests or housemaids.

5.5.6.2 Fire precautions
A system of early fire detection and warning is of paramount importance in hotels. Audible alarms and direction signs for emergency exits should be provided and should be obvious. The system may comprise a combination of heat and smoke detectors so sited as to cover all areas, including stores and ceiling and duct voids. Manual break-glass push-button alarms should be provided, linked to an adequate audible warning device. It may be necessary to interconnect the fire system with the ventilation plant, smoke doors and so on and also to give direct alarm to the local fire station. Systems should be designed to meet local Fire Officer's requirement and be to BS 5839 Part 1: 1980.

Emergency lighting can be provided from battery equipment supplying low wattage/low voltage bulbs. Alternatively, an alternator or generator set can be used with batteries supplying power to cover the time between failure and the coming onto full load of the standby plant. Systems should be designed in accordance with all Statutory Regulations, and BS 5266 Part 1: 1975.

5.5.7 References

5.5.7.1 British Standards (See also Appendix 6.2)
BS 3052 Electric Shaver Units
BS 5266 Emergency Lighting
BS 5839 Fire detection and alarm systems in buildings

5.5.7.2 Bibliography
CIBS Guide Part A1 "Environmental Criteria for Design".
CIBS (formerly IES) Code for Interior Lighting
Regulations for Electrical Installations (Institution of Electrical Engineers)

A garden restaurant

(Electricity Council)

Chapter 5.6

Catering establishments

David Taylor
Head of Electric Catering Group, The Electricity Council

5.6.1 Introduction

Catering establishments today cover a wide range of different operations designed to cater for the provision of food in a wide variety of establishments. Categorising the establishments can be undertaken, but it must be remembered that the nature of the catering installation is such that many variations and hybrids occur within any category.

The catering industry in the UK employs over 2 million full and part-time staff, making it a major employer in the country. Within this market a broad division can be drawn between the commercial 'profit making' establishments and the 'non-profit' sector. Each sector has very different requirements, but one factor is common, the industry continues to grow and diversify in size and complexity.

Legislation applies to establishments involved in catering. This is covered by The Food Hygiene (General) Regulations 1970, which require certain design and operating standards to ensure adequate protection of food within catering premises.

5.6.2 Commercial catering

Within the commercial profit making catering establishments, the most important factor is to note the almost infinite variety. These may include specialist establishments in the following areas:

(a) motorway service areas, for the traffic now using major trunk routes for business or pleasure;
(b) airline catering, including ground facilities at airports for the traveller and staff;
(c) public house catering;

(d) increase in conference and convention trade, either centred on traditional hotels (out of season) or purpose built conference centres;
(e) exhibition catering;
(f) 'fast food' chain and franchise operations
(g) speciality restaurants, such as those serving health foods, salads and pizzas;
(h) sports and leisure centres and associated catering;
(j) growth of the take-away sector, either in the form of sandwich bars or a wide range of speciality foods – fish and chips, ethnic foods, salad bars and 'lite bite' cafeterias.

5.6.3 Non-commercial catering

Within the 'non-profit' sector, there is currently considerable change in the design and principle of operating the catering facility. Economic pressures on a non-profit establishment are forcing new approaches, all aimed at improving cost and productivity or reducing the financial subsidy element required to maintain the service.

The major areas of catering in schools, colleges and universities and the institutional areas of hospitals, armed forces, prisons, etc, are all looking at major changes in the style of catering establishment required. Current financial pressures on the school meals service are producing answers based on the provision of lighter meals, snack bar and cafeteria style operations; sometimes linked to a centralised supply unit or alternatively relying on a wide range of manufactured food products. Universities and colleges may well require a wider range of services matching those found in the commercial market, i.e. 'fast food' outlets and dining/restaurant services, as well as self-service cafeteria styles.

There has been considerable change in the major institutional areas, particularly hospitals. Traditionally, this area inherited a large proportion of old Victorian-styled buildings with similar large, heavily equipped kitchens, based on the principles of bulk cooking in large oven ranges, boiling pans and steamers. Current building systems for hospitals demand more compact kitchen installations, which need compact efficient equipment, working at high efficiency and speed. This, linked to the protection of the quality of the food, aims to ensure the patient receives an attractive meal at the bedside, which should be both hot, appetising and nutritious.

Midway between the commercial and non-commercial sectors, stand those meals consumed at the place of work and together they account for some 35% to 40% of meals served. Usually attracting some form of subsidy, some 6 million of these meals are served daily and many of these operations are run by contract catering companies. Staff restaurants aim to provide a flexible type of meal service, ranging from pub-type snacks to full meals. The effects of economic pressures, changes in working patterns and flexible working times, require to be taken into account in the design and operation of the catering service.

Although the business lunch is still popular, there is an opportunity to take this in-house, in a more or less formal dining room, and even quite small firms are installing a working kitchen for just this purpose. Whether taken in an industrial canteen or staff restaurant or in a commercial establishment, the midday meal is eaten away from home by increasing number of people. This is accounted for by the greater distances travelled to and from work, the shortening of the lunch hour to something less than 60 minutes, the fact that in many families both parents are working, and the need to combine the midday break with other pursuits – shopping, sports activity, lunchtime theatre or music, for example.

5.6.4 Organisational layout

5.6.4.1 Workflow patterns

All catering establishments have a number of common elements, starting with the receipt and storage of raw materials and leading through to the service of the finished meal and the associated dining areas, as follows:

Activity	*Areas*	
Raw materials reception and storage	Bulk stores Dry stores Refrigerated stores Vegetable and fruit stores Household stores Daily stores	
Food preparation and cooking	Meat Fish Vegetables Sweets	Preparation areas
	Meat Fish Vegetables Sweets	Cooking areas
Service	Finished meal Storage Service surfaces/counters Customer areas Cashier point	
Dining	Table and seating areas Tray and 'dirty' utensil storage	
Clearing and wash-up areas	Plate collection Waste disposal Dish and utensil washing Dish and utensil storage.	

Ideally the kitchen is laid out with the system of workflow in mind, so that raw ingredients are received, prepared and processed into finished meals. The kitchen planner will take account of workflow patterns, in order to avoid unnecessary movement between sections or crossing of paths, and with attention to hygiene requirements. These dictate that supplies do not cross paths with refuse and that 'dirty' items (staff outdoor clothing, unprepared vegetables) do not penetrate into the cooking area.

He will also ensure that traffic lanes are well defined and kept clear of obstructions such as trolleys or equipment, and that work areas are separated, e.g., meat from fish preparation, vegetables from sweets, and so on. Good separation is achieved by correct siting of work areas and the use of full or half-height walls or barriers; and the correct siting of equipment in logical groupings, e.g. meat preparation adjacent to roasting and grilling equipment. Within this overall layout, each particular section has its special requirements.

Fig. 5.6.1. *Self-service from cook-chill* (Electricity Council)

5.6.4.2 Goods receipt and storage areas

Well designed goods receipt and storage areas will have a marked effect upon the profitability of the catering enterprise. The areas required will depend on a number of factors:

(a) type of meal served (fresh foods, partially prepared etc);
(b) delivery from centralised source (for example school meals service to end

kitchens, hotel group distribution systems, or patient and staff meals supplied to a group of district hospitals;
(c) frequency of deliveries;
(d) size of stocks required to be held (i.e. how many days' supply);
(e) use of special containers or packs (e.g. for prepared foods);
(f) use of returnable containers (these will require storage until collected).

Storage areas should be well lit, with a minimum of 150 lux. Apart from the illumination level, the colour of the light source and the restriction of glare is also important. Additionally, most storage areas receive dirty, refrigerated and dusty goods, so the use of vapour-proof fluorescent or filament lamp fittings is desirable.

Fig. 5.6.2. *Staff Restaurant* (Electricity Council)

Several types of stores are required. They include:

(a) *Dry Goods Store.* For bottled, canned and dry packet goods. This store should be cool and well ventilated, free from damp, with mesh guards at the windows to deter vermin and insects. Covered bins and containers are used for items such as flour etc.
(b) *Vegetable Store.* Cool and well ventilated, capable of easy washing down. Uncleaned vegetables are kept apart from washed and prepared vegetables and fruit.

(c) *Refrigerated Stores.* Used for the temporary holding of fresh ingredients and prepared items, at a temperature set to between 0 to 7°C. Smaller establishments may rely on cabinet style 'reach in' refrigerators, while in others, complete 'walk in' cold rooms will be required.

Fig. 5.6.3. *Staff dining service area* (Electricity Council)

The compressor and condenser packs would normally require low power, single-phase supply to the cabinets, with three-phase supplies being required to very large 'walk in' stores.

5.6.4.3 Preparation areas

Within preparation areas, the main electrical requirement will be for a variety of machinery used in food preparation, including mixers, peelers, chippers, slicers and mincers. These items will normally require single-phase supply for bench equipment, but three-phase supply for larger powered units, such as bowl cutters and heavy duty mixers. There may also be a need for some refrigerated storage, for the temporary holding of prepared foods, such as cold sweets and salads, before transfer to the servery. As already noted, preparation areas require to be well lit, with illumination levels of 500 lux, again ensuring good colour values and restriction of glare.

5.6.4.4 Cooking area

Numerous changes have occurred in both equipment and kitchen organisation over the last decade. Traditionally, individual equipment was allocated to each cooking task in the kitchen. Now multi-purpose equipment is available to cover a wide range of cooking tasks, enabling a minimum equipment package to be installed without limiting the range of dishes which can be produced.

Equipment may well be grouped into one of several arrangements as follows:

(a) *Centre Island.* The traditional grouping in the centre of the kitchen. All cooking units are grouped under a single ventilation canopy and essential electrical services and drainage are incorporated.
(b) *Single Cooking Units.* With the availability of pre-prepared foods, particularly frozen, very small staff feeding operations can make use of just one item of equipment, such as a convection or microwave oven.
(c) *Single line (snack or light meal).* For snacks and light meals, small (500 mm) modular equipment can be easily grouped along the back wall of the service area.

Fig. 5.6.4. *Hospital staff cafeteria* (Electricity Council)

(d) *Combination island/line (main meal).* A combination of island group in the kitchen and back-bar grouping in the service area is suitable when the menu can be divided easily into main and snack meals.
(e) *Single line (main meal).* The single line arrangement of heavy duty (700 mm) cooking units is particularly suited to waitress service in large operations.
(f) *Multiple island (large scale).* The traditional island approach can be refined to include specialised items of equipment. Not only can the main grouping be divided into 'wet' and 'dry' areas for prime cooking, but areas immediately behind the service counters or holding units can be used for fast end-cooking equipment.

(g) *Automatic Vending Machines.* Automatic vending machines are increasingly becoming part of the catering scene, particularly to provide a hot drink or even a meal in locations in which staffed service is unjustified.

5.6.5 Environmental considerations

5.6.5.1 Heating and air conditioning

In dining areas, particularly in public restaurants, the need for good quality environmental conditions is essential. Temperature levels should be maintained between 20°C and 23°C and frequently the introduction of full air conditioning will be essential to cope with a large number of diners concentrated into relatively small areas. The use of mechanical ventilation in dining areas will depend on the size, location and level of customer occupancy expected. The main aim would be to remove smoke and maintain a fresh atmosphere but care should be taken to ensure air movements do not draw in kitchen smells into the dining area.

Fig. 5.6.5. *Fast food takeaway* (Electricity Council)

5.6.5.2 Ventilation

Equipment areas must be adequately ventilated to prevent cooking smells entering dining areas, to prevent moisture and grease-laden particles entering kitchen areas and to maintain a comfortable working environment.

5.6.5.3 Heat recovery

Inevitably, there will be heat waste from various catering activities. Dishwashing and large scale refrigeration processes and ventilation are obvious areas.

A number of techniques are now available for general or specific applications including heat pipes, heat pumps, and various heat exchanger devices. Whether the heat is available from outlet water, ventilation air or refrigeration lines or condensers, there are now techniques for recovering this heat for use elsewhere in the catering establishment. The main outlets for recovered heat are into hot water and environmental heat.

5.6.5.4 Water heating and cooling

The demand for hot water is high, particularly where dish washing is carried out, therefore ample hot-water storage should be provided. Dishwashers normally incorporate electric heaters to give water at a high temperature for rinsing. In addition to the normal water services, chilled drinking water may be required for dispensers and vending machines.

5.6.5.5 Lighting

Restaurant dining areas can vary widely in their lighting requirements. The atmosphere required will depend on the type and trade it is designed to attract. At one end of the market is the tourist centre restaurant which can provide hot meals at any time from say 10 am to midnight or later. This type makes little distinction between times of day, and endeavours to create a bright and cheerful atmosphere to encourage a fast turnover in covers.

Moving from the continuous service establishments to the restaurant which caters for a distinctly separate lunch and dinner trade, it is necessary to bear in mind that these two meals are taken at very different times of day. The luncheon period may typically extend from before noon through to 3 pm and, if customers do not linger each place can accommodate two or possible three covers. The actual type of fitting could complement the general decor, but should not throw a strongly coloured light on to the table. If a rise-and-fall is chosen the fitting must be robustly made and firmly attached to the suspension. It should also be possible to adjust the height without getting burnt fingers.

The evening trade calls for different treatment with a quieter atmosphere and less bustle. The first requirement is to reduce the lighting level. This can be accomplished either by switching out selected lights or by use of dimmers. The possibilities are obviously numerous; the lunchtime ceiling fitting could be dimmed and individual candle lamps added to the tables.

The variety of lighting levels required is very wide in the catering establishments, but the following table of lighting levels may well be used as a basic guide:

Recommended Illumination Levels	Lux
Entrance area	
Reception, cashier	300
Public rooms	
Bars, coffee bars	150
Dining room, grills, restaurants	100

General cash desk	300
Cloakrooms	150
Service areas	
Kitchens	500
Cellars	150
Offices	500

Emergency lighting is required in licensed premises for places accessible to the public. It should be provided in exitways, corridors, toilets and main areas, together with exit signs. This lighting can be connected from a central battery supply at low voltage. Large installations may incorporate motor-driven generator sets. Where few emergency lights are required, self-contained fittings with integral rechargeable batteries can be used.

5.6.6 Electrical installation

The incoming supply should be 415 V three-phase. In most cases, the supply to the catering establishment forms part of the overall power distribution of the building. The catering area should be self-contained and served from a main switchboard. The bulk of the load is in the kitchen and all the kitchen equipment should be connected to a local switchboard. It is desirable to connect cold rooms and refrigerators to a circuit not liable to be disconnected in error. The kitchen control panel should form a composite assembly with separate isolating switches to each item of equipment: this makes for easy maintenance and cleaning of equipment. An isolating control should be adjacent to each piece of cooking apparatus, e.g. fryer, hotplate, so that it can be switched off in an emergency. Separate supplies should be taken from the main switchboard to local panels within the plant rooms for ventilation equipment, lifts and similar services. All electrical installation work should conform to the requirements of the IEE Wiring Regulations. Lighting and other low-current equipment should be connected to a local distribution centre and controlled by isolating switches at the main board. These distribution centres should be arranged with circuit-breakers for excess current protection. Final circuits for lighting should be so designed that some lighting is available in all areas should an individual circuit fail. Lighting switches should be grouped at convenient points for control by staff only.

An adequate number of socket outlets should be provided in all areas. In the service and kitchen areas, sockets are required at bench height for portable items of equipment and all outlet circuits should be provided with adequate earth leakage protection. It may also be necessary to earth bond other metallic equipment, i.e. tables etc, which may be used for portable electrical equipment. Outlets should not be sited in hazardous positions, e.g. near washing-up sinks. In public areas, outlets are mainly used for portable cleaning apparatus and vending machines. Socket outlets for table lamps may be required.

Equipment used for reheating or reconstituting frozen and other prepared foods, e.g. microwave ovens frequently represents a local electrical load outside of kitchen areas and wiring of adequate rating must be provided.

The wiring system should employ cables and conductors enclosed in a protective covering of non-combustible material strong enough to resist mechanical damage. Earth continuity should be provided. Suitable systems include all-armoured cables, m.i.c.s. cables, and insulated cables in screwed metal conduit or metal trunking. For public areas, it should be borne in mind that decorations are liable to be changed fairly frequently and any electrical system should take account of this. The electrical installation in kitchens, preparation areas, plant rooms and so on should be carried out with the corrosion-proof materials, e.g. galvanised conduit and fittings.

5.6.7 Communications

Telephones and public address equipment may be required. Public call boxes should be provided in circulation areas. Internal telephones should be installed on larger premises to assist in general operation and control. Direct speech systems can be employed, particularly in service areas and in conjunction with hoists. Public address systems can be provided for announcements, 'piped' music and cabaret.

5.6.8 Security

A system for fire detection and warning should be provided in accordance with local regulations or as required by the local fire officer. Where the general public is admitted and individual systems are employed, the alarm should warn staff. The system should comprise a combination of smoke and heat detectors sited in stores, ducts, ceiling voids and elsewhere. Breakglass push buttons should be provided, connected to audible alarms. Direct connection of the alarm system may be made to the local fire station. For protection of the premises, a security/burglar detection and alarm system may be required.

5.6.9 References

5.6.9.1 Legislation (See also Appendix 6.1)

Food Hygiene (General) Regulations 1970

5.6.9.2 Bibliography

Electricity Council Publications:
The Electric Catering Directory (EC 4271)
Kitchen Planning and Equipment (EC 3977)
Lighting in Hotels and Restaurants (EC 3590)
Regulations for Electrical Installations (Institution of Electrical Engineers)

All-Electric Hospital

Chapter 5.7

Hospitals

Robin Manser, B.Sc.(Eng.)(Hons.) C.Eng., F.I.Mech.E., F.I.E.E., P.P.I.Hosp.E.

5.7.1 Introduction

5.7.1.1 General

Whilst today's hospitals require highly specialised units such as operating suites, they also include within their curtilage almost all systems associated with modern life. Where these functions are carried out within individual buildings the required electrical services are substantially the same as those provided for industrial or commercial use. Thus there are administrative units which may include office machinery and computers, workshops with machine tools for maintenance, and laundries and stores areas. The electrical services for these buildings should be provided as in good general practice and in accordance with the IEE Wiring Regulations; the following paragraphs bring out only the special features required in health buildings of this kind.

5.7.1.2 Guidance documents

The UK Department of Health and Social Security (DHSS) publishes through Her Majesty's Stationery Office (HMSO) guidance documents including a number relating to electrical services in hospitals. A list of relevant publications is included in Section 5.7.21 for those who require more detailed information. The Departments' documents are updated at intervals as far as financial and staffing considerations permit.

5.7.1.3 Detailed design information

In addition to the above, a much wider range of detailed Data Sheets are produced for Hospital Service Engineering Data. These cover agreed technical policies, preferred sizes for variety reduction, etc.. The sheets are produced by collaborative effort between the DHSS and the National Health Service (NHS) and they are generally available within NHS units concerned with this work.

5.7.2 Special considerations

The special considerations for electrical services in hospitals relate largely to the patient care areas. Some of these limitations will also apply to adjacent areas, thus the need for freedom from electrical interference in ward areas must apply to adjoining rooms even when these are used for administrative purposes. These special considerations are considered in greater detail in later paragraphs but may be briefly summarised as follows:

5.7.2.1 Electrical interference

There must be freedom from mains borne and mains generated electrical interference. Modern medical practice requires the use of diagnostic electrical apparatus of great sensitivity and it is essential that medical and nursing staff should be able to use this type of apparatus freely without having to move patients to interference free zones.

5.7.2.2 Security of supply

Patients connected to life support systems and patients undergoing acute treatment require sustained electrical supplies. In addition, many of the other functions of the hospital must continue, even if with some inconvenience, in the event of medium or long term supply outage. In general this consideration requires a small provision of battery back-up supplies and a substantial diesel generator standby supply system (currently about 40% of the normal electrical demand), together with suitable distribution arrangements so that critical areas are not isolated for substantial periods due to individual component failure.

5.7.2.3 Lighting standards

In patient areas medical and nursing staff rely on good lighting standards, especially that of colour quality, so that clinical judgment and patient monitoring is not prejudiced due to poor colour judgment or other inadequacy.

5.7.2.4 Fire precautions

The integrity of the electrical services associated with these systems in a hospital is even more vital than that applying to a normal building. The difficulties in moving non-ambulant patients are such that what would normally be an inconvenient evacuation of staff in an ordinary building becomes an extremely difficult task with real possibilities of multiple deaths in a hospital.

5.7.2.5 Special electrical safety precautions.

These include anti-static floor requirements in operating rooms in which ether or cyclopropane are used as anaethetising agents.

5.7.2.6 Communication facilities

There are a number of communication requirements and systems which are special to hospitals, such as systems for the urgent location of members of staff.

5.7.3 Electricity supply and distribution

The electricity supply and distribution arrangements for hospitals are generally similar to those in industrial complexes of comparable size with the usual requirement that the system should allow for the rapid restoration of the supply in event of a fault occuring. The requirements for emergency and stand-by electricity supplies are dealt with in Section 5.7.5.

5.7.3.1 Electrical demand

Predicting the maximum demand for electricity in hospitals is extremely difficult, as demand is substantially affected not only by engineering design, but also by local medical and management practice. As a very rough indication the maximum demand figure for a modern District General Hospital of 500 beds might be 1500 kW, or 3 kW per bed. Teaching Hospitals have a somewhat higher figure per bed whilst Psychiatric Hospitals are usually about half the District General figure. Detailed information on loads and diversities is given in HMSO publications (see Bibliography). There is evidence that apart from variations in load due to physical changes such as building adaptions and extensions, there is also a continuing basic increase in the rate of electricity consumption of about 1% per annum. This probably reflects a steady increase in the amount of electro-medical apparatus in use, together with changing standards.

5.7.3.2 Supply and distribution networks

In general these follow modern practice, using buried cables. Two incoming feeds may be arranged in the interests of supply security. Where normal design economic considerations show that an HV distribution system within the hospital area is the correct choice this can be adopted, the usual distribution voltage being 11 kV. HV ring or radial systems may be adopted with design following modern practice using buried, suitably protected cables. Graded time delay relays or other recognised discriminating fault protection methods may be used to limit the extent of system outage on a fault. All the normal rules for fault protection apply as well as the management need for the appointment of Authorised Persons when HV switching will be carried out by hospital employees. 415 V 3-phase distribution, either from substations or by a main distribution network, again follows modern practice using buried cables.

5.7.4 Electrical installations within buildings

5.7.4.1 Internal wiring

Within Health Care buildings design is in accord with modern practice, the sub-mains using well-insulated and protected cables, or busbars, as considered appropriate. It should be remembered that emergency sub-mains should be physically separated with adequate fire protection between them and the normal supply cables.

Circuit wiring should follow IEE Wiring Regulation requirements but metal sheathed wiring systems should be used, that is, cable in screwed steel conduit or steel trunking, or m.i.m.s. cable. Where m.i.m.s. cable is used the sheath is not allowed to be the neutral return but it will normally be used as the circuit protective conductor. Experience has shown that only by rigid adherence to the rule on metal sheathing can the necessary freedom from interference with medical diagnostic equipment be achieved.

The NHS has an excellent record for freedom from electrical fatalities over many years. This has resulted largely from the policy of the use of conventional wiring systems, earthing and protection and good quality installations, allied to regular examination and testing by a competent electrician. Particular attention is given to the regular examination of trailing leads and plugs.

5.7.4.2 X-ray machines

These machines are characterised by heavy transient loads rarely exceeding 1 second in duration. To contain voltage fluctuation problems this load should normally be carried on circuits which should be sized on a volt basis as required by the supplier, thermal requirements being insignificant by comparison.

5.7.4.3 Lifts

Where groups of lifts are provided they should be considered for separate sub-mains to contain voltage fluctuation problems. (See also Section 5.7.13)

5.7.4.4 Vandalism and human interference

Members of the public often have time on their hands when in hospital and this frequently results in meddling with any electrical or telephone circuits to which access can be obtained by nail file or pocket knife. Even though malice may not be intended the nuisance, damage and expense can be considerable, not to mention the danger engendered to vandal and patients. It is recommended that distribution boards, telephone junction boxes etc be located in lockable cupboards or voids with lockable doors in all areas to which the public has access.

5.7.4.5 Electrical services for a typical hospital ward

Whilst it is not practicable to detail the electrical services for all hospital rooms it may be helpful to consider those in a typical modern 6 bed ward. General lighting would be provided by two fluorescent luminaires, recessed, close ceiling mounted or suspended. These would be supplemented by a ceiling mounted night light, and six patient reading lights (bedhead lights). Approximately ten 13 A socket outlets would be needed, probably four of these being on a circuit connected to the stand-by supply. Incorporated into each bedhead unit would be an outlet for a nurse-call push button with reassurance light, cancellation-button and emergency nurse-call button; also a multi-channel outlet with facilities for a hand unit incorporating radio/TV sound selector with on/off switch and volume control, nurse-call button, reassurance light and bedhead light switch. The bedhead services including the 13 A outlets may be incorporated into a bedhead trunking unit mounted on the wall just above bedhead level, also possibly incorporating facilities for piped medical gases, thermometer pockets, drip brackets etc.. Finally, a telephone socket would be provided for a trolley mounted payphone for patients' use.

5.7.5 Emergency electrical services

5.7.5.1 Requirements for standby supplies

The public electricity supply in the UK is very reliable and interruptions are likely to be few and of short duration. Where hospitals have two separate incoming feeds these risks are reduced still further. Emergency or standby electricity supply provision must however usually be made; firstly for patients on life support systems and in acute care situations – such as those in operating rooms, delivery rooms, special baby care units etc.. In these areas electrical coverage may perhaps be very slightly reduced when the public supply fails but all essential functions must continue. Secondly there are areas where lighting and some power supplies should be maintained to enable nursing and other care to continue, albeit with some inconvenience. A general ward area would typify this situation where lighting coverage might be reduced and only a limited number of 13 A outlets connected to the standby supply, patients using life support systems being placed in beds adjacent to these outlets. Thirdly there are areas which would be lit only sufficiently for safe free movement. Apart from these three categories of work areas there are other services which qualify for a standby electricity supply. Typical of these are blood banks, boiler plant, medical suction plants, telephone exchanges, and specially designated fireman's lifts. Finally there should be arrangements for certain services to be transferred manually to the standby supply in a controlled fashion when a prolonged outage occurs. Typical of such services would be water and sewage pumps, certain ventilation plants, and lifts so that those caught between floors may be brought down without resort to hand winding.

5.7.5.2 Battery back-up requirements

These are very small and are usually limited to some Acute Operating Theatre luminaires and occasionally to some 13 A outlets in the same area. Such supplies are normally arranged by the automatic changeover of the operating light (say 24 V) to a battery via a contactor, and supply to the 13 A outlets by a battery and static invertor. Small proprietary automatic battery operated luminaires may be required for escape route lighting.

5.7.5.3 Standby diesel generators

With the exception of the battery services detailed above, most other essential services are adequately served by standby diesel generators which start up automatically on mains failure, together with a distribution network and changeover facilities. These arrangements result in the standby supply being available in about

10 seconds, which is an acceptable time delay even for most of the escape route lighting, as nursing staff are trained to be familiar with the local escape routes. Where this delay is not acceptable automatic battery operated luminaires should be used. The typical 60 second start up time required by gas turbine driven standby generator sets is not acceptable for any escape route lighting. Certain areas, notably the boiler house, may be more conveniently served by a local generator set.

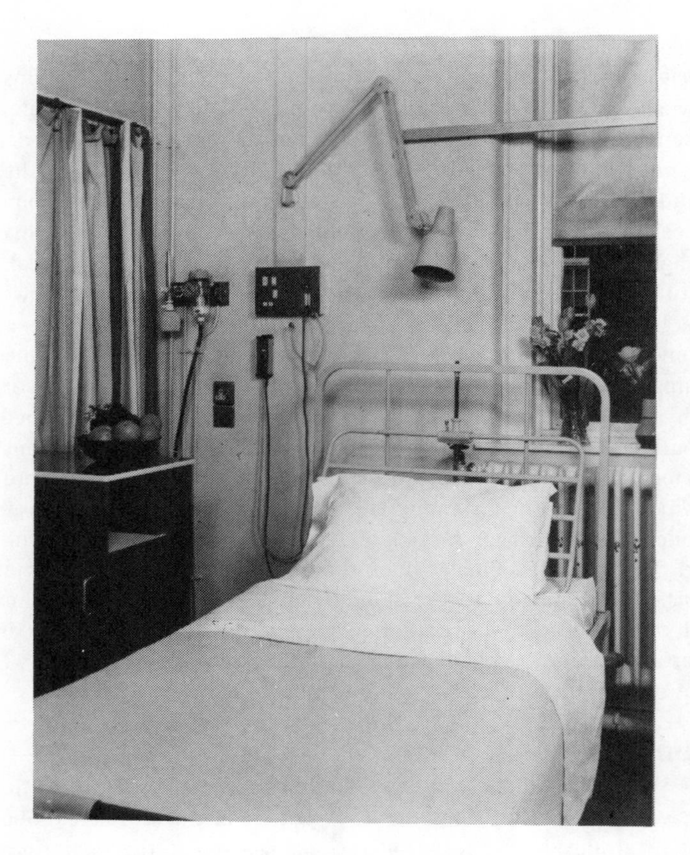

Fig. 5.7.1. *Patient Services in a Typical Ward* (Static Systems Group)

5.7.5.4 Load qualifying for emergency electricity supply

The total load is built up by the addition of the qualifying loads in the hospital concerned. The general proportion qualifying has been increasing so that in a modern Acute Hospital some 40% of the normal load qualifies. This increase reflects the more intensive hospital usage and patient turnover rate together with the increasing use of life support equipment, baby incubators etc..

5.7.6 Lighting

5.7.6.1 Internal lighting

Detailed treatment of the lighting requirements for modern hospitals cannot be adequately dealt with in a short review. Very full guidance on this subject is given in the CIBS Lighting Guide "Hospitals and Health Care Buildings" in the compilation of which both the DHSS and the NHS collaborated. The task lighting levels recommended range from 10 000 to 50 000 lux (local) under operating table luminaires, through 1000 lux (local) on examination beds in intensive therapy units, 100 lux in the circulation spaces in wards, (supplemented by bedhead lights), with night lighting of about 3–5 lux in ward corridors and 0·1 lux at bedheads.

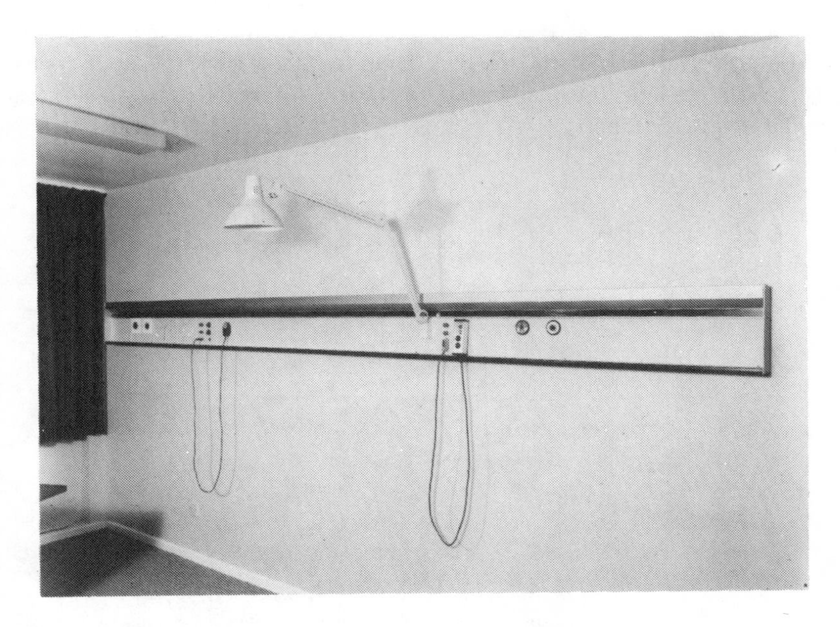

Fig. 5.7.2. *Bedhead Unit*

5.7.6.2 External lighting

External road access lighting is required generally to British Standard 5489 Part 3: 1977, Groups B8 and B5/6, whilst pedestrian ways, should be separately lit if not illuminated from adjacent roads.

External security lighting is essential round industrial zones, stores (particularly drugs stores) areas, and residential accomodation.

5.7.6.3 Escape route lighting

This should use approved fittings fed from the standby electricity supply via cable in screwed steel conduit or steel trunking, or m.i.m.s cable carefully routed as a precaution against fire damage. If this is not feasible or economic then individual automatic battery sustained lighting units which switch to internal batteries on mains failure may be used. (section 5.7.5.2)

5.7.7 Fire precautions and alarm systems

5.7.7.1 General

The Fire Precautions required for hospitals are clearly special due to the great difficulties in evacuating patients. The basic philosophy is that of compartmentisation with specific escape routes allied to fire alarm systems with fire and smoke detection systems. Each of these reflects into the electrical system design. There may also be other special fire services requiring an electricity supply, such as smoke extract systems. Lifts designated for the use of Fire Officers will also require a standby electricity supply.

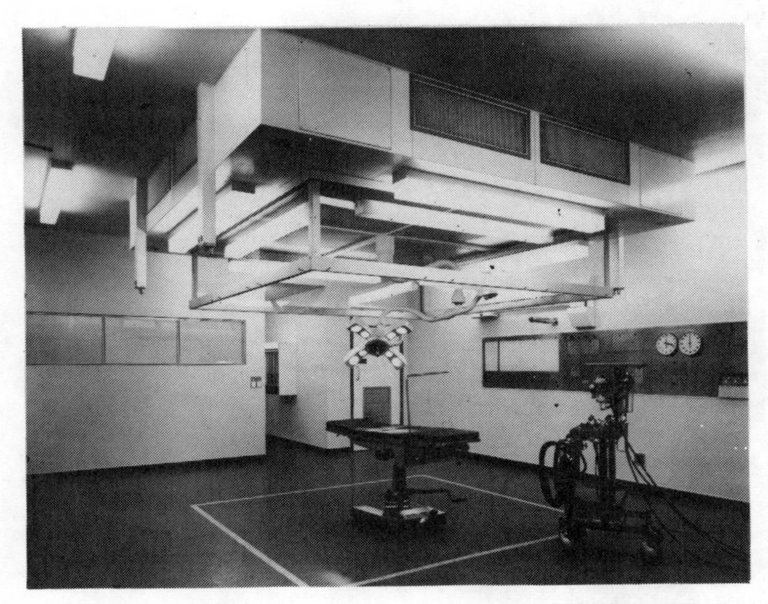

Fig. 5.7.3. *Ultra-clean operating theatre* (Howarth Air Engineering Limited)

5.7.7.2 Detection devices

Fire alarm, heat and smoke detection devices may be required separately or in combination for various areas of hospitals and the devices must be wired back to their control panels. The fire alarm system will normally include break glass units and this system may also be required to activate electrical devices such as door holding detents. The wiring for all such devices should resist fire damage for a significant period, e.g. m.i.m.s. cable, or cable in screwed steel conduit carefully routed, should be used for these circuits. Within each building (or Fire Sector) the devices are connected back to the building or sector fire alarm panel with similar hard wiring.

5.7.7.3 Fire alarm centre and network

The individual building or Fire Sector Alarm Panels are connected back to a central or Master Annunciator Panel which is normally located with the telephone exchange. This panel may be arranged not only to indicate the location of the alarm call but also to transmit a call to the Fire Brigade and alert various authorities.

It can also be arranged to illuminate indicator panels at the hospital entrances for the benefit of the Fire Brigade. The connection of the individual building or Sector alarm panels back to the main panel may be by multicore cable or by the use of multiplex signals transmitted over a simple common 2-core cable system. Multiplex systems such as this may be made self monitoring for faults and fault location and are available with Fire Offices Committee (FOC) approval.

5.7.8 Intruder alarm systems

Since hospitals are often readily accessible by members of the public consideration must be given to protecting those areas which are specially vulnerable to intruders. For example, Dangerous Drug Cupboards are required to be protected by an approved alarm system. In addition stores and other buildings, but particularly pharmaceutical stores, may require protection in the light of local circumstances.

5.7.9 Communications

5.7.9.1 Telephones

Hospitals require an extensive telephone system both for internal as well as external use. The telephone centre is also the usual focal point for relaying, either verbally or automatically, fire calls to brigades. Until recently preferred practice was for the use of PABX 3 exchange equipment, the boards being manned full time. Market forces and other considerations are now dictating a swing to the new generation of electronic exchanges. As experience is gained on electronic exchanges with their greater range of facilities there is little doubt that the service will improve and the potential for abuse will be reduced, e.g., by the barring of overseas calls from some extensions. Telephone extensions should be provided in accordance with management need but some payphones may be appropriate in public rooms. Telephone socket outlets should be provided in ward areas for trolley mounted payphones for patients' use.

5.7.9.2 Staff location systems

In general, two systems are in used, 27·12 or 31·75 MHz free-radiating transmitters at a suitable location to cover the required area, or alternatively a magnetic loop installed around the area to operate low frequency personal units carried within the loop. For either system there is a requirement for the issue and storage of units, together with battery changing or charging facilities. Speech facilities are not normally included with NHS call systems, a bleep signal only being provided. Simple systems of coloured lights are occasionally used for staff calls within individual hospital departments.

5.7.9.3 Entertainment

The locally available radio channels are normally wired into the ward bedhead units together with an extra channel for hospital use. At the main amplifier centre, facilities for a local (usually volunteer) disc jockey are sometimes provided. TV sockets should be provided in the day area of wards, normally fed from a master system.

5.7.10 Computer facilities

Computers are increasingly used in hospitals, at present mainly for administrative purposes such as payroll and stock control, but occasionally for medical use. It is likely that the long term future will take in the much greater use of computer techniques for medical record work and drug control. Services for computers should follow normal practice but where advanced hospital design is being considered useful forward thinking could include the planning or provision of routes suitable for the required cable services. Some trial work has already been carried out using trolley mounted visual display units (VDU) in wards with plug-in access to a central computer. Such methods require cable trunking facilities in the ward and these might be preplanned into the bed head unit trunking.

The use of dedicated computers for plant management and energy control is discussed in Section 5.7.11.

5.7.11 Plant management and energy control

Energy costs for hospitals are substantial and all forms of economy are practised. Apart from management techniques the most general modern equipment provision is the widespread use of optimum start heating controls in zones which are not occupied continuously. Some use has been made of more elaborate systems including data logging, plant monitoring and control and peak load lopping where suitable electrical loads exist. No pattern of general practice for computer methods has yet emerged. Potential economies are substantial but will only be realised if the facilities are integrated properly into the management system. The functions may be defined as:

(a) Command. Particularly in starting up and shutting down services at optimum times, e.g. building heating systems and boiler houses.
(b) Monitoring. To receive and possibly to print out routine figures for service status and availability.
(c) Alarm. To receive, and possibly to record, failure of services. Can be linked to automatic staff call out.

Equipment and network requirements vary from system to system. These should be considered with the hospital internal communication network.

5.7.12 Kitchen and catering facilities

5.7.12.1 Catering equipment

Catering equipment is required for kitchens of all sizes from main kitchens to ward kitchens, nursing homes and tea bars. It should be appreciated that fuel costs in a typical kitchen may represent one-tenth of total catering costs. Whilst the economics of various fuels should be evaluated due weight should be given to such matters as cleanliness, reduction of waste heat and ease of control. There is increasing use of electrical cooking equipment in modern hospitals.

5.7.12.2 Main kitchens

Here increasing emphasis is placed on energy conservation, the working environment including temperature, odour and condensation control, removal of products of combustion where appropriate, and removal of excessive or waste heat. In general these considerations require the provision of extract hoods, ventilation fans and ductwork with grease filters as well as lighting and other services.

5.7.12.3 Meals in wards

The methods of providing patients meals in wards vary from hospital to hospital. A popular method is a plated meals service from central kitchen(s) taken to the wards in electrically preheated container trolleys. Preparation of the meals may be by belt conveyor system.

5.7.12.4 Vending equipment

The use of vending equipment in hospitals is increasing. In the majority of cases this is limited at present to beverage machines and machines offering such items as individual pies. However, many new developments are incorporating a complete meal vending service, which may include microwave ovens for night staff meal service.

5.7.13 Lifts

5.7.13.1 Passenger and service lifts

Multi-storey hospital buildings may require lifts for passenger, passenger/bed, or goods service. The power systems for electric lifts in hospitals may be broadly classified as:

Single Speed a.c.
Two speed a.c.
Geared variable speed
Gearless variable speed

All these types can be appropriate to hospital use. In addition there is increasing use of the hydraulic lift, either direct acting ram or suspended type. The hydraulic power for these is derived from an electric motor/hydraulic pump unit. Lifts should be to BS and guidance on selection, traffic calculations, preferred sizes etc is given in DHSS Data Sheets.

5.7.13.2 Fire lifts

In buildings more than five storeys high there should be at least one Fire Lift. In buildings exceeding 18 m in height a Fire Lift on the basis of one lift for every 900 m^2 floor area above 18 m should be provided. These lifts must be arranged to be available for the exclusive use of firemen in an emergency, having at ground level a switch giving exclusive control over the use of the lift. A Fire Lift should have a platform area not less than 1·5 m^2 and be capable of carrying a load of 630 kg, and should be capable of reaching the top floor from ground level in one minute. It should be connected to the emergency supply.

5.7.14 Air conditioning

This service is mainly limited to operating suites although some hospitals, typically teaching hospitals sited in large cities where there is substantial noise and dirt pollution, may have large areas of air conditioned space.

5.7.14.1 Operating suites

These are normally fully air conditioned, with refrigeration. About 25 air changes per hour are provided in the operating theatre, with heating and cooling facilities capable of maintaining a room temperature variable between 15°C and 25°C in all but extreme outside conditions (i.e. about 10 hrs/year).

The electrical services are in accordance with good commercial practice and include:

(a) Fan drives, normally with duplicate motors and starters with belt transfer in case of failure.
(b) Refrigeration compressors, either motor/compressor units, sealed units, or rotary compressor units where appropriate.

(c) Controls, providing for running and standby states on reduced air flow. Temperature control within limits adjustable from the operating theatre. Indicator lights for system state.

5.7.14.2 Ultra-clean systems
In some operating theatres secondary recirculating systems are installed to provide a fast downflow of filtered (sterile) air over the operating area. These systems are usually self contained with special canopies, filters and fans with local controls, sometimes with electronically controlled variable speed. Special small profile operating table lights are used. (Fig. 5.7.3 on p. 664)

5.7.15 Domestic hot water

Due to the high consumption of domestic hot water (DHW) in hospitals, the supply is usually from calorifiers drawing heat from a primary heat source. Where there is a small local intermittent demand the economics of a local electric water heater should be assessed against the higher standing losses of a piped system. DHW should be stored at a minimum of 60°C to avoid bacterial growth.

5.7.16 Cold rooms and blood banks

Cold rooms are provided to normal commercial standards for food storage and pharmaceutical products. Blood Bank storage cabinets and cold stores should be fitted with temperature drift alarms with audible and visual signals to operate if the temperature falls below 2°C or above 8°C.

5.7.17 Mortuary and post-mortem rooms

Mortuary and Post-Mortem (PM) Rooms are provided as appropriate for the particular hospital, i.e. convalescent hospitals may have no requirement. Refrigerated body storage is provided with a normal temperature range of 3·5°C–0°C. The plant should be capable of cooling a full load of bodies from the loading temperature of 37°C to 3·5°C in 10 hours.

Teaching hospitals may require facilities to hold at a temperature of −3°C to −10°C. Electrical services are required for the refrigeration plant, circulating fans, controls as well as lighting etc..

With the quantities of liquid used in PM rooms, special precautions are necessary to reduce the risk of electric shock, as the enclosures of hand-held electrical equipment are seldom proof against the ingress of liquid.

5.7.18 Workshops and stores

Comprehensive workshop and stores facilities will be needed, with electrical services to good industrial standards.

5.7.19 Laundries and sterile supplies facilities

5.7.19.1 Laundry practice

Many hospital complexes include laundries, which may be either for the use of the hospital only or may be group laundries taking in the linen services of a surrounding district or group.

Hospital laundries are typical of good modern laundry practice but in addition allow for the safe handling and disinfection of foul material. In general this requires special (usually colour coded) bag handling facilities together with special double sided laundry machines for the disinfection process. These are barrier machines with the loading side 'foul' and the discharge side "disinfected". Hospital laundries are increasingly incorporating heat conservation and reclaim techniques. Further, it is not unusual for the laundries to provide a complete linen service, including Dry Cleaning facilities.

5.7.19.2 Sterile supplies

The bulk of sterile supplies, including standard packs for operations, are obtained from Central Sterile Supply Departments which may be on or remote from the hospital site. Sterile supplies may also be obtained commercially. Hospitals also have local facilities for sterilisation, mainly by the use of steam sterilisers. These must operate to precisely controlled cycles, (different for different products) for effective processing. Steam sterilisers are fed either from steam mains or from local boilers; electrode boilers have been used for this duty. The human and financial consequences of failure in this field are extreme and up to date expert advice must always be obtained before taking action. In particular the instrumentation performance requirements, and the regular testing and recording of these, are both critical.

5.7.20 The All-Electric hospital

The All-Electric Hospital constructed by the East Anglian Regional Health Authority on the St. John's site at Peterborough is of special interest. This hospital is of two storey construction with a floor area of $7000\,m^2$, rectangular in shape with two open quadrangles. Accomodation provides for 120 geriatric in-patients with physiotherapy and X-ray departments, together with a day clinic and a 20 bed isolation unit. The all-electric kitchen also serves all the other buildings on the site. The hospital was designed as an integrated economic concept for electric services and the fabric plus ventilation losses are approximately half those of contemporary conventional buildings at the design condition of −3°C ambient.

The electrical design is aimed at using night rate electricity as far as possible. Thus the hot water supply is from storage tanks which are heated at night rates, although additional heating by day is possible. The building carcase heat loss is made good by floor warming using embedded cables and electricity at night rates.

The hospital is mechanically ventilated throughout with fresh air and heat reclaim devices are used to minimise the heat input. Refrigeration is not provided. The general accomodation has 6 air changes per hour but the isolation ward has 15 air changes per hour. The heat reclaim devices are capable of saving over half the sensible heat losses. Ventilation air is warmed by direct electrical heater batteries.

The hospital was conceived and designed as a viable economic unit. Additionally it is expected to provide in the future a considerable amount of operational data which will be of use in determining energy policy for the NHS.

5.7.21 Bibliography

Health Technical Memoranda (published by HMSO):

1 Anti-static precautions: rubber, plastics and fabrics.
2 Anti-static precautions: flooring in anaesthetising areas.
7 Electrical services: supply and distribution.
8 Safety code for electro-medical apparatus.
11 Emergency electrical services.
14 Abatement of electrical interference.
15 Patient/Nurse call systems.
16 Fire precautions.
17 Commissioning of hospital engineering services
19 Facsimile telegraphy: the transmission of pathology reports within a hospital.
20 Staff location systems.
21 Safety Code for high voltage installations.
23 Access and accommodation for engineering services.

The similar Health Building Note series provides guidance on various Hospital Departments with the range of services, including electrical services, required by each on a room by room basis.

CIBS Lighting Guide: Hospitals and Health Care Buildings

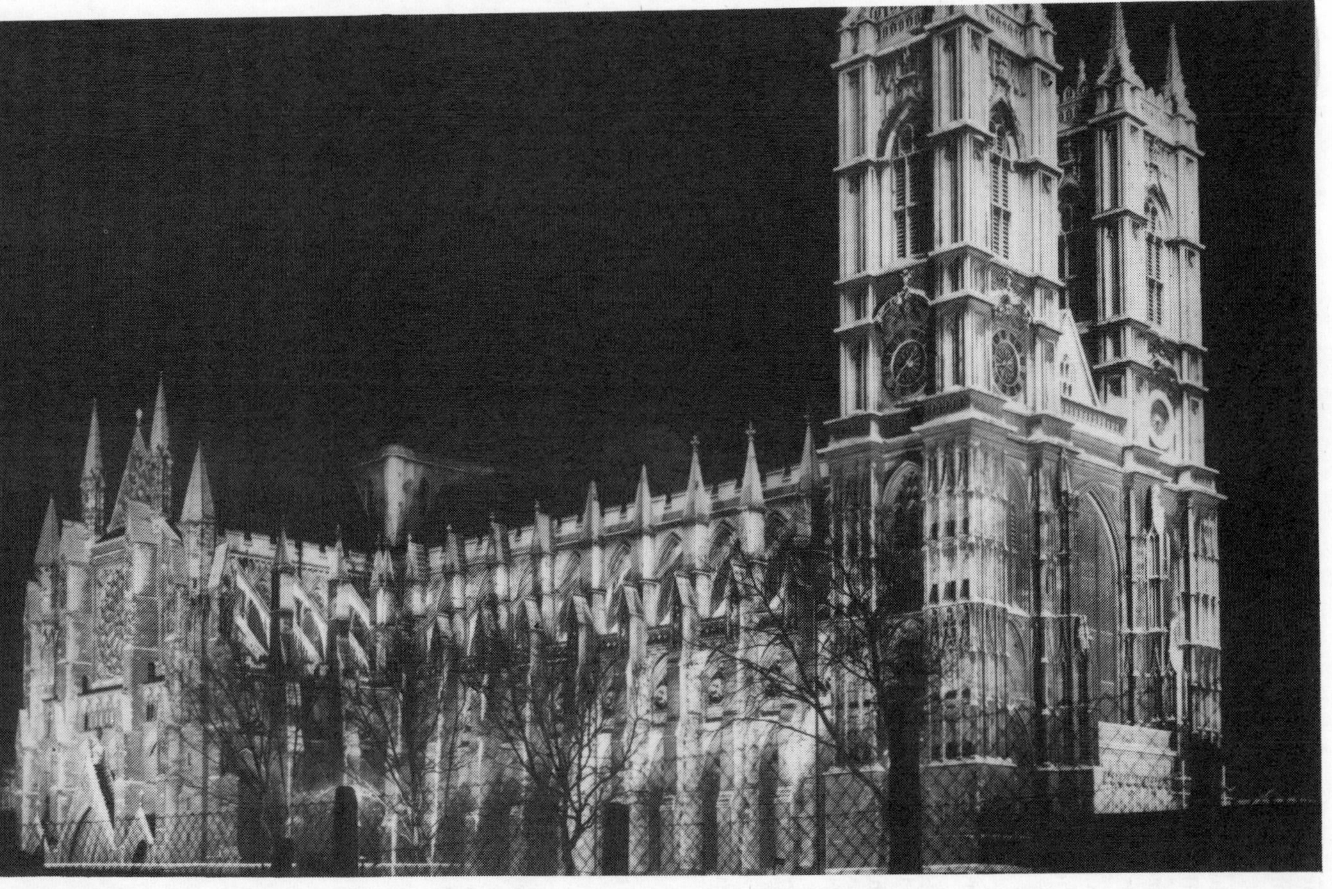

Westminster Abbey

Chapter 5.8

Religious buildings

Kenneth A. Shaw, B.Sc., C.Eng., F.I.E.E., M.I.C.B.S., M.Cons.E.
Partner, T. Harley Haddow and Partners

5.8.1 Introduction

Religious buildings vary greatly in basic layout, as they are laid out to suit particular religious requirements established over the years. The basic spatial layout will have been agreed after detailed discussion with the users with regard to their requirements and similarly the electrical installation will require detailed discussion with the users. Consequently the electrical installation in one religious building may be totally different to that in another.

We are indeed fortunate in the UK with the architectural standard of old religious buildings which we have. Many of these buildings are in category of Listed Buildings and when there is a requirement for the renewal of the electrical installation it should be appreciated that the present day usage may be somewhat different to that of the previous installation. The 'cutting of ways' in a Listed Building is a topic in itself and clear communication between the parties concerned should be achieved and the new routes marked out with chalk if necessary before the installation's 'first fix' commences.

Modern religious buildings are generally less spatial mainly due to present day financial restraints in construction, economics in heating and lighting and an overall reduction in the general maintenance of the fabric. There has also been a change in the religious habits of the population in certain areas and many newly constructed buildings have areas which are multi-purpose – a point to be carefully considered when designing the electrical installation.

Although there has perhaps been a reduction in the traditional religious population in the UK there has been a considerable increase in people from other countries and in many of the major urban areas mosques and temples have been opened. The majority of these buildings are adaptations of existing buildings, but on the other hand some new mosques have been built, many to the same dome and minaret style as would be traditional to the Middle East. The essential matter to consider before making the basic steps for the provision of electrical services is one of communication and research with the user to ensure that the final installation will provide for all their requirements in the most efficient way possible.

5.8.2 Refurbishment

Since many of the electrical services in religious buildings need renewal from time to time the authorities usually give careful thought before making such expenditure to ensure that the needs of the users will be satisfied for the period over which the renewed installation should last, say 25/30 years. In older buildings the areas

Fig. 5.8.1. *Traditional style interior*

are more than generous both in the church proper and the adjoining halls and rooms. Apart from causing difficulties with heating, these large areas are not so suitable for the wide variety of activities which are essential in a thriving present-day church community.

As a result many of the large halls which undergo refurbishment have been subdivided into a number of smaller rooms with reduced ceiling heights and in certain instances even the church itself has had remodelling of its interior in order to make more use of the space available. After the compartmentation has been agreed the renewal of the electrical services can then take place in a more logical manner. The smaller rooms and their flexibility in use provide a greater potential for electrical heating systems with individual thermostatic controls than a more traditional form of central heating system. Care should be taken to ensure that the electrical appliances do not disturb the acoustics of the building. Fan motors will get more noisy and the "cracking" noise of expanding panels may be unacceptable. Of the latter type, panel heaters or tubular heaters, they should have a physical size/wattage ratio to allow minimum expansion of the metal components. Ceiling heating and natural convectors are ideal forms which overcome these problems; ceiling heating provides the maximum flexibility in the usage of the area and usually the associated thermal insulation cover gives enhanced qualities to the acoustics.

Power outlets in refurbished rooms are often more acceptable at a height of 1500 mm as this overcomes the problems of accessibility of outlets with relocation of items of furniture.

5.8.3 Heating

The merits of electrical heating have already been mentioned in relation to the differing requirements of old and new buildings. Electricity Authorities are often able to offer special tariffs for religious buildings on the basis that their main use would be at off-peak hours. They will perhaps accept the operation of non-storage equipment e.g. tubular heaters under pews, on special off-peak tariffs, and clarification of their supply parameters at an early date will assist with the selection of the most suitable heating system. The proposed hours of operation are just as important to the Electricity Authority as to the user and these should be formally confirmed before final decisions on the heating system are made.

Electric storage heating is available in many forms; storage radiators, storage fan heaters, Electricaire, hot water storage and floor warming. The basic principles of heating as referred to in Chapter 4.2 should be observed, as intermittent or partial occupation of the building could make the operation of an electrical storage heating system uneconomic – the exception of this being storage fan heaters which are ideal for intermittent use. Direct electric heating in the form of electrode boilers coupled with a conventional low pressure hot water system, infra red heaters and radiator panels installed at high level, tubular heaters and oil filled radiators can also be used either independently or integrated with a storage heating system where the latter is providing a background heating. It is important to consider background heating with the user from the point of view of maintaining the fabric of the building in good order. Many of the fabric problems in existing churches are caused by intermittent heating and inadequate ventilation. Direct electric heating has the added attraction of flexibility of control as necessitated either by a sudden change in the weather or a change in the occupancy programme, and has a particular application in mitigating the effects of cold downdraughts from windows.

5.8.4 Lighting

Practical illumination of congregational space areas is essential to allow comfortable reading of reading material which appears to be, by tradition, in very small print.

Reference should be made to the CIBS (formerly IES) Code for Interior Lighting for guidance on the level of illumination of the various areas within a church. Note however, that the values given are minimum levels of illumination and must be carefully considered along with the proposals for colours and finished surfaces of the interiors. The standard illumination levels are as follows.

Body of church (pews) – 50 to 100 lux
Pulpit and lectern – 200 lux
Altar, communion table – 400 lux
Vestries – 200 lux

Fig. 5.8.2. *Gallery of Baptist Church*

Generally the funds available are limited, and cannot permit the use of special lighting fittings hand made to blend with the spaces provided. It is therefore preferable and sometimes more effective to keep the lighting fittings simple and focusing on the areas of religious importance. The simplicity of the fittings selected can often be beneficial when it comes to maintenance as this is generally a task for the willing laymen within the church.

As mentioned earlier, research with the user will be essential in order to determine the essentials for the lighting design. For example, in a mosque it is a basic theme that light leads one forward to prayer and the areas at the back of the building where women are assembled become quite subdued and even dark. The definition of these areas must be determined in the early stages of design. Also, mosques will have domes or minarets which have special glazing and give spectacular daylight effects. Equally spectacular effects can be achieved by illumination of these at night.

Fig. 5.8.3. *Modern Church of England interior*

Other religious buildings have spacious interiors and the structure is often exposed and interesting in detail. If monies can be made available the illumination of domes or vaulted beams can give great effect to the whole atmosphere of the building. The designer should remember to have this type of lighting installed with sufficient flexibility to allow for final adjustments and focussing when the works are completed. A similar procedure can be adopted for exterior floodlighting but in this case it is usually easier to make adjustments as the fittings are not necessarily fixed to the building structure.

Lighting should therefore be considered in the following order: practical illumination of the public areas; selection of the essential religious features; then, when finance will allow, special lighting effects, including exterior floodlighting.

A relatively new form of lighting can be used to great effect in older buildings and that is the uplighter luminaire. This form of design uses a High Intensity Discharge (HID) lamp within a bowl type upward facing reflector, and can provide excellent illumination of some feature of the structure together with adequate ground lighting. Another advantage in using this system is the relatively low power loading, between 7–10 W/m^2, which gives low running costs.

5.8.5 Electrical installation

The wiring of a religious building, no less than that of any other building, must be designed to provide those facilities which are required safely and continuously. However, particularly careful consideration requires to be given to the appearance, technical quality and adequacy of the electrical installation. Not only are these buildings often places of great architectural and historic interest, but even today may house hundreds of people whose safety must be of concern to the installation designer.

The Council for Places of Worship publishes its own booklet of recommendations and conditions, which serves as a useful guide to all Church lighting and wiring.

The lighting should be wired on at least two circuits so that the failure of any one fuse or protective device does not give rise to panic in total darkness. Control of the lighting will usually be brought to one single location – the main door or vestry – but consideration should be given to certain luminaires being separately controlled for access and inspection purposes. In larger churches some zoning of the lighting wiring will be essential, in order to provide for the various degrees of occupancy which will occur.

There is a strong preference, particularly in older stone-faced churches for mineral insulated metal sheathed cable (m.i.m.s.) because of its relatively small overall diameter and ease of installation, with little risk of subsequent problems. PVC cables either sheathed or drawn into conduits can also be used but great care is needed in unplastered buildings to conceal such cables, particularly as church authorities and others will not normally condone cutting, drilling or chasing of the structure.

It is often forgotten that religious buildings need socket outlets, with the result that those responsible for cleaning and polishing are obliged to resort to manual effort or long and often poor extension leads. The provision of a number of strategically placed sockets for floor polishers as well as any which may be needed in altar, vestry and porch areas for occasional lighting (e.g. at Christmas) will contribute to the safety of the users.

Church authorities, conscious no doubt of their responsibility to future generations, recommend that electrical installations should be inspected every two years thereafter. Such inspections should – like the whole installation – be fully in accordance with the IEE Wiring Regulations and an Inspection Certificate should be provided on completion.

5.8.6 The organ

An essential part of the electrical equipment has always been the electrically operated organ, the installation of which must be carefully planned. Damage may easily be caused by excessive heating or abnormal atmospheric conditions. The following points should be borne in mind:

(a) Hot water pipes should not pass through or near the organ.
(b) Any hot air outlets should be located well away from the organ.
(c) Rapid heating systems will make tuning difficult.
(d) Avoid having heated air drawn into the organ.
(e) In any proposed alteration or replacement of the heating system the organ builder or persons responsible for its maintenance should be consulted.
(f) Humidification is important if excessive shrinkage of existing woodwork is to be avoided.

As in other areas however the cost of the system becomes an increasingly controlling feature and the high cost of a traditional organ or even maintaining it comes within this category. The modern answer to this problem is the electronic organ which does not require the same critical environment or call for anything like the same size of power for the blower motor. These comments however refer solely to the electrical installation and cannot be taken as a comment on the quality of the sound; that is a matter beyond the scope of this chapter.

5.8.7 Public address

A study of the range of sophisticated hardware which is available for use in a public-address and amplification system will indicate that this work is of a very specialised nature. The services of the specialist should be consulted at an early date in order that locations for microphones and loud speakers can be selected and routes for the necessary interconnection can be concealed and suitably protected. Information with regard to the fabric and furnishing will also be helpful in the basic design of the system.

5.8.8 Fire precautions

Earlier mention was made of the need for safety and the suggestion of lighting being shared between at least two circuits. Religious buildings are designated by Fire Prevention Officers as non-residential public premises and as such they will require to be consulted as early as possible to ensure that their requirements for evacuation procedure and fire alarm signalling are observed. If there is sudden darkness in a large hall it is essential that the occupants are immediately aware of the location of the exits and the routes to these exits. If the hall has to be licensed under the Cinematograph Acts for a special performance then the emergency lighting system will have more stringent conditions. Most Fire Authorities will base their recommendations on BS 5266 "The Emergency Lighting of Premises" and although religious buildings may not be specifically mentioned, the fundamental proposals for safety contained in BS 5266 should be applied.

Similarly, the fire precautions may call for the installation of an electrical system of sounding devices to alert the assembly in case of fire. The design of the system should be in accordance with BS 5839 "Fire Detection and Alarm Systems in Buildings" and although it may be a fundamental requirement to ensure that all persons within the building are aware of the alarm there may be instances when the premises are unoccupied and the building is of sufficient architectural merit to consider the installation of an automatic fire detection system. Where battery supplies are used in any of the foregoing systems, if a maintenance contract is not adopted then some rigorous means of regular inspection should be established to ensure that these safety precautions are maintained.

5.8.9 Lightning protection

An important precaution to be considered is that of lightning protection. On an existing building the copper lightning conductor may have been vandalised or even removed without the users appreciating the fact. If the system is already existing then it may not have an appropriate test point; the installation of a test point would prove advantageous in subsequent inspections. The condition of the lightning conductor should be checked at regular intervals and when the periodic inspection is carried out then an item for Lightning Conductor Inspection should be included.

In new religious buildings, the prominence of steeples and spires may not be so evident but none the less to ensure safety of the structure and of the assembly, a full assessment should be made in accordance with BS Code of Practice CP 326 to check the requirements. It is possible in both old and new installations to provide some form of mechanical protection over the downlead conductors. Not only will this reduce problems from accidental damage but it will conceal the conductor sufficiently to act as a deterrent to vandals.

5.8.10 References

5.8.10.1 Legislation (See also Appendix 6.1)
Cinematograph Acts 1909–1952

5.8.10.2 British Standards (See also Appendix 6.2)
BS 5266 covers emergency lighting, BS 5839 covers fire detection and alarm systems and BS CP 326 refers to the installation of lightning conductors.

5.8.10.3 Bibliography

CIBS (formerly IES) Code for Interior Lighting
Wiring Regulations for Electrical Installations (Institution of Electrical Engineers)
"Lighting and Wiring of Churches". Church Information Office, Dean's Yard, London SW1P 3NZ.

Interior, Plymouth Civic Theatre (Plymouth City Council)

Chapter 5.9

Theatres

F. A. Abbott, C.Eng., F.I.E.E., M.C.I.B.S.
Project Director, Ove Arup & Partners

5.9.1 Introduction

5.9.1.1 Building characteristics

The major characteristic of this group of buildings is the provision of under-cover seated accommodation, usually with an area designated for performers. The principal uses are for presentation of drama, opera, ballet, music or films but may also include conference facilities. Multiple use is frequently provided for, but general purpose halls including sports accommodation are discussed elsewhere. (Chapter 5.15) There are a number of common features relating to all these buildings but also many others that are peculiar to the individual usage. It is, therefore, necessary to consider the requirements for each facility to see where these can be combined to provide for multiple usage.

5.9.1.2 Accommodation

Theatre planning is very specialized, needing to incorporate a large auditorium space with a number of inter-related smaller spaces. The auditorium will provide seating accommodation which can vary from under 200 to over 4000 and can be arranged totally to surround the performance area, be around it on three sides only, or to face it on one end. In most cases, the seating is tiered and is fixed, although movable seating is sometimes provided to enable the format to be adjusted from 'picture frame' presentation to 'in the round'.

The provision of a tiered floor and raised performance area, provides the most significant constraint on the use of the space and generally inhibits sports use.

Ancillary accommodation includes entrance foyers, cloakrooms, toilets, waiting areas, restaurants or bars, administration offices, control rooms, dressing rooms, stage workshops and plant rooms. Most theatres are provided with a fly tower over the stage with a grid suspension system and other facilities might include a scenery dock, orchestra pit, projection room, wardrobe, laundry and green room. Cinemas have particular requirements for projection facilities.

5.9.2 Environmental conditions

5.9.2.1 General

This category of buildings has particular requirements which fall under the following headings:

(a) The public at large become users and special requirements for their safety, particularly in respect of danger from fire, have to be met.
(b) Sight and sound are the principal senses involved in the appreciation by the audience of the 'work' of their performers. Acoustical quality of the building and the provision of proper lighting systems are, therefore, critical factors. There is also a growing number of technical facilities now to be provided which require careful integration into the building.
(c) In any situation, where large numbers of people meet together in close proximity, adequate fresh air and temperature control become essential.

General building services must be designed with particular reference to these requirements and special attention is necessary to ensure that they are met, since the success of this category of building is largely dependent on this. It is necessary to provide comfort for proper appreciation of the arts and if the building is to be accepted by the visiting performing companies, groups or individuals, it must be provided with, or have facilities for, the ever increasing range of technical features. It is, of course, essential that all statutory requirements are met and these are stringent when related to public safety.

5.9.2.2 Heating and ventilation

Heating and ventilation is required throughout the building with special requirements for toilets and kitchens. For comfort, the internal temperatures should be controlled at around 21°C with fresh air supplied at a minimum rate of 25 m^3/hour per person. With the use of more stage lighting equipment and greater public awareness of comfort requirements, it is becoming increasingly necessary to provide air conditioning equipment. Buildings provided only with ventilation plants experience difficulties, particularly in summer months, with present day audiences unwilling to accept internal temperatures of 30°C or more.

Particular problems are encountered in the control of the internal environment of the auditorium. Irrespective of external conditions, the sudden heating load resulting from the influx of a full house of people over a period of twenty to thirty minutes places a considerable strain on the ventilation or air conditioning plant. It is frequently the case that this load, augmented by the load from theatrical lighting, much of which is located in the auditorium, is only present for two to three hours each day, but the plant must be designed to cope with this. It is sometimes necessary to pre-cool the building to avoid excessive temperatures later, but there is a limit to the acceptability of this procedure. Air distribution patterns and noise have to be carefully controlled to avoid draughts and to prevent interference with the appreciation of the performance.

The electrical drives to all plant are straightforward but, to meet the criteria, motor speeds tend to be slower and all final connections are flexible to reduce sound transmission. Location and type of motor control gear should also be selected accordingly.

Facilities for paint spraying and for use of dyes may require special ventilation equipment in stage workshop areas. Control of smoke and fumes is essential and separate systems will be necessary where a safety curtain is fitted.

5.9.2.3 Catering

Most theatres include facilities for the sale of drinks and sometimes food for the public. Larger buildings will include a full public restaurant facility with kitchens which will require special consideration in relation to air conditioning or ventilation. Depending on location within the building, a manual or automatic hoist may become necessary to handle food supplies and waste.

Bars will be provided for the various levels of the auditorium. These require planning for fast service. Electrical supplies will be needed for normal and decorative lighting and for power supplies to pumps, refrigerators, chillers, etc. Microwave ovens are becoming popular in some locations. Mechanical handling for crates or barrels may be necessary.

5.9.2.4 Water heating

Hot and cold water services are required to all public and house toilets and to kitchen areas, vending machines, staff rooms and dressing rooms. There may also be special requirements for a laundry area including provision for the use of dyes. Because of intermittent use, localized electric water heaters may be preferred in some areas.

5.9.2.5 Acoustics

There are two principal aspects to the acoustical performance of a building. The first relates to the reverberation time of the space within which the performance is given, which affects the character of the sound. This is a very specialized design problem beyond the scope of this chapter, except that equipment can be installed to modify the natural response of the auditorium by means of microphones and loudspeakers which will require an electrical service.

The second aspect relates to noise generally. All plant and machinery must be specially designed to minimize any noise generated. This applies not only to all pumps, fans and other rotating machinery but also to water cisterns, kitchen equipment and sundry electrical items such as contactors. Lifts should also be carefully sited and specified to avoid noise from an accelerating motor or from door alarms or gongs.

Noise of two major types must be considered:

(a) airborne, which dictates flow rates, duct and air terminal configurations and acoustic isolation
(b) structural, which necessitates sprung or rubber mountings, effective foundations and flexible couplings. Recent theatre designs have aimed to limit noise from building services to extremely low levels, and this has been achieved.

5.9.3 Lighting

5.9.3.1 Housing lighting

General
Normal lighting operating from the mains supply is installed in all parts of the building. This will also include decorative lighting in foyer, auditorium, bars etc. Separate lights for cleaners may be installed to avoid use of the less efficient decorative lighting for cleaning purposes.

Fig. 5.9.1. *Services above Auditorium Ceiling* (Plymouth City Council)

Maintained
Separate lighting is kept on during a public performance or to be precise when the public are in the building even when the normal auditorium lights are dimmed out;

this is to enable the public to see to move about. Some lighting may be fed from an independent source to also act as safety lighting. By arrangement, the statutory authority may permit this lighting to be extinguished for a period of up to 30 seconds during a stage performance. This is a special dispensation, however, and has to be hand operated with self-reset.

5.9.3.2 Stage lighting

Stage lighting is arranged individually for each type of presentation and is, therefore, based on a variety of lanterns with spotlight or floodlight characteristics, each arranged to be dimmed and equipped with devices for shading, adjusting beam shape and fitting colour filters. (Fig. 5.9.2)

Fig. 5.9.2. *Stage Lighting in Studio Theatre* (Plymouth City Council)

To provide illumination for setting up and cleaning, a system of working lights is provided throughout the stage area. These are all centrally switched at the control console and are of two categories. 'White' working lights provide illumination when there is no show in progress, but separate circuits of 'Blue' lights provide safety illumination around the stage during a performance. The use of blue lamps avoids interference with the effects being achieved by the main stage lighting equipment.

5.9.3.3 Emergency lighting (non-maintained)

Emergency lighting is provided by a non-maintained safety lighting installation fed from a battery or in some circumstances a generator, and normally unlit, but arranged to come on if the normal electricity supply fails. It is designed to enable public, staff and performers to leave the building in the event of danger without the use of the general installation.

5.9.3.4 Advertising and floodlighting

External floodlighting is frequently provided on theatres to attract patrons. This will be used to emphasize architectural features of the building and to provide an inviting appearance to the entrance. Tungsten halogen or discharge lamp sources are chosen to suit the facades and features being illuminated.

On particular buildings, facilities will be required for advertising of current and future performances. Illumination of the signs may be part of the general floodlighting, but is sometimes integral with the signs themselves. Cold cathode lighting may be used for this purpose, either directly or incorporated in illuminated letters or panels. Fluorescent and other sources may also be used in panels. Specialist signs incorporating large numbers of small sources, sometimes in different colours, can be designed to have continuously varying switching patterns to give the effect of moving words or pictures. The development of solid state technology has increased the versatility of this form of advertising.

The design of all advertising signs is a specialist task, but the electrical designer must provide a suitable supply point at the sign position and if cold cathode lighting or other discharge lighting operating at higher than low voltage is used, a fireman's switch has to be installed in a prominent position.

5.9.4 Electrical installation

A number of significant electrical features need to be accommodated and these must be considered at the earliest stages of planning.

5.9.4.1 Main switchroom

Preliminary estimates of electrical load are needed to size the switchroom and substation. These should be located on the perimeter of the building, but with provision for cable routes to various sub-distribution centres for stage lighting, stage engineering, mechanical services plant and for general power and lighting. Normal building loads can be estimated on an area basis, but stage lighting needs special consideration.

As many as two or three hundred 2 kW, 5 kW or 10 kW circuits can be provided but diversity is large and the period of maximum load is frequently measured in minutes rather than hours. A careful assessment of the actual load to be designed for is, therefore, essential.

5.9.4.2 Circuit wiring

The type of wiring and distribution equipment used in the electrical installation for a theatre is similar to any other commercial building in respect to power and lighting circuits throughout the building areas. Because of the density of circuits for stage lighting, however, and the need to facilitate changes, much greater use is made of insulated wires run in surface mounted trunking. The stage lighting and stage engineering equipment will be separately fed from the intake position.

Fig. 5.9.3. *Communications Centre Off-stage* (Plymouth City Council)

5.9.4.3 Stage lighting circuits and control equipment

Equipment for lighting the performance area is located throughout that area, but also at many points in the audience space. Fixings for that equipment have to be provided together with space for connection boxes and wiring. All this equipment is arranged to be adjustable for position and orientation and to be wired with flexible cables to the plug and socket on the connection box. Individual lighting units can be rated at 500 W to 10 kW, most of which is given out as heat at the unit.

The stage lighting circuits are controlled from a single permanent position, usually by means of a desk located, ideally at the back of the auditorium, or elsewhere, such that the operator has a full view of the lit area. This desk controls dimming equipment now usually of the thyristor type, such that the output from each unit can be infinitely varied between zero and full. To facilitate setting up and rehearsals, temporary plug-in positions for a portable desk control are frequently provided at two or three other locations on stage, in the fly galleries or in the centre of the auditorium. The dimmer racks can be accommodated remote from the desk and preferably on the route between the main switchboard and the various lighting positions. It has been the custom to group all dimmer racks together, but with the development of more sophisticated control procedures these can be separated into two or more groups.

5.9.4.4 Stage wiring

Wiring to all stage lighting units is usually contained in trunking ranging from 50 mm × 50 mm up to multiple runs of 150 mm × 150 mm. Suitable routes for these have to be provided throughout the stage and auditorium.

Special consideration must be given to the sizing of this trunking to maintain the appropriate space factors laid down in the IEE Wiring Regulations. Circuits can be very long and may loop on from one connection box to another, perhaps doubling back over the same length of trunking. Strict adherence to the voltage drop requirements of the IEE Regulations can result in the use of unreasonably large conductors with consequential increases in trunking sizes, however, and in terms of satisfactory performance, a larger than normal voltage drop may be acceptable for stage lighting equipment to reduce the conductor sizes. When sizing for thermal rating, due allowance can be made for the diversity of use of the multiple outlets and the limited time of operation for theatrical performance, but care must be exercised to allow for prolonged use in rehearsal and set up periods. However, such assessments should only be made by a suitably qualified electrical engineer fully conversant with the way in which the installation is to be utilised.

5.9.5 Communications

5.9.5.1 Systems

The modern theatre is totally dependent on communications. Early planning of the building must include space for equipment and cable routes for a variety of systems, some of which require to be kept totally separate, but nevertheless run over identical routes to the same locations. The systems include:

Cue lights	Show relay
Talk-back	Close circuit TV
Call system	Staff Bell Warning
Telephones	Public Address and Sound Reinforcement

There is also a growing use of radio microphones for individual performers and of induction loop systems to provide assistance for the hard of hearing. Where a conference facility is required, this loop can also be used for simultaneous translation services.

5.9.5.2 *Wiring*

All microphone cabling is run in separate trunking or conduit and the other systems are sometimes separated into different groups to avoid interference and cross-talk. Although currents are small, the use of multicore and screened wiring techniques results in cables of up to 15–20 mm diameter. In complex installations, trunking sizes range from 50 mm x 50 mm to 150 mm x 150 mm with up to three runs in parallel on the most congested routes. The systems extend throughout the building including dressing rooms, bars, toilets, foyers and offices, and early planning for suitable routes is therefore essential to integrate trunking and terminal equipment.

5.9.6 Security

5.9.6.1 *Internal security*

A particular feature of theatres is that the permanent staff is small in relation to the size of the building and, in addition to the public use of the auditorium areas, visiting performers and part-time staff form a significant proportion of the users of the premises. There are many parts to a theatre including numerous toilets, passages and stairways and there may be several areas where money or valuable stock or property are stored. Security, therefore, is a difficult problem.

Depending on the characteristics of the premises, intruder alarms can be associated with doors, external glazing, bar grilles, safes or the box office. In addition, raid buttons may be fitted wherever cash is handled. All these alarms have to be wired to a central system and the stage doorkeeper's desk is frequently used. For security, this wiring is usually independently installed by a specialist contractor, but designated conduits can be installed during earlier stages of construction to conceal parts of the installation.

5.9.6.2 *Fire precautions*

Fire fighting requirements to the approval of the local fire authority might include hosereels, hydrants, risers, sprinkers or drenchers, depending on the size and type of building and on its location.

Again, noise is an important factor and all pumps, tanks, etc. and associated electrical equipment must be carefully sited to avoid noise intrusion into the auditorium. Suitable flexible bearings and connections must also be fitted. A fire alarm and detection system will also be required and this, together with the emergency lighting installation, have to be provided to the satisfaction of the fire authorities.

Automatic detectors of the ionization, obscuration, rate of rise or heat types are installed particularly in unoccupied areas such as scenery or wardrobe stores. Use of break-glass alarms is limited. No automatic audible warning of fire is usually allowed when the public are in the building, but visual signals, recognised by the staff, are provided followed by announcements from the stage or elsewhere to achieve evacuation without panic. Automatic signals to the fire station or a centralized security organisation may also be fitted.

5.9.7 References

5.9.7.1 Legislation (See also Appendix 6.1)

Fire Precautions Act, 1971

GLC Places of Public Entertainment: Technical Regulations

5.9.7.2 British Standards (See also Appendix 6.2)

BS 2560 Exit Signs

BS 5266 Emergency Lighting

CP 1007 Maintained Lighting for Cinemas

5.9.7.3 Bibliography

Regulations for Electrical Installations (Institution of Electrical Engineers)

BENTHAM, F. 'The Art of Stage Lighting'. (Pitman)

MILLS, E. D. (Ed.) 'Planning: Buildings for Administration, Entertainment and Recreation'. (Butterworth)

PILBROW, RICHARD. 'Stage Lighting'. (Studio Vista)

Bibliography: Building Services for Concert Halls and Theatres LB 18/81 (BSRIA)

CIBS (formerly IES) Guide for Interior Lighting

CIBS Lighting Guide: Lecture Theatres

Industry Committee for Emergency Lighting (ICEL): Emergency Lighting Applications Guide (ICEL 1003)

The Association of British Theatre Technicians (ABTT) 4 Great Pulteney Street London W1R 3DF publish a dictionary of theatre terms, 'Theatre Words' and a number of Information Sheets on specific subjects.

Library and Study Area (Thorn-EMI Lighting)

Chapter 5.10

Educational buildings

L. E. J. Piper, C.Eng., M.I.Mech.E., M.C.I.B.S.
Superintending Engineer, Department of Education and Science

5.10.1 Introduction

This Chapter covers educational buildings from nursery, primary and secondary schools to further education, higher further education, universities and polytechnics. Where subjects are taught at similar academic levels, services needs are expected to be similar and this is reflected in services provision throughout the whole education system, particularly so in the polytechnic and university field. One significant variation can be found in buildings where research work is carried out: this usually involves more space and a greater complexity and provision of services generally.

Special problems arise where buildings are grouped together in campuses, which can involve high voltage distribution networks, transformer stations and complex switching arrangements to ensure continuity of supply.

In England and Wales, S.I. 909 (1981) "The Education (School Premises) Regulations 1981" cites the statutory requirements which are in force for school buildings administered by Local Authorities. These requirements cover thermal environment, lighting, acoustics and energy conservation, and are set out in Design Note 17 published by the Department of Education and Science. No similar standards are laid down for university buildings.

5.10.2 Schools

5.10.2.1 Nursery schools

Whether as a separate building or part of a larger complex, nursery schools are usually strongly domestic in character, giving a homely, informal and friendly atmosphere. Accommodation usually consists of play rooms, quiet bays, (Fig. 5.10.1) quiet rooms, and a small dining area with a kitchen utility room which can prepare and cook a small meal or handle food from a central kitchen.

The services are basic and there are no special needs. The internal environment should be comfortable and floors should have some warm surfaces for children to play on. Air and mean radiant temperatures should be reasonably close together.

Lighting designs should aim to give a warm texture to spaces and create as far as possible a domestic atmosphere. Indoor play areas should be well lit by natural means. Direct task lighting and soft general lighting is preferable in quiet areas rather than hard overhead general illumination from fluorescent fittings. Socket outlets are required for general purposes, as well as for audio and visual aids. Television and radio are used and power will be required for a cooker and a number of outlets in the kitchen utility area. Heating and hot water service can be by any of the conventional methods, including off-peak storage and instantaneous electric water heaters. Care should be taken to ensure that surface temperatures within the reach of young infants do not exceed 43°C.

Fig. 5.10.1. *Nursery School Quiet Bay* (Department of Education and Science)

5.10.2.2 Primary and junior schools

These schools all have basically similar needs. They reflect much of what can be seen in the nursery sector with noticeable differences being the introduction of some more formal classroom spaces, and spaces where formal assembly takes place. Some assembly areas have raised stages which could have rudimentary stage lighting, others use a variety of demountable staging which can be stored away.

Power could be required in classrooms and assembly and entrance areas for fan heaters and general purpose socket outlets. A provision of 2 to 3 double outlets per general teaching area would be adequate. Additional outlets would be required for television and radio, learning machines, computers and for equipment in resource areas. Power is necessary in kitchens but requirements vary depending on the individual local authorities. Some provide a complete kitchen, others just provide rudimentary reheat facilities.

These schools are usually fed from a three phase power supply either directly from the Electricity Board mains or from a spur from another building. The supply enters the building and is generally located and controlled in a small switch room or cupboard, which should be dry and well ventilated. Separate metering may be necessary for different tariffs.

Single phase circuits will be run to local distribution boards which supply lighting and power circuits through switches and fuses. A separate supply is usually run to the boiler house and kitchen, and a three phase supply will be required where the kitchen uses electricity for cooking and in the boiler house if the plant is large enough. Some outside lighting may be necessary, particularly for illuminating road access and parking spaces.

Fig. 5.10.2. *General Teaching Area* (Department of Education and Science)

5.10.2.3 Secondary schools

The range of accommodation found in secondary schools is wide and covers a variety of special needs. All have general purpose teaching spaces handling subjects that rarely require other than basic electrical provision. (Fig. 5.10.2) This will usually consist of an adequate number of socket outlets to supply audio visual aids and for classroom cleaning purposes. Some spaces have radio and television outlets often included in a special panel which can also house a class change announcement system.

5.10.3 Specialist subjects

5.10.3.1 Drama

There are three main types of accommodation to consider: rooms for small scale drama work; drama studios; and spaces primarily for performance.

Small scale drama will take place in spaces similar in character to general teaching areas. There will be a need for socket outlets for audio-visual aids and for some local lighting effects.

Fig. 5.10.3. *Drama Studio* (Department of Education and Science)

A drama studio is a more formal space where specific facilities will be provided such as black-outs and stage lighting. It may be necessary to "stage light" all or part of the space. Individual solutions will range over many alternatives but a good basic provision of a minimum of 12 kW of power should be allowed for. It would feed possibly 15 to 20 circuits, which could be housed in purpose made pre-wired battens, or run to lights hanging on a ceiling batten, or lighting battens arranged in a variety of ways throughout the space. The whole of the stage lighting system should be controlled by a single isolator and switch. The drama space will need general purpose lighting of approximately 300 lux. There will be a need for socket outlets for audio visual aids and for cleaning purposes, and emergency lighting including exit signs. Power will be required for ventilation plant. Theatres are really a more formalised drama provision although the same lighting principles would apply. Some may have a more sophisticated and extensive arrangement of lighting and sound equipment, as well as lighting and stage management systems. (Fig. 5.10.3)

General purpose halls which have a raised formal stage with a proscenium arch are more widespread than separate theatres. There are few of the latter. It is common practice for the hall general purpose and stage theatrical lighting to be separately controlled. The general purpose lighting should be controlled in the auditorium but it is often convenient also to wire the system through a dimmer control or switch located back stage which is capable of extension to a lighting control desk for use during performances. Some general purpose circuits will be run back stage for cleaning and lighting for formal assembly, and a number of outlets located on or near the stage will be required for orchestra lighting. Electricity will be required in dressing rooms for make-up lights and for costume pressing. Much will depend on the general school plan and the proximity of the stage to teaching areas whose activities can support theatrical productions in its widest context. Power will be required for ventilation and for emergency lighting which will be required mainly for exit signs in the auditorium and for enclosed areas around the back stage. It is common for a hall of this type to have a single phase 100 A supply with a branch of 60 A capacity run to the stage to an isolator and switch. The final stage lighting arrangement will depend on available resources; it need not be decided upon until later, the essential priority being an adequate power supply.

5.10.3.2 Music

Music and drama share many facilities for performances but specialised teaching spaces designed to achieve proper acoustic privacy and sound propagation are normal. There are no special electrical requirements but adequate outlets should be provided to keep the number of multi-way adaptors to a minimum particularly where electric instruments are used. Ventilation may be needed in certain spaces, the power requirements for which would be modest.

5.10.3.3 Arts and crafts

Arts and Crafts comprise a variety of activities such as drawing and painting, printing, weaving and spinning, pottery making and wood crafts.

Equipment in use in these areas will include tape recorders, visual aids, soldering irons, photographic equipment, glue pots, electric water heaters, pug mills, grinding wheels, potter's wheels, kilns, and power drills. Most of this equipment will use single phase power from 13 A outlets, but there will be a small number of larger pieces of equipment which have a heavier power requirement. Some require a three phase supply, which is normally solid wired and controlled through a switch and starter. Emergency push button power cut-off safety devices may be necessary.

Some areas will be used for display and some for modelling. Directional lighting is often used, sometimes from high level lighting fittings fixed to proprietary brands of lighting tracks, or from a series of ceiling mounted power outlets.

5.10.3.4 Workshop areas

Most practical craft based skills are taught in schools. Traditional accommodation ranges from workshops handling metal and wood to areas arranged to teach the rudiments of engine design and the principles of electric power and rotating machines.

There is a growing interest in electronics and computer applications; this will require an additional socket outlet provision on benches for teaching packs. Single phase power is provided through standard socket outlets to drive portable tools and to energise the multiplicity of teaching equipment available. The larger fixed machines are supplied by both single and three phase. These supplies are normally solid wired to the machine via an isolator and starter.

The circuits feeding the machines must be controlled by emergency push buttons which will isolate the electrical supply and which are strategically placed and clearly marked. Reset should be by a loose key or other device that restricts the restart to a responsible person. Some authorities use residual current devices (r.c.d) as an additional safety precaution. When this is used it can be used additionally as a safety cut out provided it has a clearly marked suitably sized tripping button and a reset operated by a key switch which cannot be used by unauthorised persons. When this equipment is used it must be designed to protect young children and a residual operating current of not greater than 10 mA is a suggested figure. Typical machine equipment and loadings vary from $\frac{1}{4}$ hp (180 W) to 2 hp (1·5 kW). It is important to ensure that circular saws must be located out of reach of children.

In addition to good general lighting, all machines should ideally be provided with local lighting to concentrate the light on the task.

5.10.3.5 Home economics

13 A socket outlets will be required for all typical household equipment. A typical small furnished flat may be provided into which must be installed sufficient socket outlets to facilitate the use of vacuum cleaners, washing machines and dryers and small appliances. Cooker circuits and control units will be needed for electric cookers used for teaching purposes.

The formal teaching of cookery, sewing and ironing often takes place in specially designed spaces while the teaching of individual skills may take place in more general purpose spaces. These areas will require a more generous provision of socket outlets than ordinary classrooms.

5.10.3.6 Gymnasia

An allocation of double socket outlets placed in convenient places for cleaning with perhaps a local need for visual and audio aids is all that is normally required. Some power may be required for extra direct radiant heating in some localised areas. Ventilation to the hall and to changing room areas may be needed in some cases. Most sports halls have artificial lighting to a standard suitable for badminton and ball games generally.

5.10.3.7 Laboratories

A mains voltage electrical supply is required to operate an extensive and expanding range of teaching equipment in a variety of school laboratory layouts. Purpose designed power packs are widely used. They provide the range of frequencies, low voltage and a.c./d.c. supplies necessary to teach and demonstrate relevant subjects safely. Each laboratory should have its own separate supply with an isolator conveniently placed for operation by the person in charge. Each workstation should have one 13 A mains socket and there should be extra socket outlets provided on the side benches. Power may be taken through an r.c.d. as an additional safety measure; this should be set at a residual operating current not greater than 10 mA. (Fig. 5.10.4)

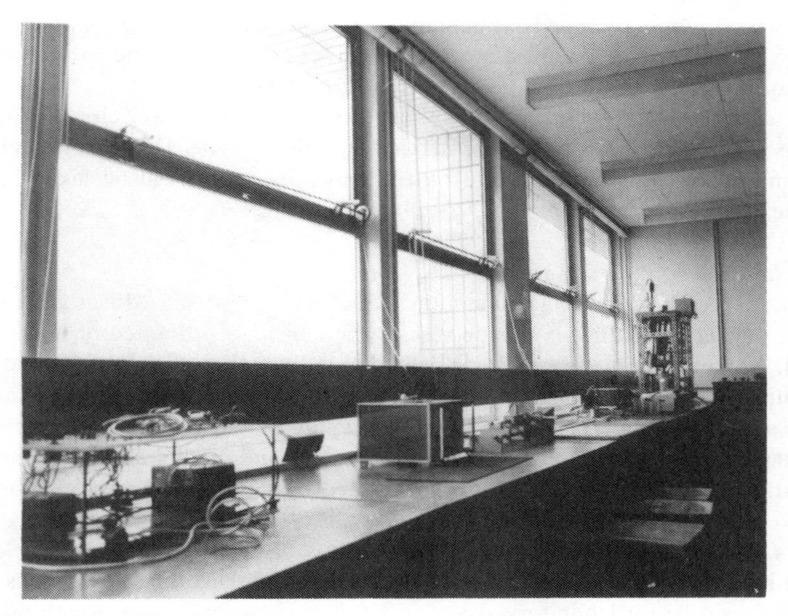

Fig. 5.10.4. *Teaching Laboratory* (Department of Education and Science)

5.10.4 Universities

5.10.4.1 General

Universities in the UK vary in size and in geographical layout. For example those like Oxford and Cambridge have approximately 10 000 students, their numerous faculties being spread widely throughout the city. The new Universities, developed in the early sixties, have between 2500 and 5000 students with their faculties and residential accommodation often concentrated on a single campus. Universities generally include faculties of Arts, Education, Social Studies and Science. In addition to this they have many research establishments covering a wide range of subjects.

The electrical services requirements can be broken down to those required for teaching, research and residential accommodation. However, it must be remembered that many Universities have large arts centre complexes, sports centres and utility areas for shops, banks, and launderettes. Indeed, such complexes are like a small town.

5.10.4.2 Main electrical installation

The main electricity supply is generally taken from the electricity supply authority as high voltage (11 kV). The University is then responsible for its own distribution network, which can be quite extensive on single campus Universities. This is achieved by establishing high voltage substations strategically placed over the campus to provide medium voltage supplies at minimum copper costs. These substations are designed for installation both inside and outside of buildings and are connected via steel wire armoured copper or aluminium cables. A strict code of supply practice has to be adhered to as laid down by the Factories Act 1961 and the Electricity (Factories Act) Special Regulations 1908 and 1944.

Discussion with the Electricity Authority will lead to the selection of the appropriate tariff which will be of the maximum demand type. Depending upon the maximum power requirement and other factors a decision will be taken on the choice of HV or LV metering.

5.10.4.3 General teaching areas

Artificial illumination to a minimum of 300 lux is desirable with a glare index of 19. Higher standards may be necessary where daylight is limited or not present at all. Socket outlets are required for audio and visual aids, also to facilitate the cleaning of spaces. A general distribution of one double outlet per 15 m^2 is a good basic provision. Additional sockets may be required in areas teaching subjects like geography, psychology and business management, and in all areas where the proliferation of electronic computation and visual display is likely.

5.10.4.4 Science laboratories

Lighting of laboratory accommodation usually means lighting large spaces. The level of lighting for laboratory spaces is 350 lux for general lighting with 500 lux for more detailed close work. The glare index for the installation should not exceed 19, and the installation should be designed using fluorescent tube lighting fittings. The fitting layout should be modular and the switching of the fittings arranged so that the row of fittings parallel with and nearest to the window can be switched off whenever the natural light is sufficient to enable work to proceed, to conserve energy. Any special requirements for a high level of artificial lighting for some particular task can be provided by local lighting. The wiring for lighting installations in laboratory buildings is usually housed in the space above the false ceiling. It is difficult to envisage mechanical damage to an installation in such a space, and therefore a system without mechanical protection can be provided. In corridors, toilets, and ancillary rooms the lighting levels will be those appropriate to such spaces.

Socket outlets are used as the method of supplying electrical energy in laboratories. Electrical loads on single pieces of equipment in laboratories are often less than 0·5 kW – but the number of pieces of electrical equipment can often be large. The provision of socket outlets on benches therefore should be generous. An investigation carried out some time ago into the need for electrical outlets in various science disciplines came to the conclusion that electrical services for science accommodation can be placed in broad classifications:

(a) Organic and physical chemistry
(b) Biological Sciences
(c) Physics

Table 5.10.1 gives an approximate socket outlet provision under definable areas within each science.

Two single outlets on benches are often installed as a double outlet where the equipment in use is known to have a low power requirement; this would be the case in most undergraduate laboratories. The socket outlets in plant rooms are for general purposes only. Additional outlets are required for fume cupboards in Chemistry and Biological sciences.

5.10.4.5 Libraries

Major libraries for Universities and for Polytechnic Colleges are generally designed within a deep square plan building. This provides accommodation in a form that the librarian can make the best use of in his layout.

The main areas provided will be:

Table 5.10.1 *Provision of Socket Outlets in Science Accommodation*

	Single Socket Outlets per 100 m^2	
	Chemistry and Biological Sciences	Physics
Laboratories (Teaching area only)	50	26
Ancillary (Preparation)	50	26
Lecture Theatres	6.3	6.3
Lecturers' Rooms	50	26
Stores Preparation	50	26
Circulation and Plant Rooms	6.3	6.3

(a) Reading area – both general and individual study areas (carrels)
(b) Book storage – Open stack easy access
Open stack restricted access
Compendium stacking
Special environmental conditions within storage areas, e.g. rare books
(c) Special reading and photo reproductive areas
(d) Book binding.

The deep planned library will be built with the minimum of window area to assist the control of the internal environment and therefore artificial lighting will be necessary at all times of occupation. Except for special areas for display and for effect lighting the artificial lighting will be provided by using fluorescent tubes with diffusers as appropriate.

The lighting levels suggested are 350 lux for general lighting in areas other than stack storage, corridors, toilets and ancillary rooms. In the book stacks the most advantageous lighting arrangement seems to be fluorescent tube batten fittings mounted on or suspended from the ceiling on the centre line between adjacent stacks. These fitting should not be fitted with a diffuser, and tubes in the output range of 600 to 800 lumens per foot of tube length are most suitable. The lighting level to be designed should be 150 lux on the horizontal plane at floor level. For corridors and toilets the lighting level for design should be 150 lux, and for ancillary rooms the level will depend upon the use of the room.

The most suitable lighting design for large reading areas is a modular spacing using fluorescent tubes in the output range 900 to 1000 lumens per foot of tube, with a suitable diffuser to ensure that the glare index does not exceed 19. Another solution for reading areas would be a coffered ceiling with recesses incorporated in the design to enable the installation of a suitable fluorescent tube. The coffer in the ceiling must be sufficient to enable a tube to be installed without a diffuser such that the tube cannot be seen by an occupant at such an angle as to cause discomfort by glare. In reading areas where the task is more difficult such as with small print, or charts, maps and drawings, it is recommended that the design lighting level should be 500 lux. This level may also be necessary in some of the ancillary spaces where detail work is carried out.

The library will have a number of socket outlets. With the exception of specialist areas such as those housing film and slide readers, copying machines etc. the socket outlets will be used for low power requirements mainly for cleaning tools and local supplementary lighting, and should be provided on the basis of one outlet point for every 15 m^2 of floor area.

In areas where visual aid machines, copiers etc are to be installed the socket outlet provision must meet the requirements of the machines in addition to outlets for cleaning tools. In ancillary spaces such as bookbinding, mess rooms, and vending machine areas, it is possible that a three phase supply may be required in addition to the socket outlet provision.

Deep plan libraries may be air conditioned; those without air conditioning will require mechanical ventilation to move air over the book stacks to prevent mould growth. A considerable demand will be made on the electrical supply for the fans, refrigeration machines and pumps for the air conditioning system and for the fans in the mechanical ventilation installations. These installations will be designed on conventional principles. There will be a requirement from the Fire Officer that the library be provided with a fire alarm system. In a building with a mechanical air movement system the requirement will also include a detection system and possibly automatic door closing and other refinements. Whatever system is required, the wiring must be carried out with a system which will not be adversely affected by fire. This suggests a mineral insulated metal sheathed (m.i.m.s) cable system with suitable fittings.

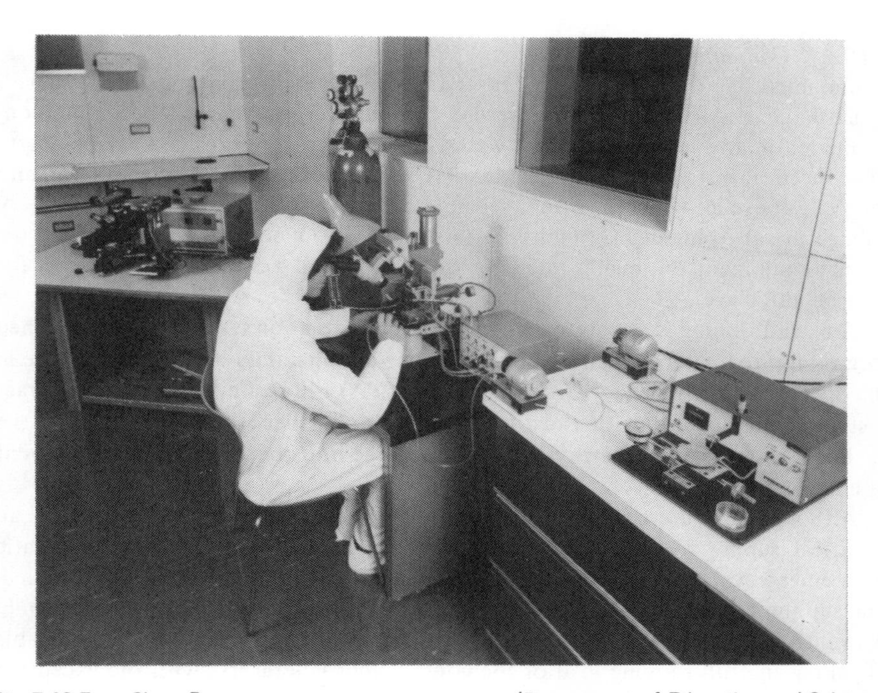

Fig. 5.10.5. *Clean Room* (Department of Education and Science)

5.10.4.6 Clean rooms (Fig. 5.10.5)

These rooms are designed to provide a dust free environment, a requirement that is both difficult and expensive to meet. Clean rooms often have full control of both humidity and temperature. Single phase 240 V 13 A socket outlets are required for monitoring equipment, soldering irons, special lighting, etc. 415 V 3-phase may be used for items such as furnaces and there may also be a requirement for 24 V d.c. supplies. All environmental plant such as ventilation fans, humidifiers and refrigeration equipment is usually 415 V 3-phase.

5.10.4.7 Computer suites

All Universities have at least one computer suite and although the development of the micro-chip will lead towards computers having greater memory capacity for less power requirements, most of the big computers still consume large amounts of electrical energy. This energy is dissipated as heat and full air conditioning is necessary.

It is essential that the manufacturer's specification for power supplies is complied with. This may be as simple as a 240 V single phase supply or for motor generators which provide a variation in frequency and/or voltage. Voltage regulators and/or transformers may also be used. It is advisable to take the supply from as close to the main supply as possible and preferably on an independent circuit from the LV side of a mains transformer.

5.10.4.8 Containment laboratories

Containment laboratories can now be found in Universities and must be designed, constructed and maintained to prevent the outside environment becoming contaminated in any way by the work which is being carried out inside the laboratory. The electrical installation will include 13 A socket outlets spaced at about 750 mm intervals above all benches, with a separate battery alarm system with low battery voltage alarm to highlight a faulty battery. 30 A 240 V sockets will be needed for special equipment too highly rated for ring mains, and a 3 phase 415 V supply for a steam autoclave.

Air conditioning is not always provided but a ventilation system must be designed to give approximately 20 air changes per hour and maintain a negative pressure in the space. High Efficiency Particulate Air (HEPA) filters are fitted on the extract system and either automatic isolating dampers or a further HEPA filter fitted to the air inlet system to prevent any harmful discharge into the atmosphere in the event of a fan failure.

Although absolute continuity of supply is not essential it is desirable to have an electrical supply reconnected within a few seconds and therefore an automatic start emergency generator that starts when mains voltage is lost should be installed, the supply being restored by an automatic voltage operated changeover switch. All ventilation plant must have autostart and the emergency supply must be capable of taking the full running load of the containment laboratory, with the exception of the refrigeration side of the air conditioning.

5.10.4.9 Workshops

University workshops are designed to give a comprehensive support to both research and teaching activities. They range from major comprehensive central facilities to small departmental workshops. The electrical requirements can be extensive and some of the largest provisions have their own high voltage sub-station sited close by.

Large central workshops are generally divided up into heavy machine shop, light machine shop, joinery shop and welding shop. The sub-dividing helps to comply with the Health and Safety at Work Act particularly with respect to extraction of dust from the joinery shop and shielding from arc flashes in the welding shop. Typical power requirements for University workshops vary from fractional horse power motors up to 20 kVA for arc welding equipment.

All machines must be fitted with local isolators to comply with the IEE Regulations and in addition to each machine having its own isolator, many will have emergency stop buttons fitted at positions that can be readily reached by supervisors and machine operators.

5.10.4.10 Centrally controlled energy and surveillance systems

Some Universities are installing computer based control systems so that heating plant and lighting can be efficiently controlled. In addition to energy management the system can be designed to include security, fire, flood and management reports.

(a) Security:	Security of doors, windows etc.,
	Access control
	Security patrol points
(b) Alarms:	Fire alarms
	Flood alarms
	Smoke alarms
(c) Energy Management:	Compensating control
	Optimum start
	Optimum stop
	Duty cycling of electric motors
	kW demand control
	Enthalpy control
	Lighting control
(d) Management Reports:	Meter readings
	Heat flow
	Savings on kW demand
	Savings on duty cycling
	Planned maintenance.

5.10.5 Residential accommodation

5.10.5.1 General

Residential accommodation can vary from self contained flats for 5 or 6 students to large halls accommodating in excess of 100 students.

5.10.5.2 Heating and ventilation

Temperatures at most Universities were designed to standards recommended by the Institution of Heating and Ventilating Engineers Guide. However, although 18°C was recommended it is found in practice that 20°C is the temperature that satisfies most residents. Residences can be heated by forced air circulation, hot water radiators, electric fires, storage heaters or under-floor heating. Storage heaters and under-floor electric heating take advantage of off-peak electricity. Domestic hot water is required for baths, showers, wash basins and kitchen sinks and is supplied at a temperature of 65°C.

Areas where cooking takes place often have extract ventilation to prevent smells penetrating into the study-bedrooms. Mechanical ventilation of internal lavatories is important. Local bye-laws are often open to interpretation by the Public Health Officer, and it is therefore advisable to obtain his opinion before final approval is sought.

5.10.3.3 Lighting

It is difficult to light a study bedroom to the required level of illumination using fixed ceiling mounted incandescent lighting fittings so that adequate levels are maintained without shadows and giving maximum amount of flexibility in positioning furniture. Fluorescent lighting would meet this requirement but as the maximum amount of light is required over the desk, and to give the rooms a feeling of warmth and comfort, study rooms are often lit with portable table lamps for the desk, as well as by general lighting.

5.10.5.4 Socket outlets

At least one double 13 A outlet is required in each study bedroom. Socket outlets are required in corridors for cleaning and in the pantry or communal area for cooking. These areas usually contain a small cooker and refrigerator and have facilities for ironing, and sometimes a washing machine and clothes dryer. Extract fans are often used in these areas to exhaust cooking smells to atmosphere.

5.10.6 Communications

Communications both internally and with the outside world play an important role in the life of all Universities and large educational centres. To meet this need most have their own Private Automatic Branch Exchange (PABX). This will operate from two sets of batteries, one being stand-by to the other at 50 V. These batteries are on constant charge from a mains transformer/rectifier so that in the event of a mains failure the exchange will continue to function. In addition to telephones, many departments have their own audio intercom systems, often sharing the same system so that instant communication is possible. HV substations will also have an independent form of communication link between them, either by telephone, radio or intercom.

5.10.7 Security

5.10.7.1 Intruder security

Three main types of intruder alarm systems are used in educational buildings:

(a) Door Contacts
These are usually in the form of magnetic switches. They protect local high risk areas e.g. principal offices, strong rooms, archives.
(b) Sound Detection
This is the most commonly used system. Sound is detected by carefully sited microphones tuned to a pre-set level which if exceeded for a given period sets up an alarm. A disadvantage is the high incidence of false alarms although special equipment can be installed to exclude known entraneous sounds.
(c) Passive Infra-Red System
This works on the principle of detecting a changing level of infra-red emission as an intruder moves through detecting sectors.

Alarms are usually bells or sirens mounted on the enternal wall or in a control room.

The use of energy management systems using intelligent outstations offers the facility for a variety of security arrangements which can send signals back to a remote manned central station.

5.10.7.2 Fire precautions
All buildings will have some form of fire alarm system, generally of the break glass type with a battery maintained separate supply to bleeper units, bells and alarms, but fire detection and smoke detection systems are only used in special circumstances. It is not possible to generalise and each system must be discussed with the local fire officer.

5.10.7.3 Emergency lighting
Lighting to provide means of evacuating buildings safely in the event of an electricity failure should be provided. This may be by a central battery system supplying fittings with LV lamps, or by a central battery system feeding through an inverter to convert to a.c. which then supplies the existing lighting system, or by individual self contained mains/battery fittings. The choice of systems should be based on economics; a central battery system can only be supported on this basis for an installation requiring a large number of fittings.

5.10.8 References

5.10.8.1 Legislation (See also Appendix 6.1)
Electricity Regulations 1937
Factories Act 1961
Health and Safety at Work, etc Act 1974
Statutory Instrument SI 909
The Education (School Premises) Regulations 1981

5.10.8.2 Bibliography

Building Bulletins, published by the Department of Education and Science

1 New Primary Schools
3 Village Schools
20 Youth Service Buildings
25 Secondary School Design 6th form and staff
26 Secondary School Design Physical Education
30 Secondary School Design Drama and Music
34 Secondary School Design Art and Crafts
35 Middle Schools
39 Designing for Science
41 Sixth Form Centres
51 Acoustics in Education Buildings
53 Guillemont Junior School, Farnborough, Hants
55 Energy Conservation
56 Nursery Education

Design Notes

1 Building for Nursery Education
9 Designing for Further Education
10 Designing for Severely Handicapped
11 Chaucer Infant and Nursery School
17 Guidelines for Environmental Design
21 Sedgefield Secondary School

Regulations for Electrical Installations (Institution of Electrical Engineers)

JENKINS, B.D. Commentary on the 15th Edition of the IEE Wiring Regulations (Peter Peregrinus Limited)

WHITFIELD, J.F. A Guide to the 15th Edition of the IEE Wiring Regulations (Peter Peregrinus Limited)

CIBS Building Services Manual

CIBS (formerly IES) Code for Interior Lighting

Health and Safety at Work Publication 39: Lighting in Offices, Shops and Railway Premises (HMSO)

Research Laboratory (Department of Education and Science)

Chapter 5.11

Laboratories

George Tuson, M.B.E., C.Eng., M.I.Mech.E., M.I.P.H.E., F.I.Hosp.E.
Consultant Engineer

5.11.1 Introduction

Electricity is a basic service requirement for laboratories. In addition to normal environmental lighting and heating applications, its main uses in experimental work are the provision of heat and the supply of power to machines and electronic instruments. Developments in the use of digital measuring equipment for recording results of experiments coupled with the use of microprocessors and computers in various applications has increased the need for careful design of laboratory electrical services.

Laboratories for education, science and technology have varying and complex requirements which are subject to change as technology advances. This has led to the general adoption of flexible or adaptable laboratory designs to allow future change with minimum reconstruction. These developments have created problems for the services engineer, leading to the development of co-ordinated system designs which are the only way to ensure flexible or adaptable solutions at acceptable cost levels. The Laboratories Investigation Unit sponsored by the Department of Education and Science and the University Grants Committee (Ref. 1) have carried out major studies on these problems and the publications of their researches are recommended for further study.

Laboratories are amongst the most costly and heavily serviced buildings. It is therefore important for the designer to be involved from the inception of a scheme in understanding user requirements and operational policies.

5.11.2 Types of laboratory

5.11.2.1 Adaptability

Laboratory spaces can be related to three principal types of activity; as knowledge advances, the requirements for these activities are subject to varying rates of change. An unexpected development in a research project, the introduction of a new teaching method or the decision to test a new product can all lead to changes affecting provision of services, furniture layout and even room layout.

5.11.2.2
Routine Testing in which the work consists of tests for quality of performance, generally against a standard.

5.11.2.3
Teaching in which the sizes of groups can vary from ten to sixty. Experimental work can be directed step-by-step or can be of a freer, exploratory nature.

5.11.2.4
Research in university, private, commercial or government establishments, usually carried out by single persons or small teams.

5.11.3 Building arrangement

From the initial planning stage, the Architect and Engineer should discuss with the client the general arrangement of the building and all aspects of service requirements. The Engineer in collaboration with the Architect should decide the philosophy of service design and determine:

(a) Plant Room sizes and locations.
(b) Switchgear Rooms sizes and locations.
(c) Distribution service routes indicating co-ordinated service requirements.
(d) Access for maintenance of services.
(e) Easy methods of replacing services.
(f) Building requirements to allow flexible or adaptable servicing system.
(g) External services to be connected.

5.11.4 Environmental requirements

5.11.4.1 General
Laboratories probably have the widest range of hazards of any technological installations of similar size because, apart from the usual range of laboratory hazards of fire, gas cylinders, acids, etc., they pose distinct problems in the handling of dangerous aerosols or vapours which arise from the incidence of bacteria and viruses, of dangerous chemicals (carcionogenic, explosive, combustible, corrosive and of radioactive substances). Environmental control is therefore a vital component in the development of a laboratory complex.

The environmental requirements fall into two categories:

(a) Personnel require comfortable working conditions where they are not exposed to risk from the work processes.
(b) Products or processes should have where necessary environmental control to ensure that procedures are not influenced by other elements to the detriment of the process, or affect personnel or other processes.

The type of environmental system to be chosen for a laboratory will depend on the analysis of the two categories. This can be a difficult process as in many cases the rapid increase in laboratory automation will have significance in decision making.

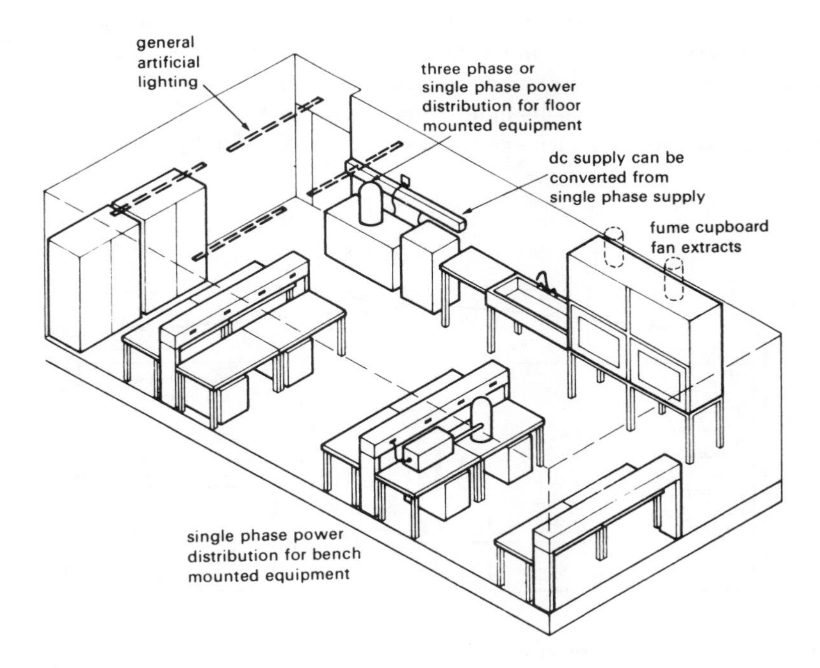

Fig. 5.11.1. *General layout of a laboratory*

The publication of Threshold Limited Values for 1977 in Guidance Note EH15/77 by the Health and Safety Executive (Ref. 2) demonstrates that many well known chemicals and other substances are far more dangerous to health than previously understood, e.g. chloroform, asbestos, formaldehyde, benzene.

5.11.4.2 Air conditioning, heating and ventilation

The provision of air conditioning, heating and ventilation is dependent on the type of laboratory and the work involved. The first consideration is to determine whether an open or closed environment is appropriate. The open environment (i.e. openable windows) would require a heating and ventilating solution, the closed environment (fixed windows or none) an air conditioning solution. Both solutions generate specific problems in dealing with fume cupboard and other extract systems and care is necessary at design stage to overcome these difficulties.

The design of an air conditioning system to provide the required operating conditions can take various forms. Basically, it must provide cooled air delivered at ceiling level and extracted at low level. Dependent on the processes involved, the space is held under negative or positive pressure in relation to the surrounding areas. With a large installation, the air system can be integrated with the lighting system using luminaires which are ventilated to remove excess heat. This heat can be usefully employed in other areas of the building and, for maximum economy, full use should always be made of waste heat. Air can be introduced through perforated ceiling diffusers. Humidity can be controlled by the usual methods but problems may arise where a number of areas are served by a central plant. It may be necessary to introduce individual humidity sources for each area. The use of steam for humidity control may be advisable to prevent contamination by solids.

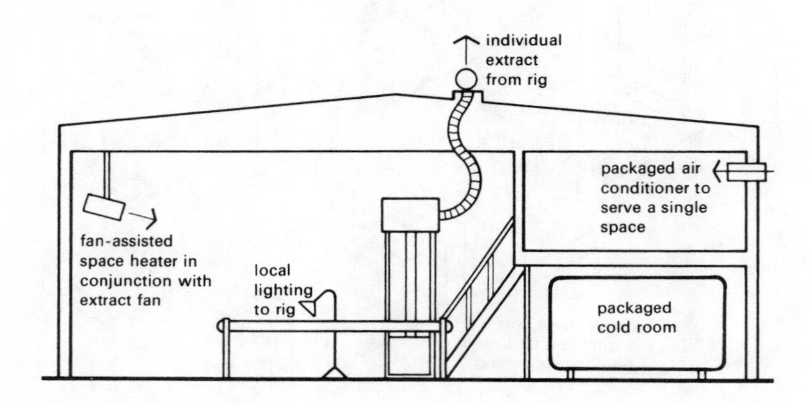

Fig. 5.11.2. *Localised environmental arrangement for a laboratory*

The elimination of dust is essential to machines, and magnetic tape is especially sensitive to the slightest contamination. The equipment provided should remove dust from the air and from operatives' clothing.

Alternative heating systems may be considered, but the following main points should be noted.

(a) Floor warming. This has the advantage that space is not taken up by the heating appliances. However, the designer should take particular care to avoid local overheating or generally high surface temperatures if a large proportion of the floor area is occupied by equipment or furniture.

(b) Radiators. These can be conveniently positioned on external walls and thus provide no restrictions on internal layout. Deep buildings with internal spaces are more difficult if floor space is to be kept free. In a deeper building, the perimeter spaces can be heated by radiators and the internal areas with warm air.
(c) Warm-air systems. These should be considered in conjunction with ventilation, as artificial ventilation is a common requirement for laboratory work. Warm-air heating is particularly suitable for laboratories as it deals with the basic problem of balancing the general heating system by warming the replacement air where intermittent extraction is necessary to counteract the fume and heat production of some experimental work. This type of ventilation requires:

(a) The introduction of heated replacement air when fume cupboard extraction is in operation. The switching of fume cupboard fans can be linked to a booster fan in the warm-air input, thus dealing with the replacement problem automatically.
(b) The provision of special air extraction to deal with excessive heat produced by engineering machinery, autoclaves and ovens. For individual items, local fan extraction should be adequate. Larger areas or rooms having this problem could be dealt with by ducted extraction, linked to the general system if the building has full artificial ventilation. The greater problem is encountered in the summer when the production of excessive heat may require a degree of cooling, extending to full air-conditioning. It is an economy to reduce the output of the heating system in winter in areas where equipment produces heat.

5.11.4.3 Lighting

The layout of lighting should be compatible with the planning module and related to bench/machine layouts, if these are regular. General recommendations for minimum illumination levels are as follows:
general laboratories, balance rooms, 400 lux, glare index 19 (schools 16)
electrical and instrument laboratories 600 lux, glare index 19
workshops, 200 to 600 lux, glare index 16 to 25.

Where accurate colour rendering is necessary, colour matching tubes should be used at the values specified above. Tungsten lighting is suitable in small ancillary spaces for intermittent use. For extremely exacting work, local lighting at the bench or machine is preferable to an attempt to increase the general lighting level.

Further lighting problems which should be considered are:

(a) Stroboscopic effects. These can cause a hazard in the machine laboratories of workshops, where the equipment has parts moving at high speed. The problem can be overcome by connecting a proportion of fittings to a separate circuit, on a different phase from the remainder. Auxiliary local lighting to machines should be tungsten.
(b) Interference. Fluorescent tubes and supply lines emit radiation at radio frequency which can interfere with very sensitive experiments in electronics. The use of rapid-start lamps with filters can reduce radiation from the supply line. Tube radiation can be reduced by shielding the lamp.

5.11.5 Special environments

The general air conditioning of a laboratory may not deal with the problems generated by aerosols and other substances and specific local applications become necessary. The following general points should be noted for installation in special rooms and enclosures:

5.11.5.1

Temperature controlled rooms (20°C to 37°C). The appropriate rating factor should apply to cables within the room if the set temperature is to be 25°C or over. The use of heat resistant cables should be considered for higher temperatures. A ceiling mounted variable speed fan may be required to prevent stratification.

5.11.5.2

Cold rooms (4°C for normal requirements down to − 20°C to − 25°C for frozen material). Alarm systems may be required. Where temperatures below − 25°C are required, usually free standing deep freeze cabinets are used.

5.11.5.3

Rooms with a high humidity or dust content. The use of water proof switches, outlets and plugs should be considered. Light fittings should be readily cleanable.

5.11.5.4

Electrical interference and screened rooms. Sources of interference may be divided into the following categories:

(a) Electro-magnetic radiation (radio waves).
(b) Electro-magnetic radiation and/or transient current surges on mains from equipment.
(c) Attenuating magnetic fields – transformers, etc.
(d) Attenuating electrostatic fields (e.g. unscreened conductors at mains potential).

Where possible when planning new laboratories, the aim should be to allow adequate physical separation between possible interfering sources and areas where sensitive apparatus may be used. Generally, the effect of radiated signals from local sources can be assumed to vary inversely as the square of the distances. It is possible to reduce the distances considerably by the use of apparatus filters and/or suppressors at source, and in general, most interference problems can be dealt with satisfactorily without resorting to the use of screened rooms.

To screen a room against external sources of interference, the walls, floor, ceiling, windows and doors must incorporate or be faced with an electrically conducting membrane which is electrically continuous throughout, with one effective low impedance earthing connection. Complete package rooms are available from manufacturers or where special localised environments are required within a laboratory, these may be provided by specially designed units.

5.11.5.5 Laboratory protective air enclosures

Depending upon the toxicity of the material being handled, these vary from simple canopy hoods which draw air over the work and vent it outside the building, to totally enclosed boxes fitted with rubber gloves for operation inside the cabinet. A microbiological safety cabinet is illustrated at Fig. 5.11.3.

5.11.6 Electrical installation

5.11.6.1 Types of supply

The type of supply and method of distribution of electrical services within the laboratory is influenced by the scale of work.

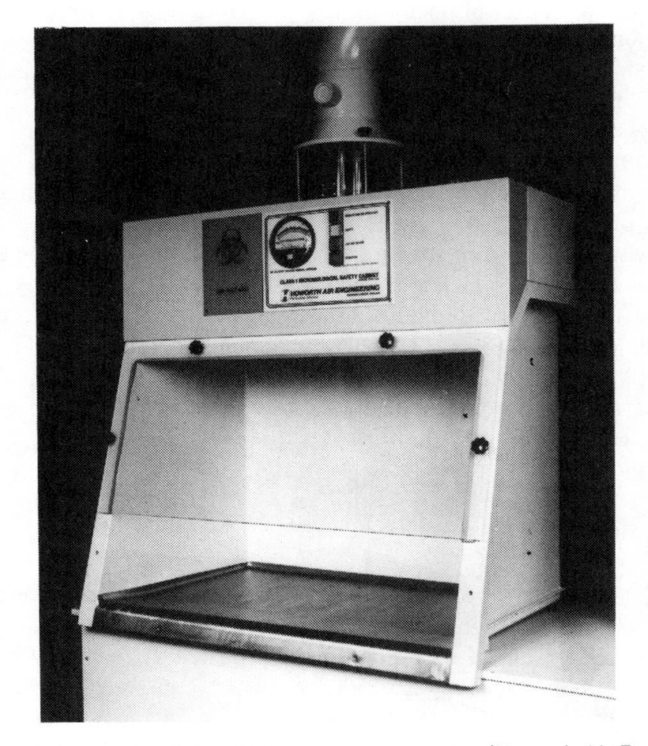

Fig. 5.11.3. *Microbiological Safety Cabinet* (Howarth Air Engineering Ltd)

Equipment

The standard 240 V single-phase supply can be conveniently converted to provide the following forms of supply within the laboratory:

(a) An electrical supply of up to 2 kW stabilised to 0·1%.
(b) A low-voltage supply for microscopes, galvanometers and balance lamps.

(c) A continuously variable voltage supply.
(d) A trickle charger d.c. supply.
(e) Vacuum from a mechanical pump and, in some cases from the same unit, compressed air.

Applied sciences are generally heavier users of electricity than the pure sciences, and more often need a 415 V supply.

5.11.6.2 Standby supply
Full standby facilities are not normally needed but a local generator to cut in when the mains fail may be provided in cases where experiments are left operating overnight which would be dangerous if a failure in the supply occured. The local authority may require independent or emergency lighting circuits in laboratories if they include fire-escape routes in open-plan layouts. Obviating failure is also important in spaces relying solely on artificial light. A proportion of the lighting to each space should be on a separate circuit from the remainder, there being less chance of simultaneous failure of both circuits.

5.11.6.3 Voltage stability
The increased use of sensitive electrical equipment in the laboratory has meant that the stability of voltage is important.

This provision of a 'clean' supply becomes essential when the same building also contains heavy machines which are large users of current.

The need for electrical durability in a supply may also extend to the need for physical stability for sensitive electronic instruments. Although local anti-vibration mountings can be used, vibration problems can also be reduced by careful planning, e.g. ensuring that laboratories housing sensitive work are not adjacent to machine laboratories, workshops or lift-shafts.

5.11.7 Security

Access to laboratories should always be controlled and where necessary authorisation permits issued. High risk laboratories, whether for health hazards or to restrict unauthorised entry, may require sophisticated alarm monitoring systems. Such systems are provided by specialist manufacturers and it is important that advice is sought to determine the levels of security required in each laboratory. Advice should also be sought from the Crime Prevention Officer of the Police Department and the responsible Fire Officer of the Fire Brigade.

5.11.8 References

5.11.8.1 References in text
(1) Papers of the Laboratories Investigation Unit, Department of Education and Science.

5.11.8.2 Bibliography

Code of Practice for the Prevention of Infection in Clinical Laboratories and Post-mortem Rooms. (Department of Health and Social Security) (HMSO)

EVERETT, K. and HUGHES, D. 'A Guide to Laboratory Design' (Butterworth)

Health Building Note no 15: Pathology Department (DHSS) (HMSO).

HUGHES, D. 'A Literature Survey and Design Study of Fume Cupboards and Fume Dispersal Systems.' Occupational Hygiene Monograph no. 4. (Science Review Ltd.)

WHITE, P. A. F. 'Protective Air Enclosures in Health Buildings' (MacMillan)

'Safety in Science Laboratories' (Safety Series no. 2) (DES) (HMSO)

'Threshold Limit Values' (Environmental Hygiene Series Guidance Note EH/15). (Health and Safety Executive). (HMSO)

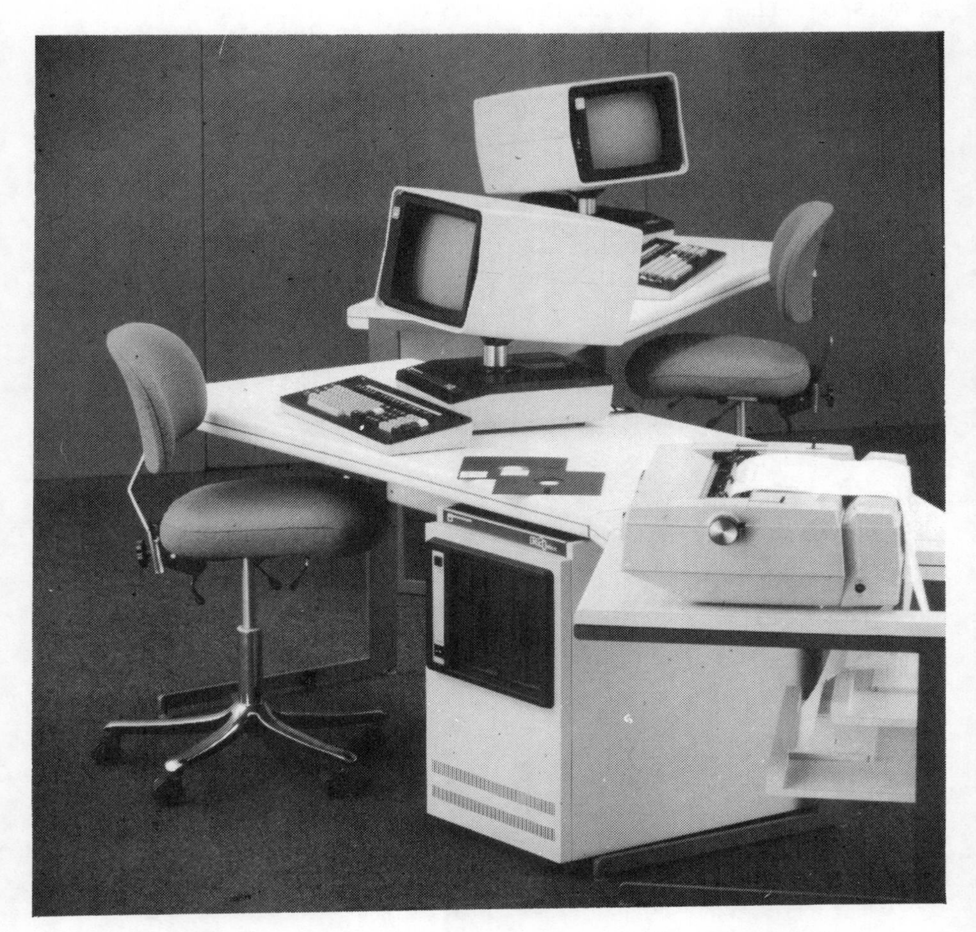

A personal computer terminal (International Computers Limited)

Chapter 5.12

Computer centres

J. K. Phillips, C.Eng., M.I.E.E.
Ove Arup & Partners

5.12.1 Introduction

A computer centre must house three categories of equipment and facilities:

(a) The computer itself:
Input and Output units, central processor, memory, control unit;
(b) Back-up facilities:
data storage, data handling, reception, administration, servicing;
(c) Ancillary Plant:
environmental plant, electrical supply equipment, fire alarm and suppression equipment.

5.12.2 Structural considerations

5.12.2.1 Accommodation

Accommodation for a small computer installation may be a single room little different from many modestly appointed offices. For the large installation it may be necessary to provide separate accommodation for each of the three categories with different environmental standards. Typically a separate room will be provided for the computer itself and its peripheral equipment, e.g. tape and disc drives, readers and printers. This room should be free from vibration, excessive noise, magnetic influence and direct sunlight. However, total lack of visual contact with the outside world is very undesirable.

Vibration is often transmitted through the building structure and fabric, and services, from a source outside the room. Careful planning may be required to eliminate this problem. In an existing building remedial measures may be necessary on existing plant or in some cases its removal to a less sensitive location.

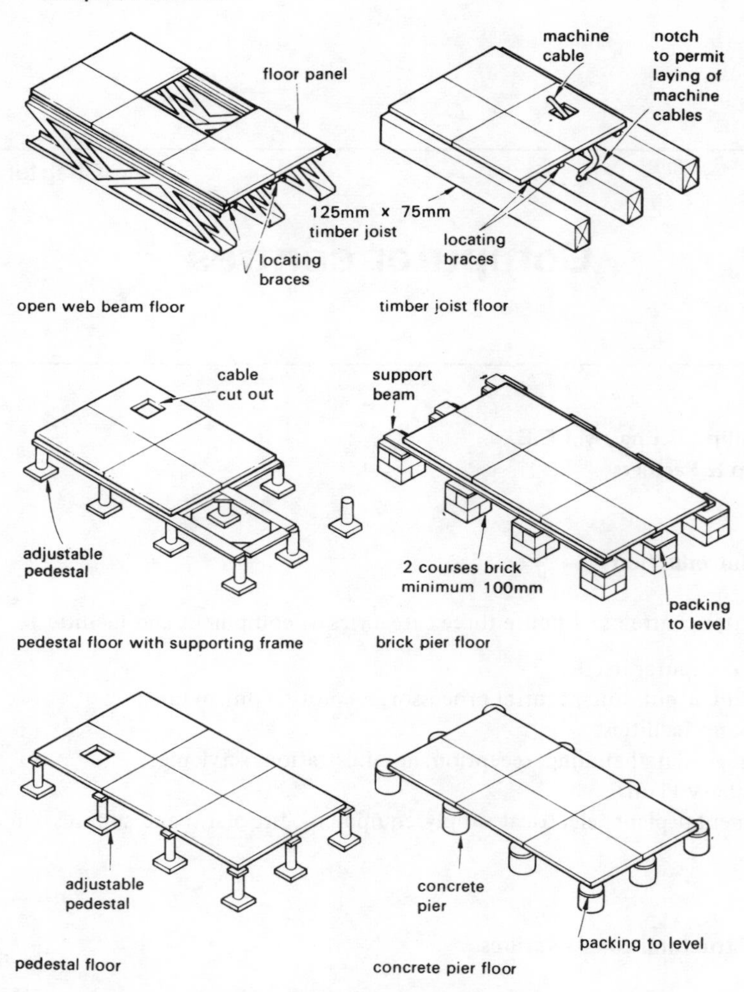

Fig. 5.12.1. *Types of suspended floors for Computer Rooms*

Much of the noise which is a problem in computer rooms is generated within the room by printers. This is best controlled at source by ensuring the machine is provided with an acoustic hood. Nevertheless, a large room having plain hard surfaces can produce an extremely unpleasant working environment. Sound absorbent materials should be adopted on ceilings and walls and where acoustic hoods cannot be used effectively, noisy machines should be screened.

5.12.2.2 Provision for services

The basic requirement will be for rooms of adequate size with features which allow facilities for the installation of all the required services and for their easy modification as the functional needs of the computer suite develop. The principal services to be considered will include general and emergency lighting, electrical power to the computer and other equipment, ventilation or air conditioning, cooling water to computers, communication links to remote locations, fire detection and alarms, fire suppression equipment and security equipment.

A suspended ceiling is usually employed to provide space for ventilation ducting, wiring for fire detection circuits and to allow the use of recessed luminaires. The space should not be used as a general route for other services as any removal of ceiling tiles for access inevitably produces a shower of dust and debris. Water and drainage pipes should not pass through the space unless absolutely unavoidable. If this is the case, special care should be taken to minimise the risk to equipment from leaks, especially during maintenance.

In all but very small installations, the advantages of the raised computer floor will prove invaluable. The void between this and the structural floor below offers, according to the type of support adopted, a degree of flexibility which will greatly simplify the installation of large quantities of data communication cables between equipment units, as well as power cables and cooling water pipes.

The floor void can also be used as a plenum for cooling air to the machines. Adjustable grilles set into floor panels can be located adjacent to the machines and by careful site adjustment very accurate cooling performances be achieved. The principal advantage of the raised floor however is the facility with which changes can be made to the locations of equipment and its connection and cooling arrangements as the needs of the installation develop.

Fig. 5.12.1 shows a variety of floor support methods. Continuous linear supports (lattice beams, joists) present difficulty when large quantities of cables have to be threaded through or removed from these supports. It follows that the method using point supports offers far greater flexibility; the optimum result is obtained by using a proprietary adjustable 'jack' system which, with well designed floor panels, can produce a perfectly flat and level floor, proof against leaks of chilled air from panel junctions which would lower the efficiency of the cooling plant. The depth of void required may vary from 150 mm to 900 mm.

5.12.3 Environmental conditions

5.12.3.1 Temperature and humidity control

The temperature and humidity of the computer room are very important and should be controlled to keep within the limits quoted by the equipment manufacturer. Typical limits quoted for optimum operating conditions are:

Temperature	21°C ± 2°C
Relative Humidity	50% ± 5%

Rapid changes in either quantity should be avoided, e.g. > 1°C or 5% RH in one hour.

If the computers and environmental plant are to be shut down over holiday periods auxiliary heating may be necessary to maintain reasonable temperatures.

5.12.3.2 Lighting

Lighting should be designed to give an even shadowless result using luminaires with good light control properties and features which limit dust collection and enable easy cleaning. Average illumination intensities at desk level should be 500 lux and the calculated glare index should not be greater than 19.

Emergency lighting should be installed to provide safe escape from the suite when normal lighting has failed. In addition it should illuminate those areas at which control of the computers and their power supplies is carried out, and of course fire alarm and control equipment.

5.12.4 Electrical supplies

5.12.4.1 Load details

The electrical supplies to a medium to large computer installation will be required to provide power to a number of categories of equipment and plant. These are listed below with typical electrical loads.

	kVA
(a) Central Processing Unit	up to 60
(b) Peripheral Equipment:	
card reader	2.2
tape (paper) reader	1
magnetic tape drive	2.6
magnetic disc drive	1.4
visual display unit	0·17
line printer	1·5–5·3
(c) Ancillary Equipment	variable
(d) General Lighting	0·02–0·03 kW/m^2
(e) Air conditioning/ventilation plant (f) Computer cooling plant	0·68 kW/m^2
(g) Fire alarms/plant alarms	–

5.12.4.2 Supply characteristics

Much computer equipment is made to operate on the UK standard voltage (415/240 V) and frequency (50 Hz). Some equipment however is rated to operate at quite different values (208 V, 60 Hz or 400 Hz) and it is generally accepted that it is the customer's responsibility to provide in his installation any voltage or frequency conversion plant that may be required. This may consist of rotary plant with associated switchgear and control panels requiring a separate plant room with a high standard of environment.

The computer itself has a limited tolerance to variations in the state of its electrical supply. Manufacturers quote limits of which the following figures are typical:

Voltage + 7% – 10%

Frequency ±0·5 Hz

Excursions outside the quoted limits can provoke computer errors so it is important to comply with maker's recommendations in the design of the installation.

5.12.4.3 'Clean' supplies

A 'clean' supply is established to power the central processing units and data signalling equipment. Other equipment and general purpose socket outlets will be fed from what may be referred to as 'dirty' supplies. Both categories of supply will usually be distributed from local switchboards at the perimeter of the computer room.

The 'clean' supply is fed to one of these local boards from a point as close to the LV supply source as possible; this is often from a separate Electricity Authority service. A corresponding 'clean' earth conductor is taken, as one core of the feeder or as a separate insulated single core cable, from the consumer's earth connection to an isolated earth busbar in the local switchboard. In addition earth continuity from the enclosing metal work of the local board and its non-isolated earth bar will be maintained via the armour or other earth continuity conductor of the feeder to the consumer's earth connection point. Power will then be taken from the local switchboard via fuses or circuit breakers to the items of computer equipment requiring a 'clean' supply via local link boxes situated in the floor void close to the equipment to be fed. The 'clean' earth conductor will in the latter case be taken through an insulated link in the box and its isolation from the common earth of the installation be maintained right up to the earth point of the computer circuits. Cables for these feeders and circuits may be m.i.m.s. or plastic insulated steel wire armoured. Both should be given a plastic oversheath. The metal sheaths or armour should be connected to the non isolated earth bar in the local board and the metal enclosures of the computer equipment.

5.12.4.4 Other supplies

Other equipment and plant within the computer room can be fed from switchboards and cables in a similar manner but without the need for a 'clean' earth. Such supplies have been referred to as 'dirty' supplies and design of these would only be constrained by normal good engineering practice for the type of equipment involved.

All power supplies in the computer room should be capable of instant isolation in an emergency. Feeders to local switchboards should be connected to the bus bars via contactors which can be open circuited from any one of a number of 'emergency power off' (EPO) push buttons located conveniently around the computer room. Re-energisation of the circuits should only be possible with the use of a key carried by authorised staff. Fig. 5.12.2 shows schematically the power distribution arrangement proposed.

Power cables should be kept to predetermined channels. Where a raised floor is used they should be located at the perimeter of the room, turning at right angles towards the point of connection to the equipment. They should not pass directly under equipment and should be kept remote from the expected routing of all data communication cables.

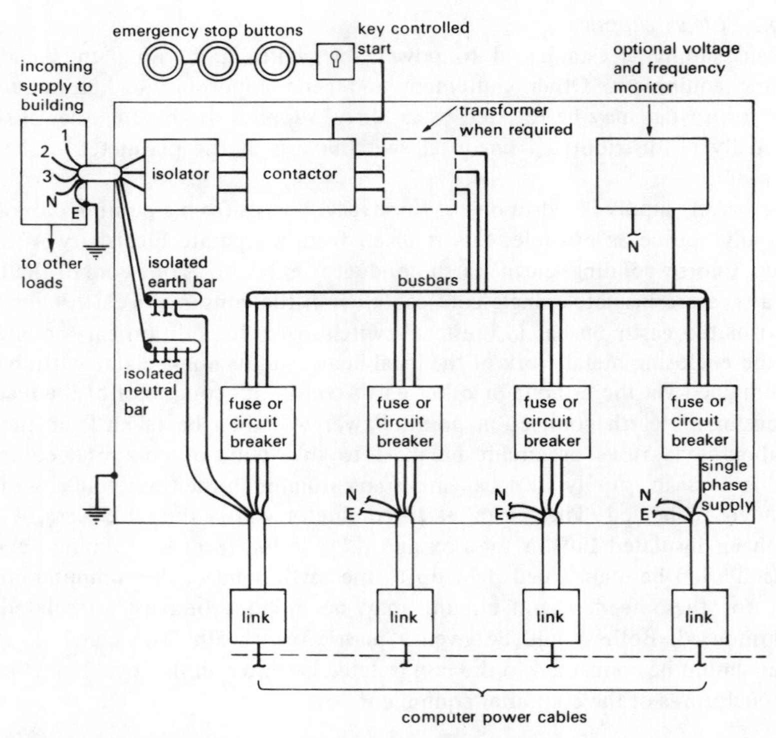

Fig. 5.12.2. *Typical Computer Power Distribution Arrangement*

5.12.4.5 Conversion equipment:

At the outset of design, consideration should be given to the possible need for ancillary plant to provide for conversion of the supply from the Electricity Authority, so that it is suitable for computer equipment requiring supplies with non-standard characteristics, and 'buffer' action to protect the computer equipment from transient or longer term variations in the voltage and frequency of the electricity supply. This can be provided by rotary or static plant which has the ability to ride through serious disturbances in supply conditions or even complete loss of supply for up to say 1 second. Ideally this plant should be placed in a separate room with good environmental standards and dust inhibiting finishes. Extract ventilation may be required to remove the heat given off by this plant.

5.12.4.6 Standby supplies

It is also necessary to consider protection of the equipment against complete loss of electricity supply, for periods lasting minutes, hours or even days. This function can be provided by a maintained battery system, possibly an Uninterrupted Power Supply (UPS – see section 2.2.2.5), an engine driven alternator or both.

A typical battery system consists of a storage battery, with sufficient capacity to supply the computer equipment for a period of up to say 15 minutes and static control gear and switchgear which will keep the battery in a fully charged condition when not in use, invert its d.c. output to a closely controlled a.c. output of required voltage and frequency when incoming mains supply fails, and automatically switch from passive to active mode and back, without unacceptable fluctuation of supply to the computer, as the condition of the normal supply dictates. A standby engine driven alternator will be required if longer periods of normal supply outage are to be covered. This can stand on its own if short breaks of supply can be accepted while the plant is started and connected – either automatically (15 secs) or manually (time dependent on availability of man power, etc.) If a continuously available supply is the minimum requirement then a UPS system supplemented by a standby alternator set, preferably fully automatic in operation, should be installed. Care is required in the location and design of the enclosure for the standby set. Major factors to be considered include:

(a) need to minimise the length of the electrical power connection;
(b) space for fuel oil storage (day tank and main storage tank); facilities for delivery of oil to the main tank.
(c) adequate access for major overhaul on site and/or for removal of the complete unit;
(d) need for large quantity of air for combustion and cooling;
(e) need for suitable measures to limit the transmission of noise, vibration and possibly heat to surrounding areas;
(f) suitable means for automatic fire detection and fire fighting.

5.12.4.7 Environmental plant supplies

In a medium to large installation the control required of temperature and humidity in the computer room will probably imply the use of a central air conditioning plant. Large computers with a high heat output may be directly cooled with chilled water and this could be supplied from the air conditioning chiller. Loss of either direct or indirect cooling can quickly result in shutdown of the computer with loss of the programme being run. This may represent a considerable financial loss. It follows therefore, that environmental cooling plant for an important installation must also operate with a high degree of reliability. To meet this need it is usual to install sufficient standby mechanical plant which on failure of running plant, will automatically take over the lost function. The changeover must take place quickly enough to avoid any threat to computer operation.

The electrical installation for the mechanical plant must therefore also be duplicated and the sensing, control and alarm circuitry be arranged to detect the loss of function, make the changeover smoothly and quickly, and give an adequate alarm and indication to the computer staff of what has taken place.

Clearly the provision of expensive standby plant is of dubious value if it cannot be given proving test runs whilst on standby status. For full reliability then the power source, cables and motor control centres must have sufficient capacity to allow this testing to be done without constraint. The most serious aspect of this operation will certainly be the starting up of the standby chiller with full standing load on the duty plant. This of course assumes that the mechanical characteristics of the chillers and chilled water circuits make it a practicable operation. As a minimum requirement it must be possible to make a manual changeover of selected plant to enable sharing of running hours or shut down for maintenance purposes.

5.12.5 Security

5.12.5.1 Intruder security

The security of computer installations is vital if risk of sabotage to equipment or unauthorised access to stored data are to be controlled. It is usual for all access doors to important areas to be monitored through detection circuits and access from outside to be gained only with the use of a coded magnetic identity card which has to be inserted into a checking head connected to a micro-processor. This determines whether access can be permitted and if so releases the door lock electrically. Closed circuit television (CCTV) may also be thought necessary in addition.

5.12.5.2 Fire precautions

Fire detection and alarm equipment should be installed to cover all the risk areas including floor and ceiling voids. A large suite needs to be zoned carefully. The computer room is usually provided with a gas flooding system (CO_2 or Halogen) to extinguish fire and this is arranged to operate automatically when the suite is not occupied. When in occupation manual control is adopted. Smoke detectors and manual break glass push buttons actuate the alarm sounders and initiate a visual indication at a control panel located at an appropriate position in the suite. Ventilation plant is often automatically shut down on operation of the sounders. Facilities are then provided for the attending fire officers to restart selected ventilation plant from the alarm control panel location.

5.12.6 References

5.12.6.1 British Standards (See also Appendix 6.2)

The following Codes of Practice are of interest:

BS 5266 Part 1: Emergency lighting of Premises

BS 5839 Part 1: Installation and servicing of fire detection and alarm systems in buildings

BS 6266 Fire Protection of electronic data processing installations

5.12.6.2 Bibliography

CIBS (formerly IES) Code for Interior Lighting
Computer Environments for the Future (Ove Arup and Partners)
Electric Power Plant International (ERA Technology Ltd)
Recommendations for the Protection of Computer Installations against Fire (Fire Offices Committee)
Services for Computer Suites, Bibliography (BSRIA LB41/80)

BP
PER LITRE
PER GALLON
CASH SALES ONLY
BP self serve
Sealand
FREE

Chapter 5.13

Commercial garages

Robert M. Bennett, Dip.E.E., C.Eng., M.I.E.E., M.C.I.B.S.
Electrical Associate, Donald Smith, Seymour and Rooley

5.13.1 General

5.13.1.1 Introduction

All commercial garages and service stations, whether separate premises or forming part of the service area of a larger commercial or industrial building, need special attention due to the inherent dangers posed by the existence of a flammable atmosphere. Hence premises of this type are subject not only to the relevant parts of the Health and Safety at Work etc Act and the Factory Acts but also to specific regulatory control. It is essential that the electrical installation is correctly designed and installed and that it is also regularly maintained in a satisfactory condition. The installation must be tested and inspected annually by a competent person acceptable to the licensing authority.

5.13.1.2 Licensing conditions

The Petroleum (Consolidation) Act 1928, requires authorities to make conditions for licensing premises used for storing petroleum spirit. The licensing conditions include exacting requirements for the electrical installation in the fuel storage and dispensing areas to avoid the danger of igniting petroleum spirit. Useful guidance is available in the Home Office publication "Model Code of Principles of Construction and Licensing Conditions". The proposed scheme should always be discussed with the local licensing authority before commencing work. The model code is intended as a guide to these authorities and some have produced their own code based on the Home Office Model Code.

The Authorities responsible for different types of premises are listed in Table 5.13.1.

Commercial garages are subject to the Electricity (Factories Act) Special Regulations 1908 and 1944. These regulations are incorporated in a booklet entitled

Table 5.13.1 *Licensing Authorities for Garage Safety Requirements*

Authority	Premises
H.M. Factory Inspectorate	Repair Workshops
Local Authority	Offices, shops and showrooms
Petroleum Licensing (e.g. County/Metropolitan authorities in England, and Regional authorities in Scotland).	Fuel dispensing and storage

"Memorandum on the Electricity Regulations" issued by the Electrical Inspectorate of the Health and Safety Executive, guidance on the application of the regulations and exemptions also being given. The Highly Flammable liquids and Liquefied Petroleum Gases Regulations (1972) (part of the Factories Act) also apply to garages and mainly concern the solvents used in painting.

The Health and Safety at Work Act 1974 applies to all types of garages, as well as those parts of the premises not covered by the Factories Act, such as offices, showrooms, shop and forecourt service areas where the electrical installation should meet the requirements of the Electricity Regulations.

5.13.1.3 Classification of areas

Areas in which flammable atmospheres occur are designated:

Zone 0 – An area where any flammable or explosive substance is continuously present in concentration within the lower and upper limits of flammability.
Zone 1 – An area within which any flammable or explosive substance is processed, handled or stored and where, during normal operations, an explosive or ignitable concentration is likely to occur in sufficient quantity to produce a hazard.
Zone 2 – An area within which any flammable or explosive substance, although processed or stored, is so well under conditions of control that the production or release of an explosive or ignitable concentration in sufficient quantity to constitute a hazard, is only likely under abnormal conditions.

Certain garage areas are classed as Zone 1 or Zone 2, depending on the quantities of flammable gas or vapour being produced and the ventilation facilities afforded. If there are any doubts regarding the adequacy of ventilation then it is safer to treat the area as Zone 1 rather than Zone 2. Zone 0 areas are not normally present in commercial garages.

5.13.1.4 Fuel dispensing areas

The areas near fuel pumps and tank vent discharge pipes are flammable zones and special precautions are required.

The Zone 1 areas are:

(a) Within 1·5 m of the vent discharge
(b) Inside the pump enclosure

(c) Up to 230 mm above forecourt ground level and within 4·25 m of any pump or tank opening.
(d) Up to 230 mm above the floor level of any kiosk having an opening within 4·25 m of any pump or tank opening.

The Zone 2 areas are:

(a) Up to 1.25 m above forecourt ground level at the pumps or the height of the pump enclosure, whichever is the greater, and then reducing uniformly to the forecourt ground level at 4·25 m from any pump or storage tank opening.
(b) The interior of any kiosk having an opening within a Zone 2 area.

5.13.2 Lighting, heating and ventilation

5.13.2.1 Forecourt lighting

Lighting of forecourt areas should be designed to give a minimum illuminance of 100 lux measured at forecourt level except for self-service petrol stations where the measuring level is at the top of each pump. However, a higher level of illuminance, commonly 300 lux, is usually required by the garage owner or petrol company to attract business. This can be achieved by the use of floodlight fittings on walls or on poles, by street lighting columns or by fluorescent or high pressure discharge lamp luminaires under a canopy. Tungsten luminaires are not usually employed due to their poor lumen efficacy compared to the alternative lamp sources. Where luminaires are required beneath a canopy over the fuel pumps, they should be mounted outside the flammable zones to avoid the need to be explosion protected. The fittings should also be weather protected to suit their mounting position.

5.13.2.2 Other lighting

Luminaires installed on the top of a pump housing must conform to the requirements for Zone 2. The Home Office Model Code also requires that the luminaires in a kiosk shall be to Zone 2 standards but fittings of an enclosed design with gaskets to prevent the entry of petrol vapour are acceptable. Lighting to other areas of garage premises must also have artificial illumination in order to comply with the Factories Act and Offices, Shops and Railways Premises Act. It is generally accepted that the illuminance levels recommended for various areas and usage listed in the CIBS (formerly IES) Code for Interior Lighting are appropriate. Extracts from this code are given in Table 5.13.2:

The illuminance levels are referred to the working plane which is typically approximately 1 metre above floor level, except for garage pit lighting which is measured at approximately 250 mm above the garage floor level and the car park, where ground level is the reference plane.

Table 5.13.2 *Recommended Illuminance Levels (Lux)*

Area	General Lighting	Supplementary Lighting
Repair Shop	300	Handlamps
Lubricating Bay	300	Handlamps or vehicle lift lights
Vehicle Wash	300	Handlamps or vehicle lift lights
Body Shop	500	Handlamps
Paint Shops	750/1000	
Stores	150	
Pits	300	
Showroom	500	
Offices	500	Desk Lamps
Car Park	50	(CIBS)

5.13.2.3 Repair shop areas

Body repair and point shop areas require particular planning. In many cases the body repair department can be a subdivision of the workshop but where the anticipated turnover is high it should be planned as a separate unit. To conform with the Factories Act, any space where cellulose solutions are stored or used should be fire-separated from other parts of the building. In paint shops the luminaires and wiring system up to the maximum spraying level should be explosion protected. Luminaires mounted at least two metres above the maximum spraying level may be of the ordinary totally enclosed industrial type, subject to confirmation from the local HSE inspector.

5.13.2.4 Spray booths

Purpose made spray booths have safety and performance benefits and make efficient use of the lighting, heating and ventilation systems. The spraying and drying chambers are flammable zones and hence it is preferable to avoid electrical apparatus within these. The lighting may be provided by means of standard non-certified luminaires above or behind sealed glazed panels. Mechanical ventilation (to give at least sixty air changes per hour in the spray booth) should use centrifugal fans with the motor outside the casing and a gas tight seal on the motor shaft where it enters the casing. Mechanical ventilation should also be used to keep the air clean during storing. Apart from the required illuminance in the body repair and paint shop, particular attention should be paid to colour temperature of the lamps.

5.13.2.5 Kiosk heating

Any heating requirements within forecourt kiosks must be by means of liquid filled radiators with flameproof thermostat units installed not less than 305 mm from the floor level.

5.13.3 Electrical installation

The complete electrical installation must be in accordance with the 15th Edition of the I.E.E. Wiring Regulations and, for Zones 1 and 2, the additional recommendations of BSCP 1003 must be strictly observed.

5.13.3.1 Service intake

The service intake and main switchgear should, whenever possible, be mounted in a "safe" area such as inside the main garage building. The main switchgear would typically comprise industrial pattern switch-fuses and incoming main isolator mounted above and below a busbar chamber. Where the earth loop impendance at the supply intake is too high for the supply authority's or consumer's main fuses to operate in the event of an earth fault, the main isolator or swith-fuse should be replaced by a residual current circuit breaker.

The prospective fault level at the intake should be obtained from the Electricity Authority in order to select adequately fault rated circuit breakers for incoming or outgoing supplies. Where fuses are employed they should be of the HRC (high rupturing capacity) type to BS 88 (1975).

5.13.3.2 Arrangement of circuits

Supplies to forecourt lighting and signs should be served from a separate distribution board to that feeding the pumps and kiosk heating and lighting. The Home Office Model Code (now administered by the HSE) requires the supply to the pumps and their integral lighting to be under a red master switch control, this switch being inaccessible to the public but readily visible with a label "Petroleum spirit pumps, switch off here". Each pump must be connected to a separate final circuit to control both the motor and the integral lighting, the circuit being controlled and protected by a suitably rated fuse or circuit breaker (Fig. 5.13.1). Each pump must also be provided with a double-pole isolating switch arranged to disconnect all circuit conductors.

5.13.3.3 Pump circuits

Blender pumps, with two motors, must be connected to a separate final circuit to protect both the motors and the integral lighting. The two motors and the integral lighting of a dual delivery pump must be connected to three separate final circuits, each protected by a suitably rated fuse or circuit breaker. An isolator switch or double-pole circuit breaker should be provided for each circuit and the three switches must be grouped together. All isolating switches or circuit breakers for control of the pumps and integral lighting must be in one central position accessible to the pump operator. These switches must be double-pole and capable of isolating all conductors to ensure safe changing of lamps. (Fig. 5.13.2).

5.13.3.4 Zone 1 areas

Wiring in the flammable zone areas should conform to BS 5345. Wiring in Zone 1 areas may be carried out in any of the following but, whichever system is used, the terminations must be made with approved flameproof boxes or cable glands:–

(a) Armoured p.v.c. insulated cables.
(b) Mineral insulated, metal sheathed cables (m.i.m.s) (with flameproof glands) and, if laid underground, with an overall extruded p.v.c. sheath.
(c) Single or multicore insulated cables enclosed in solid-drawn, heavy gauge screwed conduit (protected against corrosion), all conduit boxes or inspection fittings being of the flameproof type.

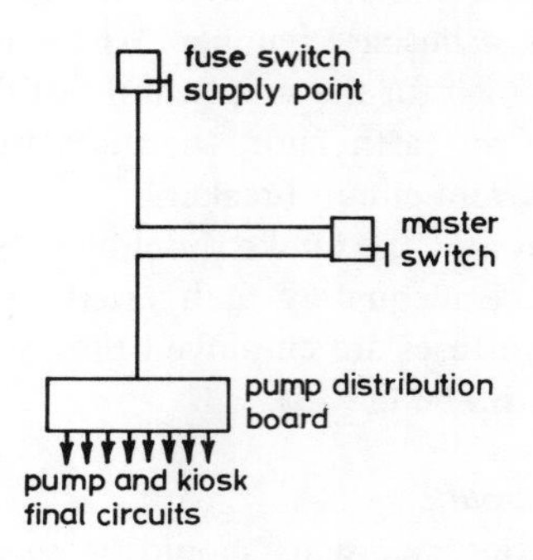

Fig. 5.13.1. *Distribution arrangement for petrol pumps*

5.13.3.5 Zone 2 areas

For Zone 2 areas, where wiring is connected to apparatus which sparks in normal operation, the systems used must be as required for Zone 1. If the apparatus does not normally spark, the following systems may be used provided that seals and barrier boxes are provided at all points where the conduit enters or leaves a safe area:–

(a) Mineral insulated metal sheathed cables with, if laid underground, an overall extruded p.v.c. sheath.
(b) Single or multicore insulated cables enclosed in heavy gauge screwed welded conduit protected against corrosion.

Electrical wiring in a safe area can be of any industrial pattern conforming to the IEE Regulations. It is normal practice to use p.v.c. insulated cables enclosed within steel or high-impact resistant p.v.c. conduits/trunking or alternatively, mineral insulated copper sheathed cables fixed to the surface. PVC insulated and sheathed cables clipped to the surface are not advisable due to their vulnerability to damage, unless further physical protection is given. In areas where there is an occasional risk of petrol spillage, or of other flammable liquids, the wiring should be installed at a minimum of one metre above floor level. Where fuel contamination may occur, oil resistant cable systems should be used.

5.13.3.6 Socket outlets

Socket outlets for use with portable equipment should preferably be used on a 110 V, centre tapped to earth, system and conform to BS 4343 for safety reasons. Similar sockets with interlocked plugs are suitable for welding sets. Socket outlets in wet areas, such as car wash area, should be fed by circuits protected by residual current circuit breakers with a trip setting of 30 mA designed to trip within 40 milliseconds. Socket outlets in entirely safe areas and for use with 240 V equipment can be to BS 1363, BS 4343 or BS 196. No socket outlets are permitted in the kiosk and any apparatus installed must be permanently wired and controlled by a double-pole switch.

With a PME supply from the Electricity Authority, bonding of all earthed metalwork on the premises to the authority's combined neutral and earth terminal will be required.

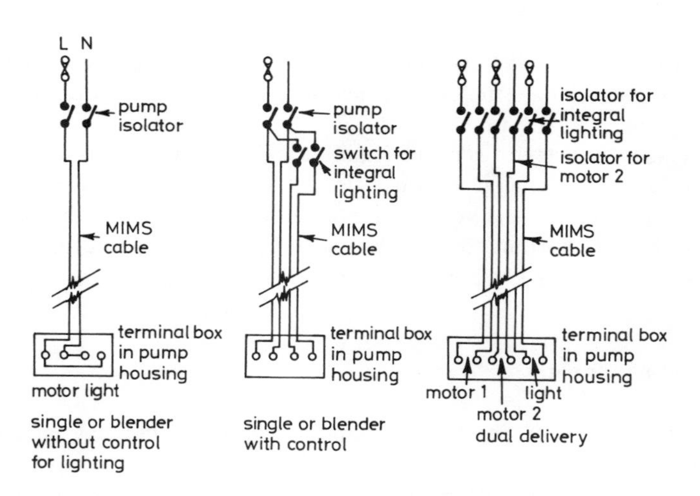

Fig. 5.13.2. *Final circuit arrangements for petrol pumps*

The Electricity Authority will be able to give detailed guidance in this respect. Where a direct earth connection cannot be obtained earth leakage circuit breakers should be employed. Conduit should preferably not be used for earth continuity – a separate conductor should be provided.

5.13.4 Miscellaneous equipment

The equipment installed in workshops, lubrication bays, washing areas etc., follows normal industrial practice and the application methods will be also under the directive of the Health and Safety Executive and other standard regulations, as referred to in this Chapter. Special precautions are only necessary where a hazardous environment exists or may exist. Where vehicle lifts are required, they should be designed in accordance with BS AU 161 (1973).

5.13.5 Self-service stations

There are a number of other important considerations which only apply to attended and unattended self-service stations. When the control of the pumps is carried out by an attendant from a control position an additional isolating switch must be provided at that point to isolate the supply to all the pumps and integral lighting. Any recording and signalling circuits which are installed between the pumps and the control point need not be controlled by the individual isolating switch for each pump provided that these are connected on extra low voltage circuits with intrinsically safe apparatus.

If the station is under the control of one attendant, a loudspeaker system must be provided to enable the attendant to instruct a customer without having to leave the control point.

In unattended self-service stations readily accessible and well marked provision must be made for the emergency operation of the master switch controlling the supply to all the pumps. In these cases, the master switch should be a contactor, operated by remote buttons located on the forecourt. To restore the supply, the contactor should be closed by a button accessible only to an authorised person.

5.13.6 Enclosed car parks

A satisfactory method of providing parking space, where building land is costly, is by multi-storey or underground car parks. For these, adequate services must be provided and this section outlines the basic requirements for heating, ventilating and lighting. Car parks can be broadly divided into two groups, public, operated on a period payment basis, and private, attached to or situated below office blocks, flats and hotels for the use of staff, tenants and visitors. The provision of a private garage or car park is often a condition of planning permission for a new building and is consequently very important. The engineering services required by public and private units, however, are practically identical and the main distinctions in the text are between multi-storey and underground car parks.

5.13.6.1 Ventilation

Ventilation of enclosed car parks is essential to reduce the risk of fire or explosion from petrol fumes and to prevent injury to health from a concentration of exhaust fumes. Natural ventilation should be provided if possible, and where this is sufficient, mechanical ventilation will not be required. The minimum free area of ventilating openings required is 2·5% of the garage floor area or sufficient for six air changes per hour, whichever is the greater. In underground car parks, and many enclosed multi-storey car parks, mechanical ventilation should always be provided. Although six air changes per hour is normally sufficient to obviate the risks of fire or explosion, where the amount of carbon monoxide is likely to be high, such as at entrances and exits, the ventilation rate should be increased. (Fig. 5.13.3)

For emergency and standby purposes it is necessary to duplicate the mechanical ventilation plant which should be arranged so that each plant works independently of the other. Each plant should remain under separate control but should be arranged so that in the event of failure of the other it will operate. This is usually achieved by providing automatic changeover switches. When considering standby facilities, a secondary source of electricity supply must be provided so that the ventilation system can operate during a mains failure. The changeover from mains to emergency supply should ideally be under automatic control. If this is not so, a competent person must be in constant attendance to supervise the plant. Where mechanical ventilation is used, even though it may not be strictly necessary, natural

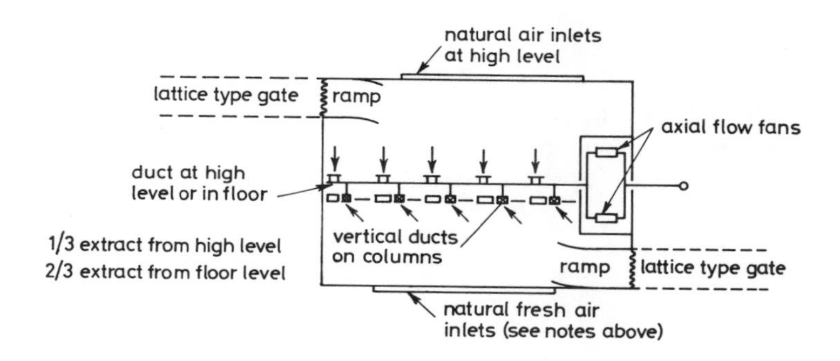

Fig. 5.13.3. *General ventilation arrangements in enclosed car parks*

ventilation provides an acceptable standby as long as it can meet the conditions previously outlined. The local licensing authority and/or other appropriate bodies must be consulted for local rules and regulations affecting ventilation, safety precautions and standby equipment for such premises.

5.13.6.2 Heating

It is neither practical nor desirable to heat open parking areas and even in a closed garage, heating is usually regarded as an unnecessary expense. However, if heating equipment is used, it should be of a type safe to use in the presence of flammable vapour. If toilet or office accommodation is included, it can be heated by suitable electric heaters. It may be considered desirable to heat the ramp surfaces to prevent the formation of ice and to melt snow. This is usually done by embedded electric heating cables.

5.13.6.3 Lighting

The lighting should be of a sufficiently high standard to enable motorists to manoeuvre without using headlamps. The illuminance should be graded to avoid excessive brightness differences when leaving by day or night. Suitable levels would be not less than 50 lux in parking areas, and 100 lux to 200 lux in access ways. Particularly in the case of underground car parks, a transitional zone may be needed during daylight hours and levels of 2000 lux or more in the entrance and exit areas will reduce contrast between the daylight and interior light. Lighting fittings should be positioned between rather than in the centre of car spaces. Sufficient light is obtained by providing about 50 W per car space. (Fig. 5.13.4) Regulations require that all electrical apparatus must be mounted not less than 1.25 m above floor level unless the equipment is approved as either totally enclosed or flameproof. The arrangement and layout of the fittings should form part of the traffic direction system and should emphasise the main routes and turnoffs. Ramps should always be well lit. The fittings themselves should be fluorescent tubes in surface-mounted vapour-proof fittings. The lamps should be controlled in groups by robust totally-enclosed switches which are in turn wired from a number of distribution boards. Emergency lighting should be provided for both motorists and pedestrians especially on stairways. This standby lighting can be provided by individual self-contained lights, supplied from an independent central source, or by non-electric self-luminous sources. An adequate number of well designed and lit signs should be so arranged as to indicate the entry and exit points.

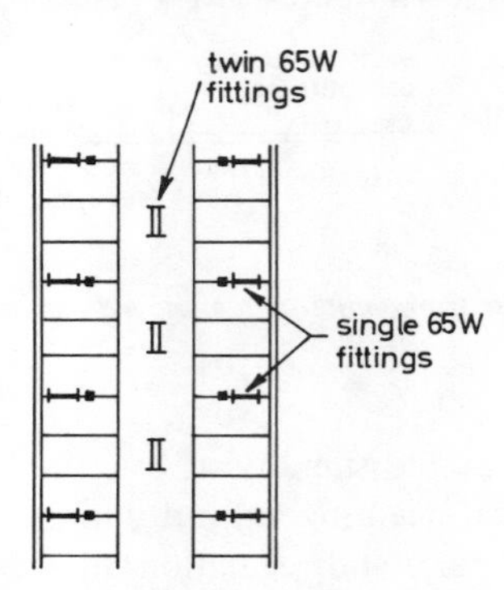

Fig. 5.13.4. *Lighting arrangements in enclosed car parks*

5.13.6.4 Electrical installation

The electrical installation needs to supply power for ventilating fans, pumps, lighting, lifts, barriers and space heating. In London, the relevant regulations make the following conditions:

(a) Electrical equipment, including electric lamps, if installed below the general garage floor level or in other hazardous positions, should be certified flameproof for Group II gases.

(b) Electrical equipment including electric lamps, if installed at garage floor level or within 1.25 m above floor level, should be certified flameproof except in car parks

or garages with natural ventilation, in which case the equipment may be of the totally-enclosed type
(c) Electrical equipment, including electric lamps, installed at a height of 1.25 m or more above floor level in car parks or garages without sufficient openings for natural ventilation should be either flameproof or totally-enclosed
(d) All electrical equipment should be adequately protected from mechanical damage
(e) Electrical equipment installed within the air stream of the extract ventilating system should be certified flameproof for Group II gases

The installation work should follow normal good practice and comply with the IEE Regulations and the various statutory requirements. The wiring should be run in galvanised conduit fixed to the surface of walls and soffits or in accordance with any other specification which meets the IEE and local regulations.

5.13.6.5 Fire precautions
Fire detection equipment should be installed with an alarm arranged to be operated automatically or manually. The alarm must be audible in all parts of the building.

In underground car parks, an automatic sprinkler system should be installed set to operate typically at 70°C, as detailed by the Fire Offices Committee (FOC) Rules. Although the use of such systems is advisable in multi-storey car parks also, it is not compulsory.

5.13.7 References

5.13.7.1 Legislation (see also Appendix 6.1)
Electricity (Factories Act) Special Regulations 1908 and 1944
Factories Act 1961
Health and Safety at Work, etc Act 1974
Highly Flammable Liquids and Liquefied Petroleum Gases Regulations 1972
Petroleum (Consolidation) Act 1928

5.13.7.2 British Standards (See also Appendix 6.2)
BS 4343 refers to industrial plugs and sockets, BS 4683, BS 5345 and BS 5501 and BS CP 1003 to electrical apparatus used in explosive atmospheres, BS 5266 to emergency lighting, BS 5839 to fire detection and alarm systems, and BS and BS 6207 to m.i.c.s cables. BS AU 161 refers to vehicle lifts.

5.13.7.3 Bibliography
CIBS (formerly IES) Code for Interior Lighting
Electrical Equipment Certification Guide (BASEEFA)
Regulations for Electrical Installations (Institution of Electrical Engineers)
Model Code of Principles of Construction and Licensing Conditions. (HSE)
K. OLDHAM SMITH: Safe Installations in Petrol Stations and Garages (The Electrical Contractor, August 1981).

Major TV production studio (BBC)

Chapter 5.14

Studios

A. D. P. Colmer, F.I.Elec.I.E.
Head of Power Distribution Section, BBC Studio Capital Projects Department

5.14.1 Introduction

The primary function of a studio is to accommodate artistic productions of one sort or another and the planning engineer's main objective must be to provide technicians, artists and directors with all the technical facilities they require to produce quality programmes with maximum efficiency and minimum distraction from the task in hand. The following recommendations relate generally to a multi-studio television production centre although many of the principles would need to be considered for the less complex requirements of individual radio, film or recording studios.

5.14.2 Facilities required

The scale of facilities provided will be determined by the volume and type of output envisaged. Studios may be required for drama, light entertainment (with or without audience) news, current affairs, sports and presentation, while the contribution of film, live or recorded programmes, outside broadcasts and imported tape or film material will influence the choice of technical facilities. A 600 m^2 studio with five or six cameras may be required for opera, ballet, main drama and light entertainment while at the other end of the scale a single camera presentation studio of 30 m^2 will suffice for announcements, trails and programme linking. Apart from the studios themselves, accommodation will be required for the associated production and technical facilities, e.g.

(a) Lighting, sound and vision control rooms.
(b) Artists areas (make-up, wardrobe and dressing rooms).
(c) Scenery construction and storage.

(d) Central Technical Area including telecine and video tape recording.
(e) Film facilities for dubbing and editing.
(f) Scenic and graphic design.
(g) Outside broadcast vehicles and garage accommodation.
(h) Offices, duty rooms, stores, PABX and maintenance areas.

5.14.3. Provision of services

5.14.3.1 TV production lighting

Modern studios employ several methods of positioning luminaires, the most popular being telescopic suspension from the ceiling or a grid or alternatively, by a number of barrels of convenient length, each designed to carry a complement of lamps. Both may be manually operated but for busy studios, the cost of remote controlled electric winching is offset by the time and labour saved. Final adjustment for height, tilt, focus and hard (focusable) or soft light function is carried out manually at the luminaire.

For major production studios computer based control systems are generally employed with up to 200 memories allowing complex lighting plots to be stored. Circuit selection and brightness level for each plot can then be recalled during the course of a production, although for News and Presentation studios simpler manual systems will generally prove to be adequate. Master control should be provided in the lighting control room together with auxiliary isolation on the studio floor.

Studio lighting sources can be divided broadly into hard and soft or diffused light usually provided in the ratio of 2:1 and supplemented with cyclorama and effects spotlights etc. Both dual purpose and dual wattage luminaires may be used. The level of illuminance required will depend upon the type of camera in use and the lens aperture considered appropriate dependent upon the depth of field required. With modern 25 mm tube colour cameras operated at f2·8 an illuminance of 800 lux should prove sufficient. A maximum lighting load of 500–600 W/m^2 should be allowed for major production studios based on the use of tungsten halogen sources.

Separate house lighting should be provided with control from the studio entrances and the lighting control room.

5.14.3.2 Lighting sources

While the more efficient fluorescent and High Intensity Discharge (HID) light sources find some favour in radio and film studios, their inadequate dimming characteristics, and the prolonged strike/restrike times of the latter, make them generally unsuitable for tv studios where tungsten halogen lamps are preferred. A similar preference exists in large music studios where the use of discharge lighting often brings complaints of reduced visual acuity from musicians. The rapid change of optical focus between conductor and well thumbed sheet music (often with poorly added annotation) can often be affected by discharge lamp flicker, which can also distort movement of the conductor's baton.

Where critical colour balancing is involved, particularly in telecine areas where a wide range of film having varying colour quality may be used, "Northlight" fluorescent tubes having a colour temperature of 6500 K should be installed to illuminate the monitor control area.

5.14.3.3 Emergency lighting

Secondary lighting should be installed in high risk areas and along all escape routes from the building. Although a non-maintained system may be satisfactory in many locations, those areas and escape routes frequented by audiences or other large numbers of people unfamiliar with the building geography will usually require maintained facilities.

5.14.3.4 Scenery hoists

While small studios usually have limited setting requirements, larger production studios will need electro/mechanical winching to enable large and complex sets to be rapidly positioned and changed.

Fig. 5.14.1. *TV Production Control Room* (BBC)

5.14.3.5 Studio control areas

Separate rooms are usually required for sound, lighting and vision control with or without an observation window to the studio. Dual lighting systems are provided so that normal lighting can be switched to the operational mode during production giving local illumination to controls and equipment and providing a better view of the studios and monitors. Power supplies are required for loudspeakers, monitors, disk reproducers and tape machines as well as control desks and consoles.

5.14.3.6 *Central technical area*

It is now common practice to locate all technical equipment associated with the studios in a central area. This will include telecine and video tape machines, camera control units, standards conversion, mixer electronics, pulse and test signal generators, together with switching and routing equipment and a master control position. This technique concentrates all equipment concerned with assembly of the station output in one area, reducing cable lengths to a minimum and simplifying signal routing and equalisation. Centralised control and monitoring also results in the most economic deployment of technical staff.

Fig. 5.14.2. *View above lighting grid showing mechanical hoists and control wiring* (BBC)

5.14.3.7 *Telecine and video tape areas*

These areas contain the equipment for the recording and transmission of programmes via magnetic tape or 8 mm, 16 mm and 35 mm film. Facilities for remote control and monitoring of the machines from the studio control areas should be provided. It should be possible to run machines singly for previewing and editing or in pairs when transmitting important programmes or producing feature films. They may also be required to run in groups of three or four when compiling a programme from a number of films or tapes.

5.14.3.8 Film editing, dubbing and review
Cutting rooms will be required for news and production film material with review theatres for rushes and general viewing. Full dubbing facilities for the addition of commentary, effects, dialogue and music will be justified if a considerable amount of film is used. Processing of film shot for production work is usually more economically undertaken in commercial laboratories, although for news contributions in-house facilities may be preferable.

5.14.3.9 Outside broadcast equipment
Mobile Control Rooms with up to six cameras and Mobile Video Tape recorders may be used extensively on location with output recorded locally or sent back to the studio centre by land line or radio link. Accommodation will be needed for garaging and servicing the vehicles at base.

5.14.4 Environmental control

Studios can pose difficult ventilation problems, particularly in television and film areas where a large amount of heat from production lighting needs to be extracted. Low velocity systems are preferred which minimise noise and possible movement of the cyclorama and luminaires. Temperature is normally controlled at 20–24°C with a diversity of 75% applied to the full production lighting load. Relative humidity control at 40–60% is recommended for film and video tape areas as well as music studios where changes in humidity can affect the pitch of musical instruments. A high degree of filtration is required in video tape areas where dust can affect quality. Critical noise rating curves should be observed in all transmission and recording areas which will require careful planning of duct routes, internal insulation, grill design and attenuation between plant and studios. In the Central Technical Area direct extract from equipment racks will help to reduce the air conditioning load.

5.14.5 Electrical installation

5.14.5.1 Specialised building requirements
Early agreement should be reached with the structural engineer and architect on the provision of specialised building requirements for the electrical installation and equipment. Switchrooms, battery, dimmer and transformer rooms will be required with interconnecting ducts and fairways, each with adequate access and space for future expansion. Separate ducts should also be planned for the routing of communication cables between the various areas with adequate segregation from power routes to minimise the possibility of electrical interference. Special plinths and floor reinforcement may be needed for heavy equipment and anti-vibration mountings together with acoustic treatment may be necessary where noise transference

may prove troublesome. The layout of studio equipment should be carefully planned so that the maximum wall area is available for acoustic treatment, and service ducts should be pugged after cable installation to maintain acoustic separation.

5.14.5.2 Power supplies

For a large studio complex a high voltage source will probably be required and early discussion with the Electricity Authority should emphasise the importance of maintaining continuity of supply. The Authority's method of control, zone protection and record of outages should be considered and often duplicated supplies from different parts of the network can be negotiated. Some merit exists in providing separate transformers for technical, production lighting and general service supplies which will avoid harmonics and heavy surges generated by dimmers and plant interfering with supplies to sensitive technical equipment. Suitable bus-coupling arrangements will then enable essential loads to be shared in the event of failure of one transformer or to meet the needs of routine servicing. Monitoring of supplies and remote control of important switchgear should be provided in the Central Technical Area.

Bulk automatic voltage regulators may be needed on feeders to areas containing voltage sensitive equipment although individual units can be installed locally for isolated requirements. Regulation may have to be provided on production lighting supplies where the voltage is likely to be unstable as a 5% voltage variation will result in a 17% change in light output with associated variation in illuminance and colour temperature. For larger studios phase balancing can be achieved by installing 415 V/240 V single phase output transformers on production lighting supplies, at the same time limiting the potential between adjacent lighting outlets to 240 V.

Duplicated services should be installed to all essential areas, suitably interlocked, with facilities for rapid changeover in the event of failure or when maintenance is required. Standby facilities, such as diesel-alternators, should be considered for first priority services to cover total supply failure. As a minimum these should allow sufficient power for the sound and vision requirements of a continuity studio so that announcements can continue, together with a telecine machine and video tape recorder to produce a single emergency programme.

5.14.5.3 Distribution

When planning the distribution network prime considerations are usually:—

(a) Security of supply.
(b) Rapid restoration after failure.
(c) Ease of expansion or alteration without interruption of other services.
(d) Total cost economics.

Discrimination between protective devices must be carefully planned so that localised faults do not interrupt costly productions or broadcasts. Fault levels in a large complex can be high and care should be taken to ensure adequate high breaking capacity back up, where low rupturing capacity protection is required for technical purposes.

All fuses, circuit breakers, isolators and control switches should be clearly identified so that their functions can be quickly recognised and rapid remedial action taken in the event of a fault. Where contactors are required, by-pass arrangements should be fitted to permit continuity of supply during maintenance or fault investigation.

Ample spare capacity on distribution panels and feeders can usually be justified as later interruption to supplies due to additions or alterations can be costly and difficult to arrange.

5.14.5.4 Noise and electrical interference

It is important that noise producing equipment is located outside sensitive areas, or noise eliminated at source. Where solid state switching is inappropriate, d.c. coils are preferable for contactors and relays, while fluorescent lighting fittings should be of rigid construction and mounting to avoid vibration at resonant frequencies. In radio studios and other high quality listening or transmission areas, chokes should be mounted remote from the fittings. Similarly, dimmers should be located in a separate room with controls only in the production areas. The routing of dimmer output cables should be planned to avoid close parallel runs with communication cables as the chopped waveform of thyristors can produce interference on low-level programme circuits. Flexible connections should be provided for conduit and trunking passing through resiliently mounted, or acoustic cavity building structures.

5.14.5.5 Signal lights

Signal lights or illuminated signs will be needed at entrances to all production areas, and duplicated within, indicating transmission or rehearsal mode inside the studios. Similar signal lights will be required for cueing artists and to replace the normal ringing tone of telephones.

5.14.5.6 Impulse clocks

Accurate timekeeping of all clocks throughout the complex is essential. A battery maintained system with duplicated crystal drive masters should be provided, with automatic correction via Greenwich Time Signal every 24 hours. Slave dials with seconds indication will be required in all technical areas although half-minute dials may suffice in less critical locations. As with dimmer circuits, clock pulses can cause interference to sensitive programme circuits, therefore the routing of all cables should be appropriately planned.

5.14.5.7 Earthing

A separate earthing system should be installed to which all technical equipment is connected. This system should be insulated from the mains earth and structure throughout the building and connected at one point only, preferably at the service intake position. Steps should be taken to avoid earth loops and parallel connections which will increase the risk of circulating currents and interference to programme circuits. Permanent monitoring should be provided to enable an increase in earth leakage to be quickly identified and corrected.

5.14.5.8 Tariffs

For a large complex the most advantageous tariff will usually be based on maximum demand rates with lower charges for HV than LV supplies. Monthly patterns of peak demand should be assessed to ensure the most favourable rates where seasonal, monthly and annual MD tariffs are offered as alternatives. Separate metering of night units may prove advantageous where considerable night operations are undertaken and special tariffs can sometimes be negotiated where the overall maximum demand occurs consistently during the board's off-peak periods. The economics of local power factor correction, compared with bulk correction, with or without selective switching, should also be considered.

5.14.6 Security

5.14.6.1 Intruder security

The need for intruder security can be high in studios where incursion by over-enthusiastic fans, political or subversive interference with live broadcasting and the theft of valuable equipment can be particular hazards. The risks will be conditioned by the location, incidence of live broadcasting and local political stability, as will the measures required to combat them.

Among the systems that may be considered are closed circuit tv surveillance, security lighting, card entry, door/window alarms and electrical movement detection supplemented by manual guarding and security patrols. Permanently surveyed access lobbies, with two interlocked doors, are particularly useful in regulating entry to sensitive areas.

5.14.6.2 Fire precautions

In all cases the Local Authority will dictate the minimum fire alarm and prevention standards although Fire Officers are usually flexible in their approach to the particular needs of studio premises.

In control rooms, visual fire indicators may be permitted in place of the usual sounders and similar units may be desirable in areas having a high ambient noise level. In studios where the sounders may interrupt a broadcast or cause consternation in an audience, the alarms are often cut by the operation of the transmission signal light key leaving the responsibility for orderly evacuation to the duty control room and fire security staff in the event of a legitimate alarm.

Automatic protection by sprinkers is often preferred by Fire Officers in studios and other high risk areas. However, considerable hazards exist to staff operating electrical equipment should sprinklers be actuated without warning and the cost of damage to equipment through accidental operation has largely restricted their use to scenery and storage areas. For technical areas an automatic fire detection system consisting of heat or smoke detectors is preferable, leaving the extinguishing to be carried out by more controlled means. Detectors may also be used automatically to control the ventilation plant to prevent a build up of smoke.

Where a high electrical risk is present in unattended areas such as HV switchrooms and diesel alternator rooms, the use of automatic carbon-dioxide extinguishing should be considered. Unless a 24 hour manned duty room is provided, automatic alarms should be connected to the local fire station or other permanently manned control centre.

5.14.6.3 Fireman's lifts

One or more 750 kg fireman's lifts should be provided with separately controlled electricity supplies and the auxiliary circuits so arranged that the Fire Brigade can take control without interference from landing call points.

5.14.7 Bibliography

As with other buildings, the IEE Regulations for Electrical Installations should be the fundamental guide to electrical services in studio premises. Appendices 1 and 2 list the related BS Specifications and Codes of Practice, together with Statutory Regulations and Associated Memoranda. Useful guidance on lighting design is given in the CIBS (formerly IES) Code for Interior Lighting. A number of other helpful publications are also produced by the Chartered Institution of Building Services, a full list of which may be obtained on application. Great care must be taken in the design of studio electrical services to ensure that acoustic design is not negated. Comprehensive guidance is given in the "BBC Guide to Acoustic Practice", copies of which are available from the BBC.

For those wishing to make a deeper study of studio technology, a number of papers written by BBC staff are available. A full list of these publications under the title "BBC Engineering", giving a record of BBC technical experience and developments in radio and television broadcasting can be obtained on application to:

Engineering Publicity Manager,
BBC Engineering Information Department,
Broadcasting House,
London, W1A 1AA.

The following papers may be of particular interest:

COURTNEY, J. P. and RATTLE, P. H. D.: 'Broadcasting Facilities in Wales' July 1980, Vol. 114.

ELLIOT, J. M., SPARKS, R. A., and NIMMY, D. G.: 'New Broadcasting House, Manchester': March 1976, Vol. 102.

NEALE, A. R.: Maida Vale: 'A Radio Music Centre': May 1974, Vol. 98.

Metal halide floodlighting of basketball court (Thorn-EMI Lighting)

Chapter 5.15

Sports arenas

John M. Chapman, M.C.I.B.S.
Partner, T. Harley Haddow and Partners

5.15.1 Introduction

5.15.1.1 General

Indoor sports stadia may comprise purpose built arenas for athletics, track and, to a degree, field events, cycling, football, tennis, badminton, bowling and many other specific sports. They will also usually contain ancillary accommodation for changing/lockers and toilets, viewing areas, restaurant/cafeteria and bar, administration offices and plant space for heating, ventilation and electrical switch and distribution equipment. There will also be storage areas for sports equipment.

Recreational Complexes will have similar ancillary accommodation requirements but are likely to combine facilities for various sports in one or more general Games Halls with, in addition, a number of Squash Courts, a Fitness (Conditioning) Room, Sauna, perhaps an area for Roller Skating or Bowling and a Swimming Pool.

Outdoor sports stadia would normally be used for all track and field athletics events and, in many cases, also for either Association or Rugby Football. They too will require ancillary accommodation and, frequently, a covered spectator area.

Swimming pools are often found in Recreational Complexes but may also be provided in some schools. The trend now is to build pools as part of a complex rather than as one-off buildings as was the case in the past.

5.15.1.2 Special requirements for services

The areas in which special requirements for services will be found are those such as

(a) Under soil warming of outdoor sports areas.
(b) Swimming pool water treatment and flow heating, and pool hall ventilation.
(c) Corrosion resistant finishes on electrical equipment installed outdoors or in conditions of high humidity or chlorinated air found in swimming pools.
(d) Possible provision of facilities for television outside broadcasts.

(e) Complex scoreboard and/or electronic timing equipment of high accuracy may be required.
(f) Luminaires will have to be robustly constructed, well fixed and guarded in areas involving ball games.
(g) Possible use of heat-recovery techniques to optimise the efficiency of energy usage principally in space heating, and possibly water heating as well.
(h) The accessibility of services for ready maintenance is important as most indoor sports arenas have such a demand on their facilities that they rarely close down for extended periods.

5.15.2 Environmental conditions

5.15.2.1 Heating and ventilation

Within one indoor sports stadium there is a requirement for varied conditions to prevail in adjoining areas, to allow comfortable conditions to be experienced by persons engaged in different sporting activities. In multi-purpose games halls, it is likely that environmental conditions will require flexibility in controls and, ideally, fast response in order to relate to the differing activities which they will house.

Indoor sports stadia frequently have very little daylighting to the sports halls to avoid the problems of glare to the players. When daylighting is provided, it is often incorporated into the roof structure in order that, both in daytime and nightime use, the lighting, whether natural or artificial, may enter the space from the same position relative to the players. It is important also to consider the alternative problems of solar heat gain through the windows in summer and building heat loss in winter, and to take the necessary precautions. Cooling may be necessary in summer to limit temperatures to about 18°C or less for energetic pursuits such as 5-a-side football. Alternatives are to place areas for such facilities internally within the building and provide high thermal insulation standards and no daylighting, or to reduce the solar gain and increase ventilation rate. Areas such as Squash Courts normally only have minimal heating, perhaps to a maximum of 10°C, and a high ventilation rate. Conditioning rooms on the other hand should have a temperature of around 16°C to 18°C. Changing Rooms, Clubrooms, Toilets, Restaurants, Reception and Administration areas should be heated to 18°C. Particular attention to ventilation (air change) rates is required in Changing Rooms and Toilet/Shower areas. Public viewing areas, if provided, should also be heated and some ventilation provided.

The ancillary accomodation of swimming pools has similar requirements for heating and ventilation to those outlined for indoor stadia but the requirements for the pool halls themselves are peculiar to these areas due to the type of environment.

The pool hall air temperature should be maintained at around 18°C by heating in winter, in order to relate to pool water temperature (normally 27°C). There is also a high level of relative humidity due to evaporation of pool water, and subsequent condensation can occur, but this can be reduced by the use of a pool cover which will also have an energy saving effect when the pool is not in use. (For details of swimming pool dehumidification, see section 4.5.8.3). A further particular condition requiring consideration is the removal of chlorinated air which, in excessive quantities, is a serious irritant. This arises from the chemical dosing of the pool water by sodium hypochlorite injection. Obviously therefore there is a requirement for effective ventilation of the pool hall, and controls for both heating and ventilation should be responsive to varying degrees of occupancy and external conditions. Attention must be paid to any summer solar heat gains and winter heat loss, occasioned by large glazing areas, in the design of heating and cooling plant.

An alternative to chlorinous disinfection is the use of ozone, which by eliminating the odour of chlorine in the air allows a greater proportion of the heated air to be recirculated and dehumidified, so reducing the need for heating fresh air.

5.15.2.2 Electric heating

In designing electric heating systems, the maximum use should be made of off-peak tariffs and heat storage systems which can be tapped during the daytime. Controls should be designed to be flexible and should be carefully zoned to allow areas not in use to be maintained at lower than design temperatures until required for use.

Because of intermittent usage of areas and, to a degree, of the whole building (Sports Arenas rarely operate for more than 12–14 hours per day) this flexibility of control coupled with the use of relatively low thermal capacity internal building materials can allow the temperature of the internal fabric surfaces to be raised rapidly.

There is a place for underfloor heating which can greatly improve comfort conditions in areas such as showers, and changing rooms. In some cases this may even extend to the poolside in pool halls. The heating elements must be protected against chemical attack and the manufacturers' advice should be sought in this connection.

The heating source requirement can readily be met electrically from an electrode boiler which can also, via a primary water circuit to a thermal storage vessel, provide space heating if required via radiators, convectors or heater batteries in ducted air systems. The boiler can in addition, via a separate calorifier to that used for pool water heating, provide domestic hot water for showers and toilet areas. Operated in conjunction with heat recovery techniques and by careful selection of tariffs in discussion with the Electricity Authority, the running costs can be minimised. (Fig. 5.15.1)

Heating in areas not fed by ducted warm air from central plant such as administration or storage areas may be by means of storage heaters, with or without fan assistance, whose charge input is controlled by an external temperature sensor system via master controllers. Care must be taken in the siting of these heaters (e.g. in storage areas) to ensure that they do not become covered.

Undersoil warming may be required for track and field areas in outdoor stadia where use of the facility is required throughout the year. This is achieved electrically by laying single core resistance element cables with protective sheathing some 150 mm below the surface of the ground (to allow deep spiking of the grass) and spaced 170 to 200 mm between runs. The electrical loading would normally be around 100 W/m^2 and automatic controls incorporating air and ground thermostats and a humidity detector would be used. In order to prevent excessive consumption, the thermostats utilised should have a differential of 0·25°C.

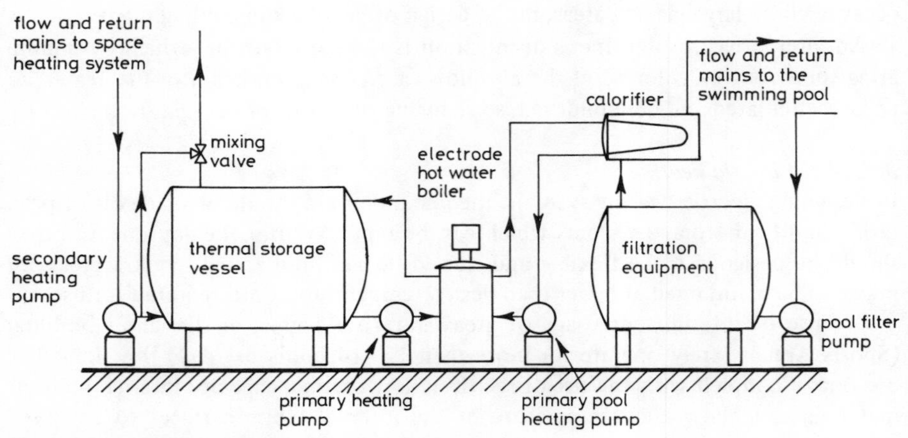

Fig. 5.15.1 *Electrode Boiler Installation*

5.15.2.3 Heat recovery

Pool hall areas are ideal cases for the use of heat-pumps with back-up electric heater batteries. In this way, the maximum use can be made of sensible and latent heat removed from the exhaust air in the extract ventilation system and transferred to the supply air heater batteries. In some cases, some heat can also be transferred to the pool water heat exchanger. Heat pumps can also provide cooling in summer. Thermal Wheels may be incorporated in larger pool halls. Use of these devices can achieve substantial economies in energy consumption. (See Secs 4.5.8.3 and 4.6.4.6).

Heat recovery techniques can also be used in other areas of indoor stadia such as large games halls heated by incoming fresh air passing through a heater battery and where there will be ducted extract ventilation by central plant. Collection of heat produced by luminaires can help substantially in reducing the requirement for prime energy to heat these premises and increase lamp efficiency by reducing the lamp envelope temperature.

Fig. 5.15.2 illustrates a typical heat recovery system for a Recreational Centre.

5.15.3 Lighting

5.15.3.1 Internal lighting

Lighting in indoor sports areas is always a critical factor in the successfulness in use of these premises. It is obvious that the lighting installation must fulfill the visual requirements of the players using the space. If there is daylighting to the space, the artificial lighting must complement it from a directional point of view as far as practicable to minimise visual distraction to players using the space during the transition from daylight to darkness.

Two of the most crucial design requirements after deciding on illuminance levels are the minimising of glare from the luminaires and achieving satisfactory uniformity of lighting over the playing area without the creation of shadows. In multi-

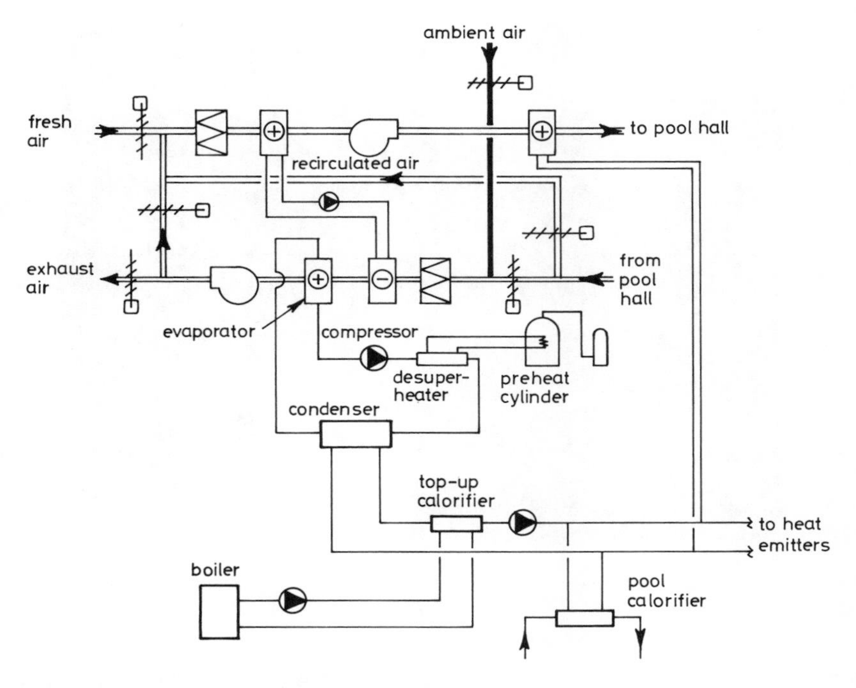

Fig. 5.15.2. *Typical heat recovery system in a leisure centre*

purpose halls, it is clear that numerous sports, each ideally requiring different lighting emphasis, will be played. It is consequently important to satisfy the requirements of the most lighting-critical sports, but it may have to be accepted that one system is unlikely to satisfy all possible needs. The switching of the lighting must be arranged to provide optimum flexibility and for total or partial use of the area. The lighting in indoor sports areas is usually achieved by use of tubular fluorescent or colour corrected high-pressure discharge source luminaires.

These must be of robust construction and securely fixed to avoid the risk of damage to the luminaire or injury to the players in the event of a luminaire being hit by a ball or other projectile. A wire guard may be a necessary provision. The luminaires should provide some upward lighting to illuminate the ceiling and thus reduce disturbing contrast between light sources and adjacent dark areas which make it difficult for the eye to follow, for example, a ball in flight. The engineer designing the lighting must take advice regarding reflectance values of the proposed floor, wall and ceiling finishes in order that these can be taken into account in his design.

In swimming pools an additional important design criterion is that the lighting be designed to allow a swimmer in difficulty underwater to be easily seen by

Fig. 5.15.3. *Swimming Pool* (Philips Lighting)

persons not in the water. This makes it essential to avoid glare, caused by reflection of light off the water surface, by careful selection and positioning of luminaires. The colour rendering properties of the light source selected are important and, together with the internal finishes, should aim to give a faintly blue appearance to the water. The luminaires and wiring systems must be corrosion resistant in view of the moisture laden, chlorinated atmosphere which may prevail in pool halls. Consideration must be given to access for maintenance and re-lamping of luminaires placed over the pool itself. In some cases, underwater lighting may be utilised to effect. When used, these luminaires are placed some 600 mm below the water surface behind water-tight glazed ports 3 to 5 metres apart.

Illuminance levels for championship pools should be 500 lux and for recreational pools around 300 lux with spectator area levels of 150 and 100 lux respectively. Illuminance levels for general purpose indoor sports stadia may vary between 400 and 600 lux. Lighting will be needed for the external access and car parks of the stadia, if not provided by the Local Authority from their street lighting network, whilst illuminated signs, both internal and external will be necessary.

Thought should be given to the possibility of televised broadcasts from the premises and the appropriate authority contacted for lighting advice.

Fig. 5.15.4. *Bowling Hall* (Thorn-EMI Lighting)

5.15.3.2 Floodlighting

Outdoor sports stadia will require floodlighting utilising colour corrected high pressure discharge luminaires for optimum colour rendition. This can be located on the roofs of side stands if they exist, or in groups on side mounted columns, or corner mounted lattice towers. Careful selection, design and aiming of floodlights are required to achieve acceptable uniformity on both vertical and horizontal planes over the entire area. A flexible switching scheme is advisable as the stadia may be used for football, athletics (track and field) and for training purposes, each requiring different emphasis. There is a relationship between the maximum spectator viewing distance, ground capacity and required illuminance for the stadium of which the designer should be aware.

Some average illuminances are:

Large Stadia	150–450 lux
Small Stadia	100 lux
Practice Purposes	30 lux

These values are in the horizontal plane and will normally give satisfactory vertical measurements provided the floodlights are correctly positioned and adjusted. They are insufficient however for television purposes.

For multi-floodlight towers, it is unlikely that all controls and ballasts will be able to be accommodated in the tower base, and weatherproof control gear pillars must be installed either adjacent or fixed to the tower itself.

Fig. 5.15.5. *Practice Fairway* (Thorn-EMI Lighting)

5.15.3.3 Emergency lighting

In order to evacuate persons from indoors sports stadia in the event of an emergency involving loss of electricity supply, it is necessary to install an emergency lighting system operated by standby batteries or generator. The minimum illuminance is usually 0·2 lux (in some parts of the UK 0·4 lux) but the level should relate to that which existed from the main lighting prior to loss of supply. The main areas to be illuminated are escape routes and the requirements are that the emergency lighting must clearly indicate the escape routes and allow safe movement along these routes. Additionally fire fighting and alarm call points must be readily seen under emergency lighting conditions. Consultation as to proposals must take place with the enforcing authority to ensure their acceptability.

5.15.4 Electrical installation

The engineer responsible for designing the electrical installation must be consulted at an early date in the outline planning stage in order that sufficient consideration is given to the location and provision of accommodation for a substation (if required), switchboards, distribution and control panels and the cabling associated with them.

Care must be taken to ensure that cabling to floodlighting towers is adequate to prevent excessive voltage drop on the long runs associated with outdoor stadia installations. Automatic voltage stabilisation equipment may be necessary in some cases to counter voltage drop.

Other aspects of electrical installations which will require consideration are:

(a) 13 A socket installation for equipment and cleaning purposes.
(b) Central control of main sports and circulation area lighting or the use of key operated switches to prevent unauthorised operation of lighting controls.
(c) Possible use of prepayment electricity meters to control lighting in areas such as squash courts and billiard tables.
(d) Electricity supplies to lifts for disabled members of the public and for goods lifts.
(e) If finance is available, it may be considered appropriate to install a standby generator set to provide power to essential services in the event of mains supply failure. Allowance will require to be made for the optimum siting for such a unit early in the planning of the building. The sub-mains distribution must be planned on the basis of essential and non-essential loads.

5.15.5 Communications

A public address system will probably be required with multi-input amplifier providing announcements from the Reception area, together with background music from a commercial cartridge tape player to selected areas with local volume control facilities. Commentary facilities via a separate microphone and local sound circuit control for main sports halls and pools and external arenas should also be provided. Loudspeakers for use outdoors will normally be of the re-entrant horn type where the sound projection is of more importance than music quality. Indoors, line source column speakers are used in the large halls with flush ceiling mounted or surface cabinet speakers in the smaller areas and corridors.

A clock installation will be needed, using synchronous or slave clocks operated from master timing equipment, which may also be utilised to operate sounders in the building to indicate the expiry of fixed time periods. Scoreboard installations suitable for operation by remote control, may also be needed.

It will be appropriate to provide a containing system (trunking, cable tray and conduit as required) for the telephone system wiring. It is normal to provide telephone lines for reservations non sequential with those for use by administrative staff in order that the admin telephones are not continuously unavailable. Public telephones are usually provided in the reception area.

5.15.6 Security

5.15.6.1 Intruder security

In view of the expensive equipment used in sports stadia and stocks of cafeterias and bars, it is advisable to provide an Intruder Alarm System to the necessary degree of sophistication to cope with the risk.

5.15.6.2 Fire precautions

A fire alarm system must be installed comprising manual and/or automatic initiation devices and sounders linked to a control panel which may allow division of the building into initiation zones in order that the area from which any alarm is initiated can be readily ascertained. Automatic initiation devices may be fixed temperature or rate of rise heat detectors or there are various forms of combustion product detectors available. Normally, the power supply for the fire alarm system must have battery back-up, the battery in question being used for no other purpose. As with emergency lighting schemes, consultation with the enforcing authority is required.

5.15.7 References

5.15.7.1 Regulations (See also Appendix 6.1)

The IEE Regulations for Electrical Installations are the principal regulations used. It will be necessary also to comply, insofar as is appropriate, with the Building Regulations and any relevant Local Authority by-laws.

5.15.7.2 British Standards (See also Appendix 6.2)

BS 5266 is the Code of Practice for Emergency Lighting, BS 5489 for Road Lighting and BS 5839 for Fire Detection and Alarm Systems. BS 5655 refers to Lifts. BS CP 326 covers the Protection of Structures against Lightning and BS CP 327 refers to Sound Distribution Systems.

5.15.7.3 Bibliography

BRAHAM, G. D. 'The Energy Factor'. (Paper to 51st Annual Conference of the Institute of Baths and Recreational Management).

CIBS Lighting Guide: "Sports"

'Facilities for Athletics (Track and Field)'. National Playing Fields Association 25 Ozington Square London SW3 1LQ

'Floodlighting of Outdoor Sports Facilities'. National Playing Fields Association.

'Light on Leisure' Article in "Building Services" Vol 2 No 4, April 1980

LUMSDEN, W. K., ALDWORTH, R. C. and TATE, R. L. C.: 'Outdoor Lighting Handbook'. (Gower Press)

STEWARD, G. W and SHARPE, R. J.: 'Sports Lighting: Indoor and Out'. Article in "Public Lighting". Vol 46 No 1 March 1981.

TUS Data Sheets:

2 Lighting in Sports Halls
3 Film and Broadcasting Requirements in Sports Facilities.
7 Swimming Pools: Solar Heating
14 Indoor Bowls Halls: Suitable Artificial Lighting Schemes
28 Energy Conservation
29 Provision of Floodlit Intensive Use Multigames Areas
40 Floodlighting for Outdoor Sports
(Technical Unit for Sport, 16 Upper Woburn Place London WC1H OQP)

The Burrell Museum, Glasgow (Barry Glasson, Architect)

Chapter 5.16

Museums and galleries

James R. Briggs, B.Sc.(Eng.), C.Eng., F.C.I.B.S., M.I.Mech.E., M.I.E.E., M.Cons.E.
James R. Briggs and Associates

5.16.1 Introduction

A museum is a space used for the exhibition of objects illustrating human and natural history. The objects may therefore be anything known to man and together may contain every conceivable material in any condition. The policy of the museum may be to exhibit in the condition the object was found or to restore it to as near original condition as possible. Whatever the policy the requirement should then be to conserve the object condition for the greatest possible period, whether the display is static in one place or travelling for exhibition in different locations.

The nature of a museum should be suited to the objects to be displayed ranging from an open site with no buildings at all to major purpose designed buildings and groups of buildings. Examples of the latter are the British and Kensington Museums in London. In some cases the building itself is a major part of the exhibition. Examples of this are the many buildings owned by the National Trust, such as Claydon House in Buckinghamshire and others owned by the community at large such as Aston Hall in Birmingham. The engineering services requirements can be as diverse as the museums and this chapter will consider the needs of a purpose designed building to house a particular collection, such as the Museum at Pollok Park in the Glasgow to house the famous Burrell Collection.

In addition to areas to contain the objects on a display such a building may, and probably will, need restaurant/kitchen, storage for objects not on display (which can be the bulk of the collection), restoration suite, temporary exhibition gallery for travelling exhibitions, lecture theatre, workshops, staff accommodation and a secure arrangement for the control of entry and exit of people, objects and all other materials.

5.16.2 Special requirements of museums

A primary objective of a museum must be to display objects for the inspection of people. The display should be arranged so that the maximum information can be gained in the shortest possible time. This requires that the objects be adequately lit, which calls for lighting of the right level, quality and direction. It also requires that the conditions of display be both pleasant and comfortable for people. At the same time a primary objective must be to protect objects against deterioration, destruction and theft.

All objects deteriorate because they comprise chemical components which may react one with another and with the components of their environment. The reaction or deterioration rate depends on the chemical components involved, the quantity and quality of light and the heat energy present. If excessive deterioration is to be avoided then it is essential to control the environment's chemical components, such as sulphur dioxide and water vapour, which may react with the object, and the light and heat energy levels, particularly light. Also it is essential to have the lowest possible fire risk.

In practical terms the factors that need to be considered are:

Air condition – temperature, humidity and purity
Light – natural and artificial
Security – destruction and theft
Fire – detection, indication, alarm and fighting
Communications – telephone, radio and public address
Electricity supply – normal and standby

For a new building the cost of providing engineering systems to give ideal protection for all these factors can easily exceed 40% of the total building cost and it is, therefore, necessary to consider the degree of protection justified for each factor.

An essential component in the design is that the services must be mutually compatible one with another and with the building architecture and structure. Consideration of the electrical services in isolation will not produce a satisfactory result.

5.16.3 Environmental considerations

5.16.3.1 Environment for objects

To establish the internal environment required the first consideration is to decide what is essential to reduce object deterioration to an acceptable rate. The person responsible for conservation must be consulted in this and an extreme requirement might be the provision of totally pollutant free air, total darkness, constant temperature in the range 15·5°C to 20°C, constant relative humidity (RH) in the range 50 to 60%, all located on high land in a vibration free fire-proof structure with full protection against shock and sound waves, total absence of all organisms (including humans), and equipped with an elaborate emergency back up system.

Clearly the requirement for absolute conservation is almost diametrically opposite to the requirement for satisfactory display and it is necessary to compromise. Fig. 5.16.1 shows one opinion of a possible range of conditions required which is based on Table 8 on page 86 of "The Museum Environment" (Ref. 1) compared to conditions needed by people based on Section A1 of the CIBS Guide (Ref. 2).

For hygroscopic objects, that is those containing moisture, such as textiles, leather, timber, paper, parchment, paints and even some types of old glass, it is important that the moisture content is held as constant as possible. This is because change of moisture content causes changes of dimension, usually of different amount in different directions. Hence warping and cracking.

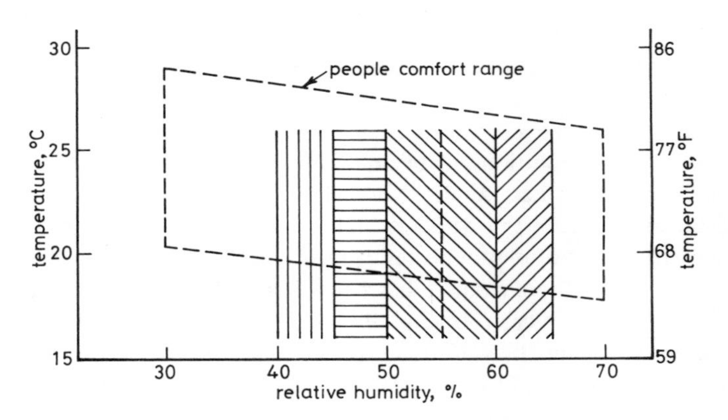

60–65% mixed collections in humid tropics (not iron)

50–60% mixed collections in temperate climates

45–50% mixed collections in cold climates if higher % RH gives condensation

40–45% mixed collections in arid climates. All metal collections anywhere

Fig. 5.16.1. *Range of conditions possibly required*
(Based on table 8 of 'The Museum Environment')

Flow of moisture between the object and the surrounding air will occur proportional to the difference between the air moisture, or vapour pressure, in the object and the air, and, at constant temperature in both, this is proportional to the % RH. To ensure the moisture in the object is held constant it follows that the % RH must be held constant and this means that the air temperature also needs to be held constant, because a one degree C change of temperature causes a 4% change of RH at a particular absolute moisture content. In practice the moisture flow between object and air is usually negligible for % RH within 5% of the required equilibrium value, and, for the objects, provided the temperature is changed slowly enough for the object temperature to follow that of the air, it is satisfactory to operate at, say, 16°C in Winter and 26°C in Summer. This will produce energy economies if acceptable to the people.

Light and dust can also be crucial. Where light contains ultra-violet radiation, as in sunlight, it will bleach coloured objects very quickly. The effects of dust, that is airborne particles settling onto objects, can be injurious in themselves in creating difficult cleaning problems but, where the air also contains agents such as the oxides of sulphur, ozone, or nitrogen dioxide, the effects can be disastrous and permanent, particularly in the presence of water.

5.16.3.2 Environment for building

Having decided the conditions needed for objects the next decision is whether or not it is necessary to provide those conditions throughout the exhibition area or whether it is feasible to place objects into showcases that have their own environmental control system. For many objects a showcase with a base filled with conditioned silica gel can provide an adequate control of relative humidity while the showcase gives protection against dirt and can also give protection against light. The general environmental control is then one of temperature only and is rather easier to achieve. This solution has been adopted at the Sainsbury Centre for the Visual Arts, University of East Anglia, Norwich. (Ref. 3).

For the Burrell Museum the whole exhibition area is required to be suitable for object conservation and display with temperature of 19 ± 1°C and a relative humidity of up to $60 \pm 5\%$. The air purity has been designed to give a particle retention efficiency of 98% for 5 micron size and 30% for 0·2 micron size with active carbon following filters to retain 95% of air entrained vapours. In addition the fresh air change rate has been selected to the minimum for odour control with a very low air infiltration rate of some one eighth of an air change per hour, by installing sealed type windows of high frame quality. The objective is for the bulk of the air repeatedly to pass through the filtration system to increase air purity to the maximum possible. In the exhibition areas the total air movement is some 9 changes per hour with fresh air adjustable between 0 (at night) and 4 to 5% during the day according to the number of people present.

For light control the building design has created deep spaces into which natural light will not penetrate although first impressions of the building may suggest there is a large proportion of glazing. Where light does penetrate the windows have either external or internal blinds, most of which are electric motor driven. The glass is also treated to reduce ultra-violet light penetration.

5.16.3.3 Means to produce the desired environment

(a) *Temperature control by heating*

Temperature may be controlled to be not less than a given value by heating, and the efficacy of control in a space will depend on both the accuracy of the sensor (usually a thermostat) and the adequacy of the circulation of heat within the space.

Most forms of heater – radiators, convectors (natural and fan types), and radiant panels – are reasonably effective in distributing heat, because a considerable proportion of their output is by convection. Heaters in several positions are clearly better than a single heat source. Heaters with a large radiant output should be avoided for conservation because they will raise local surface temperatures, leading to a local relative humidity lower than that of the space average. Hence the best form of heater for conservation is one having only convective heat output and the best of these must be heater batteries in a mechanical ventilation system in which the air, and thus the heat, is positively distributed.

The temperature control sensors provided with, or built into the unit, are usually less accurate than separately installed sensors, probably because of the heat gain to the sensor from the unit. Care is needed to locate sensors so that they are not directly affected by either the unit or any other source of heat, such as the distribution pipes.

It should be noted that heating alone will result in low relative humidities in Winter.

(b) *Temperature control by cooling*

To control temperature to a given value requires cooling in addition to heating and the control is similar to heating with the added complication that supply air streams set for correct air distribution with heating can be wrong for cooling – because a hot air stream will tend to rise and a cold to fall. Cooling is usually only available by a convective source because exposed cold surfaces would attract condensation and soon become a problem. Cooling control sensors need to be located as those for heating and are often the same sensor with a changeover device.

(c) *Humidity control by the addition of moisture*

In winter the external air moisture content is often well below that desirable and moisture may be added either centrally at the air plant or by local humidifier. All types, except possibly steam injection, must have a supply of water from which all solids have been removed, that is "de-ionised", and, unless the de-ionised water supply is 100% reliable, it is best avoided.

The efficacy of the humidifiers depends on the same factors as those for heaters because moisture is distributed by air circulation. Its natural diffusion rate through the air is negligible. Clearly, therefore, a humidifier as part of a mechanical ventilation system is to be preferred.

(d) *Humidity control by the removal of moisture*

In Summer the external air moisture content is often well above that which is desirable and this adds to the moisture exhaled by people. While there are local room dehumidifiers which do not require mechanical refrigeration, it is doubtful they could be used on any large scale. Normally the removal of moisture is only possible with mechanical refrigeration, that is in a full air conditioning system.

(e) *Air quality control*

It is possible to install a variety of local room air cleaners but to obtain standards approaching those previously mentioned, only a filtration system in a central air plant is likely to be effective.

(f) *Light control*
The ideal form of light control, meaning control of solar radiation, is to avoid windows. If windows are essential, they should be at least double glazed and equipped with an external shading device to reduce the heat gains into the space to the least possible.

5.16.3.4 *Comparison of alternatives*
Clearly for ideal conservation the only form of control likely to give fully satisfactory results is a mechanical ventilation system with air filtration, heating, cooling and humidification. Unfortunately, this is also the most expensive solution both in installation and running costs. At a lesser provision than this there is a very wide choice and Figure 5.16.2 attempts to show a comparison between the two extremes with three somewhere in the middle. The figure can only be the most approximate guide as a lot will depend on the conditions required and the building configuration, but should be sufficient to decide which systems to investigate in detail.

The text of paras 5.16.3.3 and .4 follow closely from a paper given by the author, (Ref. 4), and further details of the systems may be obtained from that paper.

5.16.3.5 *Operation and maintenance*
This subject is outside the scope of this Chapter but its importance cannot be overstressed.

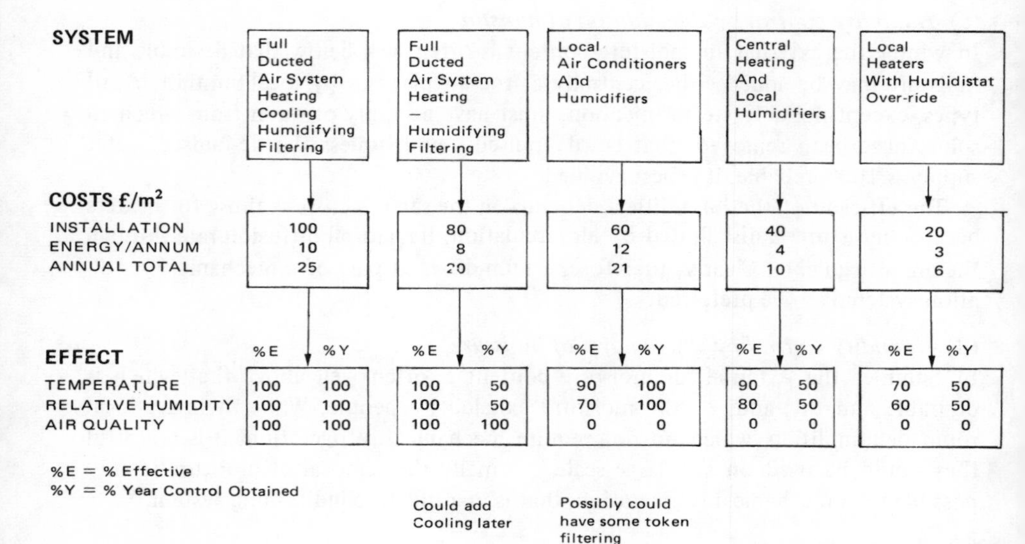

Fig. 5.16.2. *Comparison of means to control environment*

5.16.3.6 Energy conservation

A system should be installed to recover energy that would otherwise be discharged to the outside with the exhausted air, domestic hot water and similar. At the Burrell Museum the main energy recovery is from the plant room, which contains the electrical transformers and the kitchen exhaust.

5.16.4 Electrical installation

The electrical installations required are those for any building to some degree – lighting, small power outlets, connections to electrically driven plant and equipment and ancillary electrical systems for communications, fire alarms and security.

5.16.4.1 Lighting

For museums and galleries, since art is nothing if not seen, lighting is of primary importance and is needed to both illuminate exhibits and the public ways through the building – and care is needed to prevent conflict between the two functions and particularly to avoid pools of bright light against a dark background.

Unfortunately the ideal levels of light for visual comfort can be very damaging, particularly when there is an ultra-violet content and the effects depend on the illumination levels, time of exposure and the chemical composition of the object. Fabrics and paper, particularly with water colour pigments, are very sensitive and for these the illumination levels should not exceed 150 lux (50 lux for water colours) with no ultra-violet component. For maximum protection light should be excluded as much as possible and, in extreme cases, time limiting may be needed – by such as 'push button to display' techniques.

It is possible to include windows provided these are located and constructed realising the implications of natural light variations, of both level and colour temperature, and high ultra-violet content. The latter may be filtered out, and the filter should be in a permanent form that will not deteriorate with time. Window sizes and location need to be selected and controlled so that maximum internal illumination levels are not exceeded and some form of automatic blinds or shutters may be needed. It must also be realised that windows are a great source of heat gain, and loss, and lead to a greater need for air conditioning, or heating, as well as being prone to condensation and, where not sealed, to the ingress of dirt.

In any event an artificial lighting system will be needed and luminaires designed for display are available in standard ranges or may be made specifically for particular configurations. The main suitable light sources are fluorescent, tungsten filament and tungsten halogen lamps. Mercury and sodium lamps are not satisfactory because of their colour effects.

Fluorescent lighting with 1500 and 1800 mm tubes should be used as much as possible, because the energy consumption is relatively low, and when used with correctly matched tubes, shielded with a diffuser to absorb UV and to avoid glare, can supplement natural lighting very well, as has been done at the National and

Hayward Galleries in London. But, particularly where there is no natural lighting, it is difficult to use fluorescent lighting in an aesthetically pleasing way at the lower illumination levels.

Where modelling is important, and for special effects, the less efficient tungsten filament lamp is probably best, because it is possible to use different beam angles and projection to obtain precise particular effects – although the calculations are rather tedious and it is helpful to get computer assistance. Dimming can be used for final adjustment.

Flexibility of lighting is usually the main need and a plug-in or track system at high level has many uses.

5.16.4.2 Small power

Small power outlets can be needed for showcase lighting and local air conditioning units. If both are likely two separate circuits are desirable, one for lighting and items normally switched off at night, and one for items which need to run continuously. Where the showcase locations are not fixed there may be need for a system to permit additional circuits to run to wherever showcases might be. At the Burrell a system of electric floor outlets has been installed connected to two-channel under-floor trunking, one channel for 240 V small power cables and the other for security circuits.

5.16.4.3 Electrical capacity

To establish the electrical capacity required it is first necessary to analyse the total energy loads and annual consumptions to determine which loads are to be met by electricity. The analysis is not simple because of the number of variable factors. The number of people present, and hence the heating or cooling loads, can vary quite a lot. The display lighting tends to change dramatically between one display and another. Also, where there is glazing, the efficacy of the solar shading is probably variable as is the amount of air that leaks in or out of the building.

Table 5.16.1 summarises the figures produced for the Burrell Museum looking at the least, greatest and mean possibilities with the greatest heat load taken to occur when the other loads are at their least. For the most likely conditions the fans use more energy than anything else because they need to run every day of the year, although, at the Burrell, thermostats switch them off whenever the Museum is closed and the external conditions are such that the rate of change of internal condition is within the permissible tolerance.

For the Burrell, where absorption refrigeration machines were not considered appropriate, 73% of the annual energy consumption had to be electric and led to it being an all-electric building. This does not mean that all museums should be all-electric but there is a possibility that many could be and this can only be decided after an exhaustive analysis.

5.16.4.4 Security of electricity supply

It is important that the source of electricity supply be as reliable as possible. This

Table 5.16.1 *Energy loads and consumptions*

		Maximum	Maximum Watts/sq metre			Usage kWh/sq metre/annum		
		Occurs	Least	Mean	Greatest	Least	Mean	Greatest
1	Space heating (see text)	Winter	58·6	52·0	45·3	178·1	97·3	16·4
2	Domestic hot water	Always	2·5	3·8	5·0	3·5	17·6	31·7
3	Air reheat (humidity control)	Summer	0·8	3·2	5·5	1·6	7·6	13·6
4	Heat distribution	Winter	2·9	2·6	2·3	10·2	7·4	4·5
5	Catering 1 – gas, steam or electric	Always	2·1	6·5	10·9	3·7	13·1	22·5
	Sub Total 1 – Any fuel		66·9	68·1	69·0	197·1	143·0	88·7
6	Fans – air movement	Always	21·0	24·7	28·4	92·0	170·4	248·8
7	Lighting	Always	12·0	24·2	36·4	36·8	107·0	177·3
8	Cooling including distribution	Summer	13·3	27·7	42·1	28·7	59·3	89·7
9	Pumps, etc.	Always	8·0	10·8	13·5	26·0	51·1	76·1
10	Catering 2 – electric only	Always	0·6	1·4	2·2	1·5	3·6	5·7
	Sub Total 2 – Electric		54·9	88·8	122·6	185·0	391·4	597·6
	Total overall		121·8	156·9	191·6	382·1	534·4	686·3

may be achieved by arranging for the Electricity Authority incomer to be a connection to a ring main system in which the supply can come from either direction. Usually this is only feasible where the load is sufficiently high to require a supply at high voltage. For the more important circuits a standby generator should be provided.

5.16.5 Communications

Good communications are essential and a diagram of what might be desirable is given in Figure 5.16.3.

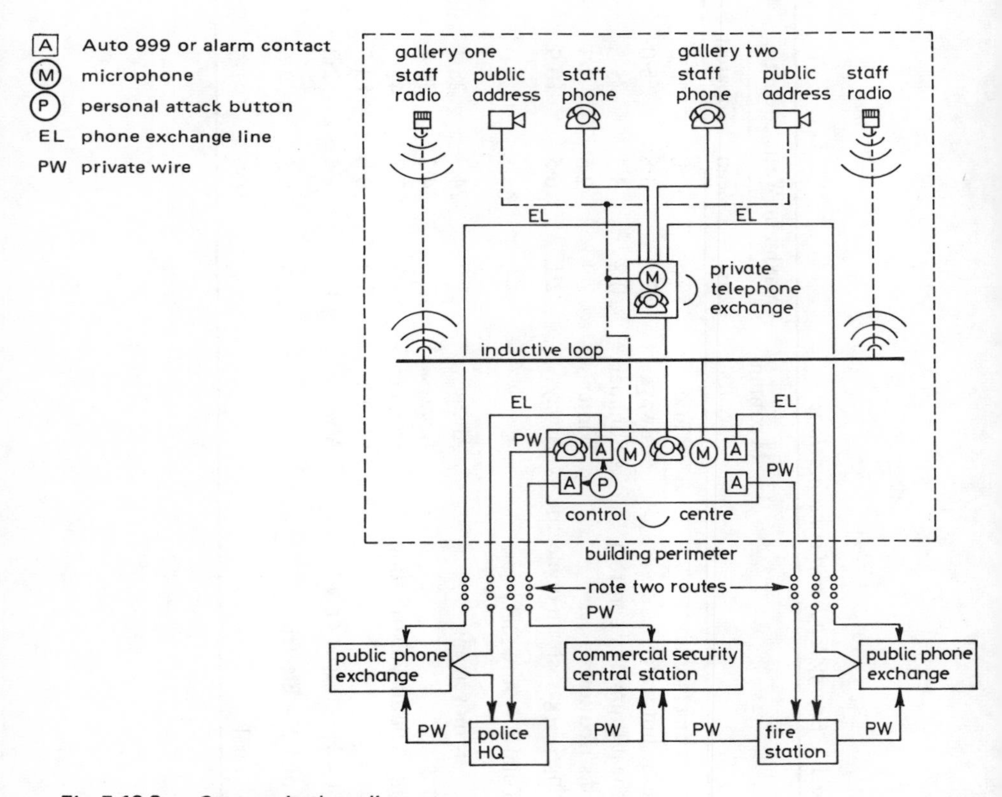

Fig. 5.16.3. *Communications diagram*

5.16.6 Security, safety and fire precautions

Before deciding on the security systems to install it is necessary to be clear as to the hazards. Apart from fire the hazards, in order of probability, are accidental damage, petty impulse damage or theft, premeditated single person damage or theft, and, premeditated syndicate damage or theft either for financial gain or political reasons. The best defence is undoubtedly the presence of uniformed personnel but there cannot be a keeper by every exhibit and it is therefore wise to have an installation of security devices which give audible warning, both locally and at a central point, and a diagram of the sort of protection available is given in Figure 5.16.4. It will be noted that closed circuit television is not included because it is difficult for watchers to detect even exceptional changes such as movement in an otherwise still scene, or very violent action in a moving scene, a fact known to all but the most ignorant of the criminal fraternity. It is thus of little deterrent value against either premeditated or impulse actions. Where there are no night patrols the system needs to be strengthened to detect movement of

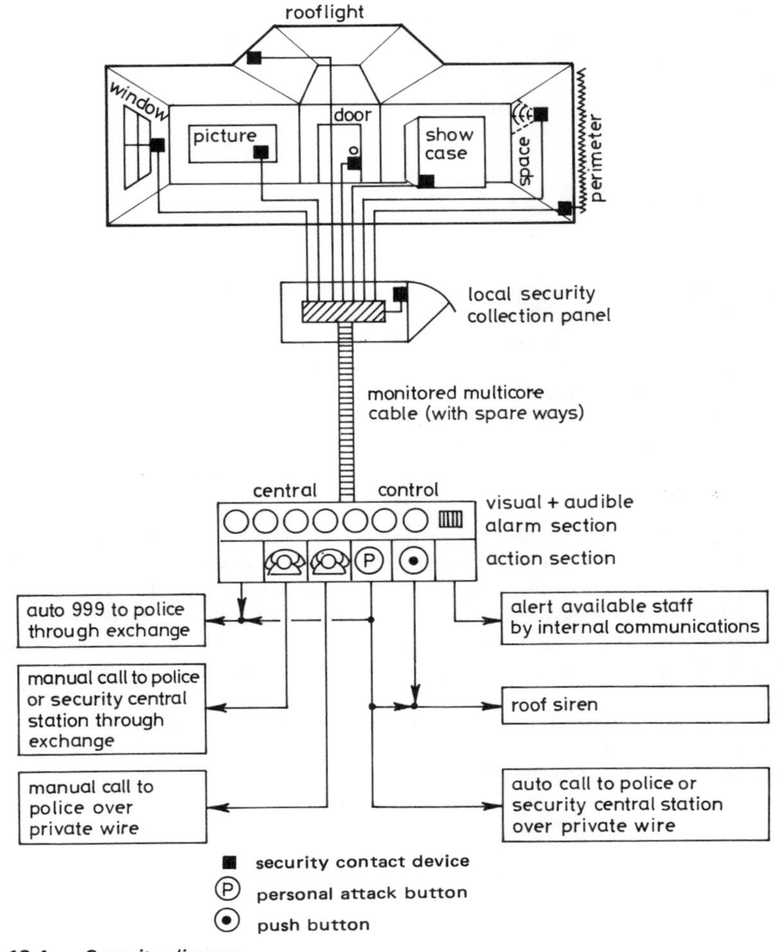

Fig. 5.16.4. *Security diagram*

people in a space, breaking of glass or break-in attempts. A factor which needs to be considered is that the Fire Prevention Officer will ask for all escape routes to be open whenever the building is occupied and this is usually diametrically opposite to the security requirement that everything is locked at all times. Explosion locks that are set to open automatically under fire conditions have not yet been found sufficiently reliable and the best compromise seems to be for all fire escape doors to be locked but easily openable from inside by breaking a glass panel.

5.16.7 Regulations, Standards, Codes of Practice

The Regulations, Standards and Codes of Practice are those applicable to any building and may also include those for places of Public Entertainment. As yet there seem to be no regulations as to the conditions required for objects but they are under consideration, particularly for the locations wishing to accept travelling exhibitions. The owners of such exhibitions may well require particular conditions before agreeing to allow the exhibition to come.

5.16.8 References

5.16.8.1 References in text

(1) THOMPSON, GARRY. Scientific Adviser, The National Gallery, London. 'The Museum Environment'. (Butterworth)

(2) CIBS Guide Section A1 'Environmental Criteria for Design'

(3) 'The Sainsbury Centre for the Visual Arts, University of East Anglia, Norwich.' The Architectural Review, December 1978.

(4) 'Environmental control of modern records' International Conference of Library and Archive Materials and the Graphic Arts, Cambridge, September 1980.

5.16.8.2 Bibliography

MONCRIEFF, ANNE: Bibliography – Control of the Museum Environment. Victoria and Albert Museum, based mainly on Art and Archaeology Abstracts. Prepared for the V & A Museum and U.K. Institute for Conservation Symposium in November 1979. Obtainable from the Publications Marketing Officer, Tate Gallery, Millbank, London, SW1P 4RG.

Bibliography – Building Services for Museums and Art Galleries. (LB10/83) Building Services Research and Information Association, Old Bracknell Lane, Bracknell, Berkshire, RG 21 4AH

BRIGGS, JAMES R and SMITH, PETER: 'Engineering systems for Galleries'. Studio International May/June 1975.

CIBS Lighting Guide: Museums and Art Galleries.

Prison Exterior (Home Office)

Chapter 5.17

Prisons

T. R. Jones, C.Eng., F.I.E.E.
Chief E & M Engineer, The Home Office

5.17.1 Categorisation

Prisons are required to hold a wide range of inmates, some for a very long time. On grounds of humane and economic containment this means that different standards become necessary and leads to categorisation of inmates and establishments. So far as secure containment is concerned this is dependent upon both the prison operational requirements and the physical security i.e. buildings, perimeter walls, fences, gates, doors and windows of adequate structural strength backed up, where management feels such facilities are required, with electrical and electronic alarm devices including closed circuit television (CCTV) and special lighting. A central control room will be required, therefore, for certain prisons, e.g. Dispersal Prisons.

Inmate categorisation in terms of security generally falls into one of four groups

(a) those whose escape would be highly dangerous to the public, the police or to the security of the State,
(b) those for whom the very highest conditions of security are not necessary but for whom escape must be made very difficult,
(c) those who cannot be trusted in open conditions but do not have the ability or resources to make a determined escape attempt
(d) those who can be trusted reasonably to serve their sentence in open conditions.

The establishments themselves are also categorised by function e.g. Local Prison, Remand Centre, Training Prison (open or closed), Youth Custody Centre (open or closed) and Detention Centre.

Several functions may be fulfilled by a particular establishment, e.g. some closed Training Prisons are known as Dispersal Prisons when they are specially organised and equipped to accommodate a proportion of the most dangerous and highest security risk prisoners.

Prisons have a very wide range of services to provide and functions to fulfil, many of which are similar to those to be found in a local community e.g. medical and dental facilities, educational and religious activities, medium and light industries including large laundries, building construction, physical recreation, crop and livestock farming and so on. Thus one can see the need for electrical, telephone, radio and public address installations and services with different levels of sophistication in order to meet the criteria already mentioned.

5.17.2 Electricity supply

5.17.2.1 Maximum demand

The electrical power supply will normally be provided by the appropriate Electricity Authority. Although it is not easy to predict the maximum demand, experience tends to show that each inmate accounts for about 0·75 kVA; i.e. for a 500 inmate prison the maximum demand will be about 375 kVA; to this must be added the demand created by the prison's industrial workshops. Unless there are specialised highly powered machines a useful figure to work on is 0·45 kVA demand for every 1 kW of installed load per 10 square metres of workshop floor area. An appropriate diversity factor which should become apparent in discussion with the client during the design stage may then need to be further applied to arrive at a realistic overall maximum demand for the prison, based on its regime.

5.17.2.2 Main switchgear

The location of the main intake switchgear, transformer if necessary and the LV distribution equipment is best arranged in the vicinity of the main entrance to the prison e.g. adjoining the Gate House rather than at the electrical centre of the load. By choosing this position the equipment is then well away from inmates, can be readily maintained and in the event of any abnormal situation developing in inmate-occupied areas the appropriate supply or service can easily be disconnected. It should be borne in mind that if the prison supply is taken at high voltage it is better to have an indoor rather than outdoor transformer which can be more easily subject to malicious damage.

5.17.2.3 Standby supply

In association with the normal power supply, consideration needs to be given to standby power facilities. In practice again it has been found sensible to locate the generator near to the prison entrance and switchroom. The rating of the generator will be governed by the requirements of the prison regime but within economic limits there is a strong case for keeping as much of the establishment operating as normally as possible. The generator, therefore, might conveniently be rated to meet the total prison load but exclude the industrial workshop demands. This condition can be met by arranging for all workshop power loads to be connected through contactors with 'no volt' coils, which can be re-energised only by an authorised works officer, after the normal power supply has been restored. The workshop lighting circuit, of course, should not be wired through such contactors.

Attention should be paid to such points as the set being able to deliver full load in about 15/20 seconds, acceptable noise levels, cooling, and reserve fuel supplies for at least one week's continuous full load operation. The generator installation must comply with relevant regulations which usually include the local supply authority's particular requirements. Special alarm and other electronic circuits should be maintained by battery systems between the mains supply failing and the generator taking over. Consideration should be given also to the need to maintain any highly critical supplies for several hours in the event of the standby generator failing to start.

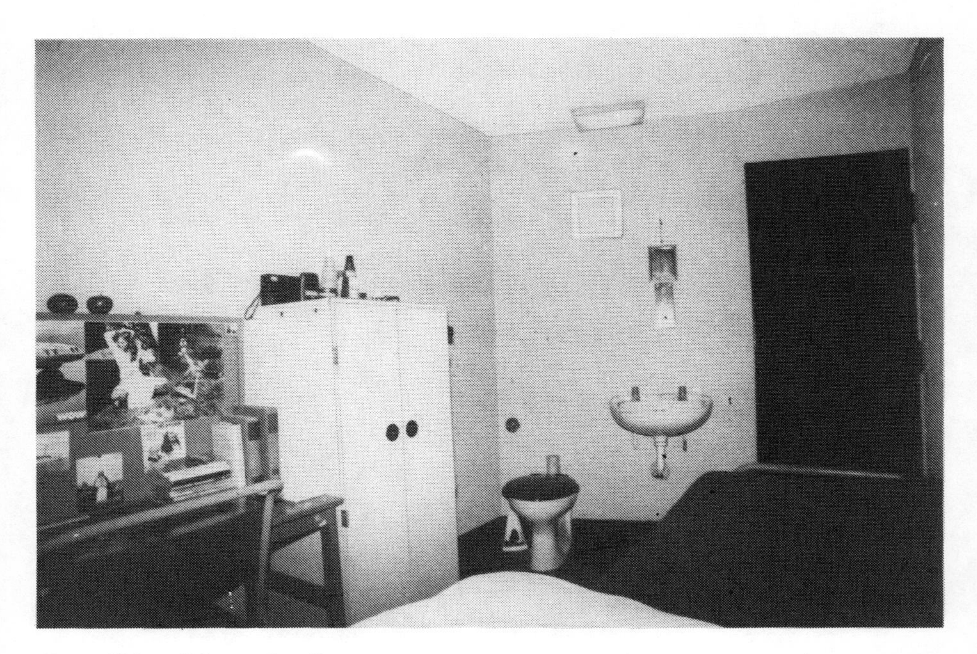

Fig. 5.17.1. *Prison cell, toilet end* (Home Office)

5.17.3 Heating

Electrical space and water heating systems will not be found to any great extent in prisons, since central coal, gas or oil fired boiler houses, or in certain cases distributed gas or oil fired boilers are usually the most economic way of providing the establishment's heating needs. Moreover if the central boiler house has to provide a steam supply for say a laundry, it is often convenient also to use steam for kitchen requirements. When this is not the case however, the possibility of an electrical kitchen should certainly be considered.

Although in general, space and water heating requirements will be met, as described above, this is not to say that alternative electrical methods should be disregarded. There may well be a good case for electrical space and domestic hot water heating when the demand is intermittent or seasonal. A typical space heating example is the prison chapel which may be in use for only a few hours each week.

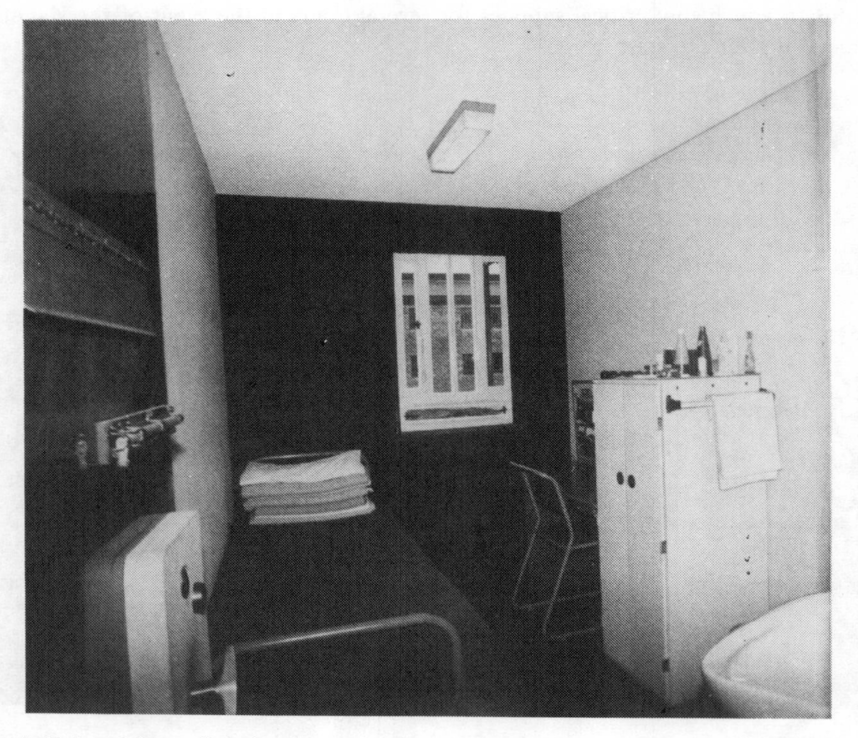

Fig. 5.17.2. *Prison cell, bed end* (Home Office)

Domestic hot water requirements which are often substantial for inmate accommodation blocks may also merit similar consideration. With a central boiler house and lengthy hot water and heating distribution mains, energy losses can be a not insignificant part of the load. During summer months with heating systems switched off, if the domestic hot water calorifiers were equipped with immersion heaters it might well be possible to shut down all the boiler plant and effect considerable savings. It will be worthwhile to bear in mind also that by increasing the hot water storage capacity it may be possible to use only a Night Rate or Off-Peak Tariff.

In comparing alternative systems it should not be overlooked that dispensing with the generation of hot water by boilers in a central boiler and using local immersion heaters throughout the year, will not only mean smaller boilers but will enable the domestic hot water distribution mains to be avoided altogether, since it is not uncommon to find separate heating and domestic hot water mains between the central boiler house and the various accommodation blocks. Experience of maintenance costs associated with steam and hot water heating mains in underground ducts and pipe in pipe systems indicates that an electrical water heating arrangement as outlined could now be quite attractive.

A wide range of electrical controls for space and water heating is now available, from the thermostat to microcomputer. In addition, comprehensive Building Management Systems are just starting to appear in prisons, for monitoring, energy control, and maintenance purposes.

A small number of prisons – those designated as Dispersal Prisons – have control rooms which need air conditioning. This is an important requirement since the staff responsible for monitoring controls and alarm devices work in rooms normally without openable windows. Good environmental conditions are essential if they are to carry out their duties efficiently.

5.17.4 Lighting

5.17.4.1 Lighting levels

The lighting levels and luminaires for the prison as a whole should follow the generally accepted standards for the particular purpose as would be the case elsewhere and be in accordance with the relevant Codes of Practice. The switching should be arranged so that vulnerable areas are under the control of prison officers. Throughout the prison it is essential that there should be an appropriate number of lighting fittings installed in key locations, which will maintain illumination from internal batteries when the electricity supply fails, pending the emergency generator providing power. Typical areas are staircases, workshops, kitchens or where groups of inmates can be in association. A suitable minimum level of illumination for cells has been shown to be about 200 lux. In a typical cell this can be obtained usually from one twin 30 watt fluorescent luminaire which so far as possible must be vandal proof, with a polycarbonate or similar diffuser fixed with cover screws needing a special tool for their removal. The fitting design should prevent the attachment of a ligature. Surface wiring must be avoided. Within the luminaire it will be convenient to locate a low wattage tungsten bulb or fluorescent tube for night inspection and reassurance purposes. With the cell occupant having the facility to switch his light from within the cell, the patrolling officer must be able to switch on either the night reassurance or full cell lighting from outside the cell. Careful attention, therefore, needs to be paid to the switching and wiring arrangements since if the cell switch toggle can be balanced in the neutral position it may prevent the lighting being switched on from outside the cell. External lighting will be necessary for general patrol, security and CCTV purposes when this is specifically required. The level of illumination will depend upon the degree of security necessary but about 7 to 8 lux will normally be adequate for general lighting around buildings, and along roads and pathways. In the vicinity of perimeter fences where it may be felt that a higher level of illumination is desirable 15 to 30 lux should be provided. In view of energy consumption considerations the lower figure might be regarded as the permanent minimum level, with the increase to 30 being actuated manually or from appropriate detectors if increased surveillance is suddenly required.

When CCTV coverage is required, experience has shown that with present day equipment a satisfactory solution is obtained with a scene illumination of about 60 lux, but this figure will no doubt fall with developing technology. Very careful siting of the cameras and luminaires is required to avoid not only possible black spots and reflections from water, but also in daytime the deliberate reflection of sunlight into the camera's lens.

5.17.4.2 Lamp types

So far as the choice of lamps is concerned for security and CCTV purposes it is important to avoid those which may have unacceptably long restrike times after a power failure. In this respect recent developments in high pressure sodium lamps have greatly helped designers who may have otherwise resorted to the high wattage tungsten type of bulb. Certain sodium lamps are now able to produce sufficient luminous lux rapidly after a power supply interruption, and thus reasonably continuous security surveillance can be maintained. Elsewhere, fluorescent tubes and lamps will meet requirements except perhaps for specialist lighting in hospital and chapels.

5.17.5 Electrical installation

5.17.5.1 Security of installation

Electrical installations must be generally robust and tamperproof to withstand high levels of vandalism. There is often a need to go beyond the non-withdrawable screw approach and provide electrical circuits which will indicate remotely when a trunking lid or switchbox cover is being removed by an unauthorised person – as for example, an inmate, to store contraband. Similarly the use of residual current devices (r.c.d.) anywhere except on final circuits needs to be considered with extreme care. Inmates may have considerable technical skill, and a good deal of time to use it for disruptive or escape purposes. Failure of lighting or power circuits at the wrong time in a prison will present difficulties which at the very least can be disconcerting and at worst might lead to an escape.

Turning to the general power and lighting installations, all supplies, trunking, wiring, and fuseboards need to be as tamper proof as possible. Fuseboards and cubicles should be padlocked unless they are already in a locked plant room.

Trunking must be routed so that as far as possible it is not taken through inmate areas where it could be tampered with unobserved. Screws in the trunking lids at strategic positions should be fitted with tamper contacts relaying an alarm signal to an agreed location.

The security of the electricity supply and distribution services if of paramount importance and this must be borne in mind at all times.

5.17.5.2 Contracts

In setting up contracts for installations, thorough attention must be given to the local site procedures which will be enforced when the work takes places in establishments holding inmates, during the course of the contract.

Almost every situation will then require the contractor's staff to be escorted at all times and this leads to much lower levels of productivity than would be the case for almost any other type of work. Realisation of this requirement at the tendering stage will minimise disruption and claims for delay in due course.

5.17.6 Security

5.17.6.1 Alarm systems

Alarm systems for various purposes are a standard requirement in any establishment and the following summary should enable the installation designer to be aware of the various needs. When regulations permit certain alarms to be integrated with others, e.g. fire with staff/inmate call or night patrol, Time Division Multiplexing (TDM) techniques can be used to achieve a considerable saving in wiring both within and between buildings.

The standard inmate cell call alarm system enables the occupant to signal for assistance by means of a press button which rings a bell or buzzer on a panel at an agreed remote central point, illuminates a call lamp outside his cell and also gives him a signal within the cell that the alarm has been transmitted to the central point. Whilst the officer on duty can mute the audible signal in his central office (leaving a warning lamp alight) he must visit the cell in order to cancel the call completely, by means of a reset button outside the cell. A general alarm system is normally provided for the staff with actuating buttons at strategic points. The signal is transmitted to a central control point with strategically placed repeater boards all as determined by the prison requirements. Officers who have specific emergency duty tasks allotted to them can then proceed quickly to the area generating the call. Depending upon the size and status of the establishment this alarm system may well need to be taken back to a fully manned control room.

Communication by radio also is used for various purposes and prison officers may need to be equipped with UHF and/or VHF personal radios, depending upon local circumstances.

5.17.6.2 Tamper alarms

Tamper alarms are strategically a very important aspect of the electrical installation and will be required on a scale commensurate with the category of the prison. The following is the order of provision to be made in relaying to the appropriately located control point, such signals as the regime requires of illegal interference to

(a) locks
(b) high security doors
(c) substation and switchroom doors
(d) equipment consoles
(e) safes for keys
(f) duct covers
(g) trunking systems
(h) call-out equipment
(j) public address systems

Depending upon the location of staff quarters, e.g. housing and bachelor accommodation, the need for a prison officer emergency call out system by the use of direct cabling should be borne in mind. Any accommodation further afield may be covered normally by the public telephone service.

5.17.6.3 Patrol signalling

Night patrols of the prison necessitate routine monitoring of this activity. Whilst the clock pegging method has been used successfully for many years it is now common practice to use a key, carried by the patrolling officer to initiate a signal, from each of the points he attends, to a central monitoring and recording facility. By such means progress of the officer whilst on his round can be noted and alarms raised if he fails to report by the appointed time.

5.17.6.4 Public address

Increasing use is being made of public address systems with provision for radio relay facilities for the general running of establishments. The microphone input should be in a secure area e.g. the communications centre or control room. Hospital areas are usually equipped with suitable switching facilities to exclude as necessary any general announcements, and to provide their own inputs as required. Typical areas covered by the general system are workshops, kitchens, dining halls and inmate association areas but not the cells themselves. (See following paragraph on electrical unlocking). The aerial arrangement for the radio p.a. system generally should allow for TV reception also, with the sets of the inmates installed in the association areas.

5.17.6.5 Video tape systems

The flexibility of this facility for both educational and recreational purpose gives a number of advantages. It can avoid the need for large gatherings in rooms which previously had to be used as cinemas. Different programmes can be shown in separate rooms with inmates grouped in smaller numbers, thus making for better management and control.

The installation arrangement will need careful assessment from the point of view of the use of existing equipment (Televisors and VCR etc) and the signal transmission distances involved. The use of base band distribution techniques therefore should not be overlooked.

5.17.6.6 Door controls

Complete electrical locking and unlocking of prisons has not found favour generally in the UK following some computer controlled installations about ten years ago. The main benefit currently appears to be in providing access for inmates in single occupancy cells to night sanitary facilities, where such permanent facilities do not exist within the cellular accommodation.

With today's cheaper microprocessor technology, however, the principle has potential and should be given careful consideration. In a somewhat reduced form, the electric locking of key doors e.g. the main prison vehicular gates and pedestrian entrances with, say, a small number of principal security doors does seem to have considerable merit in that human error in their operation can be avoided. For a basic door arrangement which is unlikely to be changed, a normally wired interlock system would suffice, but where different door opening and closing sequences may become necessary, a simple microprocessor software program would give the required flexibility. Coupled with this arrangement the opportunity is then available for staff access by passive or active magnetic cards which can be programmed to operate by grade, zone and time, together with the facility to record all door openings and closings, including any illegal attempts.

Although total electrical locking and unlocking for the prison has not become established, the power operation of the main prison entrance vehicular gates and pedestrian doors has increased markedly over the years. Several designs have emerged using hydraulic, pneumatic and electrical drives with appropriate electronic control and interlock arrangements. The two principal points which have become apparent in this area are the facility for easy manual operation in emergencies and general reliability of drive mechanisms. It needs to be remembered that if the pedestrian doors are out of action for any reason, greatly increased use will be made of the vehicular gates. Intercom systems are usually provided nowadays for the prison's main vehicular and pedestrian entrances. It is the practice to cover both the entrances to, and the exits from, the prison together with any local or intermediate doors linking the Gate House and adjacent reception areas. Where the regime so requires it, the system can be operated in conjunction with CCTV and electrically locked doors, both controlled from the Gate House.

5.17.6.7 Other alarm devices

A brief mention needs to be made of other alarm devices which may find their application in prisons. Infra-red technology, microwave devices, electrostatic fields, vibration detectors and wired mesh in walls, all have a part to play. But it is no good choosing a system with sensitive detection capability if it has a high false alarm rate. It will soon cause the user to become disenchanted and the system will tend to be ignored at the vital moment.

5.17.7 Fire precautions

The fire alarm system should follow conventional arrangements with break glass type call points covering generally all the prison's areas with the exception of the cellular accommodation. The usual remote indicator board, possibly with repeaters will be required and installed in locations to be agreed with management. Where appropriate, suitable automatic detectors e.g. rate of rise or ionization types should be installed. It should be borne in mind that it may be desirable in areas where people are restrained or locked up to use buzzers in place of bells to avert, so far as possible, any panic situation developing in which inmates may feel they are trapped. Also in maximum security establishments it may be beneficial to use the prison officer alarm call system by an appropriately coded ringing message for fire alarm signals.

Fires and fire risks in prisons have been shown to be of a very low order over the years but sabotage or arson is always a possibility. Hence automatic detectors should also be considered for those areas which are closed down for periods during the day or night after occupation by inmates e.g. industrial workshops, laundries, stores, kitchens and chapels.

The location of the various alarm boards will usually be decided by those, including appropriate Fire Officers, concerned with the prison regime, but it is important to note that at least fire alarms should be relayed to the prison entrance or Gate House so that, for example, local fire fighting appliances can be admitted without delay.

Although most doors in prisons normally are kept locked, self-closing doors with electromagnetic devices are occasionally used to control fire spread hazards, and will require to be wired into the fire alarm system at the appropriate call point, as will any ventilation fans so that they may be shut down automatically if the Fire Officer requires this action to minimise smoke spread hazards.

5.17.8 References

References (1) and (2): 'Prisons and the Prisoner'. The work of the Prison Service in England and Wales. (HMSO)

Buildings for a mixed farm

Chapter 5.18

Food production

Peter Wakeford, C.Eng., M.I.E.E., F.I.Agr.E.
Formerly Manager, Electricity Council Farm-electric Centre

5.18.1 Introduction

Methods of electricity utilisation in agriculture and horticulture differ in many ways from those in conventional buildings; for example, most of the environment is of a semi-outdoor nature, whilst livestock have a high susceptibility to electric shock. Because of this special techniques are necessary, which are described in general terms in this Chapter, reference being made to other publications for details.

5.18.2 Electricity supply

5.18.2.1 Distribution lines

The main distribution networks for rural electricity supply are usually provided by overhead lines. In most cases, these lines supply individual farms terminating close to the farm with a transformer which reduces the voltage to 240 V for domestic and farm use whilst some farms may be supplied direct from a network supplying a village. In the UK, the right to install and maintain lines over private property is secured by the Electricity Board negotiating wayleaves in exchange for an annual payment to the landowner; the consent of the occupier must also be obtained. The Electricity Board is obliged to prevent interference with cultivation as far as practicable and to ensure that the line does not provide a hazard where it crosses a route used by agricultural machinery e.g. elevators, whilst the consumer has to provide access by the Board for maintenance of poles, towers, switchgear and transformers. Where underground services are provided they must be placed below the operating level of ploughs or other soil-working implements.

5.18.2.2 Provision of electricity supply

The provision of a new electricity supply to an isolated farm or horticultural holding in the UK will usually involve the consumer in making a contribution towards the cost of its provision and possibly a guarantee of a minimum consumption over a number of years. Full details of these arrangements will be provided by the Electricity Board when a new supply is being negotiated.

5.18.2.3 Stand-by supply

A standby supply is essential when a failure in the supply is unacceptable. This could be the case with the control of environment for intensive breeding of livestock, on dairy farms and in some horticultural lighting systems. The type of plant required varies from a small lighting set to a fully-automatic set giving 15 kVA or more.

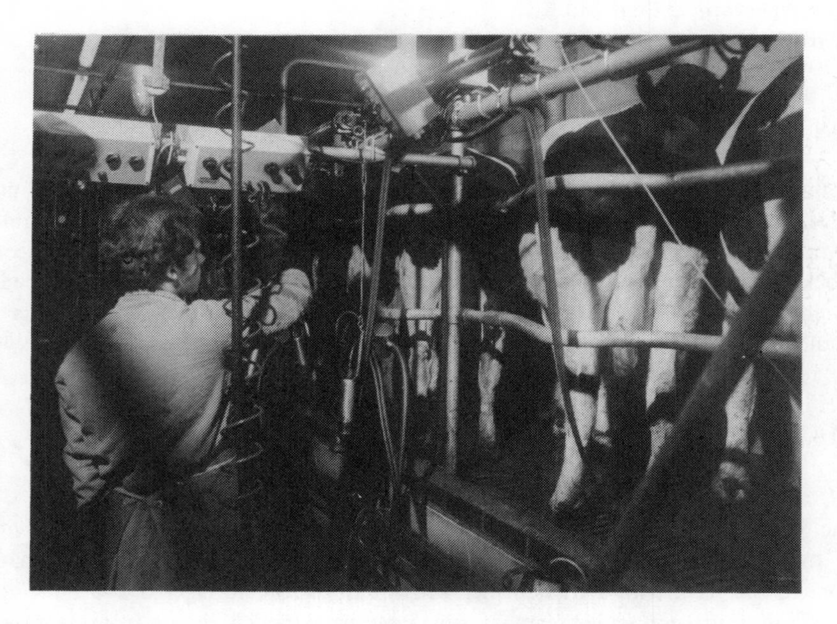

Fig. 5.18.1. *Milking parlour, showing controls for automatic feed controls and cluster removal*

(Electricity Council)

5.18.3 Dairy farming

The main uses of electricity in dairying are for the motors driving the vacuum and milk pumps, for heating water for cleaning purposes, for space heating, milk cooling and for lighting.

5.18.3.1 Motor drives

If the vacuum pump and its motor are installed in dust-proof conditions, the motor may be of the drip-proof type. Otherwise it should be totally enclosed with or without fan cooling. The releaser milk pump motor should also be totally enclosed, with or without fan cooling. Belt drives should be provided with guards. Motor starters and contactors should be constructed to BS 587 and BS 775 respectively and have weatherproof enclosures.

5.18.3.2 Water heating

Attention is drawn to the necessity for choosing a water heater of the capacity to suit the scale of the milk production. (Advice is obtainable in the UK from the Farm-electric Centre, Stoneleigh, Kenilworth, Warwickshire).

5.18.3.3 Space heating

The use of suitably protected infra-red heaters mounted centrally above the pit of milking parlours is an acceptable form of space heating, and individual heaters with loadings of 2 kW spaced at intervals of 2 m will usually provide the required environmental conditions. Time switching arranged to switch on before and off after milking occurs is a suitable control method. Thermostatic control is not usually justified.

5.18.3.4 Milk cooling

All milk produced in the United Kingdom is now collected by road tankers at a temperature usually not exceeding 4°C, from bulk tanks installed on the farm. One of the conditions under which a licence to produce milk is granted requires that it should be cooled immediately after milking, and the Milk Marketing Boards have strict specifications to ensure that the refrigeration system employed is capable of cooling all milk to below 4°C within 30 minutes of the completion of milking. Most bulk tank cooling systems employ a cooling jacket in which an ice bank surrounded by chilled water is built on expansion coils of a refrigeration unit; the chilled water is the medium by which milk in the bulk tank is cooled. Direct expansion systems have also developed in recent years, but while they reduce the running cost of milk cooling, the electrical demand imposed on the supply system is a disadvantage as it is three or four times that of the equivalent chilled water system. Potential users should therefore always consult their supply undertaking before committing themselves to a direct expansion system. The sizes and types of refrigeration units for different bulk tank capacities and advice on their suitability for operating under multi-rate tariffs can be obtained from the Farm-electric Centre.

5.18.4 Livestock

The main applications for electricity in livestock husbandry are for modifying and controlling the environment in buildings (i.e. the use of fans, heating and lighting) and for feed preparation and distribution, and slurry handling.

5.18.4.1 Control of environment

The provision of a suitable environment for livestock requires specialist knowledge. This includes an understanding of the different temperatures and air movement patterns which constitute an optimum environment for each species of farm livestock.

Most non-ruminants, i.e. pigs and poultry, respond rapidly in terms of liveweight gain and food conversion efficiency to their surrounding air temperature and air speed. For each age, weight, group size and flooring type, there are specific temperature and air speed requirements for optimum performance. As a result a narrow band of temperature and air speed is required for both pigs and poultry under specific circumstances. The only effective way to achieve these conditions in practice is to use fan ventilation systems.

Ruminants, i.e. sheep and cattle, do not respond rapidly to variations in air temperature, and have a wide band of tolerance to air temperature and, therefore, do not require a temperature controlled environment. However, both non-ruminants and ruminants require ventilation and manually controlled fan ventilation may be employed in difficult housing conversions for ruminants.

With some younger stock, e.g. young pigs, supplementary heat is essential in intensive systems, since on their own the metabolic heat of younger animals is insufficient to maintain optimum temperatures. The ways of applying such heat can best be done electrically, because electrical heating is controllable down to very low levels, resulting in low running costs. For detailed information on this and other aspects of livestock environment, potential users are referred in the UK to the Farm-electric Centre, or to the Ministry of Agriculture's livestock environment specialists. Technical Information Sheets can also be obtained from the Farm-electric Centre giving guidance on heating and ventilation for pigs.

Information is also available on the application of process lighting for laying hens in order to optimise egg production. In recent years economy in use of process lighting has become practicable since means have been found to control fluorescent lighting levels. In so doing it is now possible to substitute fluorescent lighting in place of tungsten filament lighting in buildings for laying hens, and thus achieve economies in running costs.

5.18.4.2 Animal feed preparation

Machinery is available for processing cereals on the farm and blending them with proteins, minerals, etc for feeding livestock. The advantages to the farmer of doing this himself instead of purchasing ready mixed compounds or of using a mobile milling service are:

(a) By using cereals grown on his own farm he avoids some of the transport costs associated with purchased feed.
(b) He retains control over the rations which he feeds to his stock.
(c) He can save on the cost of feed from £15–30 per tonne even after allowing for the cost of doing the processing himself.

Assessment of potential savings are demonstrated in Technical Information Sheets available from the Farm-electric Centre, and advice on equipment to use the design of layouts in existing or new buildings is also available from the same source.

5.18.4.3 Animal feed distribution

Where large numbers of livestock have to be fed within buildings, the need arises for automatic feeding systems. The Farm-electric Handbook entitled 'Automatic feeding of cattle' sets out the systems available.

Fig. 5.18.2. *Automatic ingredients proportioner and pneumatic mill for animal feed preparation*

(Electricity Council)

5.18.5 Crops

5.18.5.1 General

To enable certain crops to be kept in good condition for long periods after harvesting, it has become essential to condition them either by drying (e.g. of grain) to a safe keeping moisture content of 15/16 per cent, and by selective ventilation (e.g. of potatoes) to prevent their heating in winter. Electricity is used for driving fans and may be used for heating if required. The main crops likely to require treatment are outlined below.

5.18.5.2 Cereals

Drying, chilling and storage of grain are dealt with in the Farm-electric Handbook on 'Grain drying and storage' which outlines the design of each system. The importance is stressed of providing adequate strength in air ducts to withstand the pressure likely to be developed.

5.18.5.3 Grass

It is made clear in the Farm-electric Handbook on 'Hay drying' that electrical heating for high temperature drying of unwilted grass is not practicable, but electrically-driven fans are used to move warmed air through the crop. The drying of wilted grass with cold air is practicable, however, and the Handbook describes the types of fan suitable for this purpose. The Handbook also gives information on methods of drying grass which has been baled with 40 to 45 per cent moisture content, on big bale drying and chopped hay drying, and outlines building requirements. For some drying methods, it may be necessary to provide sufficient strength in the roof beams of a barn to sling a fan on block and tackle.

Fig. 5.18.3. *Centrifugal and axial flow fans for grass drying* (Electricity Council)

5.18.5.4 Roots and other vegetables

Advice on vegetable storage is obtainable from the Farm-electric Centre. The use of electricity is involved in the storage of seed potatoes in chitting boxes before planting, to the large-scale storage of potatoes for processing or ware, and for other root crops. Technical Information Sheets are also available from the Farm-electric Centre for onions (field wilted and direct harvested), beetroot and winter white cabbage.

5.18.6 Greenhouse crops

5.18.6.1 General

Horticultural crops comprise in the main tomatoes, lettuce and, increasing in popularity, aubergines and peppers. In the UK successful commercial production of these crops is improved where they are produced under protected structure, either glass or plastics.

For some crops, especially tomatoes and winter lettuce, artificial heat is essential and in all cases ventilation of the houses must be provided. For details of glass-house design and construction, and ventilation and heating systems, reference should be made to HMSO Bulletin 115 'Commercial glasshouses'.

Applications of electricity in greenhouse crops production are for process lighting to improve the germination and growth consistency of light sensitive subjects including tomatoes and lettuce; for heating to further assist growth promotion; and for ventilation and irrigation in which electric motors for fan drives and pumping are required.

5.18.6.2 Greenhouse lighting

Artificial light in association with heating is widely used to produce out-of-season crops as follows:

(a) To supplement daylight when increased plant growth is required during the winter months.
(b) To provide or extend the period of light in the short winter days to control the plants' seasonal functions, e.g. flowering.
(c) To provide artificially all the light requirements for plants in growing rooms from which all natural light is excluded.

There are three types of artificial light source, tungsten filament, high-pressure gas discharge and fluorescent. The type of light, its intensity and the period of use affects the rate of growth, the colour affects the height and the length of time the light is on, even at low levels of illumination, affects the plant's development towards maturity and the production of flowers and fruit.

(a) *Tungsten Filament Lamps*

Tungsten filament lamps emit light by means of a filament heated to a high temperature. They contain a good deal of infra-red in their spectrum and this produces a tendency to excessive stem elongation in many plants. These lamps are the cheapest to install and require no auxiliary gear. 100 W lamps are generally used and are quite acceptable but some growers prefer 150 W.

(b) *High-Pressure Gas Discharge Lamps*
These compact-source lamps give off light by discharging electricity through a gas or vapour, which, according to its type, determines the colour of the light. The mercury vapour (MB) lamp, producing a greenish-blue light has been superseded by the mercury fluorescent (MBF), metal halide (MBI) and high-pressure sodium (SON) lamps. The high-pressure sodium lamps have proved to be by far the most cost-effective of these in horticultural situations.

Mercury-vapour, mercury-halide and high-pressure sodium lamps require an external reflector in the form of an open-ended inverted trough. Some types of mercury-fluorescent lamps have internal reflectors which are most suited to horticultural application. Ratings of discharge lamps range from 180 W to 2000 W, and careful selection of these light sources will be needed to provide the most effective supplement to daylight in greenhouses.

(c) *Low-Pressure Gas Discharge Lamps*
Fluorescent powder on the inside of the glass tubes converts much of the ultraviolet radiation into light. The character of the powder dictates the colour of the light and, by a suitable selection of powders, a range of colours can be produced such as 'daylight', 'warm white' or 'natural'. The warm white is the most suitable for horticulture. These lamps have a low surface temperature and can be suspended close to the plants without scorching them. Because of their spectral output and linear charactor, tubular-fluorescent lamps are ideally suited for replacement lighting in growing rooms. Further information on this subject is contained in 'Lighting in Greenhouses', 'Growing Rooms', and Technical Information Sheets AGR 4-1, 4-2 and 4-3, all of which are obtainable from the Farm-electric Centre.

5.18.6.3 Heating
Most commercial greenhouse systems use solid fuel or oil-fired heating boilers which, however, require the use of electrical controls, and in many cases ancillary electrically driven pumping systems to accelerate the transfer of heat to the house.

(a) *Updating Existing Fuel Fired Heating Systems*
Grants are available from the Ministry to modernise nurseries. Many existing nurseries can benefit from this grant by providing a central boiler plant to serve a complex of greenhouses, or electrical aids can be added to existing heating systems to improve their efficiency. Fossil fuel and oil-fired low-pressure hot water or steam heating systems are common. The older systems are usually designed to operate with gravity circulation, employing large-bore pipework, while the newer systems use pumped circulation with small-bore pipes. An electric centrifugal accelerator pump (circulator) can be fitted to gravity systems. This can improve heat distribution throughout the nursery and the boiler need no longer be below ground level.

Different temperatures may be necessary in a number of houses. Electric motorised valves can be fitted to the hot water mains supplying the various houses. The temperature of each house can be controlled using a sensing element wired to:

(i) The circulating pump
(ii) The firing mechanism of the boiler
(iii) A controller such as a motorised valve.

(b) *Controlling Greenhouse Environment*
Accurate control of the greenhouse environment is essential for modern growing techniques, and the aspirated thermostat is necessary for sensing air temperature, particularly so with more sophisticated forms of controller. Controllers should be arranged to regulate automatically the heat input to the greenhouse, integrating the control of heating and ventilation systems. When heating is required, the greenhouse ventilators should be closed and the ventilation fans (where used) stopped. The ventilation and carbon dioxide enrichment should be carefully controlled ensuring that the gas is not added to the air when the ventilators are open. The heating should be controlled so that lower night running temperatures can be achieved automatically. Controls should be provided to close ventilators during heavy rain showers or winds.

5.18.6.4 Electric heating
There are some situations where, for comparatively small scale applications and where high value crops are to be grown, electric heating may be the most appropriate method of providing the required environment. It should be emphasised that heating apparatus used in greenhouses is subjected to high humidity, watering and chemical sprays. Great care must be taken therefore in selecting electric heaters and only those specially designed for horticulture should be chosen. The types of electric heater available are as follows:

(a) *Tubular Heaters*
Waterproof heaters are available 50 mm in diameter and in lengths from 0·6 m to 4·6 m. They can be installed singly or in tiers. They should be fixed to the walls with the lowest tube 100 mm to 150 mm above the soil level. This gives an efficient distribution of heat and takes up little space. If the tubes are fixed under benches there should be a space of 75 mm to 150 mm between the back of the bench and the wall. This allows the warm air to rise behind bench and circulate round the plants on the bench. The loading of the heaters is normally 180 W/m run but a loading of 250 W/m is available.

(b) *Mineral Insulated Cables (m.i.m.s)*
These can be fitted to the sides of greenhouses in similar positions to those for tubular heaters. The cable consists of a heating conductor surrounded by an inert mineral insulant and protected by a metal sheath. The cables are available in packaged units of 2 kW, 2·2 kW and 5·2 kW. Higher loadings can be supplied as required. Mineral insulated cables are cheaper to buy than tubular heaters but they cost slightly more to install.

(c) *Fan Heaters*
Care must be taken in siting fan heaters as a stream of warm air blowing directly

onto plants can cause physical damage. Recently, increasing use has been made of transparent plastic perforated ducts to give a more uniform distribution of the warm air. The size of the ducting and the perforation pattern can be varied according to requirements. In warm weather, the heating elements can be switched off and cool air drawn in from outside to assist the main ventilation system. Heaters are available with loadings of 4 kW, 8 kW, 12 kW, or 20 kW.

(d) *Convectors*
Horticultural convector heaters are quite suitable for small greenhouses and they can be placed in any part of the house.

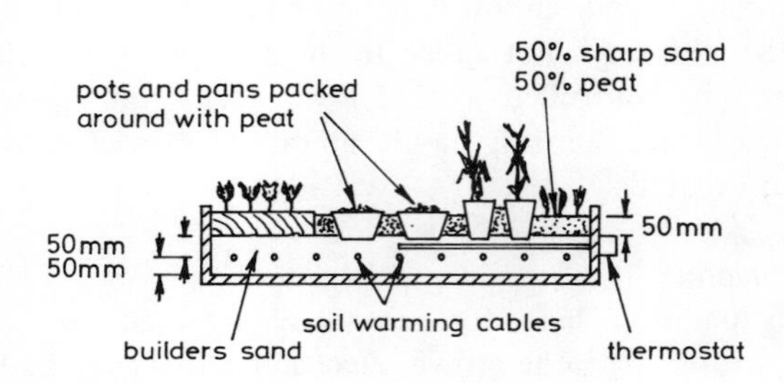

Fig. 5.18.4. *Make-up of electrically warmed bench*

(e) *Thermal Storage Heating*
Thermal storage heating is particularly suitable in buildings with a high standard of thermal insulation e.g. floor warming in mushroom houses. It can be run at cheaper off-peak rates but this requires a completely separate wiring installation.

(f) *Soil and Bench Warming*
Electrical soil warming to control root temperature offers wide possibilities. Temperature of air and roots can be maintained at optimum levels for each particular crop. Heat is provided by mains voltage cables or low voltage plastic-covered steel wire energised from a transformer. Mains voltage cables are used in most situations and are generally employed for bench warming. Where there is any risk of damage to the cables from cultivating tools, low voltage equipment should be used. Mains voltage cables should incorporate an earthed metal screen and have a p.v.c. outer sheath. They are available in packaged units from 75 W to 1000 W. Low voltage transformers are generally available in capacities up to 1000 W, and larger units are made to suit customers' requirements. Full details of the application of electric cables for soil and bench warming are given in Technical Information Sheet AGR 9 'Soil warming in horticulture', available from the Farm-electric Centre.

(g) *Soil Sterilisation*
Heat treatment at 82°C has been found to be more effective than chemicals for sterilising or pasteurising loam for seed and potting composts. Electric immersion

sterilisers are available in capacities up to 0·9 m³. At 82°C most pathogenic agents and weed seeds are destroyed. This method is much quicker than steam or chemicals and the sterilised soil can be used immediately. This method is suitable only for soil used in composts: sterilisation of greenhouse soil is normally done in situ with steam or chemicals.

5.18.6.5 Ventilation

In modern glasshouses the maximum area of ridge-vent opening should be at least one-sixth of the glasshouse floor area. In these circumstances, the ventilation gear can be power operated and automatically controlled. There are many glasshouses of the older type where ridge and side ventilation cannot meet the requirements of present day methods of crop production. In these cases, extractor fans should be used. The diameters of fans commonly used for glasshouses are 1·2 m, 0·75 m and 0·6 m. All fans should be fitted with louvres which open when the fans are

Fig. 5.18.5. *1200 mm extractor fans in a plastic bubble roofed greenhouse*

operating. Fans should be installed down one side of a glasshouse or block of glasshouses and draw air from an inlet running the length of the opposite side. Fuller details of this subject are contained in 'Ventilation for Greenhouses' and Technical Information Sheet AGR 2 'Fan ventilation', both available from the Farm-electric Centre.

5.18.6.6 Water supply

When the normal supply is not sufficient and an alternative is available e.g. a well, bore hole or river, an electric water pump is very useful. Water can be pumped from any of these sources, subject in the UK to local Water Authority approval, into a reservoir or, at pressure, directly into the irrigation lines. An average installation can ensure water at a very much cheaper rate than most mains water supplies. For further information see 'Pumping and Irrigation' available from the Farm-electric Centre.

5.18.6.7 Automatic watering

There is a variety of different methods of automatic watering. Water can be applied by overhead spray or at pot level through plastic tubes or trickle lines. A sequence controller can be used to open solenoid valves automatically in sequence. Each valve controls a spray or trickle line and can be operated for a pre-set period of time before other valves are brought in, one after the other. The length of time the valves remain open can be varied according to the need of the particular crop. Selected sequences can be arranged within a fourteen-day cycle. The watering sequence can be started by a time switch or a sequence controller.

5.18.6.8 Frost protection

A continuous spray of water applied when the temperature drops below 0°C can be used to protect fruit trees from spring frosts. The protection is provided by the latent heat produced as the water turns to ice and sufficient water must be available to allow continuous freezing until the air temperature rises above 0°C. When the water is supplied by means of an electric pump, the motor should be started with a thermostat and relay: when it is mains-supplied, a thermostatically-operated magnetic valve should be used. The pumping equipment and spraying lines normally used for irrigation are satisfactory but the nozzles may need adjusting to give the necessary spraying rate.

5.18.6.9 Hot water treatment

Hot water at specified temperatures effectively destroys a number of pathogenic organisms found in daffodils and tulips, and electricity has proved the most reliable means of heating the water for this treatment. Thermostatically controlled electric immersion heaters can provide the accurate temperature control needed and an electric pump, for efficient circulation of the water, ensures that the temperature is constant throughout the tank. A typical warm water bath has a capacity of 225 litres and can deal, for example, with 500 kg of bulbs at a time. Further information about hot water treatment can be obtained from the Farm-electric Handbook 'Electricity in Horticulture' or the UK Ministry of Agriculture.

5.18.6.10 Mist propagation

Mist propagation is a widely employed technique for rooting cuttings on electrically-warmed benches. The system consists of a sensing element, a switching controller, a solenoid valve, water lines and misting nozzles. The sensing element is placed among the cuttings being rooted so that it is exposed to the same conditions of sunlight and temperature. It is fitted with two carbon electrodes which are connected through the controller to the electricity supply. The controller operates the solenoid valve controlling the water supply. When a film of moisture bridges the exposed electrodes, the circuit is completed and the misting nozzles are switched off. When the water bridging the electrodes evaporates, which occurs at the same rate as from the plants, the circuit is broken and the solenoid valves are opened again, allowing the water to flow through and produce mist over the cuttings. Adequate drainage is essential for the bench in which the mist production equipment is installed.

Cuttings propagated by this system need a root temperature of around 21°C. This counteracts the cooling at rooting level caused by evaporation and helps the callus to form at the base of the cutting. The construction of mist propagation beds is described in Technical Information Sheet AGR 9 published by the Farm-electric Centre. A constant water pressure of 350–400 kN/m^2 is necessary to

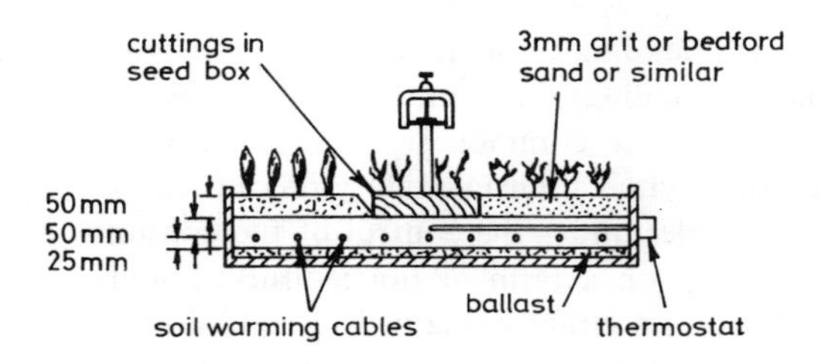

Fig. 5.18.6. *Propagation bench*

produce the fine mist required. If this is not available from the existing mains, a pressurised unit or an electric pump can be used.

5.18.7 Amenity lighting

All farm and horticultural buildings should be provided with adequate amenity electric lighting. Where stationary machinery is involved, suitable lighting is a requirement of the Farm Safety Regulations. In the dairy and wherever milk and milking appliances are handled, adequate lighting is essential to maintain the high standard of hygiene which is necessary. Evening rounds are simplified when external lighting is fitted. The lights also deter any intruders and reduce the risk of theft or vandalism. The lights may either be controlled separately or by one main switch situated at the farmhouse. Advice is contained in BS 5502 Section 3.5 'Levels of

Lighting', and in the Farm-electric Handbook 'Essentials of farm lighting', and Technical Information Sheet AGR 5-1, 'Installation techniques for lighting general purpose farm buildings'.

5.18.8 Electrical installation

5.18.8.1 Control and distribution

The main switchboard controlling the whole of the electrical installation should be not more than 1·8 m from the Electricity Board's point of supply. The site should be kept clear and have easy access. The main switchgear should be securely fixed to a framework of angle iron or slotted angle. The main controlling switch should be immediately after the Electricity Board meter. It should be capable of cutting off the supply to the whole installation in one operation. Where there is an off-peak supply, a separate switch is necessary to control this installation. Cables lead from the switchboard to the points at which electricity is used. Installations should be capable of isolation by one switch or by a number of switches in one place. Where the main service intake serves several buildings, a suitable switch must be situated in, or adjacent to, each building to isolate the wiring. Individual greenhouses should be treated as separate buildings, but multi-span greenhouses may be regarded as a single building, except where commonsense considerations make the provision of more than one isolating switch a sensible safety precaution.

Overhead lines or cables under the control of the consumer are frequently used to interconnect buildings on a farm or horticultural holding. Such cables should preferably be insulated and either contained in conduit or supported by catenary wires. The minimum ground clearance for an overhead cable on a farm should be 5·2 m increasing to 5·8 m where tall vehicles may be expected.

Alternatively, cables may be taken underground between buildings. It is essential that a route should be selected which will not be disturbed and the cable – which should be of an armoured type – should be buried at a depth of at least 0·5 m and covered with protective tiles and marker tape.

5.18.8.2 Circuit wiring

Electrical installations in farms and horticultural holdings must be designed and installed bearing in mind that exposure to one or more of the following is likely: weather, corrosive atmospheres, impact from heavy mobile machinery, abuse by operatives, interference by livestock and attack by rodents. The type of materials used should be chosen accordingly. All-insulated wiring systems are generally suitable provided that the wiring and accessories are positioned so as to avoid impact damage and interference from livestock. Where this is not possible, it is necessary to incorporate additional protection by enclosing the wiring in conduit. This conduit should be of all insulated material, preferably of high-impact heavy-duty grade. In exceptional circumstance, heavy-gauge galvanised screwed conduit may be used. On no account is light gauge or enamelled conduit acceptable for farming or horticultural installations. A circuit protective conductor (c.p.c) is required within the metal conduit system of wiring because the continuity of the conduit itself is not sufficient for earth protection.

Each building must be controlled by an individual switch placed in an easily accessible position. Trailing or other flexible cables should be kept as short as possible, therefore an adequate number of switched socket outlets should be provided.

5.18.8.3 Cables

Cables, either flat or circular in cross-section, having a suitable sheath or covering, should be used. For most farming installations, such suitable materials in order of preference are:

a Polychloroprene (p.c.p.) complying with BS 2899
b Chlorosulphonated polyethylene (c.s.p.) complying with BS 2899
c Polyvinyl chloride (p.v.c.) complying with BS 2746

Cable sheathed with vulcanised general purpose rubber compound should preferably not be used, and in any case must not be used in dairies, milking parlours or cowsheds. It may, however, be acceptable in horticultural holdings for lighting installations for chrysanthemums and where moulded lighting fittings are incorporated. The catenary or 'grid suspension' system is particularly suitable for wiring in elevated situations in steel and concrete buildings. Cables sheathed with p.c.p., c.s.p., or p.v.c must not be used in situations where they would be liable to contact with liquid creosote. It is preferable to keep cable routes outside the building, if possible under cover, and to return them into the building close to where the electricity is to be used.

5.18.8.4 Safety precautions

In the UK it is the responsibility of the consumer to provide a satisfactory means of earthing but there are circumstances when arrangements can be made jointly with the Electricity Board. When the Board is able to provide an earth it can do so in one of three ways. A connection can be made to the metal sheathing of the underground cables; the continuous overhead earth wire connected to the main earth of the supply system can be brought to the supply position; or protective multiple earthing (PME) can be used, a system in which the earth and neutral supply conductor are joined together at a number of points.

The Electricity Board will know which earthing system should be used for maximum safety in any particular situation. In some situations, none of these three methods of earthing can provide a satisfactory solution and it is necessary to use a residual current device (r.c.d) operating on the earth leakage principle. See the Farm-electric Handbook 'Safe use of electricity on the farm and in horticulture' (EC3929R) pages 13 and 14.

5.18.8.5 Electric fences

Electric fences are in wide use to prevent animals from straying. These devices usually provide a short duration pulse not exceeding 5 kV at preset intervals and can be fed from the mains supply or from a battery. In the latter case, the battery must be disconnected from the fence controller during charging to prevent the possibility of the fence becoming connected to the supply mains as a result of a fault in the charger unit. Mains operated fence controllers must comply with BS 2632.

5.18.9 References

5.18.9.1 Legislation (See also Appendix 6.1)

Agricultural (Safety, Health and Welfare Provisions) Act 1956
Agriculture (Stationary Machinery) Regulations 1959
Factories Act 1961
Health and Safety at Work etc Act 1974

5.18.9.2 British Standards (See also Appendix 6.2)

BS 196 refers to socket outlets and plugs for certain special conditions, and BS 1363 to the standard 13 A socket outlet and plug. BS 4343 refers to industrial type sockets and plugs. BS 5502 is the Code of Practice for the design of agricultural buildings.

Motor starters and contactors are covered by BS 587 and 775 respectively, BS 2746 and BS 2899 refer to certain plastic sheathing for cables, and BS 2632 is the Standard for mains operated electric fences.

5.18.9.3 Bibliography

Handbooks, Technical Information Sheets and Case Histories, produced by the Electricity Council deal with the agricultural and horticultural subjects mentioned, and subject to availability from existing stocks, may be obtained by application to the Farm-electric Centre, National Agricultural Centre, Stoneleigh, Kenilworth, Warwickshire CV8 2LS.

Farm-electric Handbooks:
- Automatic feeding of cattle
- Essentials of farm lighting
- Grain drying and storage
- Hay drying
- Potato Storage
- Pumping and irrigation

Grow-electric Handbooks:
- Growing rooms
- Lighting in greenhouses
- Ventilation for greenhouses
- Electricity in horticulture

Technical Information Sheets:

AGR1	Feed preparation on farms: milling and mixing
AGR2	Fan ventilation in horticulture
AGR3	Hay drying
AGR4-1	Growing room and supplementary lighting techniques for photosynthetic response
AGR4-2	Growing rooms and bench lighting – linear rigs
AGR4-3	Supplementary lighting in greenhouses
AGR5-1	Installation techniques for lighting general purpose farm buildings
AGR5-2	General lighting layouts for farm buildings of common sizes
AGR5-6	Daylighting of farm buildings
AGR6	Grain drying, conditioning and storage
AGR7-2	Pig creep heating
AGR7-4	The control of ventilation in livestock housing
AGR7-3	Fan ventilation systems
AGR8-1	Vegetable storage and conditioning – Potatoes
AGR8-2	Vegetable storage and conditioning – Onions
AGR8-3	Vegetable storage and conditioning – Red beetroot
AGR8-4	Vegetable storage and conditioning – Winter white cabbage
AGR9	Soil warming in horticulture
AGRIO	Heat pumps and heat recovery techniques in agriculture and horticulture

Appendix 6.1

Legislative requirements in the United Kingdom

J. H. S. Geach, Ll.B., Solicitor

6.1.1 Introduction

It is not the purpose of this Appendix to treat in detail all the enactments which may be relevant where electricity is, or is being installed, in a building in the United Kingdom. Its purpose is to provide a guide and aide memoire to any person carrying out work in a building which involves the use of electricity or installation of or alteration to, electrical equipment and wiring, so that he may consider what special precautions need to be taken. It is emphasised that the information contained in this Appendix is intended to apply to the general situation, and appropriate professional advice should be obtained in specific cases. To supplement the general information included in this Appendix many chapters elsewhere in this book make reference to specific legislation relevant to their particular subject.

6.1.2 Supply of electricity

In England and Wales electricity is normally supplied by the Area Electricity Board in whose area the building to be supplied is situated. These Boards were established and their areas in England and Wales defined by the Electricity Act 1947. In Scotland the supplying authority will, according to the location of the building, be either the North of Scotland Hydro Electricity Board (established by the Hydro Electric Development (Scotland) Act 1943) or the South of Scotland Electricity Board (established by the Electricity Reorganisation (Scotland) Act 1954). In Northern Ireland the supplying authority is the Northern Ireland Electricity Service which operates under the Electricity Supply (Northern Ireland) Order 1972 (1972 S.I. No. 1072). The Electricity (Scotland) Act 1979 consolidated the earlier Scottish Electricity Acts, and the Energy Act 1983 sets out the arrangements under which privately generated electricity may be supplied to the public network.

An Electricity Board's obligation to supply electricity and the circumstances in which an owner or occupier of premises may be entitled to a supply of electricity are, so far as England and Wales are concerned, contained in the Electricity Supply Acts 1882 to 1936 and in the Electricity Act 1947. Similar provisions operate in Scotland and Northern Ireland. These provisions cover the arrangements by which an owner or occupier of premises can obtain a supply of electricity subject to safeguards regarding payment and the adequacy of the installation on the premises for the purposes for which the supply is to be used. The reader's attention is, therefore, drawn to legal requirements which have as their main purpose ensuring safety in the use of electricity in buildings and, incidentally, preventing that use interfering with the supply to other electricity consumers.

6.1.3 Health and Safety at Work etc Act 1974

In the context of this book "building" generally has the meaning given to it by section 74 of the Health and Safety at Work etc Act 1974 ("the 1974 Act"). The definition is comprehensive and, in addition to any permanent or temporary building, extends to 'any other structure or erection of whatever kind or nature (whether permanent or temporary) and . . . shall include a vehicle . . . or other movable object of any kind in such circumstances as may be prescribed'. "Building" includes part of a building and references to the construction or erection of a building shall include references to the carrying out of operations to be treated as the construction or erection of a building as may be designated in building regulations.

6.1.4 Electricity Supply Regulations, 1937

In Great Britain the provisions governing the supply of electricity generally are to be found in the Electricity Supply Regulations, 1937. These Regulations were made under the Electricity Supply Acts and were continued in force by the Electricity Act 1947. Their main purpose was to secure the safety of the public and ensure 'a proper and efficient supply of electrical energy'. The obligations under the Regulations, therefore, fall mainly on the body supplying electricity who will almost invariably be the Electricity Board for the area concerned. Because the Regulations impose on Electricity Boards certain basic obligations with regard to the method of supplying electricity, such as minimum standards of insulation, connection of systems with earth, interconnection of systems, protection of circuits, etc., the Boards are permitted to refuse to give a supply, or to disconnect the supply, to a consumer, if the Board is not reasonably satisfied with regard to the safety of the consumer's installation. This right of the Board is set out in Regulation 27 and is concerned primarily with aspects of potential danger, including adequacy of conductors and protection against excess energy. The Regulation does not enable a Board to act arbitrarily towards a consumer for it provides that if the consumer's installation complies with the IEE Regulations currently in force it 'shall be deemed to fulfil the requirements of this Regulation'. A person, therefore, who is putting an electrical installation into a building or making alterations to an existing installation must ensure that what he proposes to do, and the manner in which it is done, complies with the current edition of the IEE Regulations if he wants to be sure that a supply of electricity will be, or continue to be, made available in that building. These Regulations are dealt with in greater detail in Chapter 3.1 and elsewhere in this book. They, and the various legislation which regulates or affects the use of electrical equipment or installations, are primarily concerned with ensuring that that use will not create danger to persons or property. Provisions which are not concerned directly or indirectly with the prevention of danger, and which a person proposing to instal an electrical installation or equipment should be aware of, as he may be affected by them, are referred to later.

In dealing with buildings as defined in the 1974 Act different requirements may apply according to the nature of the building or the purpose for which it is used. The basic distinction is between buildings in which persons are employed to work and buildings where persons are not so employed. An example of a building which is not normally a place of work for the purposes of the 1974 Act is a domestic premises, although such premises may become a place of work if a person in the course of his employment has to work in them other than as a domestic servant. In the case of premises which are not places of work there is relatively little legislation relating to safety in the use of electricity once the premises have been connected to the supply system. The 'deemed to comply' provision in Regulation 27 of the Electricity Supply Regulations 1937 will apply to any change made to the installation in the premises and will have to meet the requirements of the IEE Regulations. The protection of domestic consumers against electrical hazards once the system is properly installed is to be found mainly in Regulations made under the Consumer Safety Act 1978, which impose requirements for the safety of domestic electrical equipment and apparatus. Those requirements are chiefly concerned with such matters as insulation and earthing, accessibility of live parts, switching of heating elements, guarding moving parts, prevention of danger from excessive heat or radiation or emissions of toxic gases. For details reference should be made to the Electrical Equipment (Safety) Regulations, 1975 (S.I. 1975 No. 1366) and the Electrical Equipment (Safety) (Amendment) Regulations, 1976 (S.I. 1976 No. 1208).

6.1.5 Buildings which are places of work

Such buildings may or may not be factories within the meaning of that expression in the Factories Act 1961 ('the 1961 Act'). In the case of this Act, which was repealed by the 1974 Act, there will be a period of transition during which existing provisions will continue in force until replaced by new provisions. The 1961 Act is one of a number of Acts of Parliament (listed in the First Schedule to the 1974 Act) repealed by the 1974 Act but which continue in force for the time being by virtue of Section 1(2) of the Act. The Acts and Regulations made under them will, in the words of the Section, be 'progressively replaced by a system of regulations and approved codes of practice operating in combination with the other provisions of this Part of the Act and designed to maintain or improve the standards of health, safety and welfare established by or under those enactments'. In the case of all buildings which are places of work the 1974 Act imposes on an employer a general duty to ensure the safety of his employees at work. This duty exists, irrespective of any special requirements relating to electricity, wherever the employee may be working and the Act lays down basic standards of safety which must be observed by the employer (and, where appropriate, by the employee) to ensure, so far as is reasonably practicable, safety at the place of work. Thus, even though there may be no specific standard applicable to a particular operation, the employer has a general duty under Section 2 of the Act to ensure, so far as reasonably practicable, the health, safety and welfare of his employees; and every employee has a duty under Section 7 of the Act to take reasonable care for the health and safety of himself and other persons who may be affected by his acts or omissions at work. Section 2 of the Act also specifically requires the employer to provide and maintain safe working systems for his employees; and if an employee is injured in an accident at work which was not caused by his failure to take reasonable care, it will be for the employer to demonstrate that it was not reasonably practicable to do more than was in fact done to provide a safe system of work. The Act also imposes a general duty on persons who have control of non-domestic premises which are made available as a place of work to persons who are not their employees, to ensure that the premises (and access thereto) are safe so far as is reasonably practicable.

The enforcement of the provisions of the 1974 Act is entrusted to the Health and Safety Executive and to local authorities where authorised by regulations made by the Secretary of State. Both the Executive and the local authorities are subject to any directions given to them by the Health and Safety Commission. The Commission and the Executive were established by the 1974 Act and have taken over functions of various government agencies who had responsibilities under Acts of Parliament for supervising the safe operation of many different types of industrial process.

6.1.6 Provision for special operations

There is a considerable amount of legislation which contains special provisions which may be applicable to buildings by virtue of the operations which are carried on in those buildings. These provisions are additional to the requirements of the 1974 Act which will apply to the building by virtue of its being a place of work. The obvious examples are buildings which are factories within the definition of the 1961 Act. A factory is defined in great detail in Section 175 of that Act. In principle, it means any premises in which persons are employed in manual labour in any one of a number of processes described in the section, such as: the making of any article; altering, adapting for sale, repairing, finishing or cleaning any article; the slaughtering of cattle or other animals. Premises such as a dry dock, or where containers are filled, or printing or bookbinding carried on, are included in the definition. If a building is a factory, regulations made under, or continued in force by, the 1961 Act may apply, according to the process being carried on at the premises. Examples are: The Abrasive Wheels Regulations, 1970; The Chemical Works Regulations, 1922; The Building (Safety, Health and Welfare) Regulations, 1948; The Construction (General Provisions) Regulations, 1961; The Highly Flammable Liquids and Liquid Propane Gas Regulations, 1972; The Ionising Radiation (Unsealed Radioactive Substances) Regulations, 1968; The Iron and Steel Foundries Regulations, 1953; and various shipbuilding regulations. So far as any activity involving the generation, transformation, distribution or use of electricity is concerned the Electricity (Factories Act) Special Regulations, 1908 and 1944 will apply unless exempted by Regulations. The Regulations are directed to ensuring that electrical installations in factories comply with minimum standards so that apparatus and circuits are adequate for the purpose for which they are designed and are properly installed, insulated and earthed. For example, the Regulations require that all apparatus and conductors shall be sufficient in size and power "and so constructed, installed, protected, worked and maintained as to prevent danger"; conductors shall be covered with insulating material and every switch and circuit-breaker so constructed as to prevent danger. Throughout the Regulations the emphasis is on the prevention of danger through proper construction of all types of apparatus likely to be placed in an electrical circuit, whether the apparatus is a switch, a circuit-breaker, a transformer or a fuse. There are special requirements applicable to systems using electricity at high pressure (at present defined in the Regulations as above 650 volts but not exceeding 3000 volts) or extra high pressure (exceeding 3000 volts), particularly in relation to switchboards, to ensure that access to dangerous parts is restricted. If work has to be done on apparatus and technical knowledge or experience is necessary to avoid danger, that work may only be carried out by an authorised person (as defined in the Regulations) or by a competent person acting under his supervision. Substations have to be under the control of an authorised person and access to any part of a substation where there may be danger should be restricted to such a person or someone acting under his supervision. The main object of the 1944 Regulations was to bring the 1908 Regulations up to date by applying them to additional electrical processes, to additional places (e.g. ships) and to building operations and works of engineering construction. The Electricity Regulations 1908 (Competent Persons Exemption) Order, 1968 (S.I. 1968 No. 1454) gives exemption, on specified conditions, from the requirement in Regulation 28 of the 1908 Regulations that a competent person undertaking dangerous work described in that Regulation shall be over 21 years of age.

6.1.7 Commercial buildings

Other types of buildings, mainly commercial, to which special legislation applies are offices, shops and railway premises and cinemas. The Offices, Shops and Railway Premises Act 1963 had as its main object the welfare of workers in the premises by requiring the provision of adequate heating, ventilation and lighting. Whilst the Act and Regulations made under it are still operative it is the intention of the 1974 Act that this Act and the other Acts referred to in the First Schedule to the 1974 Act (called 'relevant statutory provision') will be replaced by a system of approved codes of practice and new regulations.

A cinema has to be licensed by the local authority under the Cinematograph Act 1909 and any person proposing to construct or operate a cinema should refer to the conditions in the licence and to the Cinematograph (Safety) Regulations 1955 (S.I. 1955 No. 1129), 1958 (S.I. 1958 No. 1530) and 1965 (S.I. 1965 No. 282). Similarly, by virtue of the Theatres Act 1968, if premises are to be used for the public performance of a play a licence must be obtained from the local authority who may impose such conditions as they consider necessary in the interests of physical safety.

If a building is not a factory (or deemed to be a factory) within the 1961 Act definition the Electricity (Factories Act) Special Regulations 1908/1944 will not strictly apply to it. In practice, however, it would seem from the Memorandum on the Electricity Regulations issued by the Health and Safety Executive (Memorandum SHW No. 928) that, so far as electrical safety is concerned, little practical distinction is likely to be made by those enforcing the 1974 Act and the 1908/1944 Regulations between a building which is a factory and one which is not. The position will eventually be clarified when new Electricity at Work Regulations (which are in preparation) come into force. These Regulations will apply to all buildings which are places of work. There will, no doubt, continue to be other regulations covering particular processes which give rise to special risks.

6.1.8 Other legal provisions

It will be clear from what has already been written that legislation relating to electricity in buildings is almost entirely concerned with preventing danger to persons and property. Mention should be made of two provisions not so orientated which a person using electricity should know about:

(1) The measurement of electricity supplied to consumers is covered by the Electricity Supply (Meters) Act 1936 under which the Secretary of State has power to appoint meter examiners and make arrangements for the certification of meters. The period of time during which a meter remains certified is at present covered by the Meters (Period of Certification) Order 1977 (S.I. 1977 No. 1970). Under the provisions of the Electric Lighting (Clauses) Act 1899 the amount of electricity

supplied to a consumer shall be ascertained by means of an appropriate certified meter – unless the consumer agrees otherwise.

(2) The use of electricity in such a way that it interferes with telephones, telegraph signals, radio or television is prohibited by Regulations made under the Wireless Telegraphy Act 1949. The Regulations currently in force are the Wireless Telegraphy (Control of Interference from Household Appliances, Tools, etc.) Regulations 1978 (S.I. 1978 No. 1267).

Appendix 6.2

British Standards

6.2.1 British Standards Institution

The BSI is the UK national standards making body, and represents the UK in international standards work. BSI publishes standards for a wide range of products and systems, including electrical equipment and components.

A valuable book of reference to all BSI activities is the BSI Catalogue, which also includes a comprehensive list of British Standards. A summary of those which appear in 'Electricity in Buildings' is given in the following section, and it is important to note that Standards may be published in a number of Parts, each dealing with specific aspects of the main subject of the Standard. In addition to the general BS series and other series dealing with particular subjects, e.g. the automobile series (AU), there are also Codes of Practice (BS CP), although Codes of Practice are now being included in the main series.

As an entirely separate function, BSI also provides a certification service for products which comply with the requirements of the relevant standards, awarding the Kitemark or Safety Mark, as appropriate. (Fig. 6.2.1).

Another BSI service, Technical Help to Exporters, (THE), provides information on the technical requirements and certification procedures of countries outside the UK.

BSI Kite Mark

BSI Safety Mark

Fig. 6.2.1. *BSI Certification Marks*

BSI Head Office: 2 Park Street, London W1A 2BS
Quality Assurance Division: Maylands Avenue, Hemel Hempstead, Herts HP2 4SQ
Sale of Standards, General Enquiries, Technical Help to Exporters: Linford Wood, Milton Keynes, MK14 6LE

6.2.2 British Standards and Codes of Practice

BS 88	Cartridge fuses for voltages up to and including 1000 V a.c. and 1500 V d.c.
BS 171	Power transformers
BS 196	Protected-type non-reversible plugs, socket-outlets, cable-couplers and appliance-couplers, with earthing contacts for single-phase a.c. circuits up to 250 V
BS 329	Steel wire ropes for electric lifts
BS 415	Specification for safety requirements for mains-operated electronic and related apparatus for household and similar general use.
BS 440	Stationary batteries (lead-acid Planté positive type) for general electrical purposes
BS 476	Fire tests on building materials and structures
BS 587	Motor starters and controllers
BS 594	Rolled asphalt (hot process) for roads and other paved areas
BS 638	Arc welding power sources, equipment and accessories
BS 699	Copper cylinders for domestic purposes
BS 764	Automatic changeover contactors for emergency lighting systems
BS 775	Contactors
BS 889	Flameproof electric lighting fittings
BS 1259	Intrinsically safe electrical apparatus and circuits for use in explosive atmospheres
BS 1361	Cartridge fuses for a.c. circuits in domestic and similar premises
BS 1362	General purpose fuse links for domestic and similar purposes (primarily for use in plugs)
BS 1363	13 A plugs, switched and unswitched socket-outlets and boxes
BS 1710	Identification of pipelines
BS 1853	Tubular fluorescent lamps for general lighting service
BS 2048	Dimensions of fractional horse-power motors
BS 2050	Electrical resistance of conducting and antistatic products made from flexible polymeric material
BS 2316	Radio-frequency cables
BS 2484	Cable covers, concrete and earthenware
BS 2560	Specification for exit signs (internally illuminated)
BS 2655	Lifts, escalators, passenger conveyors and paternosters
BS 2754	Construction of electrical equipment for protection against electric shock

BS 2769	Portable electric motor-operated tools
BS 3036	Semi-enclosed electric fuses (ratings up to 100 A and 240 V to earth)
BS 3052	Electric shaver supply units
BS 3116	Automatic fire alarm systems in buildings
BS 3198	Specification for copper hot water storage combination units for domestic purposes
BS 3456	Specification for safety of household and similar electrical appliances
BS 3767	Low pressure sodium vapour lamps
BS 4211	Steel ladders for permanent access
BS 4343	Industrial plugs, socket-outlets and couplers for a.c. and d.c. supplies
BS 4362	Rotating electrical machinery
BS 4363	Distribution units for electricity supplies for construction and building sites
BS 4533	Luminaires
BS 4579	Performance of mechanical and compression joints in electric cable and wire connectors
BS 4678	Cable trunking
BS 4683	Electrical apparatus for explosive atmospheres
BS 4727	Glossary of electrotechnical, power, telecommunication, electronics, lighting and colour terms
BS 4737	Specification for intruder alarm systems in buildings
BS 4752	Specification for switchgear and controlgear for voltages up to and including 1000 V a.c. and 1200 V d.c.
BS 4999	General requirements for rotating electrical machines
BS 5000	Rotating electrical machines of particular types or for particular applications
BS 5175	Specification for safety of commercial electrical appliances using microwave energy for heating foodstuffs
BS 5225	Photometric data for luminaires
BS 5227	AC metal-enclosed switchgear and controlgear of rated voltage above 1 kV and up to and including 72·5 kV
BS 5266	Emergency lighting
BS 5311	Specification for a.c. circuit-breakers of rated voltage above 1 kV
BS 5345	Code of practice for the selection, installation and maintenance of electrical apparatus for use in potentially explosive atmospheres (other than mining applications or explosive processing and manufacture)
BS 5419	Specification for air-break switches, air-break disconnectors, air-break switch disconnecters and fuse combination units for voltages up to and including 1000 V a.c. and 1200 V d.c.
BS 5445	Specification for components of automatic fire detection systems

BS 5446	Specification for components of automatic fire detection systems for residential premises
BS 5451	Specification for electrically conducting and antistatic rubber footwear
BS 5486	Specification for factory-built assemblies of switchgear and controlgear for voltages up to and including 1000 V a.c. and 1200 V d.c.
BS 5489	Code of practice for road lighting
BS 5490	Specification for degrees of protection provided by enclosures
BS 5501	Electrical apparatus for potentially explosive atmospheres
BS 5502	Code of practice for the design of buildings and structures for agriculture
BS 5514	Specification for reciprocating internal combustion engines: performance
BS 5615	Specification for insulating jackets for domestic hot water storage cylinders
BS 5617	Specification for urea-formaldehyde (UF) foam for thermal insulation of cavity walls
BS 5619	Code of practice for design of housing for the convenience of disabled people
BS 5655	Lifts and service lifts
BS 5656	Safety rules for the construction and installation of escalators and passenger conveyors
BS 5776	Specification for powered stairlifts
BS 5784	Specification for safety of electrical commercial catering equipment
BS 5839	Fire detection and alarm systems in buildings
BS 5900	Specification for powered home lifts
BS 5958	Code of practice for the control of undesirable static electricity
BS 5965	Specification for manually driven balanced personal homelifts
BS 5971	Safety and interchangeability of tungsten filament lamps for domestic and similar general lighting purposes
BS 5979	Specification for direct line signalling systems and for remote centres for intruder alarm systems
BS 5997	Guide to British Standard codes of practice for building services
BS 6004	PVC-insulated cables (non-armoured) for electric power and lighting
BS 6007	Rubber-insulated cables for electric power and lighting
BS 6081	Specification for terminations for mineral insulated cables
BS 6116	Elastomer-insulated flexible trailing cables for quarries and miscellaneous mines
BS 6121	Mechanical cable glands for elastomer and plastics insulated cables
BS 6179	Specification for tungsten filament lamps for general service (with lives of 2000 hours)
BS 6207	Mineral-insulated cables
BS 6231	Specification for p.v.c.-insulated cables for switchgear and controlgear wiring

BS 6266	Code of practice for fire protection for electronic data processing installations
BS 6301	Specification for safety requirements for apparatus for connection to British Telecommunications networks
BS 6305	Specification for general requirements for apparatus for connection to the British Telecommunications public switched telephone network
BS 6312	Specification for plugs for use with British Telecommunications line jack units
BS 6317	Specification for simple extension telephones for connection to the British Telecommunications public switched telephone network
BS 6320	Specification for modems for connection to the British Telecommunications public switched telephone network
BS 6328	Apparatus for connection to British Telecommunications private circuits
BS 6346	PVC-insulated cables for electricity supply
BS 6360	Specification for conductors in insulated cables and cords
BS 6387	Performance requirements for cables required to maintain circuit integrity under fire conditions
BS 6396	Code of practice for electrical systems in office furniture and screens
BS 6480	Impregnated paper-insulated cables for electricity supply
BS 6899	Specification for rubber insulation and sheath of electric cables
BS 6977	Specification for insulated flexible cables for lifts and for other flexible connections
BS AU 161	Vehicle lifts
BS CP 3	Code of basic data for the design of buildings
BS CP 153	Windows and rooflights
BS CP 324·202	Provision of domestic electric water-heating installations
BS CP 326	The protection of structures against lightning
BS CP 407	Electric, hydraulic and hand-powered lifts
BS CP 413	Ducts for building services
BS CP 1003	Electrical apparatus and associated equipment for use in explosive atmospheres of gas or vapour other than mining applications
BS CP 1007	Maintained lighting for cinemas
BS CP 1011	Maintenace of electric motor control gear
BS CP 1013	Earthing
BS CP 1014	The protection of electrical power equipment against climatic conditions
BS CP 1015	Electrical equipment of industrial machines
BS CP 1017	Distribution of electricity on construction and building sites
BS CP 1018	Electric floor-warming systems for use with off-peak and similar supplies of electricity
BS CP 1020	The reception of sound and television broadcasting
BS CP 1022	The selection and accomodation of telephone, telegraph and data communication installations

Appendix 6.3

Sources of information

A main source of reference is the 15th Edition of the IEE Regulations for Electrical Installations, and subsequent Amendments. These are best read in conjunction with the Commentary (Jenkins, B. D.) and the Guide (Whitfield, J. F.). (Peter Peregrinus Limited).

The Institution of Electrical Engineers publishes the Proceedings of the Institution each month, and together with Peter Peregrinus Limited produces a wide range of technical journals and books on all aspects of electrical and electronic engineering.

The Institution of Electrical Engineers
Savoy Place
London WC2R 0BL

Peter Peregrinus Limited
PO Box 8
Southgate House
Stevenage Herts SG1 1HQ

The Chartered Institution of Building Services publishes authoritative and comprehensive advice on many aspects of environmental design, e.g. in the several publications forming the Building Services Manual, and in the CIBS (formerly IES) Code for Interior Lighting.

The Chartered Institution of Building Services
Delta House
222 Balham High Road
London SW12 9BS

The Electricity Council have an extensive range of publications varying from 'Understanding Electricity', a series of booklets describing matters of interest to the consumer, to technical data sheets on specific aspects of domestic, commercial and industrial utilisation.

The Electricity Council
30 Millbank
London SW1P 4RD

The Build-electric Bureau
The Building Centre
26 Store Street
London WC1E 7BT

The Electricity Council Research Centre
Capenhurst
Chester CH1 6ES

In addition to these organisations, and to the specialist bodies mentioned at the end of each chapter, information may be obtained from the following:

British Electrical and Allied Manufacturers' Association (BEAMA)
Leicester House
8 Leicester Street
London WC2H 7BN

Building Services Research and Information Association (BSRIA)
Old Bracknell Lane
Bracknell
Berks RG12 4AH

Building Research Establishment (BRE)
Garston
Watford WD2 7JR

Central Electricity Generating Board (CEGB)
Sudbury House
15 Newgate Street
London EC1A 7AU

Department of Education and Science (DES)
Elizabeth House
York Road
London SE1 7PH

Department of Energy
Thames House South
Millbank
London SW1P 4QJ

Department of Health and Social Security (DHSS)
Euston Tower
286 Euston Road
London NW1 3DN

ERA Technology Limited
Cleeve Road
Leatherhead
Surrey KT22 7SA

Fire Offices Committee (FOC)
Aldermary House
Queen Street
London EC4P 4JD

HM Stationery Office
49 High Holborn
London WC1V 6HB and in the provinces

Health and Safety Executive (HSE)
Baynards House
1 Chepstow Place
London W2 4TF

Lighting Industry Federation (LIF)
Swan House
207 Balham High Road
London SW17 7BQ

Royal Institute of British Architects (RIBA)
66 Portland Place
London W1N 4AD

Royal Institute of Chartered Surveyors (RICS)
12 Great George Street
London SW1P 3AD

and in the United States

Institute of Electrical and Electronic Engineers (IEEE)
345 East 47th Street
New York NY 10017

Edison Electric Institute (EEI)
1111 19th Street NW
Washington DC 20036

Index